Procedures of Modern Network Synthesis

Procedures of Modern

NETWORK
SYNTHESIS

William C. Yengst

The Macmillan Company, New York
Collier-Macmillan Limited, London

Library of Congress catalog card number: 64-14028

The Macmillan Company, New York
Collier-Macmillan Canada, Ltd., Toronto, Ontario

Printed in the United States of America

To Betty
and the Children, Barbara and Dick

Preface

The increased complexity of modern electrical systems plus requirements of maintaining small volume, low weight, and high reliability have contributed to the development of network synthesis as a scientific basis for design. In the past, network design has been based primarily on an analysis approach in which a specific arrangement of electrical elements was tested, the results noted and compared with a specified response, and the network then modified to correct for errors. In this sense, analysis represents a "trial and error" approach to network design which relies greatly on the designer's experience. Although the analysis approach cannot be entirely discarded, it can be advantageously replaced in many instances by synthesis procedures.

The field of network synthesis is concerned with the entire problem of specifying a desired network response due to a prescribed input, formulating suitable functions to represent the network and, finally, determining an arrangement of physically realizable elements which yields the desired response within acceptable tolerances. Specification of the response and techniques pertaining to the formulation of mathematical functions which characterize the network are generally considered together and are known as the "approximation problem." Procedures for decomposition of the characterizing functions to establish an arrangement of physically realizable elements form a second area of network synthesis known as the "realization problem." Thus the field of network synthesis is conveniently separated into two major divisions—the approximation and realization problems.

A vast amount of literature has been devoted to the development and presentation of numerous approximation and realization procedures. In fact, there is such a wealth of information available on these subjects that it becomes difficult for an author to select a representative group of procedures or techniques and give proper emphasis to each. For instance, several books have been published within the last few years on various aspects of network synthesis, and in each case these books differ in the procedures and amount of detail presented, and in the level of background knowledge assumed on the part of the reader.

Following a survey of available literature, it was decided that the primary emphasis of this book should be concentrated on the realization problem. This decision was based on the fact that a designer must often work directly from specified impedance or admittance functions to obtain a suitable arrangement of physically realizable elements. Therefore, in the interest of presenting a comprehensive text for students and at the same time providing a useful reference for practicing engineers, about two-thirds of the presentation has been devoted to various realization procedures. But because students of the subject and engineers who are faced with design specifications demand that attention also be given to the approximation problem, the remainder of the text is accordingly devoted to consideration of network response in both the frequency and time domains, and to related subjects such as component variations and their effects on response.

The realization procedures covered in the earlier chapters of the book have been further restricted to the use of passive electrical elements such as resistors, capacitors, inductors, and mutual inductance associated with transformers. By limiting the subject in this manner it is possible to consider a wider selection of procedures and to investigate each in greater detail. In this case it has been the aim of the author to integrate a large number of techniques into a well-organized and logical presentation.

Emphasis has been placed on the network and its composition, with little if any attention given to the waveforms of voltages and currents applied to or observed at various points within the network. In brief, the purpose of this book is to explain in general terms—and with examples—the most useful approximation and realization procedures by which a designer can work directly from specified response requirements to obtain a suitable network arrangement of physically realizable electrical elements. Since the impedance and admittance functions considered throughout the text have been expressed in terms of complex-frequency notation, using poles and zeros as is customary in modern network synthesis, Laplace-transformation techniques can readily be employed to determine the network response to various applied voltage/current waveforms or transients.

Background requirements necessary to understand the procedures and mathematics of this book are basic network analysis, elements of differential and integral calculus, and Laplace transformations. Simplified proofs have been used whenever possible so that extensive mathematical background is not necessary. However, an acquaintance with differential equations and complex-variable theory is helpful. In many instances the realization procedures require only college algebra plus an understanding of simple electrical circuits.

The material of this book has been divided into fifteen chapters, several of which can be studied independently or in any order that is convenient. Chapter 1 contains a review of pertinent aspects of complex-variable theory, partial-fraction expansions, and complex-frequency notation. Chapter 2 discusses energy functions of electrical networks, whereas Chapter 3 develops the conditions necessary to insure physically realizable one-port networks, the tests of these conditions, and some of the techniques for realizing one-port LC canonic network forms. Chapter 4 extends the realization procedures of Chapter 3 to one-port RC and RL networks. Thus Chapters 1 through 4 serve as background for the more sophisticated procedures of Chapters 5 and 6 which are devoted to the realization of one-port RLC networks. It is seen that the procedures of Chapters 3 through 6 are restricted to one-port networks exclusively. Many of these techniques become useful in later chapters in the discussion of realization procedures for two-port networks.

Chapter 7 contains a review of transfer functions, conditions which insure physically realizable two-port networks, and a few realization procedures for two-port networks. Chapter 8 is devoted to additional techniques for realization of two-port networks, with emphasis on RC ladder configurations. Chapter 9 covers procedures for the realization of two-port symmetrical lattice networks. Consequently the material of Chapters 7 through 9 is restricted to procedures for the realization of various two-port network configurations.

Chapters 10 through 13 are concerned with practical aspects of network synthesis which relate to realization and approximation problems. For instance, Chapter 10 deals with equivalent networks and impedance-level transformations. Chapter 11 covers predistortion and higher-order approximations of commercially available elements. Chapter 12 is concerned with network response and variations in the response caused by changes in element values. Chapter 13 describes several well-known frequency transformations which find considerable use in everyday design work. Finally, Chapters 14 and 15 provide procedures which can be applied to the approximation of specified network response characteristics in the frequency and time domains respectively.

The order of presentation is arranged such that the first part of the book, dealing with realization procedures for one-port networks (Chapters 1 through 6), can be used as the basis for a one-semester course. The second part of the book pertaining to realization of two-port networks (Chapters 7 through 10) might serve for a second semester, with topics chosen from Chapters 11 through 15 being used to augment the material of the earlier sections. The two-semester approach would be advantageous for senior undergraduates or first-year graduate students who have little or no background in network synthesis, since the instructor would have sufficient time available to supplement this text with other material. For a graduate student with some knowledge of network synthesis, however, the entire text might serve as the basis for a one-semester course or as a reference.

Some synthesis procedures are sufficiently complicated so that if practical element values and frequencies were used in the discussion and examples the reader might easily become involved with mathematics or slide-rule operation and miss the fine points of the procedure. Examples throughout the text have therefore been purposely simplified in order to make the details of the procedures as clear as possible. A set of problems follows each chapter to give the reader practical experience in using the procedures and to expand on the techniques introduced in the text. These problems have been carefully chosen to develop the reader's confidence. Finally, a list of additional reading material or references also follows each chapter for the reader interested in different approaches to the subject or further details.

Having studied network synthesis under Professors E. C. Ho and F. W. Schott of the University of California at Los Angeles, I have been influenced by their approach and methods of presentation. I wish to express my sincere thanks to all those whose stimulation, writings, reviewing, and suggestions have inspired and made possible this book. Much credit is given to Hughes Aircraft Company and Aerospace Corporation for the use of their facilities during the writing of the rough draft. Special acknowledgment is made to my parents and to Professor C. R. Vail of Duke University for their continued encouragement. In particular, I am grateful to my wife, Betty, for her help in so many ways— proofreading, editing, drafting, and typing—and for her inspiration from the beginning of the first rough draft to the completion of the final manuscript.

WILLIAM C. YENGST

Contents

Procedures of Modern Network Synthesis

Chapter 1

The Complex-frequency Concept

When a source of voltage or current is applied to the input terminals of a network composed of linear, finite, passive, bilateral elements, such as resistors, inductors, or capacitors, the resulting effect of the network on the source or the response obtained at a second set of terminals depends entirely on the type and arrangement of the elements in the network. If the source delivers sinusoidal voltage or current, it is convenient to use complex notation to represent the effect of the network. For example, at a particular frequency it is customary to represent the impedance Z of a network by a complex number composed of a resistive component R and a reactive component 90° out of phase with the resistance and denoted by X. At the specified frequency, the complex vector $\bar{Z}$ can be described in terms of rectangular coordinates as $\bar{Z} = R + jX$, where the j term denotes the 90° relationship between the resistive and reactive components. The vector $\bar{Z}$ may also be described in terms of polar coordinates as magnitude Z and phase angle θ. These relationships are illustrated by the complex impedance plane of Fig. 1-1.

The complex number system is a simple method for representing quadrature relationships between two quantities represented by coplanar vectors (often called phasors when applied to alternating-current circuits). The j indicates a 90° rotation of the vector with respect to the real axis. To keep the algebraic sign correct, j must equal $\sqrt{-1}$.

In general, as the frequency ω of the applied voltage or current source is varied, the impedance and its resistive and reactive components become functions of ω. This fact can be expressed analytically as $\overline{Z(\omega)} = R(\omega) + jX(\omega)$. Resistors do not vary in response as a function of frequency; however, combinations of reactive components such as inductors L and capacitors C with reactances of $(X_L = \omega L)$ and $(X_C = -1/\omega C)$, respectively, can produce a real or resistive component, $R(\omega)$, which is a function of frequency.

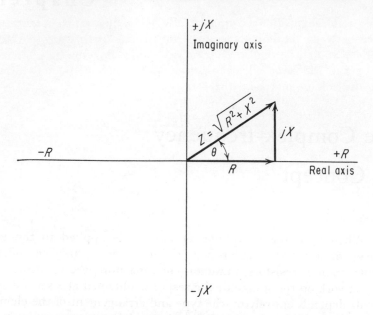

Fig. 1-1. Complex impedance or Z-plane.

If the source varies in amplitude as a function of time or if the voltages or currents supplied are nonsinusoidal, then the effects of the network's elements are not easily characterized by use of conventional complex impedance. For this reason, the concept of complex frequency has been developed to simplify the mathematics required to solve networks under these conditions. By describing the network functions in terms of complex-frequency notation, it is also possible to utilize the methods of Laplace transformations to determine the frequency or time response of the network.

The purpose of this chapter is to review complex notation briefly and to discuss the topics of complex-variable theory related to the complex-frequency concept of network representation. This review should be useful since the synthesis procedures explained in this book will be based on the complex-frequency concept.

1-1. Complex-frequency Notation in Networks

In order to thoroughly understand the complex-frequency concept, it is first desirable to investigate complex-frequency notation as applied to the analysis of some simple networks. Consider the network of Fig. 1-2 in which a sinusoidal voltage is applied to a series combination of resistance R, inductance L, and capacitance C. The rate at which the amplitude of the applied voltage varies is denoted by the real-frequency variable ω in radians per second. Because of the quadrature relationships existing between the impedance of circuit elements that are frequency-dependent and those that are not, it is common practice to include the operator j in the notation of functions of the real-frequency variable; hence, the voltage may be expressed as $e(j\omega)$.

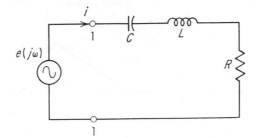

Fig. 1-2. Series *RLC* network.

The current i flowing in the network can be written in terms of the applied voltage $e(j\omega)$, and the impedance of the network elements as a function of the real-frequency variable as follows:

$$i(j\omega) = \frac{e(j\omega)}{Z(j\omega)} = \frac{e(j\omega)}{\dfrac{1}{j\omega C} + j\omega L + R} \tag{1-1}$$

The impedance of the network as a function of frequency can be written as

$$Z(j\omega) = \frac{1}{j\omega C} + j\omega L + R = \frac{-\omega^2 LC + j\omega RC + 1}{j\omega C} \tag{1-2}$$

In the case of more complicated networks, both the real and imaginary components of the impedance may be functions of frequency.

It is now possible to introduce the complex-frequency variable s which can be written as $s = \sigma + j\omega$ where σ is a real number having the units *nepers per second*. A major advantage of functions expressed in terms of the complex-frequency variable s is that they may be varied simultaneously in amplitude (at an exponential rate) and/or in angular frequency as a function of time. The complex-frequency or s-plane is shown in Fig. 1-3.

If the real-frequency variable of Eq. (1-2) is replaced by the more general complex-frequency variable, the impedance that represents the network of Fig. 1-2 becomes a function of the complex variable s.

$$Z(s) = \frac{LCs^2 + RCs + 1}{Cs} \tag{1-3}$$

This impedance function deserves further consideration; however, it is useful to first establish certain characteristics of the complex-frequency variable s.

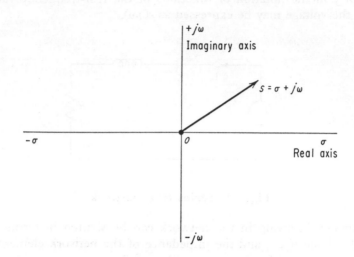

Fig. 1-3. Complex frequency or s-plane.

Networks which have only two terminals, such as Fig. 1-2 between terminals 1-1, are known as one-port networks. The reader may find networks such as these referred to in the literature as one-terminal-pair networks; however, in agreement with presently accepted terminology, "one-port networks" will be used throughout the remainder of this book. In the case of one-port networks, the reciprocal of impedance Z is known as admittance. The admittance is denoted by Y, and may also be expressed analytically as a function of the real-frequency variable ω or the complex-frequency variable s.

The linear, passive, bilateral elements (i.e., resistors, inductors, and capacitors) used in the synthesis procedures of this book can be considered to be simple one-port networks, and for this reason their impedance and admittance are reciprocal functions. The impedance and admittance of these individual elements are given in terms of real frequency and the more general complex frequency in Table 1-1. In this table it is noted that the impedance and admittance functions when expressed in terms of the complex-frequency variable are equivalent to those expressed in terms of the real-frequency variable when s equals $j\omega$.

The only operations performed in handling impedance or admittance functions are addition, subtraction, multiplication, division, integration, and differentiation. The operations of addition, subtraction, multiplication, and division are simplified by use of the complex frequency notation, since manipulation of the directional operator j is not involved. When it is desirable to find the real-frequency representation for a network, it is possible to let $\sigma = 0$ in the relationship $s = \sigma + j\omega$.

TABLE I-I

Impedance and Admittance Representation

Element	Real-frequency variable		Complex-frequency variable	
	Impedance	Admittance	Impedance	Admittance
Resistance, R	R	$\dfrac{1}{R} = G$	R	$\dfrac{1}{R} = G$
Inductance, L	$j\omega L$	$\dfrac{1}{j\omega L}$	Ls	$\dfrac{1}{Ls}$
Capacitance, C	$\dfrac{1}{j\omega C}$	$j\omega C$	$\dfrac{1}{Cs}$	Cs

The operations of integration and differentiation with respect to time are easily denoted when using the complex-frequency variable. When using linear elements, multiplication by s denotes differentiation of the function with respect to time, and division by s denotes integration with respect to time. This fact can be illustrated by considering the network of Fig. 1-2 in which the voltage is a function of time rather than a function of frequency. For simplicity, it will be assumed that there is no initial charge on the capacitor C when the voltage is applied to the network. In this case it is possible to write the following equations for the voltage drops in the network following the application of the voltage $e(t)$:

$$e(t) = \frac{1}{C} \int_0^t i \, dt + L \frac{di}{dt} + Ri(t) \qquad (1\text{-}4)$$

If the process of integration is denoted by $1/s$ and differentiation by s, then Eq. (1-4) becomes

$$e(t) = \frac{i(t)}{Cs} + Ls \, i(t) + Ri(t) \qquad (1\text{-}5)$$

Solving for the ratio of the voltage to the current,

$$\frac{e(t)}{i(t)} = \left(\frac{1}{Cs} + Ls + R \right) = \left(\frac{LCs^2 + RCs + 1}{Cs} \right) = Z(s) \qquad (1\text{-}6)$$

It is noted that this equation yields the same impedance as Eq. (1-3), which confirms that multiplication by s is equivalent to differentiating the function with respect to time, and division by s is the same as integrating the function from time $t = 0$ to time t.†

Impedance or admittance functions expressed in terms of the complex-frequency variable s are known as functions of a complex variable. The remainder of this chapter will be devoted to some of the rules which apply to the manipulation of functions of a complex variable and the complex-frequency plane. Some of the theorems and formulas mentioned in the remainder of this chapter form the basis of synthesis procedures to be developed in later chapters.

1-2. Complex Variables

If s is a complex number representing a point in a region r of the σ,ω-plane, it is called a complex variable. If a second variable w from a u,v-plane is related to s such that for each value of s in the region r there corresponds a definite value of w, then w is a function of the complex variable s and can be written $w = F(s)$. The variable w might be considered to represent the impedance or admittance of a network. The

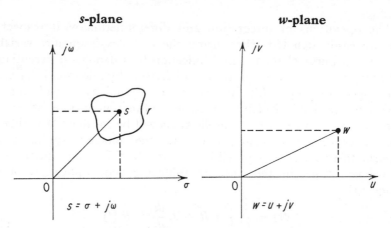

Fig. 1-4. Example of a function of a complex variable.

relationship between these variables is illustrated in Fig. 1-4, where $s = \sigma + j\omega$ and $w = u + jv$. The real and imaginary components of w do not necessarily equal the real and imaginary components of s; however, if w is a function of s, then u and v are functions of σ and ω. This can be expressed analytically as

$$u = U(\sigma,\omega) \quad \text{and} \quad v = V(\sigma,\omega) \tag{1-7}$$

† This example is not intended as proof of the above statements, since a complete proof would require discussion of the initial and final value theorems. Detailed proof of these statements can be found in M. F. Gardner and J. L. Barnes, *Transients in Linear Systems* (New York: John Wiley & Sons, Inc., 1942), pp. 267–274.

1-3. Differentiation of Complex Variables

With reference to Fig. 1-4, an incremental change in s of Δs may be made in an infinite number of directions. This would yield an infinite number of changes in w of Δw, since w is a function of s. It is of interest to determine whether the derivative or rate of change of w with respect to s is the limit of the ratio $\Delta w/\Delta s$ as the increment Δs approaches zero. Provided the ratio $\Delta w/\Delta s$ as Δs approaches zero is independent of the direction of Δs, the ratio possesses a unique value and the derivative of w with respect to s represents the limiting condition of the ratio.

The conditions under which the derivative of w with respect to s is independent of the direction of Δs can be found in the following manner. Assume that w is a continuous function of s, then

$$\frac{dw}{ds} = \frac{du + j\,dv}{d\sigma + j\,d\omega} \tag{1-8}$$

Using Eq. (1-7)

$$du = \frac{\partial u}{\partial \sigma}\,d\sigma + \frac{\partial u}{\partial \omega}\,d\omega \tag{1-9}$$

and

$$dv = \frac{\partial v}{\partial \sigma}\,d\sigma + \frac{\partial v}{\partial \omega}\,d\omega \tag{1-10}$$

If the partial derivatives $\partial u/\partial \sigma$, $\partial u/\partial \omega$, $\partial v/\partial \sigma$, and $\partial v/\partial \omega$ exist and are continuous functions, then by substituting Eqs. (1-9) and (1-10) into Eq. (1-8), it is seen that the direction of ds is determined by $d\omega/d\sigma$:

$$\frac{dw}{ds} = \frac{\left(\dfrac{\partial u}{\partial \sigma} + j\dfrac{\partial v}{\partial \sigma}\right) + \left(\dfrac{\partial u}{\partial \omega} + j\dfrac{\partial v}{\partial \omega}\right)\dfrac{d\omega}{d\sigma}}{1 + j\dfrac{d\omega}{d\sigma}} \tag{1-11}$$

This equation is independent of the direction in which Δs is taken provided that

$$\frac{\left(\dfrac{\partial u}{\partial \sigma} + j\dfrac{\partial v}{\partial \sigma}\right)}{\left(\dfrac{\partial u}{\partial \omega} + j\dfrac{\partial v}{\partial \omega}\right)} = \frac{1}{j} \tag{1-12}$$

Equating the real and imaginary parts of Eq. (1-12) yield the Cauchy-Riemann partial differential equations, which can be written as

$$\frac{\partial u}{\partial \sigma} = \frac{\partial v}{\partial \omega} \quad \text{and} \quad \frac{\partial u}{\partial \omega} = -\frac{\partial v}{\partial \sigma} \tag{1-13}$$

Whenever the real and imaginary parts of a complex function $w = F(s)$ satisfy the conditions of Eq. (1-13), the derivative of the function, if it exists, will have a unique value for any point s independent of the direction in which Δs is taken. To insure that a function will have a derivative at a particular point in a region r the Cauchy-Riemann equations must be continuous. If the function has a derivative at every point in the region, it is said to be analytic over the region and is called an analytic function. Most of the functions used in passive network synthesis satisfy these conditions; consequently, this text will deal almost exclusively with analytic functions of the complex frequency variable.

The function $w = s$, in which $u = \sigma$ and $v = \omega$, satisfies the Cauchy-Riemann conditions of Eq. (1-13) and the requirements of an analytic function. It can be shown that polynomials and also the ratio of polynomials fulfill the requirements of analytic functions.† Examples of such functions are given in Eqs. (1-14) and (1-15).

$$w = F(s) = a_n s^n + a_{n-1} s^{n-1} + \cdots + a_1 s + a_0 \qquad (1\text{-}14)$$

$$w = F(s) = \frac{a_n s^n + a_{n-1} s^{n-1} + \cdots + a_1 s + a_0}{b_m s^m + b_{m-1} s^{m-1} + \cdots + b_1 s + b_0} \qquad (1\text{-}15)$$

Most of the functions used in network synthesis, such as the example of Eq. (1-3), can be written as the ratio of two polynomials in s. The numerator of Eq. (1-15) can be divided by a_n and the denominator by b_m, and the resulting polynomials can be factored to yield the following form:

$$F(s) = K \frac{(s + s_{n*})(s + s_{n-1*}) \cdots (s + s_{2*})(s + s_{1*})}{(s + s_m)(s + s_{m-1}) \cdots (s + s_2)(s + s_1)}$$

where
$$K = \frac{a_n}{b_m} \qquad (1\text{-}16)$$

The values of s which cause the denominator of the function to be zero or the function to become infinite are known as poles. The poles of Eq. (1-16) are at $(s = -s_m)$, $(s = -s_{m-1})$, ..., $(s = -s_2)$, and $(s = -s_1)$. If h of the denominator factors are identical, then they can be grouped together as a single pole of order h.

Values of s that cause the numerator of Eq. (1-16) to be zero or the function to become zero are known as zeros. The zeros of Eq. (1-16) are at $(s = -s_{n*})$, $(s = -s_{n-1*})$, ..., $(s = -s_{2*})$, and $(s = -s_{1*})$. Functions, such as Eqs. (1-15) and (1-16), that can be expressed as the ratio of finite polynomials in s are known as rational functions. In general, a rational function is completely defined within a constant multiplier [given by K in Eq. (1-16)] by its poles and zeros.

Special points at which a function cannot be differentiated are called

† E. A. Guillemin, *The Mathematics of Circuit Analysis* (New York: John Wiley & Sons, Inc., 1949), p. 257.

singularities of the function. These singularities define the characteristics of the function and can be classified according to types as poles, essential singularities, and branch points.† The type of singularity indicates the manner in which the function (or its derivative) behaves as s approaches the point in question. At poles of a function such as Eq. (1-16) the function becomes infinite. Essential singularities and branch points are not frequently encountered in synthesis procedures; however, it is important to recognize them. Essential singularities are those points that can assume any assigned value depending on the manner in which the point is approached. Simple examples of functions having essential singularities are e^{-s}, which possesses a singularity at infinity, and $e^{-1/s}$, which has a singularity at the origin. A branch point is characterized by the fact that a complete traversal of a path enclosing the point does not result in a return to the original value. The simplest functions having branch points are of the form $\sqrt[n]{s}$. The $\sqrt{s}$ is a zero-type branch point at the origin, since $\sqrt{s}$ approaches zero as s approaches zero. The function $1/\sqrt{s}$ is a pole-type branch point at the origin.

1-4. Points at Infinity

Often in network synthesis it is necessary to consider the behavior of a function as s approaches infinity. It is awkward to assume that the s-plane goes to infinity in all directions, since this would mean that s would be infinity at an infinite number of points. Because of this difficulty, it is convenient to visualize an extended s-plane, including all finite and infinite points, as the surface of a sphere with an infinite radius on which the real and imaginary axes bend around and meet at a point as they approach infinity. This concept is shown in Fig. 1-5a. By this definition, infinity becomes a point on a complex sphere.

It is also difficult to consider the s-plane as a sphere even if its radius is infinite. This problem can be avoided by thinking of the s-plane as a flat surface, with a sphere of finite radius tangent to the plane at the origin of the coordinate axes, as seen in Fig. 1-5b. If the point of tangency is considered as the South pole of the sphere, then a given finite point s_0 in the s-plane joined with the North pole of the sphere by a straight line intersects the surface at only one point s^*. This method of projecting points from the s-plane such that each point on the sphere is uniquely associated with a point on the plane is known as stereographic projection. By this method of projection, all angles on the sphere are the same as their projections from the s-plane, and all points lying an infinite distance from the origin on the plane are projected to a single point at the North pole of the sphere. All considerations concerning

† Zeros do not qualify as singularities, since it is possible for a function to possess derivatives at these points.

regions on the s-plane can also be applied to the projection of those regions on the surface of the sphere.

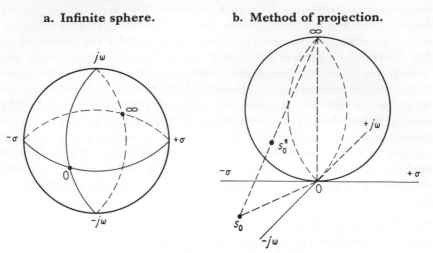

a. Infinite sphere.   **b. Method of projection.**

Fig. 1-5. Spherical concept of infinity.

1-5. Additional Properties of Analytic Functions

There are several additional properties of analytic functions which should be considered in order to better understand the usefulness of the complex plane. If $F(s)$ and $G(s)$ are two functions of s, both of which are analytic in the same region r, then the following rules can be applied to the functions.

1. The functions are still analytic in the region if multiplied by a constant K [i.e., $KF(s)$ and $KG(s)$ are analytic].

2. The sum of the two functions is analytic in the region [i.e., $F(s) + G(s)$ is analytic].

3. The product of the functions is analytic in the region [i.e., $F(s)G(s)$ is analytic].

4. A function $F(s)$ of a function $G(s)$ is analytic in the region {i.e., $F[G(s)]$ is analytic}.

5. The quotient of the functions is analytic in the region except when the denominator is zero or has a singularity [i.e., $F(s)/G(s)$ is analytic except when $G(s)$ is zero or has a singularity].

The above properties apply to almost all functions used in network analysis and synthesis procedures. Eqs. (1-14) and (1-15) are examples of functions that follow these rules.

1-6. Hurwitz Polynomials

Physical realizability is of primary importance in network synthesis, and the realizability of a network is dependent on the relative position of the poles and zeros of its characterizing function. Usually a network will be physically realizable if none of the poles and zeros of its impedance function falls within the right half of the s-plane (σ is positive and ω either positive or negative). This point will be considered in more detail later, since there are several exceptions. For instance, it is not necessary for the zeros of transfer impedance functions, representing networks which couple two or more sets of terminals, to lie in the left half-plane or on the $j\omega$-axis for the networks to be realizable. However, at this point it is convenient to study only the characteristics of functions having poles and zeros restricted to the left half of the s-plane or $j\omega$-axis.

If a polynomial of the form of Eq. (1-14) is such that all real roots and the real parts of all complex roots are either zero or negative, then the function is known as a Hurwitz polynomial. Equation (1-14) can be written in factored form as

$$F(s) = a_n(s + s_n)(s + s_{n-1})\cdots(s + s_2)(s + s_1) \qquad (1\text{-}17)$$

If this equation is multiplied out and terms of like powers of s are collected and compared with corresponding terms in Eq. (1-14), the coefficients can be equated to yield the following equations:

$$\frac{a_{n-1}}{a_n} = (s_1 + s_2 + s_3 + \cdots + s_n)$$

$$\frac{a_{n-2}}{a_n} = s_1(s_2 + s_3 + \cdots + s_n) + s_2(s_3 + s_4 + \cdots + s_n) + \cdots + s_{n-1}s_n$$

$$\cdot \quad \cdot \quad \cdot \quad \cdot \quad \cdot \quad \cdot \quad \cdot \quad \cdot \quad \cdot$$

$$\cdot \quad \cdot \quad \cdot \quad \cdot \quad \cdot \quad \cdot \quad \cdot \quad \cdot \quad \cdot$$

$$\frac{a_0}{a_n} = (s_1 s_2 s_3 \ldots s_n) \qquad (1\text{-}18)$$

For roots on the real axis of the s-plane, the zeros of Eq. (1-17) can be written as $(s = -\sigma_n)$, $(s = -\sigma_{n-1})$, $\ldots$, $(s = -\sigma_2)$, and $(s = -\sigma_1)$. If a_n is a positive real number greater than zero and each of the roots on the real axis is either zero or negative, the coefficients of Eq. (1-18) must either be zero or positive real numbers. The same results can be established for complex roots having either zero or negative real parts, provided all complex roots occur in conjugate pairs. Consequently, for a polynomial to be a Hurwitz polynomial it is necessary that the coefficients of the various powers of s be either zero or positive real numbers. Although this condition is necessary, it is not sufficient. The coefficients may all be zero or positive and real, but $F(s)$ still may not be Hurwitz. For example, $(s^3 + s^2 + s + 6)$ meets the conditions stated but when factored, $(s + 2)(s^2 - s + 3)$, it clearly has roots in the right half of the s-plane. Negative coefficients or missing powers of s may indicate the presence of zeros in the right half of the s-plane.

Consider the case of a pair of complex conjugate roots lying on the $j\omega$-axis. These roots can be written as $(s - j\omega)$ and $(s + j\omega)$ and upon combination yield:

$$F(s) = (s - j\omega)(s + j\omega) = s^2 + \omega^2 \qquad (1\text{-}19)$$

A zero at the origin can be written as s; therefore, a polynomial having zeros only on the $j\omega$-axis or at the origin will have only even powers of s or odd powers of s, and all of the coefficients will be either zero or positive real numbers.

In order to test a given polynomial to determine whether or not it is a Hurwitz polynomial, the following approach is often employed. The polynomial $F(s)$ is first broken into two parts, $M(s)$ and $N(s)$, where $M(s)$ represents the terms involving even powers of s and $N(s)$ represents the odd powers of s:

$$F(s) = M(s) + N(s) \qquad (1\text{-}20)$$

If $F(s)$ is a Hurwitz polynomial, then $M(s)$ and $N(s)$ will be Hurwitz polynomials of a special character; namely, with all their zeros on the imaginary axis, and, barring common zeros, the zeros of $M(s)$ and $N(s)$ will mutually separate each other.

To expand further on the above discussion, assume that $F(s)$ is a Hurwitz polynomial. In this case $M(s)$ and $N(s)$ are also Hurwitz polynomials having only even or odd powers of s. The ratio $M(s)/N(s)$ can be expressed as $R(s)$, where even powers of s are in the numerator and odd powers of s are in the denominator. There are two cases to be considered, depending on whether the highest power s term in $F(s)$ is even or odd. Assume the highest power is even, then the ratio becomes

$$R(s) = \frac{M(s)}{N(s)} = \frac{a_n s^n + a_{n-2} s^{n-2} + \cdots + a_4 s^4 + a_2 s^2 + a_0}{a_{n-1} s^{n-1} + a_{n-3} s^{n-3} + \cdots + a_3 s^3 + a_1 s^1} \qquad (1\text{-}21)$$

If the numerator is divided by a_n and the denominator by a_{n-1} and the resulting polynomials factored, the zeros of $M(s)$ will occur in complex conjugate pairs, since only even ordered terms are present in the numerator. Likewise, if s is factored out of the denominator, the remaining zeros of $N(s)$ or poles of $R(s)$ will occur in complex conjugate pairs. Therefore, Eq. (1-21) can be written as

$$R(s) = \frac{M(s)}{N(s)} = \frac{a_n(s^2 + s_1{}^2)(s^2 + s_3{}^2)\cdots(s^2 + s_{2n-1}^2)}{a_{n-1}s(s^2 + s_2{}^2)(s^2 + s_4{}^2)\cdots(s^2 + s_{2n-2}^2)} \qquad (1\text{-}22)$$

If $F(s)$ is truly a Hurwitz polynomial, the zeros of $M(s)$ and $N(s)$ or in other words the poles and zeros of $R(s)$ in Eq. (1-22) will alternate along the imaginary axis starting with a simple pole ($s = 0$) at the origin. This is known as the separation property of the zeros of $F(s)$. The same results are obtained if the highest power of s in $F(s)$ is odd rather than even. The poles and zeros will still mutually separate each other; however, a zero will fall at the origin rather than a pole.† Although the separation property is also a necessary condition, it is not sufficient. The necessary and sufficient conditions required to insure that $F(s)$ is a Hurwitz polynomial are

1. $F(s)$ must be a polynomial having coefficients which are either zero or positive real numbers.
2. The zeros of $M(s)$ and $N(s)$ must be simple and restricted to the imaginary axis where they mutually separate each other. Consequently, $M(s)$ and $N(s)$ may differ in their highest and lowest powers by no more than unity.

Equations such as (1-21) can be expanded in a Stieltjes continued fraction of the following form by a process of repeated division and inversion.

$$R(s) = \beta_1 s + \cfrac{1}{\beta_2 s + \cfrac{1}{\beta_3 s + \cfrac{1}{\beta_4 s + \cdots \cfrac{}{\cdots + \cfrac{1}{\beta_n s}}}}} \qquad (1\text{-}23)$$

This type of expansion can be used as a proof of a particular type of Hurwitz polynomial; namely, one which contains no roots on the $j\omega$-axis. If a polynomial $F(s)$ is known to have no roots on the $j\omega$-axis, then it may be tested to determine whether or not it is Hurwitz in the following manner. First, $F(s)$ is separated to yield the functions $M(s)$ and $N(s)$ from which the ratio $R(s)$ is established. Then if $F(s)$ is a polynomial of degree n, the continued-fraction expansion of $R(s)$ must be developed until all n coefficients $\beta_1, \beta_2, \ldots, \beta_n$ have been determined. Provided all of the β coefficients are positive real numbers, $F(s)$ is a Hurwitz polynomial. In the case of functions having roots on the $j\omega$-axis, it is possible to separate out all terms of the form s or $(s^2 + \omega^2)$ after which the continued-fraction expansion test can be made on the remainder to establish whether or not it is a Hurwitz polynomial multiplied by the removed terms.

As an example of how a polynomial can be tested by the Stieltjes continued-fraction expansion, consider the function, $F(s) = 24s^4 + 12s^3 + 18s^2 + 7s + 1$. Breaking the function into odd and even powers

† The above is not intended as proof of the separation properties of zeros nor a proof that the zeros lie on the $j\omega$-axis; however, a simple proof can be achieved by evaluating the residues of $F(s)$ at its poles. Complete proof of the separation property can be found in E. A. Guillemin, *The Mathematics of Circuit Analysis* (New York: John Wiley & Sons, Inc., 1949), pp. 400–401.

of s yields, $M(s) = 24s^4 + 18s^2 + 1$ and $N(s) = 12s^3 + 7s$. The ratio $R(s)$ can be written as

$$R(s) = \frac{M(s)}{N(s)} = \frac{24s^4 + 18s^2 + 1}{12s^3 + 7s} \tag{1-24}$$

Repeated long division and inversion gives the following continued-fraction expansion.

$$R(s) = 2s + \cfrac{1}{3s + \cfrac{1}{s + \cfrac{1}{4s}}} \tag{1-25}$$

Inspection of Eq. (1-25) reveals that all of the coefficients are positive real numbers, and since $F(s)$ contained no roots on the $j\omega$-axis, it is a Hurwitz polynomial. The same conclusion can be reached by examination of $M(s)$ and $N(s)$ in Eq. (1-24), which has a single pole at the origin and simple complex conjugate poles and zeros which mutually separate each other.

1-7. Partial Fraction Expansions

Most synthesis procedures require that network functions be broken up into a number of terms which can be identified with network elements. A continued-fraction expansion, as discussed briefly in the last section, is one procedure that can often be used to decompose a network function. A second procedure for breaking up functions is the partial-fraction expansion.

Consider a function such as Eq. (1-15) in which the denominator has been divided by b_m and factored.

$$F(s) = \frac{a_n s^n + a_{n-1} s^{n-1} + \cdots + a_1 s + a_0}{b_m(s + s_m)(s + s_{m-1}) \cdots (s + s_2)(s + s_1)} \tag{1-26}$$

This function is said to possess "simple" poles if no multiple-order poles are present, and it is possible to expand the function into a number of separate terms, as seen below. The $k_i/(s + s_i)$ terms are known as partial fractions, and this form of equation is spoken of as a partial-fraction expansion.

$$F(s) = c_q s^q + c_{q-1} s^{q-1} + \cdots + c_1 s + c_0 + \frac{k_m}{(s + s_m)}$$

$$+ \frac{k_{m-1}}{(s + s_{m-1})} + \cdots + \frac{k_i}{(s + s_i)} + \cdots + \frac{k_2}{(s + s_2)} + \frac{k_1}{(s + s_1)} \tag{1-27}$$

The polynomial, $c_q s^q + c_{q-1} s^{q-1} + \cdots + c_1 s + c_0$, will exist if the degree of the numerator of the function is equal to or greater than the degree of the denominator. If this condition exists, the polynomial can be determined by dividing the numerator by the denominator until the remainder has a numerator that is at least one degree lower than the denominator. The coefficients k_m, k_{m-1}, ..., k_2, and k_1 of the separated poles are known as residues at the poles, and they will be either real or complex constants. The following example will serve to demonstrate one procedure which can be used to determine the values of the residues.

Assume Eq. (1-28) is to be expanded into a partial-fraction expansion. For simplicity, the numerator has been chosen one degree less than the denominator.

$$F(s) = \frac{3s + 11}{s^2 + 7s + 12} = \frac{3s + 11}{(s + 3)(s + 4)} \tag{1-28}$$

The first step in the procedure is to write the partial-fraction expansion form of the function:

$$F(s) = \frac{k_2}{(s + 3)} + \frac{k_1}{(s + 4)} \tag{1-29}$$

Multiplying out Eq. (1-29) and equating its numerator with that of Eq. (1-28) yields:

$$k_2(s + 4) + k_1(s + 3) = (k_1 + k_2)s + (4k_2 + 3k_1) = 3s + 11 \tag{1-30}$$

Equating the coefficients of like powers of s

$$k_1 + k_2 = 3 \tag{1-31}$$

$$3k_1 + 4k_2 = 11 \tag{1-32}$$

Solving Eqs. (1-31) and (1-32) gives $k_1 = 1$ and $k_2 = 2$. These values can be substituted back in Eq. (1-29) to complete the partial-fraction expansion of Eq. (1-28).

$$F(s) = \frac{2}{(s + 3)} + \frac{1}{(s + 4)} \tag{1-33}$$

This procedure is satisfactory for simple functions; however, it becomes involved when the numerator and denominator are high-order polynomials.

When dealing with higher-order functions, it is sometimes desirable to compute the residue at a particular pole without solving for all of the other residues. To achieve this capability, assume that the function and its partial-fraction expansion can be written as

$$F(s) = \frac{s^n + d_{n-1}s^{n-1} + \cdots + d_1 s + d_0}{(s + s_m)(s + s_{m-1}) \cdots (s + s_2)(s + s_1)}$$

$$= \frac{k_m}{(s + s_m)} + \frac{k_{m-1}}{(s + s_{m-1})} + \cdots + \frac{k_i}{(s + s_i)} + \cdots$$

$$+ \frac{k_2}{(s + s_2)} + \frac{k_1}{(s + s_1)} \quad (1\text{-}34)$$

The numerator of $F(s)$ is assumed to be of lower order than the denominator; a result which can always be produced by removing a polynomial as discussed above. In order to evaluate the residue k_i it is possible to multiply both sides of Eq. (1-34) by $(s + s_i)$ and substitute $(s = -s_i)$ in the result. When this is done, all other factors drop out, leaving

$$k_i = [(s + s_i)F(s)]_{s = -s_i} \quad (1\text{-}35)$$

The usefulness of Eq. (1-35) can be illustrated by determining the value of the residue k_2 at the pole $s = -3$ in the example of Eq. (1-28).

$$k_2 = \left[\frac{(s + 3)(3s + 11)}{(s + 3)(s + 4)} \right]_{s = -3} = 2 \quad (1\text{-}36)$$

Note that the value of Eq. (1-36) agrees with that of the residue k_2 previously determined for Eq. (1-33). Equation (1-35) can be used to find the residues of poles only when they are simple.

When the poles are of higher order, the residues must be found by a slightly different procedure. Consider the case in which the pole at $s = -s_m$ is second-order. In this case the partial-fraction expansion must be written as follows:

$$F(s) = \frac{s^n + d_{n-1}s^{n-1} + \cdots + d_1 s + d_0}{(s + s_m)^2(s + s_{m-1}) \cdots (s + s_2)(s + s_1)}$$

$$= \frac{k_{m+1}}{(s + s_m)^2} + \frac{k_m}{(s + s_m)} + \frac{k_{m-1}}{(s + s_{m-1})} + \cdots + \frac{k_2}{(s + s_2)} + \frac{k_1}{(s + s_1)}$$

$$(1\text{-}37)$$

The value of k_{m+1} can be found by multiplying both sides of Eq. (1-37) by $(s + s_m)^2$ and substituting $s = -s_m$ in the result. Since all other terms drop out, the value of k_{m+1} becomes

$$k_{m+1} = [(s + s_m)^2 F(s)]_{s = -s_m} \quad (1\text{-}38)$$

The remaining residues, except k_m, can be found by Eq. (1-35). It can be demonstrated by a simple example that the value of k_m is given by

$$k_m = \frac{1}{1!} \left\{ \frac{d}{ds} [(s + s_m)^2 F(s)] \right\}_{s = -s_m} \quad (1\text{-}39)$$

The same general procedure can be used for determining the residues of higher-order poles. For instance, assume the pole at $s = -s_m$ is third-order. In this case the partial-fraction expansion becomes

$$F(s) = \frac{s_n + d_{n-1}s^{n-1} + \cdots + d_1 s + d_0}{(s + s_m)^3 (s + s_{m-1}) \cdots (s + s_2)(s + s_1)}$$

$$= \frac{k_{m+2}}{(s + s_m)^3} + \frac{k_{m+1}}{(s + s_m)^2} + \frac{k_m}{(s + s_m)}$$

$$+ \frac{k_{m-1}}{(s + s_{m-1})} + \cdots + \frac{k_2}{(s + s_2)} + \frac{k_1}{(s + s_1)} \qquad (1\text{-}40)$$

Multiplying both sides of Eq. (1-40) by $(s + s_m)^3$ and substituting $s = -s_m$ in the result yields

$$k_{m+2} = [(s + s_m)^3 F(s)]_{s = -s_m} \qquad (1\text{-}41)$$

The remaining residues, except for k_{m+1} and k_m, can be found by Eq. (1-35). The value of k_{m+1} and k_m can be determined from the following equations:

$$k_{m+1} = \frac{1}{1!}\left\{\frac{d}{ds}[(s + s_m)^3 F(s)]\right\}_{s = -s_m} \qquad (1\text{-}42)$$

$$k_m = \frac{1}{2!}\left\{\frac{d^2}{ds^2}[(s + s_m)^3 F(s)]\right\}_{s = -s_m} \qquad (1\text{-}43)$$

This procedure can be used to determine the residues at poles of any order, and the expressions necessary for evaluating higher-order residues should be apparent from the above cases.

To demonstrate the usefulness of the above procedures, assume it is desirable to expand the following function in a partial-fraction expansion.

$$F(s) = \frac{7s^3 + 41s^2 + 79s + 49}{(s + 2)^3 (s + 1)} \qquad (1\text{-}44)$$

The partial-fraction expansion for this function can be written as

$$F(s) = \frac{k_4}{(s + 2)^3} + \frac{k_3}{(s + 2)^2} + \frac{k_2}{(s + 2)} + \frac{k_1}{(s + 1)} \qquad (1\text{-}45)$$

The value of k_4 can be determined by substituting Eq. (1-44) into Eq. (1-41) and evaluating at the pole $s = -2$ as follows:

$$k_4 = \left[\frac{(s + 2)^3 (7s^3 + 41s^2 + 79s + 49)}{(s + 2)^3 (s + 1)}\right]_{s = -2} = 1 \qquad (1\text{-}46)$$

The value of k_3 can be determined by substituting Eq. (1-44) into Eq. (1-42) and evaluating at the pole $s = -2$.

$$k_3 = \frac{1}{1!}\left\{\frac{d}{ds}\left[\frac{(s+2)^3(7s^3 + 41s^2 + 79s + 49)}{(s+2)^3(s+1)}\right]\right\}_{s=-2}$$

$$= \left[\frac{(s+1)(21s^2 + 82s + 79) - (7s^3 + 41s^2 + 79s + 49)}{(s+1)^2}\right]_{s=-2} = 2 \tag{1-47}$$

The value of k_2 can be determined by substituting Eq. (1-44) into Eq. (1-43) and evaluating at the pole $s = -2$.

$$k_2 = \frac{1}{2!}\left\{\frac{d^2}{ds^2}\left[\frac{(s+2)^3(7s^3 + 41s^2 + 79s + 49)}{(s+2)^3(s+1)}\right]\right\}_{s=-2}$$

$$= \frac{1}{2}\left[\frac{(s+1)^2(42s^2 + 124s + 82) - 2(s+1)(14s^3 + 62s^2 + 82s + 30)}{(s+1)^4}\right]_{s=-2}$$

$$= 3 \tag{1-48}$$

Equation (1-35) can be used to determine k_1 by substituting Eq. (1-44) for $F(s)$ and evaluating at the pole $s = -1$.

$$k_1 = \left[\frac{(s+1)(7s^3 + 41s^2 + 79s + 49)}{(s+2)^3(s+1)}\right]_{s=-1} = 4 \tag{1-49}$$

Substituting the residue values determined in Eqs. (1-46) through (1-49) into Eq. (1-45), the partial-fraction expansion of Eq. (1-44) is obtained:

$$F(s) = \frac{1}{(s+2)^3} + \frac{2}{(s+2)^2} + \frac{3}{(s+2)} + \frac{4}{(s+1)} \tag{1-50}$$

It should be pointed out that the two methods described above for evaluating residues can be used advantageously to complement each other when computing the partial-fraction expansion of a function.

As a second example, consider the following function which has a pair of complex conjugate poles:

$$F(s) = \frac{8}{s^2 + 2s + 5} = \frac{k_2}{(s+1+j2)} + \frac{k_1}{(s+1-j2)} \tag{1-51}$$

Equation (1-35) can be used to determine the value of k_2 by evaluating at the pole $s = -1 - j2$.

$$k_2 = \left[\frac{(s+1+j2)8}{(s+1+j2)(s+1-j2)}\right]_{s=-1-j2} = j2 \tag{1-52}$$

Likewise, k_1 can be determined using the pole $s = -1 + j2$.

$$k_1 = \left[\frac{(s+1-j2)8}{(s+1+j2)(s+1-j2)}\right]_{s=-1+j2} = -j2 \tag{1-53}$$

Substituting k_1 and k_2 from Eqs. (1-52) and (1-53) back into Eq. (1-51) yields the partial-fraction expansion of the example function:

$$F(s) = \frac{j2}{(s + 1 + j2)} + \frac{-j2}{(s + 1 - j2)} \qquad (1-54)$$

The residues for a pair of complex conjugate poles are themselves complex conjugates, provided the coefficients of the rational function are real.

The object of this chapter has been to acquaint the reader with the complex-frequency concept, introduce some mathematical techniques, and discuss types of functions to be encountered in synthesis procedures of later chapters. Rigorous proof has not been given to support the material presented thus far, since such proof would require considerable detail that is not necessary for the application of these techniques. Indeed, many related topics have been omitted; however, if this chapter has given the reader an understanding of such terms as Hurwitz polynomial, the residue at a pole, a continued fraction, or partial-fraction expansion, it has served its purpose. The operation and significance of these concepts will become clearer as they are used in later chapters.

References

Introductory material concerning the use of complex frequency notation in network synthesis can be found in:

1. John L. Stewart, *Circuit Theory and Design* (New York: John Wiley & Sons, Inc., 1956), Chap. 2.
2. D. F. Tuttle, *Network Synthesis*, Vol. I (New York: John Wiley & Sons, Inc., 1958), Chap. 1.
3. M. E. Van Valkenburg, *Introduction to Modern Network Synthesis* (New York: John Wiley & Sons, Inc., 1960), Chap. 1.

Greater detail concerning complex-variable theory as applied to network synthesis can be found in Chaps. 2 and 3 of Ref. 2 and Secs. 4.2 and 4.3 of Ref. 3. See also the following texts:

4. E. A. Guillemin, *The Mathematics of Circuit Analysis* (New York: John Wiley & Sons, Inc., 1949), Chap. 6.
5. S. Seshu and N. Balabanian, *Linear Network Analysis* (New York: John Wiley & Sons, Inc., 1959), Appendix A.
6. L. Weinberg, *Network Analysis and Synthesis* (New York: McGraw-Hill Book Co., Inc., 1962), Chaps. 5 and 6.

Problems

1-1. Prove that the following identity satisfies the Cauchy-Riemann equations where $s = \sigma + j\omega$.

$$\cos s = \cos \sigma \cosh \omega + j \sin \sigma \sinh \omega$$

1-2. For the relationship $s = Re^{j\theta}$ and $w = F(s) = u + jv$ where R, θ, u, and v are real and $F(s)$ is a regular analytic function, show that the Cauchy-Riemann partial differential equations become

$$\frac{\partial u}{\partial R} = \frac{1}{R}\frac{\partial v}{\partial \theta} \quad \text{and} \quad \frac{\partial v}{\partial R} = -\frac{1}{R}\frac{\partial u}{\partial \theta}$$

1-3. Determine the values of s for which the following functions are analytic. Discuss the effect of these functions on the relationship between the s- and w-planes.

(a) $w = s^2 = \sigma^2 - \omega^2 + j2\sigma\omega$

(b) $w = \dfrac{1}{s} = \dfrac{\sigma}{\sigma^2 + \omega^2} - \dfrac{j\omega}{\sigma^2 + \omega^2}$.

1-4. Determine which of the following are Hurwitz polynomials. Show two different proofs for each case and discuss the results.

(a) $s^4 + 10s^3 + 35s^2 + 50s + 24$
(b) $s^5 + 2s^4 + 11s^3 + 18s^2 + 18s$
(c) $s^5 + 8s^4 + 16s^3 + 18s^2 + 95s + 150$

1-5. Determine the residues of the poles of the following function and show that they are the numerator coefficients when the function is written as a partial-fraction expansion. Is this function a Hurwitz polynomial?

$$F(s) = \frac{s + 3}{(s^2 + 8s + 12)}$$

1-6. Determine the continued-fraction expansions for the following functions by repeated division and inversion. Note that although these functions are equivalent, their expansions are different. Discuss the significance of this fact.

(a) $F(s) = \dfrac{s^2 + 8s + 12}{s + 3}$

(b) $F(s) = \dfrac{12 + 8s + s^2}{3 + s}$

1-7. Expand the following functions as partial fractions and determine the residues at each of the poles.

(a) $F(s) = \dfrac{7s^2 + 10s + 15}{(s^2 + 2s + 5)(s + 1)}$

(b) $F(s) = \dfrac{s^2 + 2s - 1}{(s - 3)^2(s + 5)}$

1-8. Determine whether or not the functions of Prob. 1-7 are Hurwitz polynomials. Expand these functions in the form of continued fractions. Discuss the possibility of obtaining a continued-fraction expansion for each with no negative terms.

1-9. Determine and plot the zeros of the following function when the residue of the pole at $(s = 0)$ has values $k = 3$, $k = 1$, $k = 0$, $k = -1$, and $k = -3$. The residues of the poles at $(s = 2)$ and $(s = 4)$ are unity for all cases. At what value of k does a zero move into the right half-plane?

$$F(s) = \frac{as^2 + bs + c}{s(s + 2)(s + 4)}$$

1-10. The Cauchy residue theorem states that the residue of a function $F(s)$ at a simple pole $(s = -s_i)$ is given by the closed integral

$$k_i = \frac{1}{2\pi j} \int_C F(s)\, ds$$

where C is any contour enclosing the point in question. Show that this integral can be used to evaluate the residues at the individual poles of Prob. 1-5. By extension of this theorem, the value of the contour integral enclosing several poles is equal to $2\pi j$ times the sum of the residues at the poles. Demonstrate this fact using the poles and residues of Prob. 1-5.

Chapter 2

Energy Functions of
a Network

Chapter 1 introduced the concept of the complex-frequency plane which will be used in the remainder of the book. It also explained that a large number of network impedance and admittance functions to be encountered in synthesis procedures of later chapters will be composed of Hurwitz polynomials. This fact will be developed in more detail here and in Chap. 3.

The realization problem of network synthesis deals with all procedures and techniques that can be used to identify a specific network with the impedance or admittance function which is either given or determined by solution of the approximation problem. However, before it is possible to solve the realization problem it is necessary that the impedance or admittance function meet certain constraints to insure that physically realizable networks having the desired characteristics may be identified with it. To determine these constraints, it is necessary to study the characteristics of physically realizable networks. The purpose of this chapter is to investigate the energy characteristics of various realizable networks and to study the "driving-point" and "transfer" impedance functions that represent them.

2-1. Energy Functions

For a single-loop network consisting of resistance R, inductance L, and capacitance C, it is possible to express the voltages around the circuit in terms of the instantaneous current through the elements. For example, in Chap. 1 the differential equation, Eq. (1-4), was used to represent the voltages around the network of Fig. 1-2, assuming no initial charge on the capacitor. This equation is repeated below for reference.

$$e(t) = \frac{1}{C} \int_0^t i \, dt + L \frac{di}{dt} + Ri(t) \tag{2-1}$$

22

Analysis similar to that performed on a single loop can be used for a multiloop network. If reciprocal capacitance, known as elastance, is denoted by S, then the elements in the loop-parameter matrices of a multiloop network can be written as L_{mk}, R_{mk}, and S_{mk}. Provided there are p loops in the network, indices m and k may assume any integer value from 1 to p and the algebraic form similar to Eq. (2-1) for the multiloop network becomes

$$\sum_{k=1}^{p}\left(L_{mk}\frac{d}{dt} + R_{mk} + S_{mk}\int dt\right)i_k = e_m$$

where $$m = 1, 2, 3, \ldots, p \qquad (2\text{-}2)$$

In this equation $e_1, e_2, e_3, \ldots, e_p$, are voltage sources in the various branches or links which connect the elements of the network, and $i_1, i_2, i_3, \ldots, i_p$ are the loop currents which flow through the same branches or links. For simplicity, it will be assumed that none of the capacitors possesses an initial charge. Although Eq. (2-2) is a compact form for the various loop equations, the reader may better understand the notation by expanding these equations in the following manner:

$$\left(L_{11}\frac{d}{dt} + R_{11} + S_{11}\int dt\right)i_1 + \left(L_{12}\frac{d}{dt} + R_{12} + S_{12}\int dt\right)i_2$$

$$+ \cdots + \left(L_{1p}\frac{d}{dt} + R_{1p} + S_{1p}\int dt\right)i_p = e_1$$

$$\left(L_{21}\frac{d}{dt} + R_{21} + S_{21}\int dt\right)i_1 + \left(L_{22}\frac{d}{dt} + R_{22} + S_{22}\int dt\right)i_2$$

$$+ \cdots + \left(L_{2p}\frac{d}{dt} + R_{2p} + S_{2p}\int dt\right)i_p = e_2$$

$$\cdot \quad \cdot \quad \cdot \quad \cdot \quad \cdot \quad \cdot \quad \cdot \quad \cdot$$

$$\cdot \quad \cdot \quad \cdot \quad \cdot \quad \cdot \quad \cdot \quad \cdot \quad \cdot$$

$$\left(L_{m1}\frac{d}{dt} + R_{m1} + S_{m1}\int dt\right)i_1 + \left(L_{m2}\frac{d}{dt} + R_{m2} + S_{m2}\int dt\right)i_2$$

$$+ \cdots + \left(L_{mp}\frac{d}{dt} + R_{mp} + S_{mp}\int dt\right)i_p = e_p \qquad (2\text{-}3)$$

The total instantaneous power delivered to the network by all the sources is given by

$$P = i_1 e_1 + i_2 e_2 + \cdots + i_p e_p \qquad (2\text{-}4)$$

The total power delivered to the network can also be expressed by multiplying both sides of Eq. (2-2) by i_m, giving an equation for each value of m from 1 to p. These equations can be substituted in Eq. (2-4) and the right-hand side summed from $m = 1$ to $m = p$.

$$P = \sum_{m=1}^{p} \sum_{k=1}^{p} \left(L_{mk} i_m \frac{di_k}{dt} + R_{mk} i_m i_k + S_{mk} i_m \int i_k \, dt \right) = \sum_{m=1}^{p} e_m i_m \tag{2-5}$$

The time differentiation and integration do not affect the current i_m.

It is now convenient to define the following three functions:

$$F = \frac{1}{2} \sum_{m=1}^{p} \sum_{k=1}^{p} R_{mk} i_m i_k$$

$$T = \frac{1}{2} \sum_{m=1}^{p} \sum_{k=1}^{p} L_{mk} i_m i_k$$

$$V = \frac{1}{2} \sum_{m=1}^{p} \sum_{k=1}^{p} S_{mk} q_m q_k \tag{2-6}$$

where q_k is the charge in the loop or time integral of the loop current, $q_k = \int i_k \, dt$. Consideration of F, T, and V reveals that F has dimensions of power, while T and V have units of energy. T represents energy stored magnetically in the network and is of the form $T = Li^2/2$, which is the magnetically stored energy of an inductor. V represents electrically stored energy and is of the form $V = Sq^2/2$, which is the electrically stored energy of a capacitor. T and V are referred to as the stored energy functions of the network, while F, which is in dimensions of power or time rate of energy, is known as the loss function of the network. Substituting the definitions of Eq. (2-6) into Eq. (2-5) yields

$$P = 2F + \frac{d}{dt}(T + V) = \sum_{m=1}^{p} e_m i_m \tag{2-7}$$

The integral sign of Eq. (2-5), which is written in terms of currents, disappears in Eq. (2-7) because V is defined in terms of charges. The actual power dissipated in the resistance of the network is $2F$, since the "loss function" of Eq. (2-6) contains a multiplier of $1/2$ to keep the form of all three definitions the same.

The definitions, F, T, and V are generally spoken of as energy functions, and Eq. (2-7) represents the total instantaneous rate of energy dissipation in an RLC multiloop network.† Resistors, inductors, and capacitors are passive elements characterized by impedance or admittance functions whose real part is greater than or equal to zero {i.e., $Re[Z(j\omega)] \geqq 0$ as illustrated in Table 1-1}. These elements are not energy sources; therefore Eq. (2-7) expresses the conservation of energy

† E. A. Guillemin, *Introductory Circuit Theory* (New York: John Wiley & Sons, Inc., 1953), pp. 510–535.

in that the time rate of energy supplied to the network equals the sum of the real power dissipated in the resistors $2F$ and the rate of change of stored energy in the electric and magnetic fields of the capacitors and inductors of the network.

2-2. Driving-point Function Characteristics

A one-port network can be drawn as indicated in Fig. 2-1, where the instantaneous voltage and current inputs $e_1(t)$ and $i_1(t)$ can be expressed as functions of complex frequency by use of the Laplace transformation.

$$E_1(s) = \int_0^\infty e_1(t)e^{-st}\,dt \quad \text{and} \quad I_1(s) = \int_0^\infty i_1(t)e^{-st}\,dt$$

$$(2\text{-}8)$$

An explicit definition for the impedance of the network is provided by the relationship $Z_1(s) = E_1(s)/I_1(s)$. The impedance $Z_1(s)$ of a one-port network is called a driving-point impedance and has many interesting aspects which will be of major importance in remaining chapters.

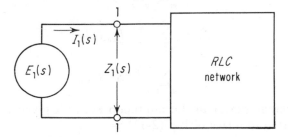

Fig. 2-1. General one-port network.

In order to determine the characteristics of a driving-point impedance, assume the available terminals 1-1 of Fig. 2-1 are the terminals of loop m of a multiloop network. Using the complex-frequency notation, it is possible to apply a voltage $e_m(t) = E_m e^{st}$ to the terminals of loop m. In this case the loop k current will be of the form $i_k(t) = I_k e^{st}$. Substituting these terms into Eq. (2-2) and factoring out the exponential e^{st} yields

$$\sum_{k=1}^{p}\left(L_{mk}s + R_{mk} + \frac{S_{mk}}{s}\right)I_k = E_m$$

where $\qquad m = 1, 2, 3, \cdots, p$ $\qquad\qquad (2\text{-}9)$

The resulting equations for $m = 1$, $m = 2$, etc., can now be multiplied respectively by the conjugate currents $\bar{I}_1, \bar{I}_2, \ldots, \bar{I}_m$ to yield the time averages of the respective powers. If this result is summed over all values of m from $m = 1$ to $m = p$, the total average power input to the network becomes

$$P_{\text{ave}} = \sum_{m=1}^{p} E_m \bar{I}_m = s \sum_{m=1}^{p} \sum_{k=1}^{p} L_{mk} I_k \bar{I}_m$$

$$+ \sum_{m=1}^{p} \sum_{k=1}^{p} R_{mk} I_k \bar{I}_m + \frac{1}{s} \sum_{m=1}^{p} \sum_{k=1}^{p} S_{mk} I_k \bar{I}_m \quad (2\text{-}10)$$

Since Eq. (2-10) expresses the average power supplied to the multiloop network, its real component must be positive. The power $R_{mk} I_k \bar{I}_m$ delivered to the resistances of the network is equal to the real part of the applied power, and this can be read on a wattmeter. The imaginary or reactive component of applied power is distributed between the electrical fields of the capacitors and magnetic fields of the inductors.

It is now convenient to define "average energy functions" which are similar in form to Eq. (2-6) but represent the time average dissipation or exchange of power.

$$F_o = \sum_{m=1}^{p} \sum_{k=1}^{p} R_{mk} I_k \bar{I}_m$$

$$T_o = \sum_{m=1}^{p} \sum_{k=1}^{p} L_{mk} I_k \bar{I}_m$$

$$V_o = \sum_{m=1}^{p} \sum_{k=1}^{p} S_{mk} I_k \bar{I}_m \quad (2\text{-}11)$$

The total average power in the multiloop network given by Eq. (2-10) can be rewritten in terms of Eq. (2-11) as

$$P_{\text{ave}} = \sum_{m=1}^{p} E_m \bar{I}_m = s T_o + F_o + \frac{V_o}{s} \quad (2\text{-}12)$$

It should be pointed out that T_o has dimensions of energy, F_o is the average dissipated power, and V_o is the time rate of change of power. Although the complex frequency variable s appears only in two places in Eq. (2-12), it should be remembered that the voltages and currents may also be expressed in terms of s. Furthermore, the average energy functions F_o, T_o, and V_o must have values which are either zero or positive and real for all values of s.†

Consider Eq. (2-12) when $m = p = 1$: this corresponds to the average power input for the network of Fig. 2-1.

$$P_{\text{ave}} = E_1 \bar{I}_1 = s T_o + F_o + \frac{V_o}{s} \quad (2\text{-}13)$$

† *Ibid.*, pp. 522–535.

The average power of Eq. (2-13) must be zero or positive and real. Dividing both sides by $I_1 \bar{I}_1 = |I_1|^2$ yields

$$\frac{E_1}{I_1} = \frac{F_o + sT_o + \dfrac{V_o}{s}}{|I_1|^2} \qquad (2\text{-}14)$$

However, E_1 and I_1 may also be functions of s; hence, the driving-point impedance can be expressed as

$$Z_1(s) = \frac{E_1(s)}{I_1(s)} = \frac{F_o + sT_o + \dfrac{V_o}{s}}{|I_1(s)|^2} \qquad (2\text{-}15)$$

The denominator of this equation must always be a positive real value, since it is a squared term. The numerator must also be positive and real, since it equals Eq. (2-13). Because F_o, T_o, and V_o must be either zero or positive and real quantities, it can be seen from Eq. (2-15) that the driving-point impedance of a passive network must have the following characteristics with respect to the complex frequency variable $s = \sigma + j\omega$:

1. When s is real, $Z_1(s)$ must be real.
2. For σ greater than or equal to zero, the real component of $Z_1(s)$ must be positive or zero.

Functions satisfying the first requirement are called real functions. If $Z_1(s)$ also satisfies the second condition {i.e., $Re[Z_1(s)] \geqq 0$ for $\sigma \geqq 0$}, it is known as a positive real (often abbreviated as p.r.) function. These results are important, since they imply that the real or "resistive component" of the impedance must be positive or zero for all real frequencies {i.e., when $s = j\omega$, $Re[Z_1(j\omega)] \geqq 0$ for all ω}.

In the above discussion it has been shown that the driving-point impedance of a one-port network must be a positive real function of s. A similar approach using energy functions can be derived on an admittance basis to demonstrate that a driving-point admittance $Y_1(s)$ must also be a positive real function. However, since $Y_1(s)$ of a one-port network is the reciprocal of the impedance, the admittance of Fig. 2-1 can be written as

$$Y_1(s) = \frac{1}{Z_1(s)} = \frac{|I_1(s)|^2}{F_o + sT_o + \dfrac{V_o}{s}} \qquad (2\text{-}16)$$

In this case the numerator and denominator are either zero or positive and real values; therefore, the same conclusions can be drawn concerning the characteristics of a driving-point admittance as were drawn for the driving-point impedance:

1. When s is real, $Y_1(s)$ must be real.

2. For σ greater than or equal to zero, the real component of $Y_1(s)$ must be positive or zero.

Therefore, the driving-point admittance of a network must also be a positive real function of s and have a real part that is either zero or positive for all values of ω. This significant result—that the driving-point impedance and admittance of a passive network must be a positive real function of s—is attributed to Otto Brune. A multiterminal or n-port network will have a driving-point impedance and admittance associated with any two of its terminals regardless of how the other terminals are terminated. The necessary conditions for a driving-point impedance or admittance to be a positive real function will be discussed in greater detail in Chap. 3.

2-3. Transfer-function Characteristics

The positive real characteristics of driving-point impedances and admittances have been discussed, but now it is desirable to determine the characteristics of a transfer function. A transfer function relates one pair of terminals of a multiterminal network to a second pair of terminals. The transfer function can be written as the ratio of output to input voltages or currents, in which case the function is dimensionally unitless. It may also be written to express output voltage as a function of input current or output current as a function of input voltage, in which case the function has units of impedance or admittance. In order to investigate the characteristics of a transfer function, an approach based on the driving-point impedances of a two-port network will be used. A two-port network is a network having four terminals which are considered in pairs of two.

Consider the two-port network of Fig. 2-2 which has an ideal transformer in the input and output circuits. The ideal transformers have turns ratios of $a:1$ and $b:1$, respectively, and their primaries are connected in series. These transformers are assumed to be circuit elements capable of changing voltage and current levels through their turns ratio; however, they do not affect the location of the poles and zeros of the network functions under consideration. Therefore, an ideal transformer is a mathematical tool and can only be approximated in practice. Finally, to simplify the figures and equations of this section, all voltages, currents, and impedances will be assumed to be functions of the complex frequency variable s.

The network between terminals 1-1 and 2-2 of Fig. 2-2 can be assumed to have two major loops containing only passive elements, represented by boxes and connected as shown in Fig. 2-3. The voltage drops around the two loops can be expressed in terms of the applied voltages, loop currents, and loop impedances as

$$E_1 = z_{11}I_1 + z_{12}I_2 \quad \text{and} \quad E_2 = z_{21}I_1 + z_{22}I_2 \quad (2\text{-}17)$$

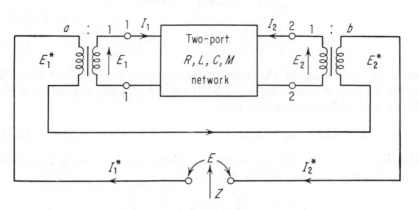

Fig. 2-2. Determination of transfer function characteristics.

The impedances z_{11} and z_{22} represent the driving-point impedance seen looking into terminals 1-1 and 2-2, respectively, with the opposite set of terminals open. The impedance z_{12} represents the impedances mutually shared by loops 1 and 2 as seen from loop 1, and z_{21} is the mutually shared impedance as seen from loop 2. These impedances are known as transfer impedances coupling loops 1 and 2, and in the case of passive networks containing no nonreciprocal elements such as gyrators, z_{12} equals z_{21}.

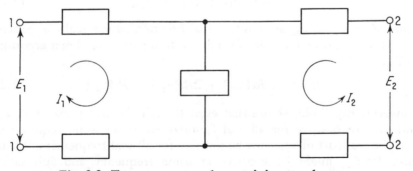

Fig. 2-3. Two-port network containing two loops.

The application of a voltage E to the network of Fig. 2-2 will produce a current I in the primaries of the transformers. This current can be written as

$$I = I_1^* = I_2^* \quad (2\text{-}18)$$

As seen from the primary terminals of the ideal transformers, Eq. (2-17) becomes

$$\frac{1}{a} E_1^* = z_{11} a I_1^* + z_{12} b I_2^*$$

$$\frac{1}{b} E_2^* = z_{21} a I_1^* + z_{22} b I_2^* \tag{2-19}$$

Since the primaries of the transformers are in series, the voltage E equals E_1^* plus E_2^*. Solving Eq. (2-19) for E_1^* and E_2^*, substituting Eq. (2-18), and adding the results gives

$$E = E_1^* + E_2^* = z_{11} a^2 I + z_{12} ab I + z_{22} b^2 I + z_{21} ab I \tag{2-20}$$

The input impedance of the network is obtained by dividing Eq. (2-20) by I and imposing the condition $z_{12} = z_{21}$.

$$Z = \frac{E}{I} = a^2 z_{11} + 2ab z_{12} + b^2 z_{22} \tag{2-21}$$

The impedance Z is a driving-point impedance, since it is the impedance seen looking into a single pair of terminals. Likewise, z_{11} and z_{22} are driving-point impedances; therefore, Z, z_{11}, and z_{22} must be positive real functions of s.

The impedance $z_{12} (= z_{21})$ does not necessarily have the characteristics of a driving-point impedance, and this fact can be demonstrated in the following manner. Assuming a turns ratio of unity for the transformers of Fig. 2-2, Eq. (2-21) becomes

$$Z = z_{11} + 2z_{12} + z_{22} \tag{2-22}$$

Since Z, z_{11}, and z_{22} are positive real functions, their real components must also be positive or zero for all real frequencies ω. Then according to Eq. (2-22)

$$Re[Z] = Re[z_{11}] + 2Re[z_{12}] + Re[z_{22}] \tag{2-23}$$

However, Eq. (2-23) shows that even though the real parts of Z, z_{11}, and z_{22} are positive for all real frequencies, there is no requirement that the real part of z_{12} must be positive for all real frequencies. Therefore, $Re[z_{12}]$ might be negative at some frequency and still satisfy Eq. (2-23). This is the major difference between a driving-point function, such as z_{11} and z_{22}, and a transfer function, such as z_{12}. If a network has several terminals, there will be a transfer impedance or admittance between any pair of terminals and a second pair of terminals regardless of how other terminals might be terminated. Specific requirements of a transfer function will be discussed in detail in Chap. 7.

References

Greater detail concerning the subject of energy functions can be found in the following references.

1. E. A. Guillemin, *Introductory Circuit Theory* (New York: John Wiley & Sons, Inc., 1953), Chap. 10.
2. S. Seshu and N. Balabanian, *Linear Network Analysis* (New York: John Wiley & Sons, Inc., 1959), Chap. 1 and Sec. 9.3.

The characteristics of impedance and admittance functions are presented in Ref. 2, Sec. 4.7 and in the following texts:

3. E. A. Guillemin, *Synthesis of Passive Networks* (New York: John Wiley & Sons, Inc., 1957), Chap. 1.
4. D. F. Tuttle, *Network Synthesis*, Vol. I (New York: John Wiley & Sons, Inc., 1958), Chap. 4.

Problems

2-1. Determine whether or not the following functions are physically realizable as driving-point impedances. This can be accomplished by substituting $s = j\omega$ and proving that the real parts of the function are positive for all frequencies from $\omega = 0$ to $\omega = \infty$. Plot the real part of the functions from $\omega = 0$ to $\omega = 4$.

(a) $Z_1(s) = \dfrac{s^2 + 5s + 6}{s^3 + 4s^2 + 5s}$ 　　　 (b) $Z_1(s) = \dfrac{s^2 + 4s + 3}{s^3 + 4s^2 + 5s}$

2-2. Plot the poles and zeros of the functions of Prob. 2-1. Note the effect on the real part of both functions, as determined in Prob. 2-1, as a result of moving a zero closer to the origin.

2-3. Check the following functions for realizability as driving-point functions by determining the real parts of the functions for $s = j\omega$. Plot the poles and zeros of the functions. Even though the real parts of these functions are zero at all frequencies, they are realizable as pure LC networks. Note the separation properties of the poles and zeros along the $j\omega$-axis. Perform a continued-fraction expansion of each function and relate the terms to a realizable network configuration.

(a) $Z_1(s) = \dfrac{s^2 + 4}{s}$ 　　　 (b) $Z_1(s) = \dfrac{s^2 + 1}{s^3 + 9s}$

2-4. Determine the driving-point impedance of the following network as a function of the complex frequency, s. Synthesize a second network for the resulting function by continued-fraction expansion.

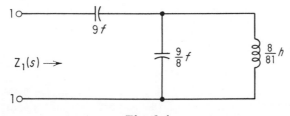

Fig. 2-4

2-5. Plot the real and imaginary parts of $Z_1(s)$ and the magnitude of $Z_1(s)$ for values of $s = j\omega$ from $\omega = 0$ to $\omega = 8$ for the following impedance. In addition, make a pole-zero plot of the function, and briefly discuss the effect of the poles and zeros on the variation of the real and imaginary parts of the function as well as the magnitude of $Z_1(s)$ when $s = j\omega$. This function is typical of a low-pass filter.

$$Z_1(s) = \frac{s^2 + 6s + 8}{s^2 + 4s + 3}$$

2-6. Repeat the requirements of Prob. 2-5, using the following impedance function:

$$Z_1(s) = \frac{s^2 + 4s + 3}{s^2 + 6s + 8}$$

2-7. Plot the magnitude of the following function for $s = j\omega$ between the frequencies $\omega = 5$ and $\omega = 15$ for $a = 1, 2$, and 5. Discuss the results of the three curves as a function of frequency and as a function of the position of the complex conjugate poles.

$$Z_1(s) = \frac{20.03}{(s + a + j10)(s + a - j10)}$$

2-8. Determine whether or not the following function is realizable as a driving-point impedance. Plot the magnitude of $Z_1(s)$ for $s = j\omega$. Compare the positions of the poles and zero with the response of the magnitude of $Z_1(s)$.

$$Z_1(s) = \frac{(s + 1)}{s^2 + 2s + 26}$$

Chapter 3

Positive Real Properties of

Driving-point Functions

In Chap. 2 it was shown that a network composed of a finite number of passive elements, such as the *RLC* network of Fig. 2-1, will have a driving-point impedance $Z_1(s)$ which can be expressed as

$$Z_1(s) = \frac{E_1(s)}{I_1(s)} = \frac{T_o s + F_o + \dfrac{V_o}{s}}{|I_1(s)|^2} \tag{3-1}$$

Based on this and a similar expression for the driving-point admittance, $Y_1(s)$, it was proved that driving-point functions must be positive real functions of s in order to insure physically realizable passive networks. Before an attempt is made to identify a physically realizable network with a given driving-point impedance or admittance function, it is worthwhile to test the function to determine whether or not it is positive real. Tests that can be performed on the functions in question and realization of various *LC* networks are the subjects of this chapter.

3-1. Properties of Positive Real Functions

In Chap. 1 it was stated that the quotient of two Hurwitz polynomials forms a rational function, and since driving-point functions can be written in this form, they must also be rational functions of s. From Eq. (3-1) it was also found that the driving-point impedance of a physically realizable passive network must be a positive real function. Consequently, three general properties of the driving-point impedance of a passive network can be listed as follows:

1. $Z_1(s)$ must be a rational function of s.
2. $Z_1(s)$ must be real for real values of s.
3. The real part of $Z_1(s)$ must be greater than or equal to zero for the real part of s greater than or equal to zero. Mathematically this can be written as

$$Re[Z_1(s)] \geqq 0 \qquad \text{for} \qquad Re[s] \geqq 0 \tag{3-2}$$

33

These properties will now be studied in more detail. Property 1 will be considered in Case A, Property 2 in Case B, and Property 3 in Cases C through I of the following discussion.

Case A. The driving-point impedance will have the form of Eq. (3-3) which is the quotient of two polynomials $P(s)$ and $Q(s)$.

$$Z_1(s) = \frac{P(s)}{Q(s)} = \frac{a_n s^n + a_{n-1} s^{n-1} + \cdots + a_1 s + a_0}{b_m s^m + b_{m-1} s^{m-1} + \cdots + b_1 s + b_0} \qquad (3\text{-}3)$$

This type of function can be rewritten as the product of a number of roots, as seen in Eq. (3-4), or it can be broken up into a partial-fraction expansion. If $Z_1(s)$ possesses these characteristics, it must be a rational function of s.

$$Z_1(s) = \frac{P(s)}{Q(s)} = K \frac{(s + s_n)(s + s_{n-1}) \cdots (s + s_2)(s + s_1)}{(s + s_{m*})(s + s_{m-1*}) \cdots (s + s_{2*})(s + s_{1*})} \qquad (3\text{-}4)$$

Case B. Since only passive elements are being considered, Property 2 requires that $P(s)$ and $Q(s)$ must have real coefficients and any complex roots of these polynomials, if present, must occur in conjugate pairs. These are the characteristics of Hurwitz polynomials.

Case C. If $Z_1(s)$ is positive real, then its reciprocal $Y_1(s)$ is also positive real except when $Z_1(s)$ is identically zero. To prove this fact, substitute $s = \sigma + j\omega$ into $P(s)$ and $Q(s)$ of Eq. (3-3), then break up the polynomials into their real and imaginary parts, $A_1 + jB_1$ and $A_2 + jB_2$, as indicated in Eq. (3-5).

$$Z_1(s) = \frac{P(s)}{Q(s)} = \frac{A_1 + jB_1}{A_2 + jB_2} \qquad (3\text{-}5)$$

The real part of $Z_1(s)$ becomes

$$Re[Z_1(s)] = Re\left[\frac{A_1 + jB_1}{A_2 + jB_2} \cdot \frac{A_2 - jB_2}{A_2 - jB_2}\right] = \frac{A_1 A_2 + B_1 B_2}{A_2^2 + B_2^2} \qquad (3\text{-}6)$$

Because of the squared terms and positive coefficients, Eq. (3-6) is positive and real. Now consider the reciprocal, the real part of $1/Z_1(s)$.

$$Re\left[\frac{1}{Z_1(s)}\right] = Re\left[\frac{A_2 + jB_2}{A_1 + jB_1} \cdot \frac{A_1 - jB_1}{A_1 - jB_1}\right] = \frac{A_1 A_2 + B_1 B_2}{A_1^2 + B_1^2} \qquad (3\text{-}7)$$

Because of the squared terms and positive coefficients, the reciprocal, $Y_1(s) = 1/Z_1(s)$ is also a positive real function of s.

Case D. There can be no poles or zeros of $Z_1(s)$ in the right half of the s-plane. This means there are no poles or zeros with positive real parts. To prove this fact, it is useful to investigate the behavior of a function in the vicinity of a pole by expanding it in a Laurent series at the pole. Therefore, assuming Eq. (3-3) possesses a pole at $s = s_o$, it is possible to expand the function in the vicinity of the pole as follows:

$$Z_1(s) = \frac{b_{-n}}{(s - s_o)^n} + \cdots + \frac{b_{-1}}{(s - s_o)} + b_0 + b_1(s - s_o) + \cdots$$

$$+ b_n(s - s_o)^n \quad (3\text{-}8)$$

A Laurent series consists of two parts known as the "principal" part and the "ascending" part. The principal part includes all terms with $(s - s_o)$ raised to negative powers, and the ascending part includes all the $(s - s_o)$ terms raised to zero and positive powers. In a region near the pole, the behavior of the function is approximated by

$$Z_1(s) \to \left. \frac{b_{-n}}{(s - s_o)^n} \right]_{s \to s_o} \quad (3\text{-}9)$$

All other terms in Eq. (3-8) become small compared with the $b_{-n}/(s - s_o)^n$ term if the magnitude $|s - s_o|$ is chosen sufficiently small.

Now let s vary around a small circle centered at $s = s_o$. In this case it is possible to write Eq. (3-9) in polar form where the terms are defined by Fig. 3-1.

$$Z_1(s) \to \left. \frac{Ke^{j\theta}}{(\rho e^{j\phi})^n} \right]_{s \to s_o} = \left. \frac{Ke^{j(\theta - n\phi)}}{\rho^n} \right]_{s \to s_o}$$

where $\qquad (s - s_o) = \rho e^{j\phi} \qquad$ and $\qquad b_{-n} = Ke^{j\theta} \qquad (3\text{-}10)$

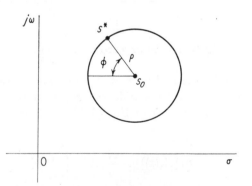

Fig. 3-1. Investigation of poles of $Z_1(s)$.

The value of θ locates the beginning point s^* on the circle, and the real part of $Z_1(s)$ becomes

$$Re[Z_1(s)] \to \left. \frac{K}{\rho^n} \cos(\theta - n\phi) \right]_{s \to s_o} \quad (3\text{-}11)$$

As s moves around the small circle, ϕ varies from 0 to 2π. Hence, $n\phi$ varies from 0 to $2n\pi$ and $Re[Z_1(s)]$ changes sign $2n$ times. Therefore,

$Z_1(s)$ can have no poles in the right half of the s-plane, since the real part of $Z_1(s)$ must be greater than or equal to zero for all values of s with real parts greater than or equal to zero.

The zeros of a driving-point function are also restricted from the right half of the s-plane. This fact can be proved by the same technique, using the poles of the admittance $Y_1(s)$ which is the reciprocal of $Z_1(s)$. In this case the zeros of $Z_1(s)$ are the poles of the admittance $Y_1(s)$. Consequently the poles and zeros of a driving-point impedance or admittance function are restricted to the left half of the s-plane or the $j\omega$-axis.

Case E. If a pole or zero is located on the $j\omega$-axis, as seen in Fig. 3-2, then as s is moved in a circle about s_o part of the circle will lie in the right half-plane and part in the left half-plane.

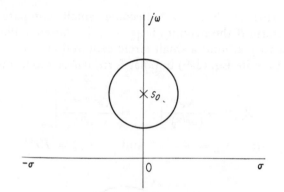

Fig. 3-2. Pole or zero on the $j\omega$-axis.

According to Case D, the real part of $Z_1(s)$ is not necessarily positive or greater than zero if it contains poles or zeros in the right half-plane. However, if $n = 1$ and $\theta = 0$ in Eq. (3-11), the real part of $Z_1(s)$ can be written as

$$Re[Z_1(s)] \to \frac{K}{\rho} \cos \phi \Big]_{s \to s_o} \tag{3-12}$$

This function is greater than zero for values of ϕ between $-\pi/2$ and $\pi/2$. Therefore, it can be concluded that positive real functions may have at least first-order poles on the $j\omega$-axis. In Case F, it will be shown that n must equal unity and θ must be zero to keep the real part of the impedance nonnegative for all real frequencies. When this is done, it can be concluded that driving-point functions may have only simple or first-order poles on the $j\omega$-axis. Similarly, by consideration of the reciprocal functions, it can be concluded that zeros of a driving-point impedance or admittance falling on the $j\omega$-axis must also be simple. Not only must the $j\omega$-axis roots of driving-point impedance and admittance functions be simple, but the residues at the simple poles on the $j\omega$-axis must be positive and real. This implies that the coefficient of the leading term in the Taylor expansion of the function at such a pole must be positive.

Case F. The number of finite poles and zeros of a driving-point function can differ at most by unity. In other words, the order of the numerator polynomial in terms of s can differ from the order of the denominator by no more than unity.

According to the definition of the s-plane given in Chap. 1, infinity can be thought of as a point which lies on the $j\omega$-axis. Poles or zeros at $s = \infty$ can be considered as poles or zeros on the $j\omega$-axis, and therefore they must satisfy the conditions discussed in Case E. As s approaches infinity, Eq. (3-3) becomes

$$Z_1(s)]_{s \to \infty} \approx K \frac{s^n}{s^m} = K s^{n-m}$$

(3-13)

This equation has three possibilities which should be investigated as s approaches infinity.

1. $Z_1(s)$ has a pole at infinity, then $n > m$ and $n - m = 1$.
2. $Z_1(s)$ has a zero at infinity, then $n < m$ and $m = n + 1$.
3. $Z_1(s)$ approaches a constant, K, then $n = m$.

These possibilities may be intuitive, since the first implies that as the frequency approaches infinity, the impedance function approaches that of an inductor. In the second case the impedance of the network approaches that of a capacitor, and in the third the impedance approaches the real component of the impedance as s approaches infinity.

On the basis of the above statements, the number of finite poles and zeros of $Z_1(s)$ or $Y_1(s)$ can differ by no more than unity. Driving-point functions that do not satisfy these conditions will be impossible to synthesize as physically realizable passive networks. However, as it will be seen in later chapters, these conditions are not necessarily true for transfer functions.

Case G. The multiplier K of a driving-point function such as Eq. (3-4) must be a positive real number. In Case F it was seen that as s approaches infinity, $Z_1(s)$ approaches K for $n = m$. In this case, due to Property 2, K must be real, and due to Property 3, K must be positive.

Case H. The lowest powers of s in $P(s)$ and $Q(s)$ can differ at most by unity. This fact can be demonstrated by approximating Eq. (3-3) for small values of s as follows:

$$Z_1(s)]_{s \to 0} \approx \frac{a_1 s + a_0}{b_1 s + b_0}$$

(3-14)

Four cases arise, since a_0 and b_0 can be either positive real values or zero.

1. If a_0, b_0, a_1, and b_1 are positive finite values, the lowest powers of s in $P(s)$ and $Q(s)$ are the same.

2. If a_1 and b_0 are zero, $Z_1(s)$ has a pole on the $j\omega$-axis at $s = 0$, so b_1 cannot be zero.

3. If a_0 and a_1 are positive finite values and if b_1 is zero, b_0 cannot be zero; otherwise there would be a simple pole at $s = 0$.

4. If a_0 is zero and b_0 and b_1 are positive finite values, then $1/Z_1(s)$ has a pole at $s = \infty$, so a_1 cannot be zero.

In the first and third cases, the impedance approaches the value of a resistance as s approaches zero. In the second case, the impedance approaches that of a capacitor, and in the fourth case it approaches that of an inductor as s approaches zero. Consequently, the lowest power of s in the numerator and denominator polynomials of a driving-point impedance or admittance function can differ at most by unity.

Case I. The real part of $Z_1(j\omega)$ is an even-ordered function, and the imaginary part is an odd-ordered function of ω. This can be proved by separating $P(s)$ and $Q(s)$ into polynomials having odd- and even-ordered values of s as shown in Eq. (3-15).

$$
\begin{aligned}
Z_1(s) &= \frac{P(s)}{Q(s)} \\
&= \frac{(a_n s^n + a_{n-2} s^{n-2} + \cdots + a_0) + s(a_{n-1} s^{n-2} + a_{n-3} s^{n-4} + \cdots + a_1)}{(b_m s^m + b_{m-2} s^{m-2} + \cdots + b_0) + s(b_{m-1} s^{m-2} + b_{m-3} s^{m-4} + \cdots + b_1)} \\
&= \frac{A_1 + sB_1}{A_2 + sB_2} = \{Ev[Z_1(s)] + Od[Z_1(s)]\}
\end{aligned}
\tag{3-15}
$$

In this equation m and n are taken as equal for convenience, and the A's and B's are even-ordered functions of s. From Eq. (3-15) the even and odd parts of the driving-point impedance can be derived as follows:

$$
\begin{aligned}
Ev[Z_1(s)] &= Ev\left[\frac{A_1 + sB_1}{A_2 + sB_2} \cdot \frac{A_2 - sB_2}{A_2 - sB_2}\right] \\
&= Ev\left[\frac{(A_1 A_2 - s^2 B_1 B_2) + s(B_1 A_2 - B_2 A_1)}{A_2{}^2 - s^2 B_2{}^2}\right] \\
&= \frac{A_1 A_2 - s^2 B_1 B_2}{A_2{}^2 - s^2 B_2{}^2}
\end{aligned}
\tag{3-16}
$$

$$
Od[Z_1(s)] = \left[s\frac{B_1 A_2 - B_2 A_1}{A_2{}^2 - s^2 B_2{}^2}\right]
\tag{3-17}
$$

Substituting $s = j\omega$ in Eqs. (3-16) and (3-17), it is seen that

$$
Ev[Z_1(j\omega)] = Re[Z_1(j\omega)] \quad \text{and} \quad Od[Z_1(j\omega)] = Im[Z_1(j\omega)] \tag{3-18}
$$

This proves that the real part of a driving-point impedance function is composed of even-ordered functions of s, and the imaginary part is composed of odd-ordered functions of s. The same results can be demonstrated for admittance functions and rational fractions for which m and n are not equal.

The highest and lowest ordered terms in a driving-point impedance or admittance function have been discussed in detail, and it is now desirable to consider the middle terms of the function. When a partial-fraction expansion is made of a driving-point impedance function, such as Eq. (3-4), the following form is obtained:

$$Z_1(s) = k_{m+2} + \frac{k_{m+1}}{s} + \frac{k_m}{(s + s_{m*})} + \frac{k_{m-1}}{(s + s_{m-1*})}$$

$$+ \cdots + \frac{k_2}{(s + s_{2*})} + \frac{k_1}{(s + s_{1*})} + k_0 s \qquad (3\text{-}19)$$

The k_{m+2}, k_{m+1}/s, and $k_0 s$ terms may or may not be present, depending on the highest- and lowest-ordered terms of the numerator and denominator polynomials of $Z_1(s)$. The impedance of Eq. (3-19) can be considered to be the sum of several individual impedances. For example, if the k_{m+2} term is present, it may be considered to represent a resistance; the k_{m+1}/s term, the impedance of a capacitor; and the $k_0 s$ term, the impedance of an inductor. The center terms of Eq. (3-19) are of the form $k/(s + s_o)$. Because the poles of the function are restricted to the left half of the s-plane or the $j\omega$-axis, there are three types of poles that can be considered.

1. Poles on the negative real or σ-axis.
2. Complex poles having finite negative real parts and occurring in conjugate pairs.
3. Poles on the $j\omega$-axis and occurring in conjugate pairs.

The entire impedance $Z_1(s)$ must meet the conditions of a positive real function as outlined in Cases A through I; however, this does not insure that each term in its partial-fraction expansion will meet these requirements. For example, consider the following positive real function and its partial-fraction expansion:

$$Z_1(s) = \frac{2s^2 + 4s + 1}{s^2 + 3s + 2} = 2 - \frac{1}{s + 1} - \frac{1}{s + 2} \qquad (3\text{-}20)$$

The $-1/(s + 1)$ and $-1/(s + 2)$ terms are clearly not positive real functions and cannot be identified as the impedances of physically realizable networks. However, if all of the terms of the partial-fraction expansion are of the form $k/(s + s_o)$ (i.e., there are no k_{m+2}, k_{m+1}/s, or $k_0 s$ terms), then it is necessary to consider the three types of poles listed above in more detail.

If a pole is of the first type, the residue k must be a positive real number in order that $k/(s + s_o)$ be a positive real function which can be identified as the impedance of a physically realizable network. If several such terms all having positive real coefficients are combined, it can be shown that all powers of s in the numerator and denominator polynomials of the resulting rational fraction will be present and will have positive real coefficients. For example, if the following positive real fractions are combined, it is seen that there are no missing powers of s between the highest and lowest powers in the numerator and denominator. It is also noted that the coefficient of each s term is positive and that the highest-ordered terms of the numerator and denominator differ in order by no more than unity. Likewise, the lowest-ordered terms differ in order by no more than unity.

$$Z_1(s) = \frac{2}{(s + 1)} + \frac{1}{(s + 2)} + \frac{3}{(s + 3)} = \frac{6s^2 + 23s + 21}{s^3 + 6s^2 + 11s + 6} \quad (3\text{-}21)$$

Poles of the second type must occur in complex conjugate pairs, and their residues must be complex conjugates of each other. When there are no terms of the form k_{m+2}, k_{m+1}/s, or $k_0 s$ present in the expansion, the real parts of the residues at complex conjugate poles will generally be positive. In this case the combination of a pair of complex conjugate terms will yield a positive real function which is physically realizable. For example, if the following complex conjugate fractions are combined, there are no missing powers of s in the numerator and denominator polynomials, and the coefficients of each s term is positive.

$$Z_1(s) = \frac{(2 + j1)}{(s + 1 - j1)} + \frac{(2 - j1)}{(s + 1 + j1)} = \frac{4s + 2}{s^2 + 2s + 2} \quad (3\text{-}22)$$

Poles of the third type must occur in conjugate pairs; however, since these poles fall on the $j\omega$-axis, their residues must be positive real numbers as stated in Case E. When conjugate poles on the imaginary axis are combined, some powers of s may be missing, but the coefficients of the s terms that are present must be positive. For example, if the following complex conjugate fractions are combined, some of the s terms are missing; however, the coefficients of the terms that are present are positive.

$$Z_1(s) = \frac{\frac{1}{2}}{(s + j1)} + \frac{\frac{1}{2}}{(s - j1)} + \frac{\frac{3}{2}}{(s + j3)} + \frac{\frac{3}{2}}{(s - j3)} = \frac{4s^3 + 12s}{s^4 + 10s^2 + 9}$$

$$(3\text{-}23)$$

Terms of the form $k/(s + s_o)$ in Eq. (3-19) comprise all powers of s in the numerator and denominator of Eq. (3-4) except for the highest- and lowest-ordered terms. Therefore, if a driving-point function contains no poles or zeros on the $j\omega$-axis, all of the s terms between the highest and lowest powers will be present in both the numerator and denominator polynomials of the function. If the function contains poles or zeros on the $j\omega$-axis, some powers of s may be missing. In addition to these constraints, the coefficients of the s terms in the numerator and denominator polynomials of a driving-point function must be positive. A number of tests, based on the above cases, can be performed to establish whether or not a given function satisfies the positive real requirements of a physically realizable driving-point impedance or admittance function. These tests will be investigated in the next section.

3-2. Tests for Positive Real Functions

Before it is possible to apply various tests to a given function, it is useful to eliminate all common factors of the numerator and denominator. For example, if $P(s)$ and $Q(s)$ both possess a common factor $(s - s_0)$ the ratio $P(s)/Q(s)$ contains the ratio $(s - s_0)/(s - s_0)$, which is obviously a positive real constant, unity. Although such a factor does not affect the positive real characteristics of a function, it may lead to erroneous conclusions. For instance, it is not immediately apparent that the following is a positive real function of s.

$$Z_1(s) = \frac{3s^2 + 4s - 20}{s^3 + 5s^2 - 2s - 24} = \frac{(3s + 10)}{(s^2 + 7s + 12)} \cdot \frac{(s - 2)}{(s - 2)}$$

$$= \frac{1}{(s + 3)} + \frac{2}{(s + 4)} \tag{3-24}$$

If all common factors in $P(s)$ and $Q(s)$ have been removed, the following observations may provide insight into the positive real characteristics of a function.

1. Check $P(s)$ and $Q(s)$ for negative coefficients. The function is not realizable if there are negative coefficients.
2. Check $P(s)$ and $Q(s)$ for missing terms. The function is probably not realizable if there are missing terms.
3. The difference in the degree of the highest-order terms in $P(s)$ and $Q(s)$ can differ at most by unity. Likewise, the degree of the lowest-order terms can differ at most by unity.

If the above observations are satisfied, the function is probably realizable as a driving-point impedance or admittance function. However, these observations are not conclusive especially if common factors exist in $P(s)$ and $Q(s)$, as shown by the example of Eq. (3-24). Furthermore, some physically realizable functions having poles and/or zeros on the $j\omega$-axis will not satisfy the above conditions. Consequently, more powerful methods designed to test the positive real characteristics of a function are required.

Test 1. The first test is designed to determine whether or not the real parts of the poles and zeros of the function are nonpositive. $P(s)$ and $Q(s)$ must both be Hurwitz polynomials, and $Z_1(s)$ can have no poles or zeros in the right half of the s-plane. The test of the poles and zeros can be made in two ways, by inspection or by consideration of the odd and even parts of $P(s)$ and $Q(s)$.

Method A. To test $P(s)$ and $Q(s)$ by inspection, both polynomials are written in factored form and considered separately. The roots of $P(s)$ and $Q(s)$ must lie in the left half of the s-plane or on the $j\omega$-axis. Consider Eq. (3-25).

$$Z_1(s) = \frac{P(s)}{Q(s)} = \frac{s+1}{s^2 + 2s + 2} = \frac{s+1}{(s+1+j1)(s+1-j1)} \quad (3\text{-}25)$$

In this example $P(s)$ has a zero $s = -1$, which is seen to lie in the left half-plane, and $Q(s)$ has roots at $s = -1 + j1$ and $s = -1 - j1$, which also lie in the left half-plane, so the roots of $P(s)$ and $Q(s)$ have real parts which are nonpositive. This method of testing is the easiest for simple functions, but when $P(s)$ and $Q(s)$ become higher-order polynomials, it is not easy to factor them, and a stronger method is needed.

Method B. In Eq. (3-15) it was seen that $P(s)$ and $Q(s)$ can be written as $P(s) = A_1 + sB_1$ and $Q(s) = A_2 + sB_2$. Since both $P(s)$ and $Q(s)$ must be Hurwitz polynomials, consideration of $P(s)$ will demonstrate a method which can also be used for testing $Q(s)$. Using the form $P(s) = A_1 + sB_1$, the continued-fraction expansion of A_1/sB_1, or its reciprocal, sB_1/A_1, must be developed. The necessary and sufficient conditions for $P(s)$ to be a Hurwitz polynomial are that the coefficients of the expansion A_1/sB_1 or sB_1/A_1 be positive. It is essential in this method that all common factors of $P(s)$ and $Q(s)$ be eliminated before the test is applied. As an example, consider the polynomial of Eq. (3-26).

$$P(s) = s^3 + 6s^2 + 11s + 6$$
$$= (6s^2 + 6) + s(s^2 + 11) = A_1 + sB_1 \quad (3\text{-}26)$$

The continued-fraction expansion of sB_1/A_1 (or A_1/sB_1) can be developed from Eq. (3-26).

$$\frac{sB_1}{A} = \frac{s(s^2+11)}{(6s^2+6)} = \frac{s}{6} + \cfrac{1}{6s\vphantom{\dfrac{1}{5s}} + \cfrac{1}{\cfrac{10}{5s}}} \over 3 \quad (3\text{-}27)$$

Since all terms of this expansion are positive, Eq. (3-26) is a Hurwitz polynomial and has no zeros in the right half of the s-plane.

If an impedance or admittance function passes Test 1, there will be no poles or zeros of the function in the right half of the s-plane. However, a necessary requirement for a driving-point function to be physically realizable is that its real part be nonnegative (positive or zero) for all real frequencies. Therefore, a second test must be made.

Test 2. The purpose of this test is to determine the sign of the real part of the function for all real frequencies between plus and minus infinity $(-\infty < \omega < \infty)$. For realizability, the real part of the function must be nonnegative over the entire range of real frequencies; however, the imaginary part can be either positive or negative, as will be seen later. The test to determine the sign can be made by inspection or in the case of higher order functions, Sturm's theorem can be applied. These methods are described below.

Method A. Inspection can be used to determine the sign of the real part of a function, provided it is not excessively complicated. A function $Z_1(s)$ can be written in terms of A_1, A_2, B_1, and B_2 according to Eq. (3-15), and its real part can be expressed in terms of real frequency from Eqs. (3-16) and (3-18). Therefore, the $Re[Z_1(j\omega)]$ becomes

$$Re[Z_1(s)]_{s=j\omega} = \frac{A_1A_2 + \omega^2 B_1 B_2}{A_2^{\,2} + \omega^2 B_2^{\,2}} \qquad (3\text{-}28)$$

The denominator of Eq. (3-28) is nonnegative for all real frequencies, since all of its terms are squared. Furthermore, because the real part of a driving-point function is even ordered with s or ω appearing only in the form $s^0, s^2, \ldots, s^{2n}$ or $\omega^0, \omega^2, \ldots, \omega^{2n}$, there is no need to test it at negative frequencies $-\infty < \omega < 0$.

Consider the example of Eq. (3-25). The real part of this example can be written in the form of Eq. (3-28), and since the denominator is always nonnegative, only the numerator must be tested:

$$Re[Z_1(s)]_{s=j\omega} = Re\left[\frac{j\omega + 1}{(-\omega^2 + 2) + j2\omega}\right] = \frac{(2 - \omega^2) + 2\omega^2}{(2 - \omega^2)^2 + (2\omega)^2} \qquad (3\text{-}29)$$

The numerator $(2 - \omega^2) + 2\omega^2$ must be positive or greater than zero for $0 < \omega < \infty$. This is seen to be true, so $Re[Z_1(s)]$ is positive for all real frequencies. Because the example of Eq. (3-25) passes both Tests 1 and 2, it is a positive real function and represents the driving-point impedance of a physically realizable network. Unfortunately, the method of inspection loses its practical usefulness when the numerator of the real part of a function $(A_1A_2 + \omega^2 B_1 B_2)$ is a complicated function of ω.

Method B. For more complicated functions, a stronger method based on Sturm's theory can be used to determine if the $Re[Z_1(s)]$ is positive for all real frequencies. Sturm's theorem states that if a function $f(x)$ has only simple roots between $x = a$ and $x = b$ and if there is a difference in the number of changes of sign for $f(x)$ at $x = a$ and $x = b$, then only odd multiples will cause changes in sign. To understand the usefulness of this theorem, it is necessary to investigate the characteristics of Sturm's functions.

In Method A it was shown that only the numerator of the real part of the function under consideration must be tested. This numerator, $(A_1A_2 + \omega^2 B_1 B_2)$, is an even-ordered function of ω; consequently, it is possible to substitute $\omega^2 = x$ which yields a polynomial in x having real coefficients:

$$f(x) = (A_1 A_2 + \omega^2 B_1 B_2)_{\omega^2 = x}$$
$$= a_n x^n + a_{n-1} x^{n-1} + \cdots + a_1 x + a_0 \qquad (3\text{-}30)$$

It is of interest to test $f(x)$ for real, positive values of x between the limits $x = 0$ and $x = \infty$ to determine whether or not the sign of the function is positive and if it changes anywhere between these limits. Sturm's theorem can be applied to $f(x)$ to yield this information by using a sequence of functions computed from $f(x)$. The sequence can be written as $f(x), f_1(x), f_2(x), \ldots, f_n(x)$, and must possess the following properties.

1. The functions must have only simple roots.

2. The functions must not vanish at the limits of the interval.

3. The second function $f_1(x)$ must have the same sign as the derivative of $f(x)$ at all roots of $f(x)$.

4. The last function $f_n(x)$ must not have a change of sign between the limits of the interval.

5. If one of the functions vanishes at some point, the preceding and following functions must have opposite signs.

A sequence of functions having these properties can be formed by selecting $f_1(x)$ as the derivative of $f(x)$. The second function is obtained by dividing $f(x)$ by $f_1(x)$ and letting $f_2(x)$ equal the negative of the remainder. The third and higher functions are obtained in the same manner as $f_2(x)$. Analytically the Sturm's sequence of functions can be written as

$$f(x) = a_n x^n + a_{n-1} x^{n-1} + \cdots + a_1 x + a_0$$
$$f_1(x) = \frac{d}{dx} f(x)$$
$$f_2(x) = (-) \text{ remainder of } f(x)/f_1(x)$$
$$f_3(x) = (-) \text{ remainder of } f_1(x)/f_2(x)$$
$$\cdots \cdots \cdots \cdots \cdots \cdots \cdots \qquad (3\text{-}31)$$

If $f(x)$ contains only simple roots, there will be no factor common to $f(x)$ and $f_1(x)$ [i.e., when $f(x)$ is zero the derivative $f_1(x)$ cannot be zero]. Furthermore, $f_1(x)$ and $f_2(x)$ can have no common factor, since it would also be a factor of $f(x)$. By this reasoning, it can be concluded that no two consecutive functions can possess common factors. The series is continued with the degree of each successive function decreasing by unity until $f_n(x)$ is simply a constant. The constant cannot be zero; otherwise, the two previous functions $f_{n-1}(x)$ and $f_{n-2}(x)$ would have common factors.

The sign of any particular function $f_g(x)$ of the sequence can only change at a root of $f_g(x)$. For instance, if x_0 is a root of $f_g(x)$, the sign of the function changes as x varies from $(x_o - h)$ to $(x_o + h)$, where h is a positive real constant. From the preceding discussion, the functions $f_{g-1}(x_o)$ and $f_{g+1}(x_o)$ cannot be zero at x_o; therefore, within a finite region defined by $(x_o - h)$ and $(x_o + h)$ neither $f_{g-1}(x_o)$ nor $f_{g+1}(x_o)$ vanishes or changes sign. However, $f_{g-1}(x_o)$ and $f_{g+1}(x_o)$ will be opposite in sign, since $f_g(x_o)$ is zero at $x = x_o$.

Because of the unique qualities described above, the sequence of functions never loses a sign reversal at a root, although the sign reversal is displaced. In the sequence $f_{g-1}(x)$, $f_g(x)$, and $f_{g+1}(x)$, the sign changes only once between $x = x_o - h$ and $x = x_o + h$. For values of x which are not roots of one of the functions, the sign remains the same. Since $f_n(x)$ is a constant, the sequence can lose a sign reversal only when x passes through a root of $f(x)$. Therefore, assuming that $f(x)$ has only simple roots and the number of sign changes are computed at $x = 0$ and also at $x = \infty$, the difference in the number of changes in sign between these limits is equal to the number of simple roots occurring at positive real values of x. Consequently it is possible to determine how many roots of $f(x)$ are at positive real values of x within the limits $0 < x < \infty$. However, only odd multiples of roots will result in a change of sign.

If $f(x)$ contains higher-order roots, its sign may or may not change as x varies from $(x_o - h)$ to $(x_o + h)$, but the sequence can still be useful by separating the function into the product $f(x) = r(x)p(x)$, where $r(x)$ contains all simple roots and $p(x)$ contains the remaining roots. Using Sturm's theorem on $r(x)$ gives the number of sign changes due to the occurrence of roots at positive real values of x. Testing $f(x)$, which possibly contains higher order roots than $r(x)$, provides the number of distinct real, positive roots.

Although the above discussion does not cover in detail the fine points of Sturm's theorem, it should suffice to give the reader a working knowledge of the method. The sign of any of the functions in the sequence at $x = 0$ is simply the sign of the constant term of that function. Likewise, the sign of any function of the sequence at $x = \infty$ is the sign of the highest-order term of the function. Consequently, the labor involved in applying the theorem is largely that of determining the sequence of functions.†

Sturm's procedure is most easily demonstrated by considering an example. Assume the following function of ω represents the numerator of the real part of a function that is being tested.

$$(A_1A_2 + \omega^2 B_1 B_2) = \omega^6 - 3\omega^4 + \omega^2 + 5 \qquad (3\text{-}32)$$

† Sturm's sequence may be replaced by Trudi's sequence, which is a series of determinants. The Trudi sequence can be written directly; however, its conversion into polynomials requires considerable calculation. See A. H. Zemanian, "Generalization of the Concept of the Positive Real Function," *IRE Trans. Circuit Theory*, vol. CT-6, no. 4 December 1959, pp. 374–383.

Substituting $\omega^2 = x$ reduces the polynomial to

$$f(x) = x^3 - 3x^2 + x + 5 \tag{3-33}$$

The derivative is given by

$$f_1(x) = \frac{d}{dx} f(x) = 3s^2 - 6x + 1 \tag{3-34}$$

To obtain $f_2(x)$, divide $f(x)$ by $f_1(x)$ and reverse the sign of the remainder.

$$3x^2 - 6x + 1 \overline{\big)\, x^3 - 3x^2 + x + 5}$$
$$x^3 - 2x^2 + \frac{x}{3}$$
$$\overline{\qquad - x^2 + \frac{2x}{3} + 5}$$

or

$$f_2(x) = x^2 - \frac{2x}{3} - 5 \tag{3-35}$$

In like manner, the remaining functions in the sequence are:

$$f_3(x) = 4x - 16$$
$$f_4(x) = -\frac{10}{3} x + 5$$
$$f_5(x) = +10 \tag{3-36}$$

Generally, the test of sign is outlined in table form known as a Sturm's table. The table for this example becomes:

Function	$x = 0$	$x = \infty$
$f(x)$	(+)	(+)
$f_1(x)$	(+)	(+)
$f_2(x)$	(−)	(+)
$f_3(x)$	(−)	(+)
$f_4(x)$	(+)	(−)
$f_5(x)$	(+)	(+)
Change of sign	2	2
Difference in Change of sign	2−2 = 0	

The difference in the number of sign changes is zero; consequently $f(x)$, given by Eq. (3-33), has no roots for real, positive values of x. Likewise, $f(\omega)$ of Eq. (3-32), has no roots for real, positive values of ω. Furthermore, since $f(x)$ is positive for $x = 0$, the real part of $f(\omega)$ from which $f(x)$ was derived is never negative on the $j\omega$-axis. Therefore the example of Eq. (3-32) satisfies the test. Although Sturm's theorem provides a powerful method for testing the sign of more complicated or higher order functions, insight into the characteristics of the function in question may prove valuable. For instance, Eq. (3-33) can be conveniently factored to give $f(x) = (x + 1)(x^2 - 4x + 5)$ which is positive for all values of x by inspection.

This concludes the tests which can be made on a function to determine whether or not it is positive real, thereby satisfying the requirements of a driving-point impedance or admittance. The steps to be taken in testing a rational function, such as Eq. (3-3), may be summarized as follows:

1. Check $P(s)$ and $Q(s)$ for negative coefficients. The coefficients must be positive and real.

2. Check $P(s)$ and $Q(s)$ for missing terms. Missing terms may indicate the function is not positive real.

3. Inspect the function to insure that the degree of the highest-order terms of $P(s)$ and $Q(s)$ differ at most by unity. The same applies to the degree of the lowest-power terms of $P(s)$ and $Q(s)$.

4. Test the function to determine the position of its poles and zeros. The real parts of the poles and zeros must be nonpositive. Poles and zeros on the $j\omega$-axis must be simple and mutually separate each other, and these poles must have positive real residues.

To be a positive real function, it is necessary that the function in question satisfies the conditions of Steps 1, 3, 4, and 5. The condition of Step 2 will not necessarily be satisfied if the function possesses $j\omega$-axis poles and/or zeros. Although the first three steps may be accomplished by inspection, the remaining tests become more difficult if the function in question is complicated. Therefore, when a relatively simple function satisfies the first three steps, it is often worthwhile to attempt to construct a network to realize the function rather than proceed with the tests of Steps 4 and 5. Consider the example of Eq. (3-37). This function satisfies the requirements of Steps 1, 2, and 3, but it is easily expanded in a continued-fraction expansion.

$$Z_1(s) = \frac{s + 1}{s^2 + 2s + 2} = \cfrac{1}{s + 1 + \cfrac{1}{s + 1}} \tag{3-37}$$

The expanded function is the reciprocal of the impedance—hence it is an admittance function. Therefore, referring to Table 1-1, the first s

term can be identified as a capacitance of 1 farad. This capacitance is in parallel with a 1-ohm resistor. The parallel admittance $1/(s + 1)$ can be considered as an impedance $(s + 1)$. From Table 1-1 it is possible to identify a series inductor of 1 henry and second 1-ohm resistor with this term. Consequently, the network of Fig. 3-3 represents the impedance function of Eq. (3-37).

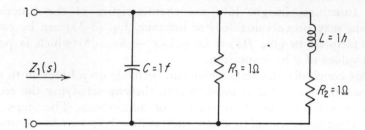

Fig. 3-3. Network for the example of Eq. 3-37.

When a network can be identified with a function such that all its elements are positive and real, it is obvious that the function is physically realizable. The above example demonstrates that it is often quicker and easier to synthesize a network than make all the tests to determine if its characterizing function is realizable. It should also be pointed out that the network of Fig. 3-3 is not the only configuration which can be derived to realize the impedance of Eq. (3-37). In fact an infinite number of different combinations of resistors, inductors, and capacitors can be constructed to yield the same driving-point impedance or admittance function. This fact will become clear in later chapters.

Biquadratic driving-point impedance or admittance functions are often encountered in network synthesis. In general, these functions can be written in the following form, where the coefficients c_1, c_2, d_1, d_2, and K must be nonnegative and real:

$$Z_1(s) = K \frac{s^2 + c_1 s + c_2}{s^2 + d_1 s + d_2} \tag{3-38}$$

The single condition necessary for this type of function to be positive real is that

$$(\sqrt{c_2} - \sqrt{d_2})^2 \leqq c_1 d_1 \tag{3-39}$$

This requirement is readily verified from the tests of Steps 4 and 5.

Finally, it should be emphasized that the various tests, procedures, and requirements outlined in this section can be utilized to check admittance as well as impedance functions. It is usually desirable to test a given function to insure that it is physically realizable before attempting the various synthesis procedures described in the following chapters.

However, before studying sophisticated synthesis techniques, it is instructive to consider characteristics of driving-point functions with poles and zeros restricted to special parts of the s-plane.

3-3. Characteristics of Reactance Functions

The characteristics of RLC driving-point functions have been considered in addition to tests that can be made to determine if a given function is physically realizable as a one-port passive network. It is now useful to consider the case of one-port networks which contain only reactive elements including mutual reactances associated with coupled coils or transformers.

Because there is no real power dissipated in a purely reactive network, the driving-point impedance of the network can be expressed in terms of Eq. (3-1) by letting the F_o term be zero.

$$Z_1(s) = \frac{E_1(s)}{I_1(s)} = \frac{T_o s + \dfrac{V_o}{s}}{|I_1(s)|^2} = \frac{1}{|I_1(s)|^2}\left(\frac{T_o s^2 + V_o}{s}\right) \tag{3-40}$$

The driving-point admittance of a pure reactance network becomes:

$$Y_1(s) = \frac{I_1(s)}{E_1(s)} = \frac{|I_1(s)|^2}{T_o s + \dfrac{V_o}{s}} = |I_1(s)|^2\left(\frac{s}{T_o s^2 + V_o}\right) \tag{3-41}$$

The poles and zeros of these driving-point functions are seen to fall at $s = 0$ and $s = \pm j\sqrt{V_o/T_o}$. Although V_o and T_o are both functions of s, it was demonstrated in Chap. 2 that they must also be positive real functions. Consequently, the poles and zeros of a driving-point reactance or susceptance are imaginary or zero.

The above conclusion can also be reached by considering the impedance of individual reactive elements such as Ls and $1/Cs$. These terms are odd-ordered functions of s, and series or parallel combination of such reactive elements yields:

$$\text{Series combination:}\quad Z_1(s) = Ls + \frac{1}{Cs} = \frac{LCs^2 + 1}{Cs}$$

$$\text{Parallel combination:}\quad Z_1(s) = \frac{1}{Cs + \dfrac{1}{Ls}} = \frac{Ls}{LCs^2 + 1} \tag{3-42}$$

The same forms are obtained on a susceptance basis, and it is noted that these functions possess only imaginary poles and zeros at $s = 0$ and $s = \pm j\sqrt{1/LC}$. It would appear that all driving-point reactance and susceptance functions have poles and zeros restricted to the imaginary axis. Indeed, since this is true, it follows from Case I of Sec. 3-1 that driving-point functions of reactance networks must be odd-ordered functions of s.

Because driving-point functions must be positive real, a driving-point reactance or susceptance can be defined as an odd-ordered positive real function. Therefore, in accordance with Eqs. (3-17) and (3-18), it must be purely imaginary {i.e., $Re[Z_1(j\omega)] = 0$}, and $Z_1(j\omega)$ can be expressed as

$$Z_1(j\omega) = 0 + jX(j\omega) \tag{3-43}$$

The derivative of this function becomes

$$\frac{dZ_1(j\omega)}{d\omega} = j\frac{dX(j\omega)}{d\omega} \tag{3-44}$$

A nonreal and/or nonpositive value for this derivative is impossible because the derivative of $Z_1(s)$ at the roots of $Z_1(s)$ must be positive and real. This follows from consideration of the Cauchy-Riemann equations of Chap. 1, Sec. 1-3, and the requirement for a driving-point function to be analytic in the right half-plane. Consequently, at real frequencies a driving-point reactance possesses a derivative which always has a positive slope, and the poles and zeros of the function must mutually separate each other. Figure 3-4 illustrates how the poles and zeros of a pure reactance function separate each other. Poles of the function are denoted in Fig. 3-4 by X's and fall at ω_1, ω_1^*, ω_3, and ω_3^* on the imaginary axis. Zeros of the function are denoted by 0's and occur at ω_0, ω_2, and ω_2^*. This notation will be used throughout the remainder of the book when plotting poles and zeros on the complex frequency plane.

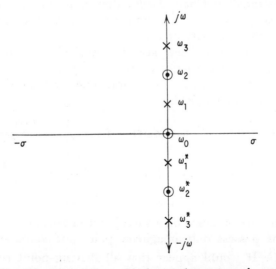

Fig. 3-4. **Separation of poles and zeros on $j\omega$-axis.**

To show that the poles and zeros of a reactance function must mutually separate each other, consider the hypothetical reactance plot of Fig. 3-5. As ω varies from the frequency ω_1 to ω_2 the reactance of the function changes continuously, provided no poles or zeros are encountered. Assume that the function has zeros at the frequencies ω_1 and ω_2 which are not separated by a pole. In this case as ω varies from the

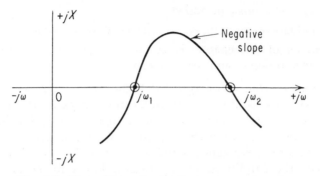

Fig. 3-5. Plot of hypothetical reactance function.

zero at ω_1 to the second zero at ω_2, the reactance must have a negative slope at some point. Under these conditions the function violates the requirement that the driving-point impedance of a reactance network must always have a positive slope. Hence, two zeros cannot lie side by side on the $j\omega$-axis. The same reasoning can be applied to poles; consequently, poles and zeros of the function must mutually separate each other.

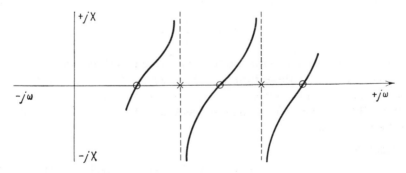

Fig. 3-6. General reactance plot as a function of frequency.

Because the poles and zeros of a pure reactance network mutually separate each other, the plot of reactance as a function of ω takes the form of Fig. 3-6.

From these considerations, two conclusions can be reached concerning the driving-point functions of pure reactance networks. These conclusions can be stated as follows:

1. Poles and zeros of $Z_1(s)$ must be simple or first order, and they must occur on the $j\omega$-axis in conjugate pairs.
2. The $j\omega$-axis poles and zeros must mutually separate each other.

Because the impedance or admittance must be a positive real function, a third characteristic must be added.

3. The residues at each of the poles must be positive real values.

The remainder of this chapter is devoted to the various forms which a pure reactance function and network can assume.

In a pure reactance function the highest-order terms (and lowest-order terms) of $P(s)$ and $Q(s)$ must differ in order by unity. If the orders of the numerator and denominator were equal, division would result in a constant term, indicating the presence of a resistance. Furthermore, even though a pure reactance network is being considered, its real part must satisfy the conditions of Eq. (3-28). For a physically realizable network, the $Re[Z_1(j\omega)]$ must be positive and real; therefore, it follows from Eq. (3-28) that $A_1A_2 + \omega^2 B_1B_2 \geq 0$. A limiting case of this equation occurs when $A_1A_2 + \omega^2 B_1B_2 = 0$, and this limiting condition applies to reactance networks except in the trivial cases when $Z_1(s) = 0$, $Z_1(s) = \infty$, or $Z_1(s) = s$. Consequently there are only two possibilities for the real part of the function to be zero: Either A_1 and B_2 must be zero or A_2 and B_1 must be zero in Eq. (3-28). Under these conditions, the driving-point impedance will have one of two forms:

$$Z_1(s) = \frac{P(s)}{Q(s)} = \frac{sB_1}{A_2} \tag{3-45}$$

or

$$Z_1(s) = \frac{P(s)}{Q(s)} = \frac{A_1}{sB_2} \tag{3-46}$$

By substituting $s = j\omega$ in Eq. (3-45), two general reactance functions are formed. Both of these functions have zeros at $\omega = 0$; however, one has a pole as ω approaches infinity, whereas the second has a zero at infinity. These forms will be denoted as Cases A and B, respectively, and can be written as

Case A:

$$Z_1(j\omega) = j\omega \, K \frac{(\omega^2 - \omega_2{}^2)(\omega^2 - \omega_4{}^2) \cdots (\omega^2 - \omega_n{}^2)}{(\omega^2 - \omega_1{}^2)(\omega^2 - \omega_3{}^2) \cdots (\omega^2 - \omega_{n-1}^2)} \tag{3-47}$$

Case B:

$$Z_1(j\omega) = j\omega \, K \frac{(\omega^2 - \omega_2{}^2)(\omega^2 - \omega_4{}^2) \cdots (\omega^2 - \omega_{n-1}^2)}{(\omega^2 - \omega_1{}^2)(\omega^2 - \omega_3{}^2) \cdots (\omega^2 - \omega_n{}^2)} \tag{3-48}$$

Likewise, if $s = j\omega$ is substituted in Eq. (3-46), a second pair of reactance functions results, both having poles at $\omega = 0$. One of these functions has a pole as ω approaches infinity, and the other has a zero at infinity. These two forms will be denoted as Cases C and D, respectively, and can be written as

Case C:

$$Z_1(j\omega) = \frac{K}{j\omega} \frac{(\omega^2 - \omega_1{}^2)(\omega^2 - \omega_3{}^2) \cdots (\omega^2 - \omega_n{}^2)}{(\omega^2 - \omega_2{}^2)(\omega^2 - \omega_4{}^2) \cdots (\omega^2 - \omega_{n-1}^2)} \quad (3\text{-}49)$$

Case D:

$$Z_1(j\omega) = \frac{K}{j\omega} \frac{(\omega^2 - \omega_1{}^2)(\omega^2 - \omega_3{}^2) \cdots (\omega^2 - \omega_{n-1}^2)}{(\omega^2 - \omega_2{}^2)(\omega^2 - \omega_4{}^2) \cdots (\omega^2 - \omega_n{}^2)} \quad (3\text{-}50)$$

F. M. Foster is given credit for these equations in which the poles and zeros are denoted by $\pm\omega_1, \pm\omega_2, \ldots, \pm\omega_{n-1}, \pm\omega_n$. Mutual separation of the poles and zeros is accounted for, since $\omega_1 < \omega_2 < \omega_3 \cdots \omega_{n-1} < \omega_n$, and K is a positive real constant. From these four forms, it is possible to synthesize several different physically realizable reactance networks. It should also be pointed out that susceptance functions having the same forms as Eqs. (3-47) through (3-50) can be derived and synthesized as physically realizable networks.

3-4. Canonic Forms of LC Networks

The driving-point reactance functions of Eqs. (3-47) through (3-50) will now be discussed and characteristics of these functions as well as networks which can be used to realize them will be investigated. For instance, consider Eq. (3-47) which has a zero at $\omega = 0$ and a pole at

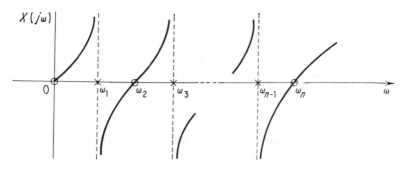

Fig. 3-7. Reactance plot for Eq. 3-47.

$\omega = \infty$. The reactance plot for this function takes the form of Fig. 3-7. A network with these characteristics behaves like an inductor at low and high frequencies. However, the actual composition of the networks for these cases will be considered later in the section.

The reactance function of Eq. (3-48) has zeros at $\omega = 0$ and $\omega = \infty$ and possesses a reactance variation with frequency similar to that of Fig. 3-7, the only exception being that the reactance approaches zero as ω approaches infinity. Networks having reactance functions of this form behave like an inductor at low frequencies and a capacitor at high frequencies. In like manner, Eq. (3-49) has poles at both $\omega = 0$ and $\omega = \infty$. The characteristic variation of reactance for a network with this type of driving-point function is shown in Fig. 3-8, and the network will behave like a capacitor at low frequencies and an inductor at high frequencies. Finally, Eq. (3-50) has a pole at $\omega = 0$, but a zero at $\omega = \infty$. Therefore, the characteristic variation of reactance for this function will be similar to that of Fig. 3-8, the only exception being that the reactance approaches zero as ω approaches infinity. Networks having reactance functions of this form behave like capacitors at both high and low frequencies.

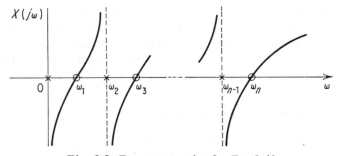

Fig. 3-8. Reactance plot for Eq. 3-49.

The various networks which can be synthesized to realize these four cases will now be considered. If a partial-fraction expansion is made of Cases A or B, Eqs. (3-47) or (3-48), using the conjugate poles as the denominators, the residues k_i of the conjugate poles $\pm \omega_i$ must be of equal magnitude. Combining the conjugate poles causes the partial-fraction expansion to take the following form:

$$Z_1(j\omega) = j\left[k_0\omega + \frac{2k_1\omega}{(\omega^2 - \omega_1{}^2)} + \frac{2k_3\omega}{(\omega^2 - \omega_3{}^2)} + \cdots\right] \quad (3\text{-}51)$$

Replacing $j\omega$ by s and the constant factors by new constants, Eq. (3-51) takes the form

$$Z_1(s) = K_0 s + \frac{K_1 s}{s^2 + \omega_1{}^2} + \frac{K_3 s}{s^2 + \omega_3{}^2} + \cdots \quad (3\text{-}52)$$

The $K_0 s$ term represents an inductor of K_0 henrys; however, the 2nd, 3rd, 4th, etc., terms are of the form $K_i s/(s^2 + \omega_i{}^2)$. These terms are of the same form as the impedance of a parallel combination of inductance and capacitance as indicated in Eq. (3-42). The form of the last term of Eq. (3-52) will depend on whether the expansion was derived from Case A or Case B. In Case A the last term will be of the form $K_i s/(s^2 + \omega_i^2)$, but the expansion of Case B will yield a last term of the form K_n/s, which represents a capacitor.

From the above discussion it is seen that the first term of Eq. (3-52) represents an inductance, and the remainder of the terms is a series of parallel LC elements, except the last term, which will depend on the nature of the original function. The last term must be of the form K_n/s if it is present, since there can be no constant terms, and a term of the form $K_n s$ could be combined with the first term. Because Eq. (3-52) represents the sum of a series of impedances derived from Eqs. (3-47) and (3-48), Cases A and B can be realized as LC networks of the form seen in Fig. 3-9.

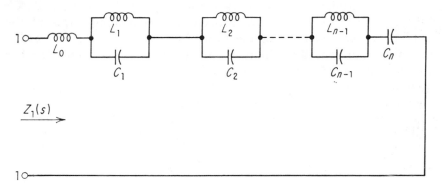

Fig. 3-9. First form of LC network.

In Case A, Eq. (3-47), there is no K_n/s term present when the function is expanded, so the network of Fig. 3-9 will have no series capacitor as its last element. It will have an inductor as the first element. In Case B a K_n/s term will be present, so the network will have an inductor as its first element and a capacitor as the last element.

It is now of interest to consider Cases C and D, Eqs. (3-49) and (3-50). These functions can also be expanded in partial fractions using the conjugate poles as the denominators. The residues k_i of the conjugate poles $\pm \omega_i$ must be of equal magnitude; therefore, combining conjugate terms of the partial-fraction expansion yields

$$Z_1(j\omega) = j\left[\frac{k_0}{\omega} + \frac{2k_2\omega}{(\omega^2 - \omega_2^2)} + \frac{2k_4\omega}{(\omega^2 - \omega_4^2)} + \cdots\right] \qquad (3\text{-}53)$$

Replacing $j\omega$ by s and the constant terms by new constants gives

$$Z_1(s) = \frac{K_0}{s} + \frac{K_2 s}{s^2 + \omega_2^2} + \frac{K_4 s}{s^2 + \omega_4^2} + \cdots \qquad (3\text{-}54)$$

The first term K_0/s of Eq. (3-54) represents a series capacitor, and the 2nd, 3rd, etc., terms of the function represent parallel LC combinations similar to Eq. (3-52). The last term of the expansion depends on which case is being considered. In Case C, the last term will be $K_n s$, indicating the presence of a series inductor, and in Case D the last term will be of the form $K_i s/(s^2 + \omega_i^2)$. As a result, Eq. (3-54) reveals that the same type of networks can be realized for Cases C and D as were formed for Cases A and B.

The reactances of Eqs. (3-47) through (3-50) can also be realized by using the admittance functions $Y_1(s) = 1/Z_1(s)$. When the admittance functions are expanded in partial-fraction expansions, similar to the method used for the impedance functions, terms of the form Ks, K/s, and $K_i s/(s^2 + \omega_i^2)$ result. The first and/or last terms of the expansion, if they are present, are of the form Ks or K/s. Since admittance functions are being considered, Ks denotes a capacitor of K farads, and K/s represents an inductor of $1/K$ henrys. The remaining terms of the admittance expansion are of the form $K_i s/(s^2 + \omega_i^2)$, and are readily shown to represent the admittance of a series LC combination. For instance, in Eq. (3-42) it was seen that the impedance of a series LC combination is given by $(LCs^2 + 1)/Cs$; therefore, the admittance of such a network becomes $Cs/(LCs^2 + 1)$. Consequently, the impedances of Eqs. (3-47) through (3-50) can be realized as admittance functions to yield a second form of network of the type shown in Fig. 3-10. The presence of the parallel inductor or capacitor as the first or last element of the network will depend on the four possible cases, A, B, C, and D.

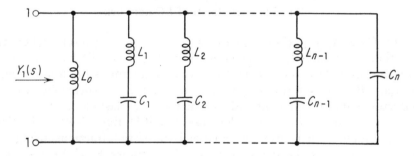

Fig. 3-10. Second form of LC network.

Figures 3-9 and 3-10 are the first two canonic forms of pure reactance networks, and they are sometimes called the Foster canonic forms.[†] A canonic form implies a network that is capable of representing any impedance function of a given type while using a minimum number of elements. A pure reactance network will have a minimum of $(n + m + 1)/2$

[†] Ronald M. Foster, "A Reactance Theorem," *Bell System Technical Journal*, vol. 3 April 1924, pp. 259–267.

elements, where n is the degree of the highest-order term in the numerator polynomial and m is the degree of the highest-order term in the
denominator of the driving-point function.

The driving-point impedance for a pure LC network can be expressed
as the ratio of two Hurwitz polynomials, and since the highest-order
terms of the numerator and denominator must differ in degree by unity,
it is convenient to assume the numerator is nth order and the denominator is of order $(n - 1)$. In this case the impedance can be written as

$$Z_1(s) = K \frac{s^n + a_{n-2}s^{n-2} + a_{n-4}s^{n-4} + \cdots}{s^{n-1} + a_{n-3}s^{n-3} + a_{n-5}s^{n-5} + \cdots} \tag{3-55}$$

This type of function can be expanded by a process of long division and
inversion to yield a continued-fraction expansion of the following form:

$$Z_1(s) = L_1 s + \cfrac{1}{C_1 s + \cfrac{1}{L_2 s + \cfrac{1}{C_2 s + \cdots}}} \tag{3-56}$$

The multiplying constants in the expansion have been replaced by new
constants, L_1, C_1, L_2, C_2, etc., in which case Eq. (3-56) suggests a third
form of network as illustrated in Fig. 3-11. The manner in which this
network is terminated is determined by whether the last term of the
continued-fraction expansion corresponds to an inductor or a capacitor.

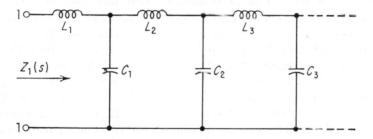

Fig. 3-11. Network for expansion of Eq. 3-56.

The impedance function of Eq. (3-55) can also be inverted to give
an admittance $Y_1(s) = 1/Z_1(s)$ which can be expanded in turn to yield
a continued fraction of the following form:

$$Y_1(s) = \frac{1}{Z_1(s)} = \cfrac{1}{\cfrac{1}{C_1 s} + \cfrac{1}{\cfrac{1}{L_1 s} + \cfrac{1}{\cfrac{1}{C_2 s} + \cfrac{1}{\cfrac{1}{L_2 s} + \cdots}}}} \tag{3-57}$$

Again the multiplying constants of the expansion have been replaced by C_1, L_1, C_2, L_2, etc., and Eq. (3-57) suggests a fourth network form shown in Fig. 3-12. The manner in which the network of Fig. 3-12 is terminated also depends on the last term of the continued-fraction expansion.

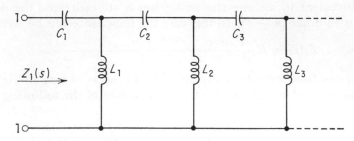

Fig. 3-12. Network for expansion of Eq. 3-57.

The networks of Figs. 3-11 and 3-12 could also have been derived by assuming the driving-point impedance of Eq. (3-55) had a denominator of order n and a numerator of order $(n - 1)$. In this case, expansion of $Y_1(s) = 1/Z_1(s)$ would have led to the network form seen in Fig. 3-11, whereas expansion of $Z_1(s)$ would yield a network of the form seen in Fig. 3-12. Furthermore, these networks represent two additional canonic forms for reactance functions. This fact can be verified by consideration of the continued-fraction expansion. In Chap. 1, Sec. 1-6, a continued-fraction expansion was used as a test of Hurwitz polynomials. In this test the given polynomial was separated into $M(s)$ and $N(s)$, where $M(s)$ represented all even powers and $N(s)$ represented odd powers of s. To test the polynomial, the expansion of $R(s) = M(s)/N(s)$ or $R(s) = N(s)/M(s)$ must be developed until all coefficients are determined. For an nth order polynomial to be positive real, the expansion will yield only n coefficients all of which must be positive real numbers.

Assume that n is an even number, then for a reactance function $M(s)$ is an even-ordered polynomial of order n and $N(s)$ an odd-ordered polynomial of order $(n - 1)$. The ratio $R(s) = M(s)/N(s)$ has the same form as the driving-point reactance of Eq. (3-55), and if it is to be positive real, its continued-fraction expansion must have only n terms. If n is an odd number, then $N(s)$ will be of order n and $M(s)$ will be of order $(n - 1)$, in which case the expansion of $R(s) = N(s)/M(s)$ must have only n terms. Consequently, since the highest-order terms of the numerator and denominator of a reactance function must differ by unity, the continued-fraction expansion of these functions will always yield n terms.

A canonic reactance network has $(n + m + 1)/2$ elements, where n

is the degree of the highest-order term in the numerator and m the degree of the highest-order term of the denominator of the reactance function. For a numerator of degree n and denominator of degree $m = n - 1$, there are n elements in the canonic form; hence, the network which represents the continued-fraction expansion of the reactance function must be canonic. A similar argument can be given if the highest-order term of the denominator is greater than that of the numerator by unity. Credit for the canonic forms of Figs. 3-11 and 3-12 is given to W. Cauer.†

It is now useful to investigate some examples of the four LC canonic forms described above.

Example 1. Consider the driving-point impedance of Eq. (3-58) which has been expanded by the procedure of repeated division and inversion.

$$Z_1(s) = \frac{s^4 + 4s^2 + 3}{s^3 + 2s} = s + \cfrac{1}{\cfrac{s}{2} + \cfrac{1}{4s + \cfrac{1}{\cfrac{s}{6}}}} \tag{3-58}$$

A continued-fraction expansion developed by dividing the highest-order numerator term by the highest-order denominator term or vice versa is equivalent to consistently removing only the poles of the function at $s = \infty$. When a function is written with its highest-order terms first, as in Eqs. (3-55) and (3-58), it is considered to be written in the forward direction. The network corresponding to the expansion of Eq. (3-58) is one of Cauer's canonic forms as seen in Fig. 3-13.

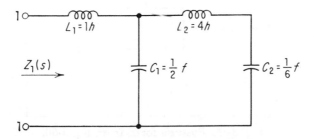

Fig. 3-13. Cauer's form from Eq. 3-58.

Example 2. Now consider Eq. (3-58) written in the reverse direction and expanded. An equation written with its lowest-order terms first, as in Eq. (3-59), is said to be written in the reverse direction. A continued-fraction expansion developed by dividing the lowest-order term of the numerator by the lowest-order term of the denominator or vice versa is equivalent to consistently removing only the pole at $s = 0$.

† W. Cauer, "Die Verwirklichung von Wechselstromwiderständen vorgeschriebener Frequenzabhängigkeit," *Arch. Elektrotech.*, vol. 17 1926, pp. 355–388.

$$Z_1(s) = \frac{3 + 4s^2 + s^4}{2s + s^3} = \frac{3}{2s} + \cfrac{1}{\cfrac{4}{5s} + \cfrac{1}{\cfrac{25}{2s} + \cfrac{1}{5s}}} \tag{3-59}$$

This expansion represents the network of Fig. 3-14, and since both Figs. 3-13 and 3-14 were derived from the same driving-point impedance, they must be two equivalent canonic forms. Figure 3-14 is the second Cauer form for Eq. (3-58).

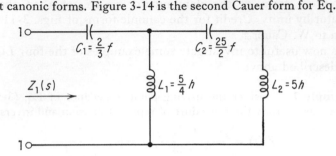

Fig. 3-14. Cauer's form from Eq. 3-59.

Example 3. If the denominator of Eq. (3-58) is divided into the numerator once and the remainder expanded by partial-fraction expansion, it yields Eq. (3-60).

$$Z_1(s) = \frac{s^4 + 4s^2 + 3}{s^3 + 2s} = s + \frac{2s^2 + 3}{s^3 + 2s} = s + \frac{\frac{s}{2}}{s^2 + 2} + \frac{3}{2s} \tag{3-60}$$

This expansion leads to the network of Fig. 3-15, which is one of Foster's canonic forms for the driving-point impedance of Eq. (3-58).

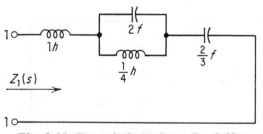

Fig. 3-15. Foster's form from Eq. 3-60.

Example 4. Finally, consider the impedance of Eq. (3-58) expanded in the following manner.

$$Z_1(s) = \frac{s^4 + 4s^2 + 3}{s^3 + 2s} = \cfrac{1}{\cfrac{s^3 + 2s}{s^4 + 4s^2 + 3}} = \cfrac{1}{\cfrac{1}{\cfrac{2s}{s^2 + 3}} + \cfrac{1}{\cfrac{2s}{s^2 + 1}}} \tag{3-61}$$

The network representing this expansion is the second Foster canonic form as shown in Fig. 3-16.

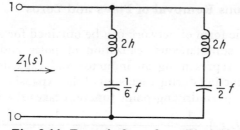

Fig. 3-16. Foster's form from Eq. 3-61.

The above examples illustrate that it is possible to synthesize a given driving-point reactance function as any one of the four Cauer and Foster forms. In some cases it may be more desirable to synthesize one form than another, due to practical considerations. Perhaps the element values for one form of network are not realistic from the standpoint of physical

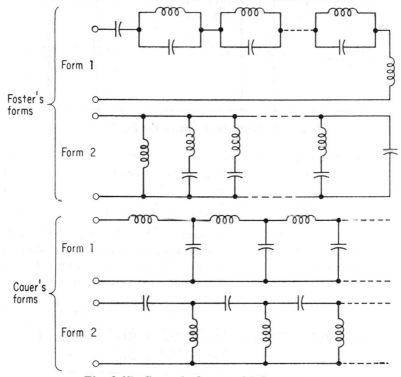

Fig. 3-17. Canonic forms of *LC* networks.

size, cost, weight, or commercial availability. The procedures for obtaining the various expansions in the examples should be apparent; however, details of these procedures will be discussed at greater length in the following chapter. The Foster and Cauer canonic forms are summarized in Fig. 3-17.

3-5. Simultaneous Removal of Poles and Zeros

A fifth canonic form of network can be obtained for a pure reactance function by the simultaneous realization of poles and zeros. In this procedure terms representing an inductor and capacitor are removed from the given function during each step of the expansion. As a result, the expansion of the given driving-point function takes the following form:

$$Z_1(s) = L_1 s + \cfrac{1}{C_1 s} + \cfrac{1}{C_2 s + \cfrac{1}{L_2 s} + \cfrac{1}{L_3 s + \cfrac{1}{C_3 s} + \cdots}}$$

(3-62)

This type of expansion yields a network of the form shown in Fig. 3-18.†

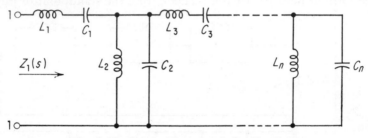

Fig. 3-18. Form of network for Eq. 3-62.

The impedance of Eq. (3-63) will serve to illustrate the manner in which a reactance function can be expanded to give a network similar to Fig. 3-18.

$$Z_1(s) = \frac{24s^8 + 92s^6 + 84s^4 + 18s^2 + 1}{24s^7 + 56s^5 + 24s^3 + 2s}$$

(3-63)

The expansion of Eq. (3-63) is formed by the following method. The denominator is divided into the numerator, as seen in Eq. (3-64), and the division is carried out until the $as + b/s$ terms are obtained. These terms represent the first series LC combination of the network.

$$
\begin{array}{r}
s + \dfrac{1}{2s} \\[4pt]
\hline
24s^7 + 56s^5 + 24s^3 + 2s\,\big)\,24s^8 + 92s^6 + 84s^4 + 18s^2 + 1 \\
24s^8 + 56s^6 + 24s^4 + 2s^2 \\
\hline
36s^6 + 60s^4 + 16s^2 + 1 \\
12s^6 + 28s^4 + 12s^2 + 1 \\
\hline
\end{array}
$$

remainder $\rightarrow 24s^6 + 32s^4 + 4s^2$ (3-64)

---

† T. C. Fry, "The Use of Continued Fractions in the Design of Electrical Networks," *Bull. Am. Math. Soc.*, vol. 35 July 1929, pp. 463–498.

To obtain the first parallel LC combination, the remainder of the first division is divided into the divisor of the preceding step. This procedure is continued until there is no remainder, and provided the function is a pure reactance there will be no constant terms. The expansion of Eq. (3-63) developed in the manner described above is given by

$$Z_1(s) = s + \frac{1}{2s} + \cfrac{1}{s + \cfrac{1}{2s} + \cfrac{1}{2s + \cfrac{1}{s} + \cfrac{1}{s + \cfrac{1}{3s}}}} \tag{3-65}$$

This expansion can be identified with the network of Fig. 3-19; however, it is not a Stieltjes continued-fraction expansion as discussed in Chap 1, Sec. 1-6. Finally, it is easily demonstrated that the network of Fig. 3-19 is a fifth canonic form which can be developed on either an impedance or admittance basis.

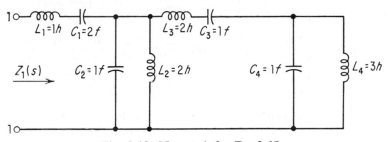

Fig. 3-19. Network for Eq. 3-65.

This concludes a discussion of tests that can be made on driving-point functions and several forms which a pure reactance network can assume. In addition, a few simple procedures for synthesizing reactance networks have been investigated. It will be noted in the next chapter that RL and RC networks have canonic forms similar to the LC cases covered in this chapter.

References

Tests for positive real functions are described in detail in the following references.
1. D. F. Tuttle, *Network Synthesis*, Vol. I (New York: John Wiley & Sons, Inc., 1958), Chaps. 5 and 6.
2. M. E. Van Valkenburg, *Introduction to Modern Network Synthesis* (New York: John Wiley & Sons, Inc., 1960), Chaps. 3 and 4.

3. L. Weinberg, *Network Analysis and Synthesis* (New York: McGraw-Hill Book Co., Inc., 1962), Secs. 6-2, 6-3, and 6-4.

Additional material concerning reactance functions and networks can be found in Ref. 2, Chaps. 4 and 5; and in Ref. 3, Sec. 9-2. See also the following texts:

4. E. A. Guillemin, *Synthesis of Passive Networks* (New York: John Wiley & Sons, Inc., 1957), Chaps. 1, 2, and 3.
5. M. B. Reed, *Electric Network Synthesis: Image Parameter Method* (Englewood Cliffs, N.J.: Prentice-Hall, Inc., 1955), Chap. 1.

Problems

3-1. Using the procedure outlined in Sec. 3-2, determine which of the following functions are realizable as driving-point impedances. Discuss the results in each case.

(a) $Z_1(s) = \dfrac{s + 3}{s^2 + 2s + 2}$ (d) $Z_1(s) = \dfrac{(s^2 + 1)(s^2 + 4)}{s(s^2 + 2)(s^2 + 3)}$

(b) $Z_1(s) = \dfrac{s^2 - s + 2}{s^2 + 2s + 1}$ (e) $Z_1(s) = \dfrac{s^3 + 6s^2 + 3s + 2}{s^4 + 3s^3 + 2s + 1}$

(c) $Z_1(s) = \dfrac{s^2 + 3s + 2}{s^2 + s + 1}$ (f) $Z_1(s) = \dfrac{s^2 + 5s + 6}{s^2 + 6}$

3-2. Using the positive real function, $Z_1(s)$, of Prob. 2-1, Eq. b, show that $Z_1^*(s)$, given in terms of $Z_1(s)$ and H according to the following relationship, will be positive real for all real and positive values of H.

$$Z_1^*(s) = \frac{HZ_1(s) - sZ_1(H)}{HZ_1(H) - sZ_1(s)}$$

This function represents Richard's theorem which is presented in Chap. 5, Sec. 5-4.

3-3. Write the expression for an LC driving-point impedance having a pole at $s = 0$ and critical frequencies at $\omega = 2$, 4, and 6. Realize this impedance by expanding it in four different ways to yield each of the four canonic forms.

3-4. Determine whether or not the following function is realizable as a driving-point admittance.

$$Y_1(s) = \frac{s^4 + 7s^3 + 19s^2 + 13s}{s^3 + 2s^2 + s + 2}$$

3-5. Prove that the following functions are realizable as driving-point impedances using Sturm's tables.

(a) $Z_1(s) = \dfrac{8s^2 + 36s + 15}{6s^2 + 3s}$ (b) $Z_1(s) = \dfrac{38s^3 + 53s^2 + 8s + 8}{2s^4 + 3s^3 + 32s^2 + 44s}$

3-6. Determine two equivalent networks for the following reactance network.

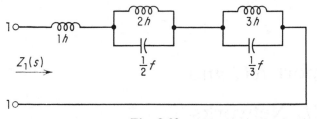

Fig. 3-20.

3-7. Plot the reactance as a function of ω for the network of Prob. 3-6. Discuss the reactance plot, particularly the slope of the curve.

3-8. Realize the following impedance functions by forward and reverse continued-fraction expansions to yield two different canonic network forms for each.

$$(a) \quad Z_1(s) = \frac{3s^4 + 45s^2 + 50}{s^3 + 10s} \qquad (b) \quad Z_1(s) = \frac{3s^8 + 24s^6 + 50s^4 + 24s^2 + 3}{3s^7 + 15s^5 + 15s^3 + 3s}$$

3-9. Realize the impedance functions of Prob. 3-8 by partial-fraction expansions to yield two different canonic forms for each.

3-10. Realize the impedance functions of Prob. 3-8 by simultaneous removal of poles and zeros.

3-11. Invert the impedance of Eq. (3-63) to form an admittance function, then realize the admittance by simultaneous removal of poles and zeros. Discuss the resulting network.

Chapter 4

One-port RC and

RL Networks

One-port reactance networks have been discussed and their characteristics determined in Chap. 3. Furthermore, it was seen that reactive driving-point functions can be expanded and identified with several different canonic network forms. In this chapter RC and RL one-port networks will be considered, and it will be seen that their driving-point functions can be expanded to yield canonic forms similar to the LC cases. In addition, certain characteristics of RC and RL networks will be investigated.

4-1. One-port RC Networks

The driving-point impedance of a one-port passive network is expressed in terms of "average energy functions" in Eq. (2-15). For a network restricted to resistance and capacitance elements the magnetically stored energy represented by T_o is zero; therefore, Eq. (2-15) becomes

$$Z_1(s) = \frac{E_1(s)}{I_1(s)} = \frac{1}{|I_1(s)|^2}\left(\frac{F_o s + V_o}{s}\right) \tag{4-1}$$

The driving-point admittance of a one-port RC network is given by

$$Y_1(s) = \frac{I_1(s)}{E_1(s)} = |I_1(s)|^2\left(\frac{s}{F_o s + V_o}\right) \tag{4-2}$$

Although F_o and V_o may be complicated functions of s, they must be real and positive as explained in Chap. 2, Sec. 2-1. Poles and zeros of $Z_1(s)$ or $Y_1(s)$ in Eqs. (4-1) and (4-2) occur at $s = 0$ and $s = -V_o/F_o$. Therefore, because F_o and V_o must be positive real functions of s, the poles or zeros at $s = -V_o/F_o$ must be real and negative. Consequently, the poles and zeros of a driving-point impedance or admittance of an RC network must lie on the negative real axis or at the origin of the *s*-plane. It will also be seen that these poles and zeros must mutually separate each other similar to those of reactance functions. Finally, at real frequencies, the driving-point functions of *RC* networks will have both real and imaginary components. In other words $Z_1(j\omega)$ will be a combination of resistance and reactance, and $Y_1(j\omega)$ will be a combination of conductance and susceptance.

That the poles and zeros of an *RC* driving-point function must lie at the origin or on the negative real axis can be illustrated by considering the impedance of a series and parallel combination of resistance R and capacitance C.

$$\text{Series combination:} \quad Z_1(s) = R + \frac{1}{Cs} = \frac{RCs + 1}{Cs}$$

$$\text{Parallel combination:} \quad Z_1(s) = \frac{1}{\dfrac{1}{R} + Cs} = \frac{R}{RCs + 1} \tag{4-3}$$

In the series combination, there is a pole at $s = 0$ and a zero at $s = -1/RC$; whereas, the parallel combination has a pole at $s = -1/RC$. Similar results are obtained on an admittance basis. A network composed of a number of series or parallel *RC* combinations will have a driving-point function with poles and zeros restricted to the origin and the negative real axis.

To demonstrate that the poles and zeros of an *RC* driving-point function must mutually separate each other, the current in Eq. (4-1) can be chosen as one ampere. In this case the impedance becomes

$$Z_1(s) = F_o + \frac{V_o}{s} = F_o + \frac{V_o}{\sigma + j\omega}$$

$$= \left(F_o + \frac{\sigma V_o}{\sigma^2 + \omega^2}\right) + j\left(\frac{-\omega V_o}{\sigma^2 + \omega^2}\right)$$

$$= R(\sigma,\omega) + jX(\sigma,\omega) \tag{4-4}$$

where $R(\sigma,\omega)$ and $X(\sigma,\omega)$ represent the real and imaginary components of $Z_1(s)$. Taking the partial derivative of the imaginary part of Eq. (4-4) with respect to ω yields

$$\frac{\partial X}{\partial \omega} = \frac{\partial}{\partial \omega}\left(\frac{-\omega V_o}{\sigma^2 + \omega^2}\right) = \frac{-V_o(\sigma^2 - \omega^2)}{(\sigma^2 + \omega^2)^2} \tag{4-5}$$

Since the poles and zeros of the impedance function are restricted to the negative real axis, it is only necessary to consider this derivative for real values of *s*. In other words, ω may be set equal to zero. In addition,

V_o must be real and positive; therefore, Eq. (4-5) may only go to zero at $\sigma = \infty$. Consequently, it is possible to write

$$\frac{\partial X}{\partial \omega} = \frac{-V_o}{\sigma^2} < 0 \tag{4-6}$$

The Cauchy-Riemann conditions of Chap. 1, Eq. (1-13), require that $\partial R/\partial \sigma = \partial X/\partial \omega$, so it follows from Eq. (4-6) that

$$\frac{\partial R}{\partial \sigma} = \frac{-V_o}{\sigma^2} < 0 \tag{4-7}$$

Because the Cauchy-Riemann derivative is independent of the direction of the computation, $\partial R/\partial \sigma$ is always negative. Therefore, it follows from Eqs. (4-6) and (4-7) that for real values of s (i.e., $s = \sigma$), the slope of the driving-point impedance function is always negative. In a similar manner, it can be demonstrated that the slope of an RC driving-point admittance function for real values of s is always positive. An exception to these rules occurs at $s = \sigma = \infty$, where the impedance may have a simple zero due to the capacitance or approach some positive, nonzero value determined by the resistance. An RC driving-point admittance will either have a simple pole due to the capacitance at $s = \sigma = \infty$ or a positive, nonzero value determined by the conductance. The fact that poles and zeros at $s = \sigma = \infty$ must be simple is dictated by the positive real characteristics of driving-point functions defined in Chap. 3, Sec. 3-1. This conclusion can also be reached by considering individual elements. As frequency becomes infinite, the impedance of a capacitor $(1/Cs)$ approaches zero; however, the impedance of a resistor is not a function of frequency. Therefore, as s approaches infinity the impedance of an RC network approaches either zero or a finite value determined by the real part of the driving-point impedance.

The positive real characteristics of an RC driving-point function also exclude the possibility of multiple order poles or zeros at the origin, $(s = \sigma = 0)$. Furthermore, the impedance will either have a pole or a positive, nonzero value and the admittance will have a zero or positive, nonzero value at $s = 0$. In terms of individual elements at zero frequency, a resistor gives a finite impedance, but a capacitor yields an infinite impedance. Therefore, when s equals zero, a finite or infinite impedance can be obtained.

Returning to the separation properties of the poles and zeros of RC driving-point functions, consider a hypothetical impedance function in which the zeros fall side by side. In this case the function will have a positive slope for some value of σ as s moves from one zero to the other. The same reasoning can be used if two poles fall side by side. This violates the above conclusions; therefore, the poles and zeros must mutually separate each other. The requirement that the slope of the impedance be negative (i.e., a finite, negative, nonzero value) implies that as σ varies through a pole or zero, the pole or zero must be first-order or simple. As a consequence of the fact that poles and zeros of an *RC* driving-point function are simple and restricted to the negative real axis where they mutually separate each other, it is possible to show the behavior of the functions as σ varies in a manner similar to that used to

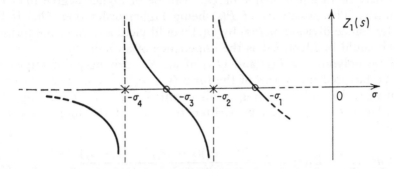

Fig. 4-1. General behavior of *RC* driving-point impedance functions.

show the change in reactance as a function of ω in the *LC* cases. Typical curves of this behavior are given for an *RC* impedance function (negative slope) in Fig. 4-1 and an *RC* admittance function (positive slope) in Fig. 4-2.

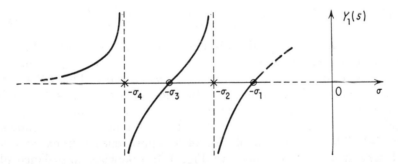

Fig. 4-2. General behavior of *RC* driving-point admittance functions.

An *RC* driving-point impedance or admittance function may assume four different forms, depending on the behavior of the function at $s = \sigma = 0$ and $s = \sigma = \infty$. These four forms can be classified for an impedance function as follows:

Case A. The impedance has a positive, nonzero value at both $s = 0$ and $s = \infty$.

Case B. The impedance has a pole at $s = 0$ and a zero at $s = \infty$.

Case C. The impedance has a positive, nonzero value at $s = 0$ and a zero at $s = \infty$.

Case D. The impedance has a pole at $s = 0$ and a positive, nonzero value at $s = \infty$.

When the impedance is written as $Z_1(s) = P(s)/Q(s)$, the highest-order terms of $P(s)$ and $Q(s)$ may be of equal degree or $Q(s)$ can be of higher degree than $P(s)$ by unity. Likewise, the lowest-order terms of $P(s)$ and $Q(s)$ may be of equal degree or $Q(s)$ can be of higher degree than $P(s)$ by unity. The possibility of $P(s)$ being higher-order than $Q(s)$ is forbidden, since division of $P(s)$ by $Q(s)$ would yield a term of the form Ks which could be identified as the impedance of an inductor.

The polynomials $P(s)$ and $Q(s)$ of an RC driving-point impedance can be factored into terms of the form $(s + \sigma_n)$, where the σ_n terms are positive real numbers. Using terms of this form, the RC driving-point impedance functions can be written for each of the four cases listed above.

Case A.
$$Z_1(s) = K\frac{(s + \sigma_2)(s + \sigma_4)\cdots(s + \sigma_n)}{(s + \sigma_1)(s + \sigma_3)\cdots(s + \sigma_{n-1})} \qquad (4\text{-}8)$$

Case B.
$$Z_1(s) = K\frac{(s + \sigma_2)(s + \sigma_4)\cdots(s + \sigma_{n-1})}{s(s + \sigma_3)\cdots(s + \sigma_n)} \qquad (4\text{-}9)$$

Case C.
$$Z_1(s) = K\frac{(s + \sigma_2)(s + \sigma_4)\cdots(s + \sigma_{n-1})}{(s + \sigma_1)(s + \sigma_3)\cdots(s + \sigma_n)} \qquad (4\text{-}10)$$

Case D.
$$Z_1(s) = K\frac{(s + \sigma_2)(s + \sigma_4)\cdots(s + \sigma_n)}{s(s + \sigma_3)\cdots(s + \sigma_{n-1})} \qquad (4\text{-}11)$$

The K term in these equations is a constant, and the poles and zeros of the functions occur at $s = -\sigma_1, s = -\sigma_2, \ldots, s = -\sigma_{n-1}$, and $s = -\sigma_n$, where $0 > \sigma_1 > \sigma_2 > \sigma_3 > \sigma_4 \cdots \sigma_{n-1} > \sigma_n$. The behavior of the impedance, when plotted as a function of σ for Cases A and B is seen in Figs. 4-3 and 4-4, respectively. The impedance of Eq. (4-8) approaches a positive, nonzero value at $\sigma = 0$ and $\sigma = \infty$ as shown in Fig. 4-3. The impedance of Eq. (4-9) approaches infinity at $\sigma = 0$ and zero at $\sigma = \infty$ as shown in Fig. 4-4. Likewise, impedance plots can be drawn for Cases C and D. Furthermore, similar results can be derived for one-port RC networks on an admittance basis.

It is seen that a number of similarities exist between RC and LC driving-point functions. The poles and zeros of RC functions must be simple and mutually separate each other on the negative real axis $(s = \sigma)$, whereas in the LC case simple poles and zeros mutually separate each other on the imaginary axis $(s = j\omega)$. The slope of an RC driving-point impedance with respect to σ must be negative; whereas, the slope of an LC driving-point impedance with respect to ω is always positive.

Finally, the four *RC* driving-point impedances of Eqs. (4-8) through (4-11) are similar to the four *LC* cases of Eqs. (3-47) through (3-50). Consequently, it is logical to suspect that canonic forms similar to the *LC* networks of Fig. 3-19 can be derived to represent *RC* driving-point functions.

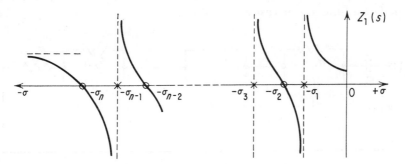

Fig. 4-3. Behavior of $Z_1(s)$ for Case A, Eq. 4-8.

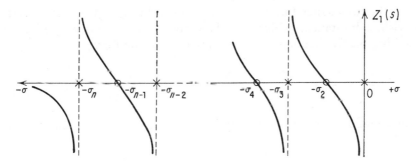

Fig. 4-4. Behavior of $Z_1(s)$ for Case B, Eq. 4-9.

4-2. Canonic Forms of *RC* Networks

The partial-fraction expansions of Eqs. (4-8) through (4-11) lead to functions of the form

$$Z_1(s) = \frac{K_0}{s} + \frac{K_1}{(s + \sigma_1)} + \frac{K_3}{(s + \sigma_3)} + \cdots + \frac{K_i}{(s + \sigma_i)} + \cdots + K_n$$

$$(4\text{-}12)$$

In this expansion the presence of K_0/s or K_n as the first and last terms, respectively, depends on the case under consideration. For instance, in Case A there will be a K_n term but no K_0/s term. In Case B there will be a K_0/s term but no K_n term. Case C will have neither terms, whereas Case D will possess both terms. The K_0/s term can be identified with a capacitor of $1/K_0$ farads, and the K_n term represents a resistor of

K_n ohms. Consequently, a resistor and/or a capacitor may terminate the RC network. The center terms of the expansion $K_i/(s + \sigma_i)$ are of the same form as the impedance of a parallel combination of resistance and capacitance as given by Eq. (4-3). Therefore, the first RC canonic network takes the form shown in Fig. 4-5. The presence of the capacitor C_0 and/or resistor R_n in the network of Fig. 4-5 will depend on the impedance function or case in question.

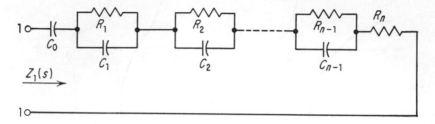

Fig. 4-5. First canonic form for RC networks.

If the impedance functions of Eqs. (4-8) through (4-11) are inverted to yield admittances which are then divided by s and expanded, the resulting partial-fraction expansions will be of the form

$$\frac{Y_1(s)}{s} = \frac{K_0}{s} + \frac{K_2}{s + \sigma_2} + \frac{K_4}{s + \sigma_4} + \cdots + \frac{K_{n-1}}{s + \sigma_{n-1}} + K_n \tag{4-13}$$

This equation can then be multiplied through by s, giving the following result.

$$Y_1(s) = K_0 + \frac{K_2 s}{s + \sigma_2} + \frac{K_4 s}{s + \sigma_4} + \cdots + \frac{K_{n-1} s}{s + \sigma_{n-1}} + K_n s \tag{4-14}$$

The first and last terms of this expansion represent a resistor and capacitor, respectively, whereas the center terms of the form $K_i s/(s + \sigma_i)$ represent series combinations of RC elements. The latter fact is readily verified from Eq. (4-3), since the admittance of a series RC combination can be written as $Y_1(s) = 1/Z_1(s) = Cs/(RCs + 1)$. Therefore, the expansion of Eq. (4-14) represents a network composed of a number of series combinations of RC elements, a resistor, and/or a capacitor all connected in parallel as illustrated in Fig. 4-6. The single resistor and capacitor may or may not be present, depending on the four possible cases previously outlined. The network of Fig. 4-6 is the second RC canonic form.

Figures 4-5 and 4-6 are analogous to Figs. 3-9 and 3-10 for LC networks. There are two more RC canonic network forms which can be derived as follows. The driving-point impedances of Eqs. (4-8) through (4-11) can be multiplied out and written in the form

$$Z_1(s) = K \frac{s^n + a_{n-1}s^{n-1} + \cdots}{s^m + b_{m-1}s^{m-1} + \cdots}$$

(4-15)

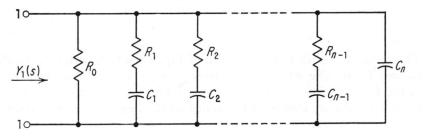

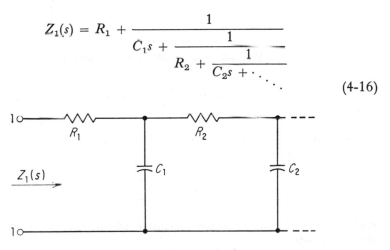

Fig. 4-6. Second *RC* canonic form.

There are only two realizable cases of this expression leading to pure *RC* networks, one when $n = m$ and one when $n = m - 1$. If $n = m$, Eq. (4-15) can be expanded in a continued-fraction expansion of the form

$$Z_1(s) = R_1 + \cfrac{1}{C_1 s + \cfrac{1}{R_2 + \cfrac{1}{C_2 s + \cdots}}}$$

(4-16)

Fig. 4-7. Third *RC* canonic form.

In developing this expansion from Eq. (4-15), constant terms have been identified as resistors R_1, R_2, etc., and the coefficients C_1, C_2, etc., of the *s* terms represent capacitors. Therefore, the expansion of Eq. (4-16) can be identified with the network of Fig. 4-7, which is a third *RC* canonic form.

If $n = m - 1$ in Eq. (4-15), the continued-fraction expansion of the function will be of the form

$$Z_1(s) = \frac{1}{C_1 s} + \cfrac{1}{\cfrac{1}{R_1} + \cfrac{1}{\cfrac{1}{C_2 s} + \cfrac{1}{\cfrac{1}{R_2} + \cdots}}} \qquad (4\text{-}17)$$

This expansion leads to the network of Fig. 4-8 which is the fourth RC canonic form. The RC canonic forms of Figs. 4-7 and 4-8 are similar to the LC networks of Figs. 3-11 and 3-12, and the manner in which these networks are terminated depends on the last term of their respective continued-fraction expansions.

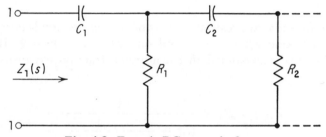

Fig. 4-8. Fourth RC canonic form.

It is now instructive to consider examples of the four RC canonic forms.

Example 1. Assume it is desirable to synthesize an RC network with the following driving-point impedance:

$$Z_1(s) = \frac{s^2 + 4s + 3}{s^2 + 2s} \qquad (4\text{-}18)$$

Performing a continued-fraction expansion of this function in the forward direction yields

$$Z_1(s) = \frac{s^2 + 4s + 3}{s^2 + 2s} = 1 + \cfrac{1}{\cfrac{s}{2} + \cfrac{1}{4 + \cfrac{1}{\cfrac{s}{6}}}} \qquad (4\text{-}19)$$

The network that represents this expansion is shown in Fig. 4-9.

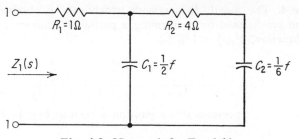

Fig. 4-9. Network for Eq. 4-19.

Example 2. As a second method for developing a network for Eq. (4-18), it is possible to expand the function in the reverse direction.

$$Z_1(s) = \frac{3 + 4s + s^2}{2s + s^2} = \frac{3}{2s} + \cfrac{1}{\cfrac{4}{5} + \cfrac{1}{\cfrac{25}{2s} + \cfrac{1}{\cfrac{1}{5}}}}$$

(4-20)

This expansion leads to the network of Fig. 4-10.

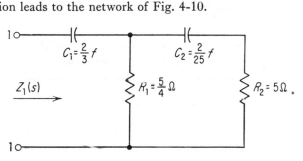

Fig. 4-10. Network for Eq. 4-20.

Example 3. It is also possible to form a partial-fraction expansion of Eq. (4-18) as follows:

$$Z_1(s) = \frac{s^2 + 4s + 3}{s^2 + 2s} = 1 + \frac{\frac{1}{2}}{s + 2} + \frac{\frac{3}{2}}{s}$$

(4-21)

This expansion yields the network of Fig. 4-11.

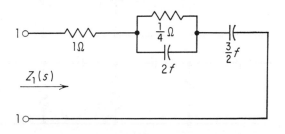

Fig. 4-11. Network for Eq. 4-21.

Example 4. The fourth RC network which can be obtained from Eq. (4-18) can be synthesized by performing a partial-fraction expansion of the admittance function, $Y_1(s) = 1/Z_1(s)$.

$$Y_1(s) = \frac{s^2 + 2s}{s^2 + 4s + 3} = \frac{\dfrac{s}{2}}{(s + 1)} + \frac{\dfrac{s}{2}}{(s + 3)} \qquad (4\text{-}22)$$

The network which represents this expansion is seen in Fig. 4-12.

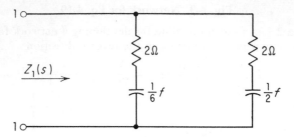

Fig. 4-12. Network for Eq. 4-22.

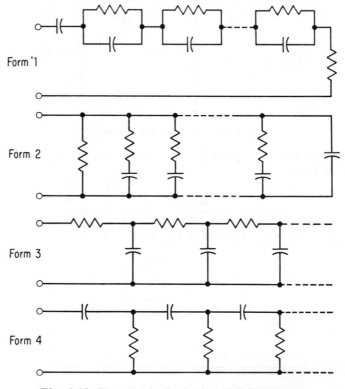

Fig. 4-13. Four canonic forms of RC networks.

The above examples demonstrate that it is possible to synthesize any one of four canonic *RC* networks, similar to the *LC* networks of Chap. 3, for a driving-point function with *RC* characteristics. The four *RC* canonic forms have been summarized in Fig. 4-13. The manner in which Forms 3 and 4 are terminated depends on the nature of the driving-point function.

4-3. *RC* Networks at Real Frequencies

The variation of the impedance of a one-port *RC* network as a function of σ has been investigated; however, it is also instructive to consider the variations in impedance as a function of ω. To accomplish this end, it is useful to consider the impedance of a simple network composed of a resistor and capacitor in parallel. The impedance of such a combination is given in Eq. (4-3) and can be expressed in terms of real frequency as

$$Z_1(j\omega) = \frac{R}{1 + j\omega RC} \tag{4-23}$$

The real and imaginary parts of this function become

$$Re[Z_1(j\omega)] = \frac{R}{1 + \omega^2 R^2 C^2} \tag{4-24}$$

$$Im[Z_1(j\omega)] = \frac{-j\omega CR^2}{1 + \omega^2 R^2 C^2} \tag{4-25}$$

In the case of simple series and parallel combinations of *RC* elements, the behavior of the real and imaginary parts of the impedance or admittance as a function of ω can best be illustrated by use of circle diagrams. For example, in the above equations the real part of the impedance has a maximum value R at $\omega = 0$. As frequency increases, the real part of the impedance decreases steadily, approaching zero at $\omega = \infty$. The imaginary part of the impedance is negative for all ω, with a value of zero at $\omega = 0$ and $\omega = \infty$. Both the real and imaginary parts have a magnitude of $R/2$ at $\omega = 1/RC$. A plot of the complete phasor locus of the real and imaginary parts of $Z_1(j\omega)$ yields a semicircle, as shown in Fig. 4-14.

Each parallel *RC* combination of the first *RC* canonic form (Fig. 4-5) will have an impedance with real and imaginary components defined by Eqs. (4-24) and (4-25), respectively. The behavior of the real and imaginary parts of the impedance, resulting from the series connection of these parallel *RC* combinations, will be similar to that shown in Fig. 4-14 at and near $\omega = 0$ and $\omega = \infty$. However, at intermediate frequencies the behavior of the real and imaginary parts of the impedance may be complicated functions of ω. This is particularly true if a large number of parallel RC combinations are contained in the network. The series resistor R_n if it is present, contributes to the real part of the impedance, and the capacitor C_0 if it is present, contributes $(-j1/\omega C_0)$ to the imaginary part of the impedance.

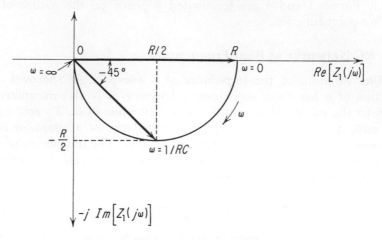

Fig. 4-14. Circle diagram for $Z_1(j\omega)$ of Eq. 4-23.

From the above discussion and consideration of Fig. 4-14, the following conclusions can be reached concerning the variations of the real and imaginary parts of the driving-point impedance of the first RC canonic form (Fig. 4-5) as a function of ω.

1. The real part of the impedance is maximum at $\omega = 0$ and decreases as frequency increases, reaching a minimum value at $\omega = \infty$.

2. The reactance or imaginary part of the impedance is negative for all values of ω. At $\omega = 0$ the reactance may be either zero or infinite (zero if C_0 is missing and infinite if C_0 is present). However, at $\omega = \infty$ the reactance will always be zero.

Because all four canonic network forms of Fig. 4-13 can be derived from the same driving-point function, each will possess the same general characteristics for its real and imaginary components as a function of frequency. Although this fact may not be apparent, it can be demonstrated by evaluating the real and imaginary parts of the impedance of other canonic forms for real frequencies from $\omega = 0$ to $\omega = \infty$.

Conclusions reached concerning the behavior of the real and imaginary parts of a driving-point admittance function bear a reversed relationship to those obtained when considering the impedance function, since $Y_1(s) = 1/Z_1(s)$. In other words, conductance as a function of frequency must act in a manner similar to the reciprocal of the real or resistive component of the impedance. Likewise, susceptance behaves in a manner similar to the reciprocal of reactance. Therefore, the following conclusions can be reached concerning the variation of the real and imaginary parts of the driving-point admittance of an *RC* network as a function of ω.

1. The real part of the admittance is minimum at $\omega = 0$ and increases as frequency increases, reaching a maximum value at $\omega = \infty$.

2. The susceptance or imaginary part of the admittance is positive for all values of ω. At $\omega = 0$ the susceptance must be zero. However, at $\omega = \infty$ the susceptance will either be infinite or zero depending on the function in question.

To illustrate the above statements, consider the admittance of a simple series *RC* combination. The admittance for such a combination can be written in terms of real frequency from Eq. (4-3) as follows:

$$Y_1(j\omega) = \frac{j\omega C}{1 + j\omega RC} \tag{4-26}$$

From this equation the real and imaginary parts of $Y_1(s)$ become

$$Re[Y_1(j\omega)] = \frac{RC^2\omega^2}{1 + R^2C^2\omega^2} \tag{4-27}$$

$$Im[Y_1(j\omega)] = \frac{j\omega C}{1 + R^2C^2\omega^2} \tag{4-28}$$

It is seen from Eq. (4-27) that the real part of the admittance is zero at $\omega = 0$. It increases steadily with frequency, reaching a maximum value

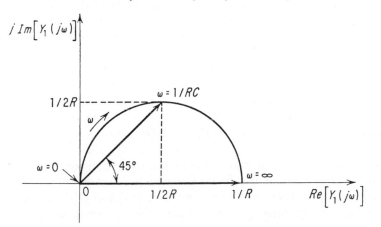

Fig. 4-15. Circle diagram for $Y_1(j\omega)$ of Eq. 4-26.

of $1/R$ at $\omega = \infty$. The imaginary part of the admittance, Eq. (4-28), is positive for all ω. Its value is zero at $\omega = 0$ and $\omega = \infty$. Both the real and imaginary parts have a magnitude of $1/2R$ at $\omega = 1/RC$. A plot of the complete phasor locus of the real and imaginary parts of $Y_1(j\omega)$ yields the circle diagram of Fig. 4-15.

In the second RC canonic form (Fig. 4-6), the behavior of the real and imaginary parts of the admittance resulting from the parallel connection of a number of series RC combinations will be similar to that of Fig. 4-15 at and near $\omega = 0$ and $\omega = \infty$. For intermediate frequencies, the behavior of the real and imaginary parts of the resulting admittance may become complicated functions of ω. The resistor R_0 if it is present in Fig. 4-6 contributes to the real part of the admittance; and the capacitance C_n if it is present contributes $(j\omega C_n)$ to the imaginary part of the admittance.

From the above analysis, it is seen that the conclusions reached concerning the variation of the real and imaginary parts of the driving-point admittance of an RC network as a function of ω are true for the second RC canonic form. Furthermore, because all four canonic forms may be derived from the same driving-point admittance, the behavior of the real and imaginary parts of the admittance as a function of ω will be the same for all forms.

4-4. Canonic Forms of RL Networks

The characteristics of RC networks have been considered in the first part of this chapter, and it was seen that there are four RC canonic network forms just as there were for LC networks. In like manner, there are four canonic forms for RL networks which are analogous to the forms of Figs. 3-17 and 4-13. In order to obtain the four RL forms, the same procedures used for RC networks can be repeated. In view of this fact, the analogy between RC and RL driving-point functions will be utilized to minimize the required discussion.

If the driving-point impedance of an RL network is written as $Z_1(s) = P(s)/Q(s)$, the highest-order terms of $P(s)$ and $Q(s)$ may be of equal degree or $P(s)$ can be of higher degree than $Q(s)$ by unity. This fact can be stated in terms of Eq. (4-15) as $n = m$ or $n = m + 1$. Likewise, the lowest-order terms of $P(s)$ and $Q(s)$ may be of equal degree or $P(s)$ can be of higher degree than $Q(s)$ by unity. The possibility of $Q(s)$ being higher-order than $P(s)$ is forbidden, since division of $P(s)$ by $Q(s)$ would yield a term of the form K/s which could be identified as the impedance of a capacitor. The polynomials $P(s)$ and $Q(s)$ can be factored into terms of the form $(s + \sigma_n)$, where the σ_n terms are positive real numbers.

An RL driving-point impedance or admittance function may assume four different forms depending on the behavior of the function at $s = \sigma = 0$ and $s = \sigma = \infty$. These forms can be classified on an impedance basis as follows:

Case A. The impedance has a positive, nonzero value at both $s = 0$ and $s = \infty$.

Case B. The impedance has a zero at $s = 0$ and a pole at $s = \infty$.

Case C. The impedance has a positive, nonzero value at $s = 0$ and a pole at $s = \infty$.

Case D. The impedance has a zero at $s = 0$ and a positive, nonzero value at $s = \infty$.

The impedance functions associated with these four forms can be written in a manner similar to the *RC* cases of Eqs. (4-8) through (4-11). However, because the *RL* functions are so nearly the same as the *RC* cases, they will not be tabulated here, although the expansion of these functions will be considered in some detail.

If an *RL* driving-point impedance is divided by s, expanded in a partial-fraction expansion, then multiplied through by s, it yields an expansion of the following form:

$$Z_1(s) = K_0 + \frac{K_1 s}{s + \sigma_1} + \frac{K_3 s}{s + \sigma_3} + \cdots + \frac{K_{n-1} s}{s + \sigma_{n-1}} + K_n s \qquad (4\text{-}29)$$

The first and last terms of the expansion K_0 and $K_n s$, if either or both are present, represent a resistor of K_0 ohms and an inductor of K_n henrys, respectively. The intermediate terms of the expansion are of the form $K_i s/(s + \sigma_i)$ and can be identified as the impedance of simple parallel combinations of resistance and inductance. For example, the impedances of a network composed of resistance R and inductance L in parallel can be written as

$$Z_1(s) = \frac{1}{\dfrac{1}{R} + \dfrac{1}{Ls}} = \frac{Rs}{s + \dfrac{R}{L}} \qquad (4\text{-}30)$$

Therefore, the intermediate terms of Eq. (4-29) represent parallel *RL* combinations, giving the first *RL* canonic form as shown in Fig. 4-16.

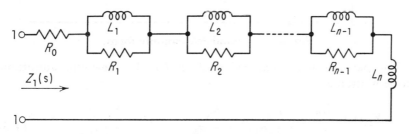

Fig. 4-16. *RL* canonic form from Eq. 4-29.

Consideration of Eq. (4-30) reveals that the zero of the function falls at the origin. The pole of Eq. (4-30) falls on the real axis at $\sigma = -R/L$. In like manner the poles and zeros of the *RL* driving-point impedance given by Eq. (4-29) fall on the negative real axis the same as for the *RC* networks. This is also true for the driving-point admittance of an RL network. It turns out that the slope of the driving-point impedance of an RL network with respect to σ is positive. This is just the reverse of the RC impedance characteristics and can be proved by taking the partial derivative of the RL impedance with respect to σ. The poles and zeros of RL networks must also be simple and mutually separate each other as in the RC case.

It should be pointed out that the impedance of a simple parallel RL combination given by Eq. (4-30) is of the same form as the admittance of a series RC combination $Y_1(s) = Cs/(RCs + 1)$. Likewise, the driving-point admittance of a simple RL series circuit has the same form as the driving-point impedance of a parallel RC circuit given by Eq. (4-3). To illustrate, the admittance of a simple RL series combination of elements is given by

$$Y_1(s) = \frac{1}{Z_1(s)} = \frac{1}{Ls + R} = \frac{Rs}{s + \dfrac{R}{L}} \tag{4-31}$$

The above conclusions indicate that the form of the driving-point impedance function of an RL network are similar to the driving-point admittance of an RC network. The converse of this statement is also true.

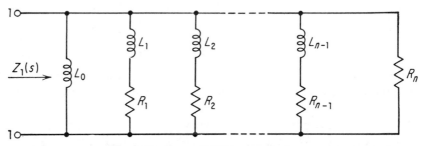

Fig. 4-17. Second RL canonic form.

The partial-fraction expansion of an RL driving-point admittance can be written as

$$Y_1(s) = \frac{K_0}{s} + \frac{K_1}{s + \sigma_1} + \frac{K_3}{s + \sigma_3} + \cdots + \frac{K_{n-1}}{s + \sigma_{n-1}} + K_n \tag{4-32}$$

The intermediate terms of Eq. (4-32) are of the same form as Eq. (4-31); whereas, the terminating terms K_0/s and K_n, if they are present, represent a shunt inductor of $1/K_0$ henrys and resistor of $1/K_n$ ohms, respectively. Consequently, the second RL canonic network form can be derived from Eq. (4-32) and is shown in Fig. 4-17.

Two of the four *RL* forms have been obtained, and the remaining two are similar to Forms 3 and 4 of Figs. 3-17 and 4-13. From the analogy between *LC*, *RC*, and *RL* networks, the third and fourth forms of an *RL* network are almost obvious. For this reason no attempt has been made to synthesize these forms; however, they can be derived by forward and reverse continued-fraction expansions of the *RL* driving-

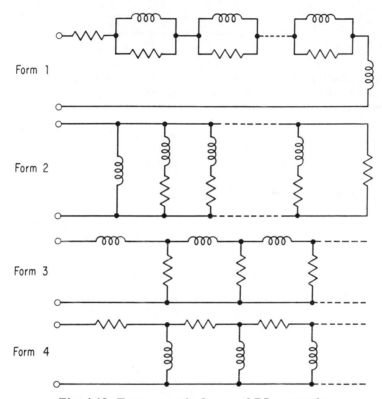

Form 1

Form 2

Form 3

Form 4

Fig. 4-18. Four canonic forms of *RL* networks.

point functions as in the case of *LC* and *RC* networks. The four *RL* canonic forms are summarized in Fig. 4-18. The manner in which Forms 3 and 4 are terminated depends on the nature of the driving-point function in question.

The following examples will serve to demonstrate the synthesis of *RL* networks.

Example 1. Assume the driving-point impedance of Eq. (4-33) is to be realized as an *RL* network of the second form.

$$Z_1(s) = \frac{6s^3 + 14s^2 + 4s}{11s^2 + 13s + 2} \tag{4-33}$$

Since the second form is composed of a parallel combination of elements, the admittance function is easier to work with. The terms for the expansion of the admittance function must be of the form K/s, $K/(s + \sigma_n)$, or K: therefore, the following expansion is appropriate.

$$Y_1(s) = \frac{1}{Z_1(s)} = \frac{11s^2 + 13s + 2}{6s^3 + 14s^2 + 4s}$$

$$= \frac{1}{2s} + \frac{1}{s + 2} + \frac{\frac{1}{3}}{s + \frac{1}{3}} \qquad (4\text{-}34)$$

The first term represents a 2-henry inductor, and the second and third terms are series RL combinations as in Eq. (4-31). The network resulting from this expansion is shown in Fig. 4-19.

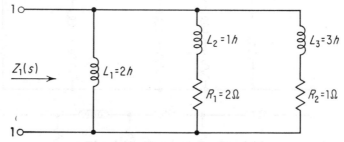

Fig. 4-19. Network for Eq. 4-34.

Example 2. The third RL form for Eq. (4-33) can be obtained by performing a forward continued-fraction expansion. In this case Eq. (4-33) becomes

$$Z_1(s) = \frac{6}{11} s + \cfrac{1}{\cfrac{121}{76} + \cfrac{1}{0.825s + \cfrac{1}{6.66 + \cfrac{1}{0.63s}}}} \qquad (4\text{-}35)$$

This expansion leads to the network of Fig. 4-20.

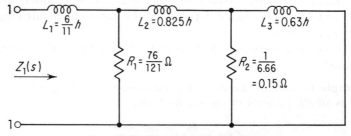

Fig. 4-20. Network for Eq. 4-35.

In many cases commercially available elements cannot be obtained to fit the requirements of a specific network. For example, all inductors possess a finite resistance. Therefore, when designing networks which require inductors, the problem of realizing the network with commercially available elements is simplified if each inductor of the synthesized network has a resistance in series with it. For this reason one canonic form may be preferable to another. For example, Form 2 of Fig. 4-18 might be more easily realized than Forms 1, 3, or 4.

4-5. *RL* Networks at Real Frequencies

Because of similarities existing between *RL* and *RC* networks, it is not considered necessary to explain in detail the behavior of the real and imaginary parts of *RL* driving-point functions at real frequencies. Therefore only a brief discussion of these functions will be presented in this section. Consider the driving-point admittance of Eq. (4-31) for a simple series *RL* network. When $j\omega$ is substituted for s, this function becomes

$$Y_1(j\omega) = \frac{1}{R + j\omega L} \tag{4-36}$$

The real and imaginary parts can be written as

$$Re[Y_1(j\omega)] = \frac{R}{R^2 + \omega^2 L^2} \tag{4-37}$$

$$Im[Y_1(j\omega)] = \frac{-j\omega L}{R^2 + \omega^2 L^2} \tag{4-38}$$

The intermediate terms of Eq. (4-32) are the same form as Eq. (4-36) (substituting $s = j\omega$), and the K_0/s and K_n terms represent a shunt inductor and resistor, respectively. Consequently, the behavior of the real and imaginary parts of Eq. (4-32) at and near $\omega = 0$ and $\omega = \infty$ can be surmised by studying the behavior of $K_0/j\omega$, K_n, and Eqs. (4-37) and (4-38). The behavior of Eqs. (4-37) and (4-38) as a function of ω can be iilustrated by use of circle diagrams as in the *RC* cases. When this is done and the $K_0/j\omega$ and K_n terms are taken into account, the following conclusions can be drawn concerning the behavior of the real and imaginary parts of an *RL* driving-point admittance at real frequencies.

1. The real part of the admittance is maximum at $\omega = 0$ and decreases as frequency increases, reaching a minimum value at $\omega = \infty$.

2. The susceptance or imaginary part of the admittance is negative for all values of ω. At $\omega = 0$ the susceptance may be either zero or infinite (zero if L_0 is missing and infinite if L_0 is present). However, at $\omega = \infty$ the susceptance will always be zero.

It should be noted that the behavior of the real and imaginary parts of *RL* driving-point admittance functions at real frequencies is similar to that of *RC* driving-point impedance functions (see Sec. 4-3). Likewise, the behavior of the real and imaginary parts of an *RL* driving-point impedance is similar to that of an *RC* driving-point admittance for real frequencies. This behavior can be described as follows:

1. The real part of the impedance is minimum at $\omega = 0$ and increases as frequency increases, reaching a maximum value at $\omega = \infty$.
2. The reactance or imaginary part of the impedance is positive for all values of ω. At $\omega = 0$ the reactance is always zero. However, at $\omega = \infty$ the reactance is either zero or infinite (zero if L_0 is missing and infinite if L_0 is present).

Because all four canonic forms can be derived from the same *RL* driving-point function, the behavior of the real and imaginary parts of the impedance or admittance of each network form will be as outlined above. It should also be pointed out that because the driving-point admittance is the reciprocal of the impedance, the conductance and susceptance have a frequency variation similar to the reciprocal of the real and reactive components, respectively, of the impedance function. These facts are readily verified by an analysis of the type performed on *RC* networks in Sec. 4-3.

4-6. Summary of *LC*, *RC*, and *RL* Driving-point Function Characteristics

A brief summary of the characteristics of *LC*, *RC*, and *RL* driving-point functions may help the reader at this point to more easily recognize these functions. Driving-point impedances will be reviewed, and because admittance functions possess a reciprocal relationship to the impedances, a discussion on an admittance basis is not considered necessary. Therefore, assume the driving-point impedance is written in the following form.

$$Z_1(s) = K \frac{P(s)}{Q(s)} = K \frac{s^n + a_{n-1}s^{n-1} + \cdots + a_1 s + a_0}{s^m + b_{m-1}s^{m-1} + \cdots + b_1 s + b_0} \quad (4\text{-}39)$$

In order for this function to be the driving-point impedance of an *LC*, *RC*, or *RL* network, it must possess the characteristics outlined in Table 4-1.

A set of characteristics similar to those of Table 4-1 can be derived for *LC*, *RC*, and *RL* driving-point admittance functions. These characteristics should make it possible for the reader to more easily recognize functions that can be realized as two-element kind, *LC*, *RC*, or *RL* networks. Furthermore, a number of procedures have been explained in Chaps. 3 and 4 for testing and synthesizing these special driving-point functions to realize various canonic network forms.

TABLE 4-I

Characteristics of *LC*, *RC*, and *RL* Driving-point Impedance Functions

Function characteristics in terms of Eq. 4-39	LC	RC	RL
The degree of the highest order terms of $P(s)$ and $Q(s)$ ...	Must differ by unity ($n = m - 1$ or $n = m + 1$)	Must be either $n = m$ or $n = m - 1$	Must be either $n = m$ or $n = m + 1$
The degree of the lowest order terms of $P(s)$ and $Q(s)$ ...	Must differ by unity (a_0 and b_0 cannot both be present)	May differ by unity (a_0 and b_0 may be present)	May differ by unity (a_0 and b_0 may be present)
Coefficients of all s terms must be positive real values, and $P(s)$ and $Q(s)$ will contain ...	Only even- or odd-ordered terms (i.e., if $P(s)$ has s^0, s^2, s^4, etc., terms, then $Q(s)$ can have only s^1, s^3, s^5, etc., terms)	All powers of s between the highest and lowest orders	All powers of s between the highest and lowest orders
Poles and zeros of $Z_1(s)$ must be simple and mutually separate each other ...	On the $j\omega$-axis, where they occur in conjugate pairs	On the negative real or σ-axis	On the negative real or σ-axis

References

The following references provide further reading concerning the synthesis of RC and RL one-port networks.

1. Wilhelm Cauer, *Synthesis of Linear Communication Networks*, Vols. 1 and 2 (New York: McGraw-Hill Book Co., Inc., 1958), Chap. 5.
2. E. S. Kuh and D. O. Pederson, *Principles of Circuit Synthesis* (McGraw-Hill Book Co., Inc., 1959), Chap. 10.
3. D. F. Tuttle, Jr., *Network Synthesis*, Vol. I (New York: John Wiley & Sons, Inc., 1958), Chap. 7.
4. M. E. Van Valkenburg, *Introduction to Network Synthesis* (New York: John Wiley & Sons, Inc., 1960), Chap. 6.
5. L. Weinberg, *Network Analysis and Synthesis* (New York: McGraw-Hill Book Co., Inc., 1962), Secs. 9-3 and 9-4.

Problems

4-1. Expand the following driving-point impedance to yield four RC canonic forms.

$$Z_1(s) = \frac{8s^2 + 36s + 15}{6s^2 + 3s}$$

4-2. Expand the following function to yield four RL canonic forms.

$$Z_1(s) = \frac{s^2 + 11s + 12}{2s + 10}$$

4-3. An RC network is to be designed with a pole at $\sigma = -2$, a zero at $\sigma = -4$, and a pole at $\sigma = -6$. In addition, the magnitude of the impedance is to be 2.5 ohms at $\omega = 2$. Determine the impedance function and plot its poles and zeros. Sketch the impedance plot of this function versus σ and discuss the results.

4-4. Synthesize two RC canonic network forms for the impedance determined in Prob. 4-3. Also realize one canonic network when the impedance of Prob. 4-3 is 25 ohms at $\omega = 2$.

4-5. Decompose the following driving-point impedance to yield an RC network, removing a series resistor and a shunt capacitor, by continued-fraction expansion. Following the removal of the first two elements, prove that the remaining expression is still physically realizable. Demonstrate that it is always possible to decompose a function by one of the canonic form methods to yield part of a network, then reverse the procedure and develop the remainder of the network as a different canonic form.

$$Z_1(s) = \frac{20s^3 + 127s^2 + 92s + 12}{4s^3 + 23s^2 + 10s}$$

4-6. An RL network is to be designed with zeros at $\sigma = -1$, $\sigma = -3$, and $\sigma = -5$. Two poles are to be used in the design in order to keep the order of the denominator within unity of the order of the numerator. On the basis of these requirements, choose the most likely poles for the function by making a pole-zero plot. Adjust the level of the resulting function to give an impedance of 50 ohms when $\omega = 4$. Synthesize a canonic *RL* network to realize this function.

4-7. Discuss the possibility of realizing the following driving-point impedance as either an *RC* or *RL* canonic network. Realize one *RC* and *RL* canonic form to demonstrate the results.

$$Z_1(s) = \frac{s^3 + 19s^2 + 108s + 180}{s^3 + 13s^2 + 44s + 32}$$

4-8. Synthesize two additional *RL* canonic network forms to realize the impedance of Eq. (4-33). Do not use the networks of Figs. 4-19 and 4-20.

4-9. Plot the real and imaginary parts of the impedance of Prob. 4-2 as a function of real frequency. Construct a locus of the impedance $Z_1(j\omega)$ similar to the circle diagram of Fig. 4-14 using this data. Discuss the results and how they will change if considered on an admittance basis.

4-10. Repeat the requirements of Prob. 4-9, using the impedance function of Prob. 4-7.

Chapter 5

Synthesis of *RLC* One-port

Networks

The synthesis of *LC*, *RC*, and *RL* canonic network forms has been discussed in Chaps. 3 and 4, and it was seen that a particular driving-point function might lead to a pure *RC* network while another function yields an *RL* or *LC* network. In circuit design, it is not necessary nor is it always desirable to restrict the synthesis procedure to pure *LC*, *RC*, or *RL* networks. Depending on such factors as the characteristics of a specified driving-point function or availability and cost of components, it may be useful to utilize *R*, *L*, and *C* elements in the same network. This possibility provides the designer with more freedom concerning the form of the resulting network, and in some cases it may be possible to realize the desired function with fewer elements than required for the pure *LC*, *RC*, or *RL* cases.

5-1. Series-parallel Withdrawal

The canonic network forms of Chaps. 3 and 4 were obtained by expanding driving-point functions by different procedures. One procedure used several times was the continued-fraction expansion. This process of repeated division and inversion can be generalized in the following manner. If the numerator polynomial $P(s)$ is of higher order than the denominator $Q(s)$, then it is divided by the denominator. The result of this division gives one term which can be identified with an element of the network. The remaining polynomial fraction is then inverted and the procedure repeated until each of the terms is obtained and identified with network elements. If the denominator is of higher order than the numerator, the function is first inverted before performing the first division.

Assume an impedance function is to be expanded by repeated division and inversion. If the numerator is of higher order than the denominator, the first division will yield a series-inductance term. At this point the remaining polynomial fraction can be inverted to form an admittance function. Division of this fraction will yield an admittance term which can be realized as a shunt element. If the numerator of the assumed impedance function is of lower order than the denominator, inversion will yield an admittance from which a shunt element can be identified as a result of the first division. When repeated division and inversion is employed to synthesize an *RLC* network, it is called a series-parallel withdrawal procedure. This terminology is used, since it is often possible to realize several series elements by division before inverting the remainder to remove parallel elements. For this reason the technique might be termed a "brute-force" method for expanding a function, although it cannot be used on all functions, as will be seen later in this section. However, series-parallel withdrawal can be used to realize many *RLC* networks.

Analysis of a specific example will make it easier to understand the procedure of series-parallel withdrawal. Assume the driving-point impedance of Eq. (5-1) is to be realized as an *RLC* network.

$$Z_1(s) = \frac{s^3 + 5s^2 + 8s + 4}{s^3 + 6s^2 + 13s + 9} \tag{5-1}$$

Before an attempt is made to realize this function, it should be tested by the procedures of Chap. 3, Sec. 3-2, to insure that it is a driving-point function and will lead to a physically realizable network. When this is done, close inspection reveals that the denominator is generally larger than the numerator; therefore the driving-point admittance should probably be considered for the removal of the first term. Dividing the numerator of $Y_1(s) = 1/Z_1(s)$ by the denominator yields a constant plus a remainder admittance which can be written as

$$Y_1(s) = 1 + \frac{s^2 + 5s + 5}{s^3 + 5s^2 + 8s + 4} = Y_2(s) + Y_3(s) \tag{5-2}$$

The admittance $Y_1(s)$ has been split into two admittances, $Y_2(s)$ and $Y_3(s)$, where $Y_2(s)$ is a conductance of 1 mho. One parallel element has been realized from $Y_1(s)$, so the problem is reduced to breaking up $Y_3(s)$. By inspection, $Y_3(s)$ has a denominator of higher order than its numerator; consequently, the impedance is easier to work with than the admittance.

$$Z_3(s) = \frac{1}{Y_3(s)} = \frac{s^3 + 5s^2 + 8s + 4}{s^2 + 5s + 5} \tag{5-3}$$

By long division, Eq. (5-3) is broken up into two series impedances, $Z_4(s)$ and $Z_5(s)$.

$$Z_3(s) = s + \frac{3s + 4}{s^2 + 5s + 5} = Z_4(s) + Z_5(s) \tag{5-4}$$

The first of these impedances, $Z_4(s)$, represents an inductor of 1 henry. At this point the denominator of $Z_5(s)$ is larger than the numerator and of higher order, so it is easier to work with the admittance $Y_5(s)$. By long division, $Y_5(s)$ is broken up into three admittances, $Y_6(s)$, $Y_7(s)$, and $Y_8(s)$.

$$Y_5(s) = \frac{1}{Z_5(s)} = \frac{s^2 + 5s + 5}{3s + 4} = \frac{1}{3}s + \frac{11}{9} + \frac{\frac{1}{9}}{3s + 4} = Y_6(s) + Y_7(s) + Y_8(s)$$

(5-5)

From Eq. (5-5) it is seen that $Y_6(s)$ is a capacitance of 1/3 farad, and $Y_7(s)$ is a conductance of 11/9 mhos, or a resistance of 9/11 ohm. The only remaining elements to be determined are included in the admittance $Y_8(s)$. The denominator of $Y_8(s)$ is of higher order than the numerator, so the impedance is easier to work with. This impedance is broken up by division to give two impedances in series, $Z_9(s)$ and $Z_{10}(s)$.

$$Z_8(s) = \frac{1}{Y_8(s)} = \frac{3s + 4}{\frac{1}{9}} = 27s + 36 = Z_9(s) + Z_{10}(s)$$

(5-6)

The impedance $Z_8(s)$ represents a series inductor of 27 henrys and resistor of 36 ohms. This completes the expansion of Eq. (5-1) which can be written as

$$Z_1(s) = \cfrac{1}{1 + \cfrac{1}{s + \cfrac{1}{\frac{s}{3} + \frac{11}{9} + \cfrac{1}{27s + 36}}}}$$

(5-7)

The network which realizes this expansion is shown in Fig. 5-1.

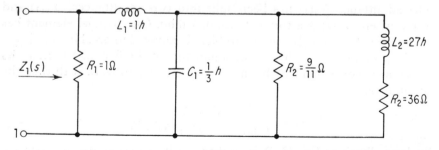

Fig. 5-1. Final form of *RLC* network for Eq. 5-1.

From the above example, it is seen that terms can sometimes be removed from a driving-point impedance or admittance by long division, alternating between realization of series and parallel elements. It would seem that this method of decomposition is desirable under most conditions due to its simplicity, but there are several drawbacks to the method. With some driving-point functions, a negative sign will be obtained in the remaining polynomial fraction of the division process if the proper terms are not removed in the correct order. This causes a great deal of trouble, since negative elements are not realizable in terms of passive elements. It sometimes requires a painful process of trial and error to find the correct solution.

A second example will help to illustrate the difficulties encountered in the application of the series-parallel withdrawal procedure. The impedance of Eq. (5-8) has been checked and fulfills the requirements necessary to insure a realizable network. An attempt will be made to synthesize a network for this function, using series-parallel withdrawal.

$$Z_1(s) = \frac{5s^2 + 3s + 4}{s^2 + 2s + 2} \qquad (5\text{-}8)$$

The numerator of this function appears to be larger than the denominator by inspection; however, division of the numerator by the denominator results in negative terms.

$$Z_1(s) = 5 + \frac{-7s - 6}{s^2 + 2s + 2} \qquad (5\text{-}9)$$

A series 5-ohm resistor can be realized from $Z_1(s)$, but the next term will be negative and is not realizable in terms of passive elements. Perhaps if a parallel element is realized first, the function will break down; therefore, expanding the admittance $Y_1(s)$ yields

$$Y_1(s) = \frac{1}{Z_1(s)} = \frac{s^2 + 2s + 2}{5s^2 + 3s + 4} = \frac{1}{5} + \frac{7s + 6}{25s^2 + 15s + 20} = Y_2(s) + Y_3(s) \qquad (5\text{-}10)$$

A 5-ohm resistor can be realized, and the remaining admittance is still positive. If $Y_3(s)$ is converted to an impedance, so that series terms can be removed, the following results are obtained.

$$Z_3(s) = \frac{1}{Y_3(s)} = \frac{25s^2 + 15s + 20}{7s + 6} = \frac{25s}{7} + \frac{-45s + 140}{49s + 42} \qquad (5\text{-}11)$$

A series inductance of 25/7 henrys can be realized, but again the remainder is negative, so this approach has also led to a nonrealizable solution. Consequently, it is seen that decomposition of complicated driving-point functions by the series-parallel withdrawal technique may involve a tedious process of trial and error. Fortunately, procedures such as zero shifting and partial removal of terms can be helpful in this process and will be described in later chapters.

Because the driving-point impedance of Eq. (5-8) passes all the tests of Chap. 3, Sec. 3-2, it must yield a realizable network. Generalized *RLC* synthesis procedures will be developed in the remaining sections of this chapter to synthesize driving-point functions such as Eq. (5-8) in a direct manner. For instance, Brune's procedure employs what may be called a "minimum impedance" approach to decompose a function until a particular combination of three inductors, including one negative inductance, can be realized in the form of a transformer with a specified mutual inductance. Details of this procedure will be investigated following a discussion of minimum-impedance functions.

5-2. Minimum-impedance Functions

The driving-point impedance of an *RLC* network must be a positive real function of *s* which consists of real and imaginary parts for $(s = j\omega)$ as described in Chap. 3. The impedance can be expressed in terms of real frequency as

$$Z_1(j\omega) = Re[Z_1(j\omega)] + jIm[Z_1(j\omega)] = R_1(\omega) + jX_1(\omega) \quad (5\text{-}12)$$

It is seen from this equation that the real part $R_1(\omega)$ as well as the reactance $X_1(\omega)$ may change as ω varies. For example, consider Eq. (5-13).

$$Z_1(s) = \frac{s^2 + s + 1}{s^2 + s + 4} \quad (5\text{-}13)$$

In terms of real frequency, this function becomes

$$Z_1(j\omega) = \frac{-\omega^2 + j\omega + 1}{-\omega^2 + j\omega + 4} \quad (5\text{-}14)$$

Rationalizing and separating terms, the real and imaginary parts can be expressed as

$$Re[Z_1(j\omega)] = \frac{(1 - \omega^2)(4 - \omega^2) + \omega^2}{(4 - \omega^2)^2 + \omega^2} = \frac{\omega^4 - 4\omega^2 + 4}{(4 - \omega^2)^2 + \omega^2} \quad (5\text{-}15)$$

$$Im[Z_1(j\omega)] = \frac{\omega(4 - \omega^2) - \omega(1 - \omega^2)}{(4 - \omega^2)^2 + \omega^2} = \frac{3\omega}{(4 - \omega^2)^2 + \omega^2} \quad (5\text{-}16)$$

Therefore, the driving-point impedance can be written as a function of ω as

$$Z_1(j\omega) = \frac{\omega^4 - 4\omega^2 + 4}{(4 - \omega^2)^2 + \omega^2} + j\frac{3\omega}{(4 - \omega^2)^2 + \omega^2} = R_1(\omega) + jX_1(\omega) \quad (5\text{-}17)$$

From Eqs. (5-15) and (5-17) it is clear that the real part $R_1(\omega)$ varies with frequency, but because it is the real or resistive part of the driving-point impedance it can never be negative. At some frequency ω_1 this function will have a minimum value. Assume that $R_1(\omega)$ varies as illustrated in Fig. 5-2.

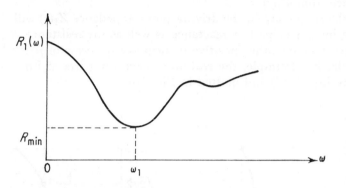

Fig. 5-2. Resistive part of impedance as a function of frequency.

The largest resistance that can possibly be removed from a driving-point impedance is the minimum resistance R_{min}. If a larger resistance than R_{min} is removed the real part of the remaining function will be negative at some frequency, and as a result, it will not be realizable in terms of passive elements. If the minimum resistance is removed, the driving-point impedance becomes

$$Z_2(s) = Z_1(s) - R_{min} \qquad (5-18)$$

The network takes the form seen in Fig. 5-3.

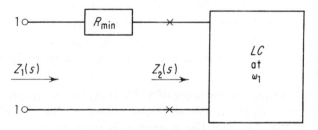

Fig. 5-3. Network after the removal of R_{min}.

After R_{min} has been removed, the new driving-point impedance $Z_2(s)$ will be positive and real, but it will have a real or resistive component that is zero at ω_1. Functions of this type are referred to as minimum-resistance functions. In some cases R_{min} occurs at $\omega = 0$ or $\omega = \infty$. This fact can be checked by testing the limit of $Re[Z_1(j\omega)]$ at $\omega = 0$ and $\omega = \infty$. Testing $Re[Z_1(j\omega)]$ for minimum values at intermediate frequencies may require considerable work for complicated functions. However, for $Z_2(s)$ to be a positive real function, its real part must be nonnegative at all frequencies including $\omega = 0$ and $\omega = \infty$. Therefore, it is important to accurately establish the value of R_{min} before removing resistance from $Z_1(s)$.

At the frequency ω_1 the driving-point impedance $Z_1(s)$ will generally have an imaginary part or reactance as well as the resistance R_{min}. This reactance may be either positive or negative in terms of $j\omega$ and still be realizable. For example, the real and imaginary parts of Eq. (5-13) are given by Eq. (5-17) and plotted in Fig. 5-4.

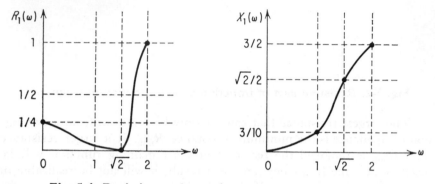

Fig. 5-4. Resistive and reactive components of Eq. 5-17.

It is seen from this figure that the minimum value of resistance R_{min} is zero and occurs at the frequency $\omega_1 = \sqrt{2}$. For this reason no resistance can be removed from the example of Eq. (5-13) without causing the real part of the remaining impedance function to be negative at the frequency $\omega_1 = \sqrt{2}$. However, Fig. 5-4 also shows that $Z_1(j\omega)$ possesses a reactance of $X_1(\omega) = \sqrt{2}/2$ at $\omega_1 = \sqrt{2}$. If this reactance is removed from $Z_2(s)$, the resulting impedance $Z_3(s)$ will be zero at the frequency $\omega_1 = \sqrt{2}$.

In order to remove a reactance of $\sqrt{2}/2$ from the minimum-resistance function $Z_1(s) = Z_2(s)$ the nature of the reactance must be considered. It is seen in Fig. 5-4 that the reactance is positive at ω_1 and can be synthesized at this frequency by a term of the form $j\omega L$ or in terms of complex frequency by Ls. Assuming the reactance is of this form, an inductance of $1/2$ henry will supply the correct reactance at $\omega_1 = \sqrt{2}$.

$$X_L = \omega_1 L = \sqrt{2}/2 \qquad \text{so} \qquad L = 1/2 \text{ henry} \qquad (5\text{-}19)$$

If this inductance is removed from the driving-point impedance $Z_2(s)$ an impedance $Z_3(s)$ results which has zero reactance at the frequency ω_1.

$$Z_3(s) = Z_2(s) - Ls = \frac{s^2 + s + 1}{s^2 + s + 4} - \frac{1}{2}s = \frac{-s^3 + s^2 - 2s + 2}{2s^2 + 2s + 8} \qquad (5\text{-}20)$$

Removal of the reactance of $Z_2(s)$ at ω_1 causes $Z_3(s)$ to have zero reactance at that frequency. Hence, $Z_3(s)$ is known as a minimum-reactance function. But more important is the fact that $Z_3(s)$ also has zero real part at ω_1. An impedance function possessing these characteristics (i.e., both real and imaginary parts of the function vanish at ω_1, where ω_1 may be any real frequency, including $\omega = 0$ or $\omega = \infty$) is defined as a minimum-impedance function.

At first glance it would appear that $Z_3(s)$ is a completely impossible function to synthesize and more complex than before the minimum resistive and reactive terms were removed. However, $Z_3(s)$ is a minimum-impedance function and forms the basis of the Brune procedure. Finally, it should be clear that the above procedure can also be used to remove conductance and susceptance from an admittance function. A minimum-conductance function is an admittance with zero conductance at some real frequency ω_1. In like manner, a minimum-susceptance function has zero susceptance, and a minimum admittance has zero admittance at the frequency ω_1.

5-3. Brune's Synthesis Procedure

The Brune procedure for the synthesis of an *RLC* network can be stated as a series of distinct steps based on the removal of the minimum resistance and reactance of the specified function at the frequency ω_1.[†] This method of decomposition will be explained in general terms after which the example of Eq. (5-8) will be considered again. Assume that a driving-point impedance function $Z_1(s)$ is under consideration and must first be tested in order to determine if it will yield a realizable network. If the function passes these tests, then the Brune procedure can be used to decompose it. The steps involved in the decomposition process will be outlined in the following discussion.

Step 1. If the numerator and denominator of $Z_1(s)$ are of unequal order, a network composed of series or parallel combinations of inductors and/or capacitors can be removed by series-parallel withdrawal or the procedures of Chap. 3. The purpose of this step is to remove all $j\omega$-axis poles and zeros from the driving-point function. Once the $j\omega$-axis poles and zeros have been removed from $Z_1(s)$, the remaining function $Z_2(s)$ will have a numerator $P(s)$ and denominator $Q(s)$ which are of equal degree. At this point the *LC* network between terminals 1-1 and *a-a* of

† O. Brune, "Synthesis of a Finite Two-Terminal Network Whose Driving-Point Impedance is a Prescribed Function of Frequency," *J. Math. Phys.*, vol. 10, August 1931, pp. 191–236.

Fig. 5-5 has been realized, and the remaining impedance $Z_2(s)$ can be written as

$$Z_2(s) = \frac{P(s)}{Q(s)} = \frac{a_n s^n + a_{n-1} s^{n-1} + \cdots + a_0}{b_n s^n + b_{n-1} s^{n-1} + \cdots + b_0} \qquad (5\text{-}21)$$

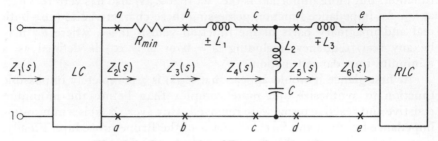

Fig. 5-5. One cycle of Brune's procedure.

Step 2. Writing $Z_2(s)$ in terms of $j\omega$, Eq. (5-21) becomes

$$Z_2(j\omega) = Re[Z_2(j\omega)] + jIm[Z_2(j\omega)] \qquad (5\text{-}22)$$

From this equation the values of R_{min} and the frequency ω_1 are determined as explained in Sec. 5-2. The value of R_{min} can be removed from $Z_2(s)$ leaving a minimum resistance function $Z_3(s)$.

$$Z_3(s) = Z_2(s) - R_{min} \qquad (5\text{-}23)$$

At this point in the decomposition, the network between terminals 1-1 and $b\text{-}b$ of Fig. 5-5 has been realized. Furthermore, $Z_3(s)$ is a pure reactance at ω_1, but at any other frequency it possesses a finite real or resistive component.

Before continuing to the next step, it is always useful to check to see if one of the earlier steps can be applied again. For instance, removal of R_{min} may introduce new poles and/or zeros on the $j\omega$-axis or at $s = 0$ or $s = \infty$.

Step 3. The minimum resistance has been removed from $Z_2(s)$ by using the $Re[Z_2(j\omega)]$. Now using the $Im[Z_2(j\omega)]$, the value of the reactance is determined at the frequency ω_1. This reactance may be either positive or negative, but for reasons which will become clear, it is desirable to remove a positive or negative inductor $\pm L_1$ from $Z_3(s)$ such that $j\omega_1 L_1$ or $j\omega_1(-L_1)$ equals the reactance at ω_1. Removal of an inductance gives

$$Z_4(s) = Z_3(s) - \boxed{+ L_1 s \quad \text{or} \quad - L_1 s} \qquad (5\text{-}24)$$

Following this step, the network has been realized from terminals 1-1 to $c\text{-}c$ in Fig. 5-5. In addition, $Z_4(s)$ is a minimum impedance function at the frequency ω_1. Since $Z_4(s)$ is zero at ω_1, it is possible to remove a zero producing impedance which can be realized as a shunt *LC* combination.

Step 4. In order to remove a shunt *LC* combination, it is easier to work with the admittance $Y_4(s) = 1/Z_4(s)$. The admittance of the shunt *LC* combination to be removed from $Y_4(s)$ will be of the form

$$Y = \frac{1}{L_2 s + \dfrac{1}{Cs}} = \frac{\dfrac{1}{L_2} s}{s^2 + \dfrac{1}{L_2 C}} \qquad \text{where} \qquad \omega_1 = \sqrt{1/L_2 C}$$

$$(5\text{-}25)$$

Because $Z_4(s)$ is zero at the frequency ω_1, $Y_4(s)$ is infinite and can be realized by a series *LC* combination as given by Eq. (5-25). The admittance $Y_5(s)$ is found by removing the function of Eq. (5-25) from $Y_4(s)$.

$$Y_5(s) = Y_4(s) - Y = Y_4(s) - \frac{\dfrac{1}{L_2} s}{s^2 + \dfrac{1}{L_2 C}}$$

$$(5\text{-}26)$$

The elements L_2 and C, which compose the admittance Y, must be positive; however, the manner in which they are determined will become clear following the discussion of the next step. At the conclusion of this step, the network of Fig. 5-5 will be realized between terminals 1-1 and *d-d*.

Step 5. Using the impedance, $Z_5(s) = 1/Y_5(s)$, it is possible to realize a third inductor L_3 which has the opposite sign of the inductor L_1. The value of L_3 is determined from the relationship

$$-L_3 = \frac{L_1 L_2}{L_1 + L_2}$$

$$(5\text{-}27)$$

The sign of L_3 will be negative if a positive value of L_1 is removed in Step 3, Eq. (5-24). A positive L_3 results when L_1 is negative. This point will also become clear later. The realization of this inductor can be expressed as

$$Z_6(s) = Z_5(s) - \boxed{-L_3 s \quad \text{or} \quad +L_3 s}$$

$$(5\text{-}28)$$

Although it is not obvious from the above discussion, $Z_6(s)$ will be a driving-point impedance with characteristics similar to those of $Z_2(s)$. Therefore, one cycle of the procedure ends when the network between terminals 1-1 and *e-e* of Fig. 5-5 has been realized. The entire process can be applied again to $Z_6(s)$ until the remaining function is fully realized.

Before continuing, it is worthwhile to reconsider the nature of the functions resulting from the above five steps. If $Z_1(s)$ is a positive real driving-point function, removal of all $j\omega$-axis poles and zeros to form an LC network yields a remainder $Z_2(s)$ which is also positive real. The removal of $R_{\min}$ at a frequency ω_1 from $Z_2(s)$ gives $Z_3(s)$ which is a minimum-resistance function and is still positive real. At this point the reactance is removed from $Z_3(s)$ at the frequency ω_1 as a positive or negative inductor L_1. If the reactance is negative requiring that L_1 be negative, then $Z_4(s)$, Eq. (5-24), will have a positive residue at its pole $(s = \infty)$ and must be a positive real function. However, if the reactance of $Z_3(s)$ is positive at ω_1, requiring that L_1 be positive, then $Z_4(s)$ will not be positive real because its pole at $(s = \infty)$ will have a negative residue. In either case it appears that an impossible situation exists.

Ignoring these problems for the moment, consider the case in which L_1 is negative. In this case $Z_4(s)$ is positive real but has a simple pole at the frequency ω_1. The removal of the simple pole of $1/Z_4(s)$ at ω_1 by realization of the series $L_2 - C$ combination yields $1/Z_5(s)$ which must be positive real since removal of $j\omega$-axis poles from a positive real function must leave a positive real remainder. Furthermore, $Z_5(s)$ will have a pole at $s = \infty$. This fact can be proved in the following manner. Analytically, $Y_5(s)$ can be written as

$$Y_5(s) = Y_4(s) - Y(s) = \frac{1}{Z_3(s) - L_1 s} - \frac{\dfrac{1}{L_2}s}{s^2 + \dfrac{1}{L_2 C}} \tag{5-29}$$

The reciprocal $Z_5(s)$ is given by

$$Z_5(s) = \frac{-L_1 s^3 + s^2 Z_3(s) - \dfrac{L_1 s}{L_2 C} + \dfrac{Z_3(s)}{L_2 C}}{\left[1 + \dfrac{L_1}{L_2}\right]s^2 - \dfrac{s Z_3(s)}{L_2} + \dfrac{1}{L_2 C}} \tag{5-30}$$

In this equation $Z_3(s)$ is a positive real function which is regular and approaches a finite value as s approaches infinity; consequently, near $(s = \infty)$, $Z_5(s)$ becomes

$$Z_5(s)\Big]_{s \to \infty} \longrightarrow \frac{-L_1 s^3}{\left[1 + \dfrac{L_1}{L_2}\right]s^2} = \frac{-L_1 L_2 s}{L_1 + L_2} = L_3 s \tag{5-31}$$

Clearly, $Z_5(s)$ has a pole at $(s = \infty)$, and if L_1 is negative, $Z_5(s)$ approaches a positive reactance for large s which can be identified as $L_3 s$. This verifies the relationship of Eq. (5-27).

Removal of $L_3 s$ from $Z_5(s)$ yields $Z_6(s)$, which again must be positive real and will have no $j\omega$-axis poles or zeros. In other words, $Z_6(s)$ will possess the same properties as $Z_2(s)$, although its numerator and denominator will be two degrees lower than $Z_2(s)$. Since $Z_6(s)$ is a positive real function of s, the entire process can be repeated by first removing a resistor, R^*_{min}, similar to Step 2. The cycle of steps is then repeated until the last element is realized.

It is now possible to return to the problem of realizing the negative inductor $(-L_1)$ or the nonpositive real function generated by the removal of a positive L_1s term from $Z_3(s)$. Consider first the case in which L_1 is negative. In Fig. 5-5 it is seen that the negative inductor $(-L_1)$ forms a branch of a T network with the positive inductors, L_2 and L_3. Such a T network can be replaced by a pair of positive mutually coupled inductors which form a transformer as indicated in Fig. 5-6.

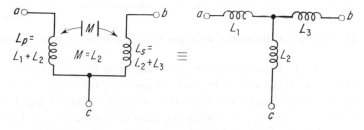

Fig. 5-6. Transformer equivalent of T network.

The T network of Fig. 5-6 has an equivalent transformer in which $L_p = L_1 + L_2$ and $L_s = L_2 + L_3$. The primary inductance L_p and the secondary inductance L_s of the transformer must be greater than zero, and the magnitude of the mutual inductance $|M|$ must equal L_2. From transformer theory, the coupling coefficient Ψ for the transformer can be written as

$$\Psi = \frac{|M|}{\sqrt{L_p L_s}} = \frac{|L_2|}{\sqrt{(L_1 + L_2)(L_2 + L_3)}} \qquad (5\text{-}32)$$

For perfect coupling, which can only be approximated in practice, Ψ is unity, and Eq. (5-32) becomes

$$\sqrt{(L_1 + L_2)(L_2 + L_3)} = |L_2| \qquad (5\text{-}33)$$

Squaring both sides and solving for L_3 yields

$$L_1 L_2 + L_1 L_3 + L_2 L_3 = 0 \qquad \text{or} \qquad L_3 = \frac{-L_1 L_2}{L_1 + L_2} \qquad (5\text{-}34)$$

It is seen that Eqs. (5-27), (5-31), and (5-34) give the same result; consequently, it is possible to substitute a transformer with perfect coupling for the three inductors L_1, L_2, and L_3, as indicated in Fig. 5-6. The network of Fig. 5-5 is transformed to that of Eq. (5-7) by this step.

The above discussion satisfies the case in which the value of L_1 is negative, with a possible question remaining concerning the usefulness of the procedure in view of the requirement for a perfectly coupled transformer. It is now of interest to consider the case in which L_1 is positive such that removal of L_1s from $Z_2(s)$ yields $Z_3(s)$, a nonpositive real function. Ignoring this fact for the present, removal of L_1s causes the

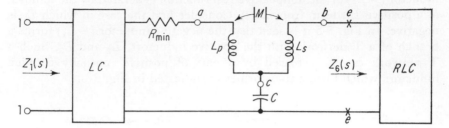

Fig. 5-7. Final form for a single cycle of Brune's procedure.

input impedance of the network to have a pole at $(s = \infty)$ because of the series inductor. However, $Z_2(s)$ had no $j\omega$-axis poles or zero; therefore, a second series term must be removed to offset the effect of L_1. The shunt combination is necessary to realize the zero of $Z_3(s)$ at ω_1, and the series inductor $-L_3$ offsets the effect of $+L_1$.

In effect the perfectly coupled transformer which replaces L_1, L_2, and L_3 cancels the net series inductance of the circuit. Consequently, when L_1 is positive causing $Z_3(s)$ to be nonpositive real, it is possible to continue the realization process by recognizing the subtle fact that removal of a negative inductor $-L_3$ restores the positive real character of the remaining function. Substantiation of this fact can be obtained from consideration of the example driving-point impedance of Eq. (5-8), which is rewritten below.

$$Z_1(s) = \frac{5s^2 + 3s + 4}{s^2 + 2s + 2} = \frac{P(s)}{Q(s)} \tag{5-35}$$

Step 1. In the first step, LC elements are removed from $Z_1(s)$ until $P(s)$ and $Q(s)$ are of the same order. By observation it is seen that $P(s)$ and $Q(s)$ are both second order polynomials, so no LC elements can be removed. Therefore, $Z_2(s)$ will equal $Z_1(s)$.

Step 2. In the second step the resistance R_{min} is removed. In order to find the value of R_{min}, the $Re[Z_2(j\omega)]$ must be studied. In terms of $j\omega$, $Z_2(s)$ becomes

$$Z_2(j\omega) = \frac{(4 - 5\omega^2) + j(3\omega)}{(2 - \omega^2) + j(2\omega)} = Re[Z_2(j\omega)] + jIm[Z_2(j\omega)] \tag{5-36}$$

The real and imaginary parts of $Z_2(j\omega)$ are

$$Re[Z_2(j\omega)] = \frac{(4 - 5\omega^2)(2 - \omega^2) + (2\omega)(3\omega)}{(2 - \omega^2)^2 + (2\omega)^2} = \frac{5\omega^4 - 8\omega^2 + 8}{\omega^4 + 4} \quad (5\text{-}37)$$

$$Im[Z_2(j\omega)] = \frac{(3\omega)(2 - \omega^2) - (2\omega)(4 - 5\omega^2)}{(2 - \omega^2)^2 + (2\omega)^2} = \frac{(7\omega^3 - 2\omega)}{\omega^4 + 4} \quad (5\text{-}38)$$

The value of R_{min} can be determined by differentiating the $Re[Z_2(j\omega)]$, Eq. (5-37), with respect to ω and solving for the minimum. In the case of Eq. (5-37), the maximum and minimum points occur at $\omega = 0, +1, -1, +j2$, and $-j2$. The imaginary and negative values of frequency are extraneous roots. The root at zero frequency is a trivial case, which leaves only $\omega = +1$ of any interest. If Eqs. (5-37) and (5-38) are plotted as a function of frequency, the curves of Fig. 5-8 result. In most cases it is easier to determine the minimum value of $Re[Z_2(j\omega)]$ by differentiating the function and solving for the minimum. However, when the function is not easily differentiated, it can be plotted carefully to determine the minimum.

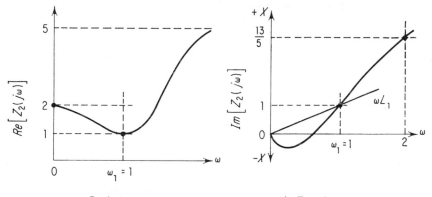

a. Real component   b. Imaginary component

Fig. 5-8. Real and imaginary parts of Eq. 5-36.

From the curve of the $Re[Z_2(j\omega)]$, the value of R_{min} is seen to be 1 ohm and occurs at $\omega_1 = 1$. Removing the value of R_{min} from $Z_2(s)$ gives

$$Z_3(s) = Z_2(s) - R_{min} = \frac{5s^2 + 3s + 4}{s^2 + 2s + 2} - 1 = \frac{4s^2 + s + 2}{s^2 + 2s + 2} \quad (5\text{-}39)$$

Step 3. The impedance $Z_3(s)$ has a 1-ohm reactance at the frequency ω_1 as shown by the curve of the $Im[Z_2(j\omega)]$ in Fig. 5-8b. It is possible to realize this reactance as a positive inductance L_1.

$$X_L = \omega_1 L_1 = 1 \text{ ohm} \quad \text{where} \quad \omega_1 = 1 \quad \text{so} \quad L_1 = 1 \text{ henry}$$
$$(5\text{-}40)$$

An inductance of 1 henry can be removed from $Z_3(s)$ to yield $Z_4(s)$.

$$Z_4(s) = Z_3(s) - L_1 s = \frac{4s^2 + s + 2}{s^2 + 2s + 2} - 1s = \frac{-s^3 + 2s^2 - s + 2}{s^2 + 2s + 2} \qquad (5\text{-}41)$$

$Z_4(s)$ has zero impedance at the frequency ω_1. The reciprocal admittance, $Y_4(s)$, becomes infinite at ω_1; consequently, it is now possible to remove the shunt L_2C combination. However, before this is done, a check can be made on the progress of the method by determining the value of the residue at the pole of $Y_4(s)$. In this case the residue k becomes

$$k = \left[\frac{s^2 + 2s + 2}{(s^2 + 1)(-s + 2)} \right]_{s = j\omega_1 = j1} = \frac{1}{2} \qquad (5\text{-}42)$$

This residue is positive and real, so it is possible to remove the L_2C combination.

Step 4. The admittance $Y_4(s)$ can be expanded in the following manner:

$$Y_4(s) = \frac{s^2 + 2s + 2}{-s^3 + 2s^2 - s + 2}$$

$$= \frac{2}{-s + 2} + \frac{s}{s^2 + 1} = Y_5(s) + Y(s) \qquad (5\text{-}43)$$

The $Y(s)$ term represents the admittance of the shunt L_2C branch.

$$Y(s) = \frac{\dfrac{1}{L_2} s}{s^2 + \dfrac{1}{L_2C}} = \frac{s}{s^2 + 1} \qquad \begin{array}{l} \text{so} \;\; L_2 = 1 \text{ henry} \\ \text{and} \;\; C = 1 \text{ farad} \end{array} \qquad (5\text{-}44)$$

Step 5. Using the impedance $Z_5(s)$ a series inductance L_3 can be realized. This inductance must be negative since the inductance L_1 was positive.

$$Z_5(s) = \frac{1}{Y_5(s)} = \frac{-s + 2}{2} = \frac{-s}{2} + 1 = L_3 s + Z_6(s) \qquad (5\text{-}45)$$

The value of L_3 is seen to be $-1/2$ henry, and the remainder $Z_6(s)$ is 1 ohm.

Step 6. At this point the procedure can be repeated using $Z_6(s)$; although in this example it is seen that $Z_6(s)$ is a 1-ohm resistor which can be identified as $R^*_{\min}$. The circuit for the example takes the form of Fig. 5-9.

The three inductors L_1, L_2, and L_3 form a T network as in Fig. 5-6, so a transformer with perfect coupling can be substituted in the network.

The primary, secondary, and mutual inductance of the transformer can be found as follows:

$$L_p = L_1 + L_2 = 1 + 1 = 2 \text{ henrys}$$

$$L_s = L_2 + L_3 = 1 - 1/2 = 1/2 \text{ henry}$$

$$M = L_2 = 1 \text{ henry} \tag{5-46}$$

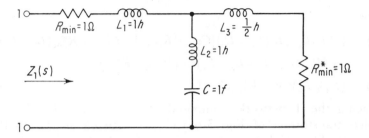

Fig. 5-9. Partial determination of network for Eq. 5-35.

Substituting the transformer for the T network composed of L_1, L_2, and L_3 in Fig. 5-9 converts the network to that of Fig. 5-10.

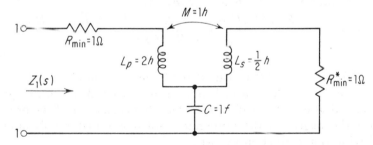

Fig. 5-10. Final network for Eq. 5-35.

This example demonstrates a case in which the inductor L_1 is positive; thereby, making it necessary to remove a negative inductor $-L_3$ during Step 5 of the procedure to restore the positive real character of the remaining function. It is also noted that the network of Fig. 5-10 realizes the *RLC* driving-point impedance of Eq. (5-35) or (5-8) which was found difficult to synthesize by the series-parallel withdrawal procedure of Sec. 5-1.

A question remains concerning the usefulness of Brune's procedure when transformer-coupling coefficients less than unity are employed in the realization process. A measure of the effect caused by various coupling coefficients may be obtained by investigating the sensitivity of pole-zero locations of the impedance function to changes in Ψ. For example, consider a single cycle of Brune's procedure starting with $Z_2(s)$ (a positive real function having no $j\omega$-axis poles or zeros) and ending with $Z_6(s)$ which possesses the same characteristics. More specifically, the driving-point impedance for a single cycle of Brune's network composed of R_{min}, $\pm L_1$, L_2, C, $\mp L_3$, and R_{min}^* can be written as

$$Z(s) = \frac{P(s)}{Q(s)}$$

where

$$P(s) = [\mp L_3 L_2 \pm L_1(L_2 \mp L_3)]Cs^3 + [R_{min}(L_2 \mp L_3) + R_{min}^*(L_2 \pm L_1)]Cs_2$$
$$+ (R_{min}R_{min}^*C \mp L_3 \pm L_1)s + (R_{min} + R_{min}^*)$$
$$Q(s) = (L_2 \mp L_3)Cs^2 + R_{min}^*Cs + 1 \tag{5-47}$$

Replacing the T network, composed of $\pm L_1$, L_2, and $\mp L_3$, by the coupled transformer of Fig. 5-6 yields a network similar to that of Fig. 5-10. The driving-point impedance for the transformed network can be obtained by substituting the relationships of Eq. (5-32) in Eq. (5-47) to give

$$Z(s) =$$

$$\frac{(1 - \Psi^2)L_p L_s Cs^3 + (L_p R_{min}^* + L_s R_{min})Cs^2 + (R_{min}R_{min}^*C + L_p + L_s - 2\Psi\sqrt{L_p L_s})s + R_{min} + R_{min}^*}{L_s Cs^2 + R_{min}^*Cs + 1}$$

$$\tag{5-48}$$

Inspection of Eq. (5-48) reveals that for perfect coupling ($\Psi = 1$) the impedance for a single cycle of Brune's procedure reduces to the quotient of two quadratics. This reaffirms the fact that each cycle of the procedure reduces the degree of the numerator and denominator polynomials of the driving-point function by two.

For coupling coefficients less than unity, the numerator of Eq. (5-48) becomes a cubic, and $Z(s)$ possesses a pole at $s = \infty$. As a result, the accuracy with which the network with ($\Psi < 1$) approximates the desired driving-point impedance for a network with ($\Psi = 1$) becomes worse as s increases. For large values of s, Eq. (5-48) becomes

$$Z(s)\Big]_{s \to \infty} \longrightarrow \frac{(1 - \Psi^2)L_p L_s Cs^3}{L_s Cs^2} = (1 - \Psi^2)L_p s \tag{5-49}$$

It is seen that the error which results at large values of s because of imperfect transformer coupling can be partially compensated for by readjusting the primary inductance of the transformer L_p by a factor $(1 - \Psi^2)$. However, zeros of the driving-point impedance will still possess errors because of the coupling coefficient present in the co-efficient of the s term of the numerator of Eq. (5-48).

To demonstrate the sensitivity of pole-zero locations to changes in the transformer coupling coefficient, it is useful to reconsider the example of Eq. (5-35) or Fig. 5-10. Substituting the element values of Fig. 5-10 in Eq. (5-48), which represents the generalized driving-point impedance for a single cycle of Brune's procedure, yields

$$Z(s) = \frac{P(s)}{Q(s)} = \frac{2(1 - \Psi'^2)s^3 + 5s^2 + (7 - 4\Psi')s + 4}{s^2 + 2s + 2} \tag{5-50}$$

It is seen that the poles of this function, represented by $Q(s)$, do not change as Ψ' varies; however, the zeros of $P(s)$ shift as the coupling coefficient changes. The zeros of Eq. (5-50) have been computed for several values of Ψ' and are presented in Table 5-1. It should be noted that for ($\Psi' = 1$) there are only a pair of complex conjugate zeros, and Eq. (5-50) reduces to Eq. (5-35). For Ψ' less than unity, a third zero is introduced, and the original complex conjugate zeros shift to new positions.

TABLE 5-I

Variation of Zero Positions with Changes in Coupling Coefficient for the Example of Fig. 5-10

Ψ'	Complex conjugate zeros	Real zero
1.00	$s = -0.300 \pm j0.843$	(none)
0.95	$s = -0.312 \pm j0.850$	$s = -25.018$
0.90	$s = -0.324 \pm j0.858$	$s = -12.510$
0.80	$s = -0.352 \pm j0.876$	$s = -6.242$
0.70	$s = -0.383 \pm j0.895$	$s = -4.136$
(trivial case) 0.00	$s = -0.750 \pm j1.199$	$s = -1.000$

The above example illustrates the manner in which the sensitivity of pole-zero positions can be tested when transformers with less than perfect coupling are employed in the realization process. It should also be noted that the resistors R_{min} and R^*_{min} are in series with L_p and L_s, respectively. Commercially available transformers possess distributed resistance in their primary and secondary circuits. Consequently, R_{min} and R^*_{min} can be reduced in value to partially or completely compensate for the distributed resistance of the transformer.

It is seen that Brune's procedure is powerful and can be used to decompose a general *RLC* driving-point impedance. Because the procedure is general, it can also be carried out on an admittance basis; however, in either case a perfect transformer is required to realize the driving-point function exactly.† A perfect transformer can never be achieved in practice even though a close approximation can often be obtained. When adjustments are made in the network to compensate for deficiencies in the transformer, it may still be impossible to approximate the specified driving-point function within the required degree of accuracy. In this event it may be desirable or necessary to employ a realization procedure which avoids the use of transformers. The remainder of this chapter is devoted to synthesis procedures, based on mathematical transformations, which can be used in the realization of RLC driving-point functions without employing transformers.

5-4. Richards' Theorem

Brune's procedure is based on minimum impedance functions and zero producing. Several additional synthesis procedures have been developed which follow the same steps to the point at which Brune realized the perfect transformer. However, at this point a transform, based on Richards' theorem, is used to replace the transformer with a more complicated but more easily realized RLC network. Before discussing the steps involved in these procedures, it is instructive to consider Richards' theorem, which is a special case of Schwarz's lemma.‡

Richards' theorem states that if a function $Z(s)$ is positive real and if $Z(s)/Z(1)$ is not identically equal to s or $1/s$, then the function $Z^*(s)$ can be written as

$$Z^*(s) = \frac{Z(s) - sZ(1)}{Z(1) - sZ(s)} \qquad (5\text{-}51)$$

The function $Z^*(s)$ will also be a positive real function of s, and this fact can be proved in the following manner. Consider the new variable p in which the magnitude of p is less than unity for values of σ greater than zero.

$$p = \frac{s - 1}{s + 1} = \frac{\sigma - 1 + j\omega}{\sigma + 1 + j\omega}$$

where $$|p| \leq 1 \quad \text{for} \quad \sigma \geq 0 \qquad (5\text{-}52)$$

Also consider the linear fractional transformation given by

$$f(p) = \frac{Z(s) - Z(1)}{Z(s) + Z(1)} \qquad (5\text{-}53)$$

† This subject is presented from a different viewpoint in the following reference, V. Belevitch, "An Alternate Derivation of Brune's Cycle," *IRE Trans. Circuit Theory*, vol. CT-6, no. 4, December 1959, pp. 389–390.

‡ Paul I. Richards, "A Special Class of Functions with Positive Real Part in a Half Plane," *Duke Mathematical Journal*, vol. 14, no. 3, September 1947, pp. 777–786.

In this transformation it is assumed that $Z(s)$ is a positive real function, and $Z(1)$ is clearly positive and real. Using Eqs. (5-52) and (5-53), it is possible to write

$$\frac{f(p)}{p} = \left[\frac{Z(s) - Z(1)}{Z(s) + Z(1)}\right]\frac{(s + 1)}{(s - 1)} = \frac{Z(1) - sZ(s) - Z(s) + sZ(1)}{Z(1) - sZ(s) + Z(s) - sZ(1)}$$

$$= \frac{1 - \dfrac{Z(s) - sZ(1)}{Z(1) - sZ(s)}}{1 + \dfrac{Z(s) - sZ(1)}{Z(1) - sZ(s)}} = \frac{1 - Z^*(s)}{1 + Z^*(s)} \tag{5-54}$$

This equation is a special form of Schwarz's lemma which states that if $f(p)$ is analytic and if the magnitude of p is less than unity, then under these conditions the magnitude of $f(p)/p$ is less than unity. These are the conditions which were set up by Eqs. (5-52) and (5-53), so the magnitude of $f(p)/p$ is less than unity.

$$\left|\frac{f(p)}{p}\right| = \left|\frac{1 - Z^*(s)}{1 + Z^*(s)}\right| < 1$$

where
$$|p| \leqq 1 \tag{5-55}$$

From this result, it follows that the $Re[Z^*(s)]$ must be greater than zero for σ greater than zero; hence, $Z^*(s)$ is a positive real function of s. In general, Eq. (5-51) can be written as

$$Z^*(s) = \frac{KZ(s) - sZ(K)}{KZ(K) - sZ(s)} \tag{5-56}$$

If K is a positive real number and $Z(s)$ is positive real, then $Z(Ks)$ is also positive real as well as $Z^*(s)$. It should be understood that $Z(K)$ is simply $Z(s)$ with K substituted for s. With this transformation, it is now possible to investigate the Bott-Duffin method for synthesis.

5-5. The Bott-Duffin Synthesis Procedure

The Bott-Duffin procedure can be stated as a series of steps similar to the Brune method; furthermore, the first part of the procedure is the same as that used by Brune.† These steps will be explained in general terms after which an example will be studied.

Step 1. The first step of the Bott-Duffin procedure is the same as that of the Brune procedure. If the numerator and denominator of $Z_1(s)$ are of unequal order, a network composed of series or parallel combinations of inductors and/or capacitors can be realized. The purpose of this

---

† R. Bott and R. J. Duffin, "Impedance Synthesis Without Use of Transformers," *J. of Appl. Phys.*, 20, 1949, p. 816.

step is to remove all $j\omega$-axis poles and zeros from $Z_1(s)$. The remaining function $Z_2(s)$ will possess a numerator and denominator which are of equal degree.

Step 2. Once the numerator and denominator polynomials are of equal degree, it is possible to remove R_{min} from $Re[Z_2(j\omega)]$. The resistance R_{min} is the minimum value of $Re[Z_2(j\omega)]$ and occurs at the frequency ω_1. When R_{min} is removed from $Z_2(s)$, $Z_3(s)$ results which is a pure reactance at ω_1. This portion of the procedure is identical to the first two steps of Brune's procedure, and the impedance $Z_3(s)$ is expressed analytically by Eq. (5-23). The network between terminals 1-1 and *b-b* of Fig. 5-5 has been realized; however, the Bott-Duffin procedure departs from Brune's approach at this point.

Step 3. The impedance $Z_3(s)$ is a minimum resistance function with a pure reactance at the frequency ω_1. The $Im[Z_3(j\omega)]$ equals X_1, and this reactance X_1 can be either positive or negative. For convenience, assume that it is positive and can be realized by an inductor L_1.

$$Z_3(j\omega_1) = jX_1 = j\omega_1 L_1 \qquad \text{where} \qquad L_1 > 0 \qquad (5\text{-}57)$$

It is now possible to make use of the transformation of Eq. (5-56) by choosing a value of K such that

$$\frac{Z_3(K)}{K} = \frac{Z_3(j\omega_1)}{j\omega_1} = \frac{jX_1}{j\omega_1} = L_1 \qquad (5\text{-}58)$$

This is always possible since the value of K varies from zero to infinity as L_1 varies from infinity to zero. Using this value of K, determine $Z^*(s)$ from Eq. (5-56). The impedance $Z^*(s)$ will have a zero at $s = j\omega_1$ because of the manner in which it was determined. This can be proved as follows:

$$Z^*(s) = \frac{KZ_3(s) - sZ_3(K)}{KZ_3(K) - sZ_3(s)} = \frac{K\left[Z_3(s) - s\dfrac{Z_3(K)}{K}\right]}{KZ_3(K) - sZ_3(s)} \qquad (5\text{-}59)$$

Substituting Eqs. (5-57) and (5-58) in the above and letting $s = j\omega_1$ yields

$$Z^*(s) = \left[\frac{K(j\omega_1 L_1 - j\omega_1 L_1)}{KZ_3(K) - sZ_3(s)}\right]_{s=j\omega_1} = 0 \qquad (5\text{-}60)$$

When the transformation is solved for $Z_3(s)$ in terms of K, L_1, and $Z^*(s)$, the following expansion results:

$$Z_3(s) = \frac{1}{\dfrac{s}{K^2 L_1} + \dfrac{1}{KL_1 Z^*(s)}} + \frac{1}{\dfrac{1}{L_1 s} + \dfrac{Z^*(s)}{KL_1}} \qquad (5\text{-}61)$$

This expansion of $Z_3(s)$ suggests a network of the form seen in Fig. 5-11.

The blocks enclosed in the dashed lines of Fig. 5-11 represent the beginning of two new circuits which can be considered as opposite branches of a bridge network. This fact will be discussed in more detail later.

Continuing the realization of Eq. (5-61), a series combination $L_a C_a$ can be removed in parallel with the capacitor C_1 in the first block of Fig. 5-11. The reason this combination should be realized is that

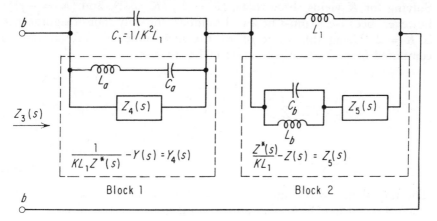

Fig. 5-11. Network resulting from Eq. 5-61.

$1/KL_1 Z^*(s)$ contains a $j\omega$-axis zero which if removed causes $Z_4(s)$ to possess the same characteristics as $Z_2(s)$. Consequently, following removal of $L_a C_a$ the transformation may be employed again on $Z_4(s)$, and the process can be repeated as many times as necessary to complete the realization of Block 1. In a similar manner, the function representing the second block $Z^*(s)/KL_1$, has a $j\omega$-axis pole. Realization of a parallel $L_b C_b$ combination removes this pole and yields a series impedance $Z_5(s)$ which has the same characteristics as $Z_2(s)$. Therefore, the transformation may also be employed again on $Z_5(s)$ and the process repeated as often as necessary to complete the realization of Block 2. The first elements to be removed from $Z_4(s)$ and $Z_5(s)$ will be minimum resistances R^*_{min} and R^{**}_{min}, respectively. It is seen that this procedure yields a rather complex network but does not involve any transformer.

Example. As an example of the Bott-Duffin procedure, reconsider Eq. (5-35) which was used as the example of Brune's procedure. Because the first two steps are identical to those of Brune's procedure, it is not necessary to repeat them. Consequently, it is possible to begin this example with the third step of the procedure and the impedance $Z_3(s)$ given by Eq. (5-39). The impedance $Z_3(s)$ has a 1-ohm reactance at the frequency $\omega_1 = 1$. It was shown in Eq. (5-40) that this reactance can be removed by realizing an inductor $L_1 = 1$ henry. The third step of the Bott-Duffin procedure requires that a value of K be chosen such that $Z_3(K)/K = L_1$ according to Eq. (5-58). In this case $Z_3(K)$ is $Z_3(s)$ of Eq. (5-39) with K substituted for s.

$$\frac{Z_3(K)}{K} = \frac{\dfrac{4K^2 + K + 2}{K^2 + 2K + 2}}{K} = L_1 = 1 \text{ henry} \tag{5-62}$$

Solving for K yields three roots, $(K = 2)$, $(K = j1)$, and $(K = -j1)$; however, because K must be a real number, the only root of significance is $K = 2$. Using this value of K, the new impedance $Z^*(s)$ can be computed from the transformation of Eq. (5-59).

$$Z^*(s) = \frac{KZ_3(s) - sZ_3(K)}{KZ_3(K) - sZ_3(s)} = \frac{2\left(\dfrac{4s^2 + s + 2}{s^2 + 2s + 2}\right) - s\left(\dfrac{4(4) + 2 + 2}{4 + 2(2) + 2}\right)}{2\left(\dfrac{4(4) + 2 + 2}{4 + 2(2) + 2}\right) - s\left(\dfrac{4s^2 + s + 2}{s^2 + 2s + 2}\right)}$$

$$= \frac{2(s^2 + 1)}{4s^2 + 5s + 4} \tag{5-63}$$

The impedance $Z_3(s)$ can now be written in the form of Eq. (5-61), where $L_1 = 1$ henry, $K = 2$, and $Z^*(s)$ is given by Eq. (5-63).

$$Z_3(s) = \frac{1}{\dfrac{s}{4} + \dfrac{1}{\dfrac{4(s^2 + 1)}{4s^2 + 5s + 4}}} + \frac{1}{\dfrac{1}{s} + \dfrac{s^2 + 1}{4s^2 + 5s + 4}} \tag{5-64}$$

Referring to Fig. 5-11 and Eq. (5-61), it is seen that the first term of Eq. (5-64) is composed of two admittances. The first admittance is a capacitance of $1/4$ farad, and the second admittance can be written as

$$Y(s) = \frac{4s^2 + 5s + 4}{4(s^2 + 1)} \tag{5-65}$$

A series $L_a C_a$ combination can be realized by performing a partial-fraction expansion of $Y(s)/s$, then multiplying through by s to give

$$Y(s) = \frac{5s}{4(s^2 + 1)} + 1 = \frac{\dfrac{s}{L_a}}{s^2 + \dfrac{1}{L_a C_a}} + Y_4(s) \tag{5-66}$$

This expansion shows that $L_a = 4/5$ henry and $C_a = 5/4$ farads. The admittance, $Y_4(s)$ can be synthesized by the same procedure, but for this simple example $Y_4(s) = 1$ mho, or $R^*_{\min} = 1$ ohm. This portion of the network can be seen in Fig. 5-12.

Returning to Eq. (5-64), it is seen that the second term is composed of two admittances. The first admittance is the inductance $1/L_1 s$. The remaining term can be written as an impedance.

$$Z(s) = \frac{4s^2 + 5s + 4}{s^2 + 1}$$

(5-67)

A parallel $L_b C_b$ combination can be realized from this function by performing a partial-fraction expansion.

$$Z(s) = \frac{5}{s^2 + 1} + 4 = \frac{\dfrac{1}{C_b}}{s^2 + \dfrac{1}{L_b C_b}} + Z_5(s)$$

(5-68)

This expansion reveals that $L_b = 5$ henrys and $C_b = 1/5$ farad. It is also seen that $Z_5(s)$ is 4 ohms, so $R^{**}_{min} = 4$ ohms. Since all of the element values have been determined for the example impedance of Eq. (5-35), the final network, synthesized by the Bott-Duffin procedure, can be constructed as shown in Fig. 5-12.

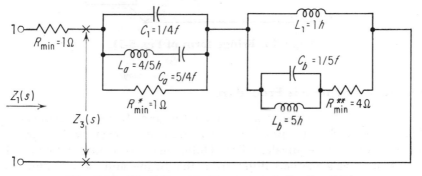

Fig. 5-12. Final Bott-Duffin network for Eq. 5-35.

The network of Fig. 5-12, although more complex than the Brune network, has the same impedance function as the example of Fig. 5-10. However, this complicated network does not require a transformer and is, therefore, more easily realized in terms of practical elements. It should be pointed out that although the above discussion and example assumed a positive reactance and inductor L_1 at the critical frequency ω_1 analogous structures exist for the negative case. When the reactance is negative or $[Z_2(j\omega_1) = -jX_1]$, it is possible to switch to an admittance basis $[Y_2(j\omega_1) = 1/Z_2(j\omega_1) = +jB_1]$. A positive capacitance C_1 can then be realized from $Y_2(s)$ at the frequency ω_1 after which Richards' transformation of Eqs. (5-58) and (5-61) with impedances replaced by admittances may be applied to $Y_3(s)$.†

† A detailed description of the procedure for negative values of X_1 may be found in D. F. Tuttle, *Network Synthesis*, Vol. I (New York: John Wiley & Sons, Inc., 1958), Chap. 10.

From Fig. 5-11 it is seen that there are two blocks formed each time the transform is used. Consequently, there will be $2n$ blocks for n uses of the transformation. Closer inspection of Fig. 5-11 reveals that the entire network for $Z_3(s)$ can be redrawn as a balanced Wheatstone bridge circuit. Figure 5-13 shows this bridge in simplified form. Because the bridge is balanced, terminals c-d may be left open-circuited, short-circuited, or contain any arbitrary impedance. This point will become important in the following sections.

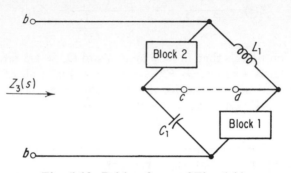

Fig. 5-13. Bridge form of Fig. 5-11.

5-6. Reza's Synthesis Procedure

F. M. Reza unified the Bott-Duffin and Brune procedures by demonstrating that it is possible to convert a Brune cycle with its perfect transformer to an equivalent Bott-Duffin network configuration.† The details of Reza's method differ from the Brune and Bott-Duffin procedures only after R_{min} has been removed from the driving-point impedance. According to the notation of Secs. 5-3 and 5-5, the remaining impedance function after removal of R_{min} is $Z_3(s)$ which is a pure reactance at the frequency ω_1.

For the purpose of this discussion, it will be assumed that the reactance of $Z_3(s)$ is positive at ω_1, and a positive inductor L_1 can be realized. The reactance $L_1 s$ is removed from $Z_3(s)$ to yield $Z_4(s)$, which is a minimum impedance function at ω_1. At this point the constant K is determined as in the Bott-Duffin procedure [see Eq. (5-58) where $Z_3(K)/K = L_1$]. This value of K should then be held while the remainder of the network is solved by the Brune procedure to give a network of the form shown between terminals b-b and e-e of Fig. 5-5. From the resulting Brune network, the values of L_1, L_2, L_3, and C can be used along with the constant K to solve the following conversions.

---

† F. M. Reza, "Conversion of a Brune Cycle with an Ideal Transformer into a Cycle without an Ideal Transformer," *J. Math. Phys.*, 33, July 1954, pp. 194–198.

$$A = \frac{1}{L_1 K^2} \quad \text{farads} \qquad\qquad E = \frac{L_1^2(K^2 L_2 C + 1)}{L_2} \quad \text{henrys}$$

$$B = \frac{K^2(L_2)^2 C}{K^2 L_2 C + 1} \quad \text{henrys} \qquad F = \frac{(L_2)^2 C}{L_1^2(K^2 L_2 C + 1)} \quad \text{farads}$$

$$D = L_1 \quad \text{henrys} \qquad\qquad G = \frac{K^2 L_2 C + 1}{K^2 L_2} \quad \text{farads}$$

$$\frac{1}{Z_a} = \frac{1}{KL_1 Z_c} - \frac{(K^2 L_2 C + 1)s}{K^2 L_2(L_2 C s^2 + 1)} \qquad Z_b = \frac{L_1 K}{Z_c} - \frac{L_1^2(K^2 L_2 C + 1)s}{L_2(L_2 C s^2 + 1)}$$

where

$$\frac{1}{Z_c} = \frac{L_1 K^2 - s Z_3(s)}{K[Z_3(s) - L_1 s]} \tag{5-69}$$

Using these values, the equivalent Bott-Duffin balanced-bridge shown in Fig. 5-14 can be obtained.

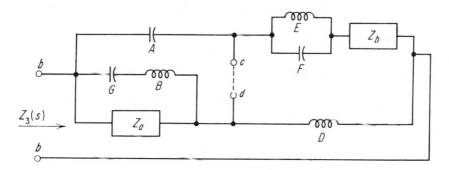

Fig. 5-14. Bott-Duffin network for the conversions of Eq. 5-69.

The terminals *c-d* of Fig. 5-14 may be open- or short-circuited since the bridge is balanced, and the impedances, Z_a and Z_b, can be decomposed by using Brune's procedure and Reza's conversions of Eq. (5-69) again. This method for obtaining the Bott-Duffin bridge network is sometimes more convenient than employing the transform method of Sec. 5-5. It should also be pointed out that an analogous set of conversions can be derived for transforming the Brune cycle for an impedance possessing a negative reactance at the critical frequency ω_1 to an equivalent Bott-Duffin configuration. The Brune and Bott-Duffin network forms are not the only configurations which can be used to realize a general *RLC* driving-point function. A third synthesis procedure, developed by R. H. Pantell, avoids the use of perfect transformers but realizes the function with a network which requires one less element per cycle of application than the Bott-Duffin procedure.

5-7. Pantell's Synthesis Procedure

R. H. Pantell is given credit for employing Richards' transformation, Eq. (5-56), in what might be considered a two-port network approach to driving-point impedance realization.† Consider the network of Fig. 5-15, where $Z_3(s)$ is a minimum resistance function {i.e., $Re[Z_3(j\omega)]$ is zero at ω_1}. The impedance $z_{11}(s)$ represents the driving-point impedance seen looking into terminals a-a of the two-port network with terminals b-b open. Similarly, $y_{11}(s)$ represents the driving-point admittance of terminals a-a with terminals b-b short-circuited, and $y_{22}(s)$ is the driving-point admittance seen looking into terminals b-b with terminals a-a short-circuited. (These terms are described in detail in Chap. 7.)

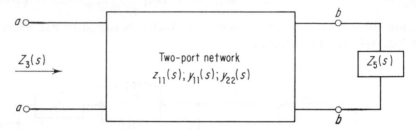

Fig. 5-15. **Two-port network approach to driving-point synthesis.**

The terminating impedance $Z_5(s)$ can be written in terms of $Z_3(s)$ and the parameters of the two-port network as

$$Z_5(s) = \frac{z_{11}(s)[1 - Z_3(s)y_{11}(s)]}{y_{22}(s)[Z_3(s) - z_{11}(s)]} \qquad (5\text{-}70)$$

The real part of $Z_3(s)$ is zero at the frequency ω_1; and the reactance may be removed at ω_1 by realization of an inductor L_1 as in the Brune and Bott-Duffin procedures [i.e., $Z_3(j\omega_1) = j\omega_1 L_1$]. Assume that L_1 is positive, in which case the driving-point impedance of the two-port network can arbitrarily be expressed as

$$z_{11}(s) = L_1 s + \cfrac{K^2 L_1}{\cfrac{K^2 L_1 - sZ_3(s)}{Z_3(s) - L_1 s} + \cfrac{\omega_1^2 s}{s^2 + \omega_1^2}}$$

where

$$K = \frac{Z_3(K)}{L_1} \qquad (5\text{-}71)$$

Because L_1 was assumed to be positive and the $[K^2 L_1 - sZ_3(s)]/[Z_3(s) - L_1 s]$ term is a Richards' function, $z_{11}(s)$ must be positive real.

---

† R. H. Pantell, "A New Method of Driving-point Impedance Synthesis," *Proc. IRE*, vol. 42, no. 5, May 1954, p. 861.

It is now possible to realize $z_{11}(s)$ as a network of the form shown in Fig. 5-16, where $Z_4(s)$ is given by

$$Z_4(s) = \cfrac{K^2L_1}{\cfrac{K^2L_1 - sZ_3(s)}{Z_3(s) - sL_1} - \cfrac{As}{s^2 + \omega_1{}^2}} \qquad (5\text{-}72)$$

If the elements of Fig. 5-16 are to be positive, it is necessary that the constant A be selected in such a manner that

$$A \leq 2 \text{ Residue} \left[\frac{K^2L_1 - sZ_3(s)}{Z_3(s) - sL_1}\right]_{s=j\omega_1} \qquad \text{for } A > 0$$

or $\qquad A \geq (-\omega_1{}^2) \qquad\qquad\qquad\qquad \text{for } A < 0 \qquad (5\text{-}73)$

Following selection of A, $Z_4(s)$ will in general possess a zero at $(s = j\omega_1)$.

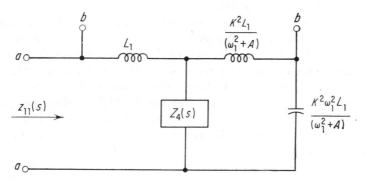

Fig. 5-16. Network to realize Eq. 5-71 where $Z_4(s)$ is given by Eq. 5-72.

Using the network of Fig. 5-16 and Eq. (5-70), it is possible to compute the impedance $Z_5(s)$ which must be placed across terminals $b\text{-}b$ such that the impedance seen looking into terminals $a\text{-}a$ will become $Z_3(s)$ as in Fig. 5-15. $Z_5(s)$ is given by

$$Z_5(s) = \frac{L_1[L_1K^2 - sZ_3(s)]}{Z_3(s) - sL_1} + \frac{(K^2A)L_1s}{(\omega_1{}^2 + A)(s^2 + \omega_1{}^2)} \qquad (5\text{-}74)$$

From the network of Fig. 5-16 and Eq. (5-74), it is seen that two important cases exist in the selection of A.

Case 1. The first term of Eq. (5-74) is positive real since it represents L_1 times Richards' function; however, for $Z_5(s)$ to be realizable A must be selected such that

$$\frac{K^2A}{(\omega_1{}^2 + A)} \geq -2 \text{ Residue} \left[\frac{L_1K^2 - sZ_3(s)}{Z_3(s) - L_1s}\right]_{s=j\omega_1} \qquad (5\text{-}75)$$

In this case A will be negative; although, from Fig. 5-16 it is clear that for positive elements it is also necessary that A be greater than $(-\omega_1^2)$. If A is selected from Eq. (5-75), $Z_5(s)$ will in general possess a pole on the $j\omega$-axis at $(s = j\omega_1)$. However, if A is chosen equal to (-2) times the residue, the pole of $Z_5(s)$ will be removed, and $Z_5(s)$ will be of degree two less than $Z_3(s)$. The procedure may be repeated on $Z_5(s)$ starting with the removal of a minimum resistance $R_{\min}^*$.

Case 2. The second case of importance is when A is selected according to the following

$$A = 2 \text{ Residue} \left[\frac{K^2 L_1 - s Z_3(s)}{Z_3(s) - s L_1} \right]_{s=j\omega_1} \qquad (5\text{-}76)$$

In general, a positive A causes a zero in $Z_5(s)$ at $(s = j\omega_1)$; however, if A is chosen according to Eq. (5-76), the zero is removed and $Z_5(s)$ will be of degree two less than $Z_3(s)$.

As an example of Pantell's procedure, reconsider the driving-point impedance of Eq. (5-35). Steps 1, 2, and 3 of the procedure may be accomplished in a manner identical to that of the Bott-Duffin procedure. There are no $j\omega$-axis poles or zeros in Eq. (5-35); therefore, Step 1 does not apply and $Z_1(s) = Z_2(s)$. In Step 2 the minimum resistance is removed at the frequency ω_1 to give $Z_3(s)$ [see Eq. (5-39)]. In this example, $R_{\min}$ is one ohm at a frequency $\omega_1 = 1$. Step 3 involves removal of the reactance from $Z_3(s)$ at ω_1 by realizing an inductor L_1. Using L_1 and $Z_3(K)$, it is possible to determine the value of K. Step 3 for this example is outlined in Sec. 5-5, Eq. (5-62), where the value of L_1 is one henry and K equals two. At this point $Z_3(s)$ is a minimum-resistance function, and the necessary parameters have been established for application of Pantell's procedure.

Step 4. In the application of Pantell's procedure, it is first necessary to calculate the constant A. Two values of A are useful as described by Cases 1 and 2, Eqs. (5-75) and (5-76). Using Eq. (5-75), A becomes

$$\frac{K^2 A}{(\omega_1^2 + A)} = \frac{4A}{(1 + A)} = -2 \text{ Residue} \left[\frac{L_1 K^2 - s Z_3(s)}{Z_3(s) - L_1 s} \right]_{s=j\omega_1}$$

$$= -2 \text{ Residue} \left[\frac{4 - s \left(\dfrac{4s^2 + s + 2}{s^2 + 2s + 2} \right)}{\left(\dfrac{4s^2 + s + 2}{s^2 + 2s + 2} \right) - s} \right]_{s=j1} = -2 \left[\frac{5}{2} \right]$$

$$(5\text{-}77)$$

Solving for A yields $(A = -5/9)$. Before exploring the second value of A, the remainder of the procedure will be developed with $(A = -5/9)$.

Step 5. Using $(A = -5/9)$, the impedances of Fig. 5-16 are computed, where $Z_4(s)$ is given by Eq. (5-72).

$$\frac{K^2 L_1 s}{(\omega_1{}^2 + A)} = \frac{4s}{\left(1 - \dfrac{5}{9}\right)} = 9s$$

$$\frac{K^2 L_1 \omega_1{}^2}{(\omega_1{}^2 + A)s} = \frac{4}{\left(1 - \dfrac{5}{9}\right)s} = \frac{9}{s}$$

$$Z_4(s) = \frac{4}{\dfrac{(4s^2 + 5s + 4)}{(s^2 + 1)} + \dfrac{5s}{9(s^2 + 1)}} = \frac{1}{1 + \dfrac{1}{\dfrac{18s}{25} + \dfrac{18}{25s}}}$$

$$(5\text{-}78)$$

The impedances of Eq. (5-78) can be realized as a network similar to Fig. 5-16 and are shown in Fig. 5-17.

Step 6. The driving-point impedance $Z_5(s)$ can now be computed from Eq. (5-74). For this example, $Z_5(s)$ becomes

$$Z_5(s) = \frac{4s^2 + 5s + 4}{(s^2 + 1)} - \frac{5s}{(s^2 + 1)} = 4 \qquad (5\text{-}79)$$

This impedance is placed across terminals b-b of Fig. 5-17 to complete the realization of Eq. (5-35).

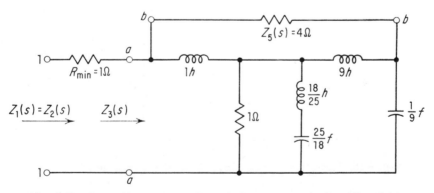

Fig. 5-17. Pantell network (Case 1) for the example of Eq. 5-35.

It is now useful to consider the second case in which A is determined from Eq. (5-76). Substituting K, L_1, $Z_3(s)$, and ω_1 in Eq. (5-76) [similar to the approach used in Step 4, Eq. (5-77)], the value of A becomes $(A = 5)$. With this value of A, the procedure of Steps 5 and 6 may be repeated. From the network of Fig. 5-16 and Eq. (5-72), the following impedances are determined:

$$\frac{K^2 L_1 s}{(\omega_1{}^2 + A)} = \frac{4s}{(1 + 5)} = \frac{2s}{3}$$

$$\frac{K^2 L_1 \omega_1{}^2}{(\omega_1{}^2 + A)s} = \frac{4}{(1 + 5)s} = \frac{2}{3s}$$

$$Z_4(s) = \frac{4}{\dfrac{4s^2 + 5s + 4}{(s^2 + 1)} - \dfrac{5s}{(s^2 + 1)}} = 1 \tag{5-80}$$

The impedance $Z_5(s)$ can be computed from Eq. (5-74) as follows:

$$Z_5(s) = \frac{4s^2 + 5s + 4}{(s^2 + 1)} + \frac{20s}{(1 + 5)(s^2 + 1)} = 4 + \frac{1}{\dfrac{3s}{25} + \dfrac{3}{25s}} \tag{5-81}$$

The impedances of Eqs. (5-80) and (5-81) can be combined with $R_{\min}$ to realize a network similar to that of Fig. 5-16, where $Z_5(s)$ is the impedance connecting terminals b-b. This completes the realization of Eq. (5-35) for the second case of the constant A. The network which represents this realization is seen in Fig. 5-18.

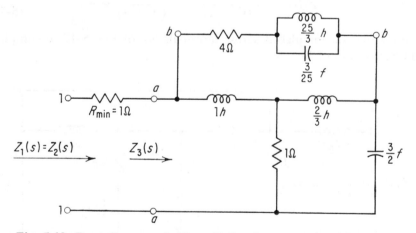

Fig. 5-18. Pantell network (Case 2) for the example of Eq. 5-35.

In either of the above two cases, the network realization is accomplished with one less element per cycle of application than the Bott-Duffin procedure. Furthermore, the realization is accomplished without use of perfect transformers. Finally, it should be pointed out that the network forms resulting from Pantell's procedure represent unbalanced bridge structures. This fact accounts for the saving of one element per cycle, as can be demonstrated by a transformation of the Bott-Duffin balanced bridge suggested by J. E. Storer.†

5-8. Storer's Procedure

Storer has suggested that since the Bott-Duffin bridge of Fig. 5-14 is balanced, it is possible not only to open or short terminals *c* and *d*, but to insert any type of impedance element between these two terminals without changing the driving-point function of the network. If the impedance is chosen as an inductor of appropriate value, the Bott-Duffin balanced bridge can be converted by a T to Pi transformation to the network configuration developed by Pantell with a saving of one element per cycle of application. This fact is most easily demonstrated by considering the example Bott-Duffin network of Fig. 5-12. The portion of Fig. 5-12 which represents $Z_3(s)$ is redrawn in Fig. 5-19a with an arbitrary inductor *m* inserted between terminals *c* and *d*.

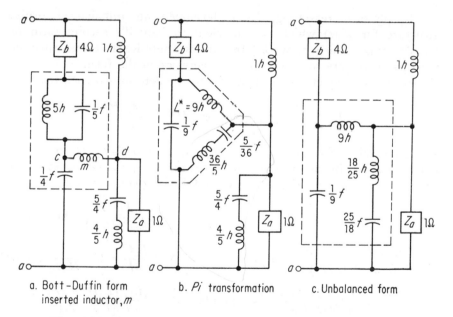

a. Bott-Duffin form   b. *Pi* transformation   c. Unbalanced form
inserted inductor, *m*

Fig. 5-19. Storer's conversion of the Bott-Duffin network.

The T network contained in the dashed lines of Fig. 5-19a can be replaced by an equivalent Pi network. If the element values of the Pi are computed in terms of the T network element values, proper selection of

---

m reduces one branch of the Pi to a single inductor L^*. In this example, choice of ($m = 4h$) yields the transformed network of Fig. 5-19b where the Pi section is enclosed by dashed lines and L^* becomes 9 henrys. Following the T to Pi transformation, it is possible to combine the series LC combination of the Pi with the series LC combination of 5/4 farads and 4/5 henrys. This combination leads to the unbalanced bridge network of Fig. 5-19c. Therefore, using the T to Pi transformation, two series LC branches are combined to yield one series LC branch and a single inductor, thereby eliminating one element. Closer inspection of Fig. 5-19c reveals that it is identical to the Pantell network following terminals a-a of Fig. 5-17. Furthermore, the impedances Z_a and Z_b of Fig. 5-19 are not involved in the transformation; consequently, it is possible to save one element per cycle of application of the Bott-Duffin procedure.

5-9. Reza's Unbalanced Form

By physical reasoning, Reza developed an unbalanced bridge structure for $Z_3(s)$ which is equivalent to Pantell's second form by transforming Brune's network.† In order to apply Reza's transformation, it is first necessary to realize Brune's network in the form of Fig. 5-5. When this is complete, a constant H must be determined such that

$$L_3 H + Z_6(H) = 0 \quad \text{or} \quad H = \frac{-Z_6(H)}{L_3} \tag{5-82}$$

Using the value of H along with L_1, L_2, L_3, C, and $Z_6(s)$ determined by completing the Brune cycle for the network, it is possible to determine the element values for Fig. 5-20 by the following conversions:

$$D = L_1 \quad \text{henrys} \qquad\qquad M = \frac{L_3 L_2 C H^2}{L_3 C H^2 - 1} \quad \text{henrys}$$

$$E = \frac{L_1{}^2 (H^2 L_2 C + 1)^2}{L_2 (1 - C L_3 H^2)} \quad \text{henrys} \qquad\qquad N = \frac{L_2 C}{M} = C - \frac{1}{H^2 L_3} \quad \text{farads}$$

$$F = \frac{L_2 C}{E} = \frac{(L_2)^2 C (1 - C L_3 H^2)}{L_1{}^2 (H^2 L_2 C + 1)^2} \quad \text{farads} \qquad Z_b = \frac{(L_1)^2 [L_3 H^2 + s Z_6(s)]}{L_3 [L_3 s + Z_6(s)]}$$

$$Z_a = \frac{H^2 L_3 [L_3 s + Z_6(s)]}{s Z_6(s) + L_3 H^2} \tag{5-83}$$

Due to the unbalancing of the bridge, corresponding elements of the balanced Bott-Duffin bridge of Fig. 5-14 and those of Fig. 5-20 will not

† F. M. Reza, "A Bridge Equivalent for a Brune Cycle Terminated in a Resistor," *Proc. IRE*, vol. 42, no. 8, August 1954, p. 1321.

necessarily have the same values. This fact can be seen by comparing the transformation of Eqs. (5-69) and (5-83).

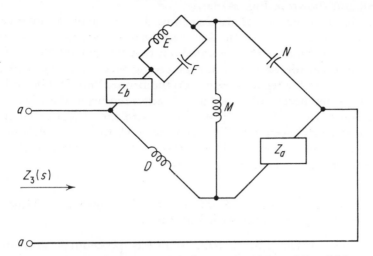

Fig. 5-20. Reza network for the conversions of Eq. 5-83.

As an example of Reza's unbalanced bridge, the impedance of Eq. (5-35) can be evaluated. The Brune network representation for this example is given in Fig. 5-9, where

$$L_1 = 1 \text{ henry}; \qquad L_2 = 1 \text{ henry}; \qquad L_3 = -1/2 \text{ henry}$$

$$R_{\min} = 1 \text{ ohm}; \qquad C = 1 \text{ farad}; \qquad Z_6(s) = R^*_{\min} = 1 \text{ ohm} \quad (5\text{-}84)$$

The first step in converting the Brune network to an unbalanced form is to determine the value of H using Eq. (5-82). Since the value of $Z_6(s)$ is one ohm and L_3 is $-1/2$ henry, it follows from Eq. (5-82) that

$$H = \frac{Z_6(H)}{-L_3} = -\frac{1}{-\dfrac{1}{2}} = 2 \tag{5-85}$$

Using this value of H and the element values of Eq. (5-84), it is possible to compute the conversions of Eq. (5-83). It is convenient to compute D, E, F, M, and N in the order listed, after which $Z_a(s)$ and $Z_b(s)$ may be found. The conversion values for this example become

$$E = 25/3 \text{ henrys}; \qquad F = 3/25 \text{ farads}; \qquad D = 1 \text{ henry}$$

$$N = 3/2 \text{ farads}; \qquad M = 2/3 \text{ henrys}; \qquad Z_a = 1 \text{ ohm}$$

$$Z_b = 4 \text{ ohms} \tag{5-86}$$

It should be remembered that $R_{\min} = 1$ ohm, since it is not a part of the conversion cycle which starts at $Z_3(s)$ in Fig. 5-9. The network which results when these element values are substituted in Fig. 5-20 with R_{min} as a series resistor is a structure identical to the second form derived by Pantell and shown in Fig. 5-18.

Similar conversion techniques can be derived on an admittance basis and for situations in which the reactance is negative at the critical frequency. It should also be pointed out that the general RLC synthesis procedures considered in this and preceding sections do not necessarily exhaust all possible techniques nor do the Brune, Bott-Duffin, or Pantell network forms necessarily yield a realization requiring the least number of elements. In brief, these procedures, with the exception of Brune's procedure, have been based on reduction of the given driving-point function to a minimum-impedance form, which in turn is realized as a balanced or unbalanced bridge structure.

5-10. Bridge Network Realization for Special Minimum-resistance Driving-point Functions

Of the various general RLC synthesis procedures developed in preceding sections, Brune's procedure requires the least number of reactive elements per cycle, a perfect transformer and a capacitor, in order to realize a minimum-resistance driving-point function. The Bott-Duffin procedure, which bypasses the perfect transformer, realizes a minimum-resistance function with a balanced bridge requiring six reactive elements per cycle. Pantell, Storer, and Reza unbalanced the bridge configuration reducing the number of reactive elements per cycle to five. Kim, Van Valkenburg, and Seshu have investigated conditions under which it is possible to realize certain specially restricted minimum-resistance functions with an unbalanced bridge configuration requiring only three reactive elements per cycle.† The purpose of this section is to present these specialized unbalanced bridge networks.

Kim studied all possible combinations of elements in the bridge network of Fig. 5-21 for cases in which the design was restricted to only two reactive elements. As a result it was found that none of the combinations possessed driving-point functions with minimum-resistance characteristics. For clarity in this discussion, a minimum-resistance impedance is considered to be one for which $Z(j\omega)$ is finite at both $(\omega = 0)$ and $(\omega = \infty)$, $Re[Z(j\omega)]$ is zero at some frequency ω_1 but $Im[Z(j\omega)]$ is nonzero at ω_1. A special class of driving-point functions possessing these characteristics can be realized by a bridge network when three reactive

† Wan H. Kim, "On Non-Series-Parallel Realization of Driving-Point Functions," IRE National Convention Record, Part 2, Circuit Theory and Ultrasonic Engineering, March 24–27, 1958, pp. 76–81. Also M. E. Van Valkenburg, "Special Case of a Bridge Equivalent of Brune Networks," Proc. IRE, vol. 44, no. 11, November 1956, p. 1621; S. Seshu, "Minimal Realizations of the Biquadratic Minimum Function," IRE Trans. Circuit Theory, vol. CT-6, no. 4, December 1959, pp. 345–350.

elements are employed. Furthermore, since there are no series or parallel combinations of two reactive elements which possess these characteristics, it is concluded that the lowest bound on the number of reactive elements necessary to realize a minimum-resistance driving-point function without application of a transformer is three.

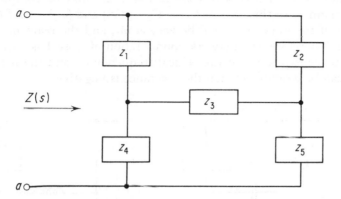

Fig. 5-21. General bridge network configuration.

The mechanism by which the bridge network realizes a minimum-resistance function cannot be visualized in terms of zero or pole-producing combinations of impedances as in the Brune, Bott-Duffin, or Pantell procedures. The driving-point impedance for the general bridge network of Fig. 5-21 is given by

$$Z(s) =$$

$$\frac{z_1 z_2 z_4 + z_1 z_2 z_3 + z_2 z_3 z_4 + z_1 z_2 z_5 + z_1 z_3 z_5 + z_1 z_4 z_5 + z_2 z_4 z_5 + z_3 z_4 z_5}{z_1 z_3 + z_1 z_4 + z_1 z_5 + z_2 z_3 + z_2 z_4 + z_2 z_5 + z_3 z_4 + z_3 z_5}$$

$$(5\text{-}87)$$

In this equation z_1, z_2, z_3, z_4, and z_5 may all be functions of s; therefore, it would be difficult to comprehend the manner in which the real parts of the eight double and triple products of the function add to zero at some frequency ω_1.

It is now of interest to consider the network of Fig. 5-21 for two special cases in which three reactive elements are employed. These two cases are shown in Fig. 5-22. The driving-point impedance for the network of Case 1 can be written as

$$Z(s) = K \frac{\left[s^3 + \dfrac{(C z_2 z_4 L_1 + C z_2 z_4 L_2 + L_1 L_2)}{L_1 L_2 C K} s^2 + \dfrac{(L_1 z_2 + L_2 z_4)}{L_1 L_2 C K} s + \dfrac{z_2 z_4}{L_1 L_2 C K} \right]}{\left[s^3 + \dfrac{(L_1 z_4 + L_2 z_2)}{L_1 L_2} s^2 + \dfrac{(L_1 + L_2 + C z_2 z_4)}{L_1 L_2 C} + \dfrac{K}{L_1 L_2 C} \right]}$$

where $\qquad\qquad K = (z_2 + z_4) \qquad\qquad\qquad (5\text{-}88)$

This impedance function will have a real part that goes to zero at the frequency ω_1 if $(L_1 = L_2 = L^*)$ and $(\omega_1^2 = 1/L^*C)$. Furthermore, the reactance or imaginary part of the impedance is positive at ω_1; consequently, regardless of the values of z_2 and z_4, the network will represent a minimum-resistance driving-point function. The driving-point impedance for the network of Case 2, Fig. 5-22, may be computed in a similar manner. In this case if $(C_1 = C_2 = C^*)$ and $(\omega_1^2 = 1/LC^*)$, the real part of the impedance will be zero at ω_1, and the reactance will be negative. Therefore, the network configuration of Case 1 is useful when the reactance is positive at the critical frequency ω_1 and the network of Case 2 can be employed when the reactance is negative.

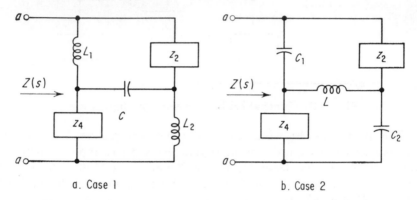

a. Case 1   b. Case 2

Fig. 5-22. Two special cases of the bridge of Fig. 5-21.

Both the numerator and denominator of Eq. (5-88) reduce to cubic polynomials when z_2 and z_4 are resistors. In this case substitution of L^* for L_1 and L_2 yields the following relationships:

$$Z(s) = K \frac{(s^3 + a_1 s^2 + a_2 s + a_3)}{(s^3 + b_1 s^2 + b_2 s + b_3)}$$

where $K = R_2 + R_4$

$$a_1 = \frac{(2CR_2R_4 + L^*)}{L^*CK} \qquad b_1 = \frac{K}{L^*}$$

$$a_2 = \frac{1}{L^*C} \qquad b_2 = \frac{(2L^* + CR_2R_4)}{(L^*)^2C}$$

$$a_3 = \frac{R_2R_4}{(L^*)^2CK} \qquad b_3 = \frac{K}{(L^*)^2C} \qquad (5\text{-}89)$$

For the impedance of Eq. (5-89) to be a minimum-resistance function, certain restrictions must be imposed on the a and b coefficients. The numerator of the $Re[Z(j\omega)]$ goes to zero, and hence $Re[Z(j\omega)]$ becomes zero at the frequency ω_1 if $(\omega_1{}^2 = a_2 = b_3/b_1)$. To insure that the denominator of the $Re[Z(j\omega)]$ does not vanish at ω_1, it is necessary that $(b_1 b_2 - b_3 > 0)$. For a positive reactance at ω_1, it is also necessary that $(a_1 b_3 - a_3 b_1 > 0)$. Finally, for physically realizable passive elements, it is required that $(b_3 - 4a_3 \geqq 0)$. These restrictions on the coefficients of Eq. (5-89) are summarized below and insure that the function can be realized in the form of Fig. 5-22, Case 1.

$$a_2 = \frac{b_3}{b_1} = \omega_1{}^2 \qquad \frac{a_2}{b_1}(b_1 b_2 - b_3) = (a_1 b_3 - a_3 b_1) > 0$$

$$b_1 b_2 - b_3 > 0 \qquad\qquad b_3 - 4a^3 \geqq 0 \qquad\qquad (5\text{-}90)$$

The element values for the network may be computed in terms of the a and b coefficients of Eqs. (5-89) and (5-90) as follows:

$$L^* = L_1 = L_2 = \frac{K}{b_1} \qquad C = \frac{b_1}{a_2 K} = \frac{(b_1 b_2 - b_3)}{K(a_1 b_3 - a_3 b_1)}$$

$$R_2 = \frac{2a_3 K}{b_3 \pm \sqrt{b_3 A}} \qquad\qquad R_4 = \frac{2a_3 K}{b_3 \mp \sqrt{b_3 A}}$$

where
$$A = b_3 - 4a_3 \qquad\qquad (5\text{-}91)$$

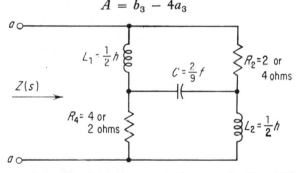

Fig. 5-23. Example network realization for Eq. 5-92.

As an example of the above procedure, consider the following minimum-resistance driving-point impedance which satisfies the restrictions of Eqs. (5-89) and (5-90).

$$Z(s) = 6\,\frac{s^3 + \dfrac{72}{12}s^2 + 9s + 24}{s^3 + 12s^2 + 50s + 108} \qquad\qquad (5\text{-}92)$$

The critical frequency for this impedance is $(\omega_1 = 3)$, at which $[Z(j\omega_1) = 0 + j3/2]$. Using Eq. (5-91), the element values for this example become $(L^* = L_1 = L_2 = 1/2$ henry$)$, $(C = 2/9$ farad$)$, $(R_2 = 2$ or 4 ohms$)$, and $(R_4 = 4$ or 2 ohms$)$. Combining these elements in a network of the form of Fig. 5-22, Case 1, yields the configuration of Fig. 5-23.

A similar procedure can be used for the network of Case 2, Fig. 5-22. When the capacitances are equal, $(C^* = C_1 = C_2)$ and z_2 and z_4 represent resistors, the driving-point impedance of Case 2 becomes

$$Z(s) = K \frac{s^3 + a_1 s^2 + a_2 s + a_3}{s^3 + b_1 s^2 + b_2 s + b_3}$$

where

$$K = \frac{R_2 R_4}{(R_2 + R_4)}$$

$$a_1 = \frac{1}{KC^*} \qquad\qquad b_1 = \frac{C^* R_2 R_4 + 2L}{LC^*(R_2 + R_4)}$$

$$a_2 = \frac{2C^* R_2 R_4 + L}{R_2 R_4 L (C^*)^2} \qquad\qquad b_2 = \frac{1}{LC^*}$$

$$a_3 = \frac{1}{L(C^*)^2 K} \qquad\qquad b_3 = \frac{1}{L(C^*)^2(R_2 + R_4)} \qquad (5\text{-}93)$$

For this impedance to be a minimum-resistance function, it is necessary to restrict the a and b coefficients in the following manner. The $Re[Z(j\omega_1)]$ goes to zero if $(\omega_1{}^2 = b_2 = a_3/a_1)$; however, to insure that it does not become indeterminant at ω_1, it is necessary that $(b_1 b_2 - 2b_3 > 0)$. For the reactance to be negative at ω_1, it is necessary that $(b_1 a_3 - 2a_1 b_3)$ also be greater than zero. Finally, for physically realizable elements, it is required that $(a_3 - 4b_3 \geq 0)$. These restrictions on the coefficients of Eq. (5-93) are summarized below and insure that the function can be realized in the form of Fig. 5-22, Case 2.

$$b_2 = \frac{a_3}{a_1} = \omega_1{}^2 \qquad\qquad b_2{}^2 = (b_1 a_3 - 2a_1 b_3) > 0$$

$$b_1 b_2 - 2b_3 > 0 \qquad\qquad a_3 - 4b_3 \geq 0 \qquad (5\text{-}94)$$

The element values for the network may be computed in terms of the a and b coefficients from Eqs. (5-93) and (5-94) as follows:

$$C^* = C_1 = C_2 = \frac{1}{a_1 K} \qquad\qquad L = \frac{a_1 K}{b_2} = \frac{K b_2}{b_1 b_2 - 2b_3}$$

$$R_2 = \frac{2K a_3}{a_3 \pm \sqrt{a_3 A}} \qquad\qquad R_4 = \frac{2K a_3}{a_3 \mp \sqrt{a_3 A}}$$

where

$$A = a_3 - 4b_3 \qquad (5\text{-}95)$$

Provided a driving-point impedance of the form of Eq. (5-93) meets the restrictions of Eq. (5-94), it may be realized as a network of the form of Fig. 5-22, Case 2. The relationships of Eq. (5-95) can be used to determine the element values for the network directly from the coefficients of the driving-point impedance.

It should be emphasized that the network configuration of Fig. 5-22, Case 1, is useful in realizing minimum-resistance driving-point impedances, having positive reactance at the frequency ω_1 which also satisfy the requirements of Eqs. (5-89) and (5-90). The network configuration of Case 2 is useful in realizing minimum-resistance driving-point impedances, having negative reactance at ω_1, which also satisfy the requirements of Eqs. (5-93) and (5-94).

The procedures outlined above can be applied to realize certain specially restricted biquadratic minimum-resistance driving-point impedances, provided they can be put in the same form as Eqs. (5-89) and (5-93). This can be accomplished by multiplying both numerator and denominator of the biquadratic function by a surplus factor $(s + \beta)$ as follows:

$$Z(s) = K \frac{(s^2 + c_1 s + c_2)}{(s^2 + d_1 s + d_2)} \cdot \frac{(s + \beta)}{(s + \beta)}$$

$$= K \frac{s^3 + (c_1 + \beta)s^2 + (c_2 + c_1\beta)s + c_2\beta}{s^3 + (d_1 + \beta)s^2 + (d_2 + d_1\beta)s + d_2\beta} \qquad (5\text{-}96)$$

If the biquadratic impedance is to be realized by a network of the form of Fig. 5-22, Case 1, it is necessary from Eq. (5-90) that $(a_2 = b_3/b_1)$. Imposing this condition on Eq. (5-96) yields

$$(c_2 + c_1\beta) = \frac{d_2\beta}{(d_1 + \beta)} \qquad (5\text{-}97)$$

The necessary and sufficient conditions for a biquadratic to be a physically realizable minimum-resistance function is that $[c_1 d_1 = (\sqrt{c_2} - \sqrt{d_2})^2]$. (See Chap. 3, Sec. 3-2.) Consequently, substituting this relationship in Eq. (5-97), it is possible to solve for the value of β which can be used to convert the biquadratic to a bicubic function similar to Eq. (5-89).

$$\beta = \frac{\sqrt{c_2 d_2} - c_2}{c_1} \qquad (5\text{-}98)$$

Using the surplus factor β as indicated in Eq. (5-96) causes the resulting bicubic to be a minimum-resistance function which can be realized by Eqs. (5-89) through (5-91) as a network of the form of Fig. 5-22, Case 1.

In like manner, if the biquadratic is a minimum-resistance function possessing a negative rather than positive reactance at the critical frequency, it can be realized as a network of the form of Fig. 5-22, Case 2. In this case the biquadratic can be converted to a form similar to Eq. (5-93) by employing the surplus factor β. However, analysis similar to that carried out in Eqs. (5-97) and (5-98) reveals that β must be chosen such that

$$\beta = \frac{\sqrt{c_2 d_2} - d_2}{d_1} \qquad (5\text{-}99)$$

Using this value of β, the biquadratic of Eq. (5-96) can be converted to a bicubic minimum-resistance function which can be realized by Eqs. (5-93) through (5-95) as a network of the form of Fig. 5-22, Case 2.

As an example of the realization of a biquadratic, consider the following minimum-resistance driving-point impedance:

$$Z(s) = K \frac{s^2 + c_1 s + c_2}{s^2 + d_1 s + d_2} = 4 \frac{s^2 + 2s + 8}{s^2 + s + 2} \tag{5-100}$$

The critical frequency for a minimum-resistance biquadratic impedance is given by $\omega_1{}^2 = \sqrt{c_2 d_2}$. For this example ($\omega_1 = 2$) and the impedance at ω_1 is $[Z(j\omega_1) = 0 - j8]$. Because the reactance is negative, the network will be realized in the form of Fig. 5-22, Case 2. The surplus factor for this case is given by Eq. (5-99) and becomes ($\beta = 2$). Multiplying Eq. (5-100) by this factor yields

$$Z(s) = 4 \frac{(s^2 + 2s + 8)(s + 2)}{(s^2 + s + 2)(s + 2)} = 4 \frac{s^3 + 4s^2 + 12s + 16}{s^3 + 3s^2 + 4s + 4} \tag{5-101}$$

This function satisfies the conditions of Eqs. (5-93) and (5-94); therefore, element values for the network can be determined from Eq. (5-95). These values become ($C^* = C_1 = C_2 = 1/16$ farad), ($L = 4$ henrys), and ($R_2 = R_4 = 8$ ohms). Connecting these elements in the configuration of Fig. 5-22, Case 2, completes the realization of Eq. (5-100).

The unbalanced-bridge structure in the above discussion was restricted to three reactive elements for z_1, z_3, and z_5 of Fig. 5-21. Other combinations of three reactive elements may be useful for some realization problems. Furthermore, minimum-resistance functions can be realized in the form of Fig. 5-22, Cases 1 and 2, even when z_2 and z_4 are arbitrary impedance functions representing additional resistance and/or reactance elements. Finally, certain nonminimum-resistance driving-point functions can also be realized in the bridge form with fewer elements than required for a realization by series-parallel withdrawal or other procedures previously considered.

5-11. Total Impedance Required for the Realization of a Network

Emphasis in the last few sections has been placed on reducing the number of reactive elements required to realize a specified driving-point function. It has been pointed out by A. Bar-Lev that, although this is a worthwhile objective, it may not be the most practical.† The distribution and size of element values should also be taken into account in the

---

† A. Bar-Lev, "On the Total Amount of Inductance and Capacitance Needed in the Bott-Duffin Realization and its Modifications," *IRE Trans. Circuit Theory*, vol. CT-9, no. 2, June 1962, pp. 188–189.

selection of a synthesis procedure. This point will be developed in greater detail in Chap. 11, Consideration of Practical Elements; however, it is worthwhile to digress briefly to consider Bar-Lev's comments which apply to the procedures of this chapter.

The concept of total impedance is most easily developed by considering one type of element at a time. In other words, it is of interest to determine which procedure is most economical in terms of total resistance, capacitance, and/or inductance required to realize a given driving-point function. Each cycle of application of the various procedures outlined in Secs. 5-3 through 5-10 reduces the degree of the specified function by two; therefore, it is possible to compare the impedance of each approach on a per cycle basis. Furthermore, for comparison purposes, it is possible to consider differences in impedance from one network to the next rather than deal with absolute magnitudes. Finally, it is convenient to select the Brune network of Fig. 5-5 as a reference, because most of the other procedures can be derived from it.

In the preceding sections, it was seen that two possible balanced- and unbalanced-bridge configurations can be derived from Fig. 5-5, depending on the sign of L_1 and L_3. It is desirable to compare the total resistance R^t, inductance L^t, and capacitance C^t of each combination with that of Brune's configuration. It would also be desirable to compare the total impedance of each configuration with all others; however, space does not permit such a comprehensive study. Therefore, the total impedance for the example networks of Figs. 5-12, 5-17, and 5-18 will be compared with that of the Brune network of Fig. 5-9, since all of these structures were derived from the same driving-point impedance, Eq. (5-35). Following this example, some generalized conclusions will be stated concerning the total impedance of the various network configurations.

The total resistance, inductance, and capacitance of Brune's network can be written from Fig. 5-9 as $R_b{}^t = R_{min} + R^*_{min} = 2$ ohms, $L_b{}^t = L_1 + L_2 + L_3 = 3/2$ henrys, and $C_b{}^t = C = 1$ farad. Similarly, the total impedance of the Bott-Duffin balanced bridge of Fig. 5-12 can be denoted by subscripts bd, the unbalanced form of Fig. 5-17 by $p1$, and the unbalanced form of Fig. 5-18 by $p2$. Using these subscripts, the differences in the total resistance ΔR^t, inductance ΔL^t, and capacitance ΔC^t can be derived from the networks of the figures listed above as follows:

Bott-Duffin (Fig. 5-12):

$$\Delta R^t_{bd} = R_b{}^t - R^t_{bd} = 2 - 1 - 1 - 4 = -4 \text{ ohms}$$
$$\Delta L^t_{bd} = L_b{}^t - L^t_{bd} = 3/2 - 1 - 9 - 18/25 = -5.3 \text{ henrys}$$
$$\Delta C^t_{bd} = C_b{}^t - C^t_{bd} = 1 - 1/4 - 5/4 - 1/5 = -0.7 \text{ farad}$$

Pantell, Case 1 (Fig. 5-17):

$$\Delta R_{p1}^t = R_b^t - R_{p1}^t = 2 - 1 - 1 - 4 = -4 \text{ ohms}$$
$$\Delta L_{p1}^t = L_b^t - L_{p1}^t = 3/2 - 1 - 9 - 18/25 = -9.22 \text{ henrys}$$
$$\Delta C_{p1}^t = C_b^t - C_{p1}^t = 1 - 25/18 - 1/9 = -0.5 \text{ farad}$$

Pantell, Case 2 (Fig. 5-18):

$$\Delta R_{p2}^t = R_b^t - R_{p2}^t = 2 - 1 - 1 - 4 = -4 \text{ ohms}$$
$$\Delta L_{p2}^t = L_b^t - L_{p2}^t = 3/2 - 1 - 2/3 - 25/3 = -8.5 \text{ henrys}$$
$$\Delta C_{p2}^t = C_b^t - C_{p2}^t = 1 - 3/25 - 3/2 = -0.62 \text{ farad} \qquad (5\text{-}102)$$

TABLE 5-1

Comparison of Synthesis Procedures of Secs. 5-3 through 5-10

Procedure	Reference network	Elements per cycle	Reactive elements per cycle		Total impedance compared to Brune's network
			L	C	
Brune (Sec. 5-3)	Fig. 5-5	5	3	1	This reference network has lowest total R^t, L^t, and C^t per cycle
Bott-Duffin balanced bridge (Secs. 5-5 and 5-6)	Fig. 5-11 or Fig. 5-14	7	3	3	This form generally has higher R^t, L^t, and C^t than Brune but less L^t than unbalanced forms
Unbalanced bridge (Secs. 5-7, 5-8, and 5-9)	Fig. 5-20	6	3	2	Two cases exist which have same R^t, about the same C^t, and higher L^t than Bott-Duffin
Special bridge networks (Sec. 5-10)	Fig. 5-22a	5	2	1	These cannot be compared, since the forms are not general
	Fig. 5-22b	5	1	2	

Several interesting results can be derived from this type of analysis. For example, it is seen in Eq. (5-102) that ΔR^t is the same for each case. This is because the Bott-Duffin and Pantell networks are based on Richards' transformation and only the number of reactive elements are different from one configuration to the next. Generally, the total resistance per cycle is the same for the Bott-Duffin network and its modifications. It is also seen in Eq. (5-102) that all of the ΔR^t, ΔL^t, and ΔC^t

results are negative. This implies that the balanced- and unbalanced-bridge configurations require more total impedance per cycle to realize a given driving-point function than a Brune network. Both of Pantell's unbalanced forms require less capacitance but more inductance per cycle than does the Bott-Duffin configuration. The unbalanced form of Case 2, Fig. 5-18, always requires less total inductance and more total capacitance than that of Case 1, Fig. 5-17.

Table 5-1 summarizes some of the comments made in the above discussion in addition to showing the number of elements required per cycle of application for the procedures of Secs. 5-3 through 5-10. Comments concerning total impedance are referenced in each case to Brune's network of Fig. 5-5. The procedures of this chapter summarized in Table 5-1 do not exhaust all possible *RLC* driving-point synthesis techniques. Several additional procedures based on continued-fraction expansion techniques are described in Chap. 6.

References

Further reading on the subjects of minimum-impedance functions and Brune's procedure can be found in the following references:

1. E. A. Guillemin, *Synthesis of Passive Networks* (New York: John Wiley & Sons, Inc., 1957), Chap. 9.
2. D. F. Tuttle, *Network Synthesis*, Vol. I (New York: John Wiley & Sons, Inc., 1958), Chaps. 8 and 9.
3. L. Weinberg, *Network Analysis and Synthesis* (New York: McGraw-Hill Book Co., Inc., 1962), Secs. 10-1 and 10-2.

Chapter 10 of all three of these references is devoted to the Bott-Duffin procedure. For the unbalanced-bridge procedures described in Secs. 5-6 through 5-11, the best references are those listed in the footnotes of each section.

Problems

5-1. Using the series-parallel withdrawal procedure, synthesize *RLC* networks for the following driving-point functions:

(a) $\quad Z_1(s) = \dfrac{14s^3 + 112s^2 + 72s + 6}{s^3 + 15s^2 + 3s}$

(b) $\quad Z_1(s) = \dfrac{2(3s^3 + 2s^2 + 21s + 10)}{3(3s^2 + 2s)}$

(c) $\quad Y_1(s) = \dfrac{10s^3 + 33s^2 + 89s + 15}{20s^4 + 116s^3 + 373s^2 + 565s + 225}$

5-2. Realize a network for the following driving-point impedance, which is the series combination of two impedances, such that the magnitude of one impedance is twice that of the second. Realize the two impedances by series-parallel withdrawal of elements. What can be said of the relationship of the series- and shunt-element values of the two subnetworks? Show that these subnetworks can be combined physically to yield a single network equivalent to the network which results when series-parallel withdrawal is practiced directly.

$$Z_1(s) = \frac{15s^2 + 39s + 63}{5s + 3}$$

5-3. Determine the minimum resistance for the following functions and the frequency ω_1 at which it occurs. Remove the minimum resistance, then determine the reactance that must be removed from each function in order that the remaining functions will have zero impedance at the frequency ω_1.

(a) $Z_1(s) = \dfrac{12s^2 + 13s + 12}{s^2 + 3s + 3}$ (b) $Z_1(s) = \dfrac{19s^2 + 22s + 36}{2s^2 + 12s + 24}$

5-4. Realize the Brune network for the following function according to the procedure of Sec. 5-3.

$$Z_1(s) = \frac{10s^2 + 18s + 32}{s^2 + 8s + 8}$$

5-5. Realize the Brune networks for the functions of Prob. 5-3 according to the procedures outlined in Sec. 5-3.

5-6. Determine the driving-point impedance for the network of Fig. 5-24.

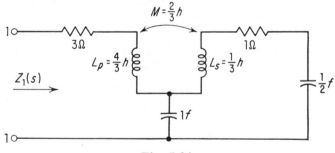

Fig. 5-24.

5-7. Design a Brune network in which the minimum resistance of the first cycle is 4 ohms and occurs at $\omega_1 = 3$. The impedance of the second cycle is a resistor of 2 ohms, and the primary, secondary, and mutual inductance of the transformer is 1/6 henry. After obtaining the T-network form of the transformer, determine the value of C necessary to yield a minimum resistance at $\omega_1 = 3$. Determine the driving-point impedance.

5-8. Synthesize the Bott-Duffin network for Prob. 5-4 by the procedure outlined in Sec. 5-5. Remember that the minimum resistance must be removed from the impedance function before the transformation can be used. Using the transformations of Eq. (5-69), check the resulting network.

5-9. Synthesize a Bott-Duffin network equivalent to the Brune network of Prob. 5-6, Fig. 5-24. Use the transformations of Sec. 5-6, Eq. (5-69). Repeat the problem using Reza's transformations of Sec. 5-9, Eq. (5-83), to realize an equivalent unbalanced-bridge network.

5-10. Using the transformations of Sec. 5-9, Eq. (5-83), determine the Reza unbalanced networks for the impedances of Prob. 5-3.

5-11. Realize the impedance of Prob. 5-4 by Pantell's procedure to yield two different network configurations, one for each of the values of A determined from Eqs. (5-75) and (5-76). Check the results by applying the transformations of Reza's unbalanced form or Storer's conversion from the balanced Bott-Duffin configuration.

5-12. Determine which of the following driving-point impedance functions can be realized as bridge networks of the form of Fig. 5-22. Synthesize bridge networks to realize the impedances that satisfy the necessary requirements:

(a) $\quad Z(s) = \dfrac{4s^3 + 5s^2 + 16s + 16}{s^3 + 4s^2 + 3s + 8}$ (c) $\quad Z(s) = \dfrac{2s^2 + 4s + 16}{s^2 + s + 4}$

(b) $\quad Z(s) = \dfrac{2s^3 + s^2 + 4s + 2}{2s^3 + 6s^2 + 4s + 12}$ (d) $\quad Z(s) = \dfrac{s^2 + 4s + 16}{s^2 + s + 4}$

5-13. Show that the use of surplus factors increases the total impedance required to realize a given driving-point function. Select a biquadratic function which leads to a bridge network similar to Fig. 5-22 to demonstrate this fact.

Chapter 6

Additional Driving-point
Synthesis Procedures

With exception of the series-parallel withdrawal procedure, which is more or less an iterative approach to synthesis, all of the *RLC* synthesis techniques described in Chap. 5 employed reduction of the given function to a minimum impedance or admittance form as a preliminary step in the realization. At this point all but Brune's procedure completed the synthesis by realizing the minimum driving-point function in the form of a balanced- or unbalanced-bridge structure. This is by no means the only approach that can be taken in solving the realization problem for *RLC* driving-point functions. One obvious technique is to reduce in the beginning the given driving-point function to the sum of a number of simplified impedance or admittance functions, the realization of which is more easily performed. This approach is considered in Secs. 6-2 through 6-4 of this chapter.

Decomposition of a driving-point impedance or admittance into the sum of several simplified functions may actually be a complicated process, since each of the simplified functions must be positive real in order to be physically realizable. A procedure for satisfying this condition has been suggested by F. Miyata.† Consider the following driving-point impedance where A_1 and B_1 are, respectively, the even and odd parts of the polynomial $P(s)$; and A_2 and B_2 are the even and odd parts of $Q(s)$. It is also convenient to assume that poles and zeros of the function are restricted from the $j\omega$-axis. The reason for this will become clear later.

$$Z(s) = \frac{P(s)}{Q(s)} = \frac{a_n s^n + a_{n-1} s^{n-1} + \cdots + a_1 s + a_0}{b_n s^n + b_{n-1} s^{n-1} + \cdots + b_1 s + b_0} = \frac{A_1 + B_1}{A_2 + B_2} \qquad (6-1)$$

† F. Miyata, "A New System of Two-Terminal Synthesis," *IRE Trans. Circuit Theory*, vol. CT-2, no. 4, December 1955, pp. 297–302.

The real part of $Z(s)$ can be written as

$$Re[Z(s)]_{s=j\omega} = \frac{(A_1 + B_1)}{(A_2 + B_2)} \cdot \frac{(A_2 - B_2)}{(A_2 - B_2)}\Big]_{s=j\omega} = \frac{A_1 A_2 - B_1 B_2}{A_2^2 - B_2^2}\Big]_{s=j\omega}$$

$$= \frac{N_n \omega^{2n} + N_{n-1} \omega^{2n-2} + \cdots + N_1 \omega^2 + N_0}{D_n \omega^{2n} + D_{n-1} \omega^{2n-2} + \cdots + D_1 \omega^2 + D_0} = \frac{N(\omega^2)}{D(\omega^2)}$$

$$(6-2)$$

In abbreviated form $N(\omega^2)$ and $D(\omega^2)$ represent the numerator and denominator polynomials, respectively, of the $Re[Z(j\omega)]$. The denominator $D(\omega^2)$ is positive for all ω, since it is a perfect square; therefore, Eq. (6-2) can be broken up as follows:

$$Re[Z(j\omega)] = \frac{N_0}{D(\omega^2)} + \frac{N_1 \omega^2}{D(\omega^2)} + \cdots + \frac{N_{n-1} \omega^{2n-2}}{D(\omega^2)} + \frac{N_n \omega^{2n}}{D(\omega^2)}$$

$$(6-3)$$

Each term of Eq. (6-3) having a numerator with a positive coefficient may be considered to represent the real part of a physically realizable driving-point impedance. However, a question remains concerning the approach to be taken when one or more of the N_i coefficients are negative. Furthermore, the problem of converting each positive term of Eq. (6-3) to an impedance, having only the real part of the function at $(s = j\omega)$, must be solved. Finally, cases for which poles and zeros of the driving-point function are not restricted from the $j\omega$-axis must be examined. Provided these items can be satisfied, $Z(s)$ can be realized as the sum of several individual impedances possessing simplified properties. This summation of simplified functions can be expressed as follows:

$$Z(s) = Z_0(s) + Z_1(s) + \cdots + Z_{n-1}(s) + Z_n(s) \qquad (6-4)$$

Before investigating the details of Miyata's procedure, it is of interest to consider techniques whereby a driving-point impedance or admittance can be determined as a function of s when only its real part is known as a function of ω.

6-1. Impedance Determination from its Real Part

In some situations, such as that described above, the real part of an impedance function is known, and the problem is to find the related imaginary part so that they can be combined to yield the desired impedance function. Clearly an infinite number of different reactance functions or imaginary parts may be associated with a given real part. However, there exists a minimum imaginary part related to a given real part. Additional reactance above this minimum results in addition of $j\omega$-axis poles and/or zeros to the desired impedance function. In other words, addition of a reactance function to any given impedance does not affect the resulting real part, and so the impedance which can be constructed from the real part cannot have $j\omega$-axis poles or zeros. For this reason the imaginary part, which is to be determined, will be restricted to a minimum-reactance function, and consequently the restriction imposed on Eq. (6-1) becomes meaningful.

The problem of determining the impedance function when only its real part is specified can be solved (within the minimum-reactance restriction mentioned above) by a technique suggested by C. Gewertz.† Gewertz's procedure relies on the fact that the real part of an impedance function is composed of only even-ordered functions of s such as s^2, s^4, s^6, etc. This fact was established in Chap. 3, Sec. 3-1, where it was shown that the $Re[Z(j\omega)]$ equals $Ev[Z(s)]$ when $s = j\omega$. Suppose that the real part of a driving-point impedance is known, in which case the even-ordered terms are known. The entire impedance can be written as

$$Z(s)]_{s=j\omega} = Re[Z(j\omega)] + jIm[Z(j\omega)] \qquad (6\text{-}5)$$

Because only the real part is known, it is necessary to find the imaginary or reactive part of the function. In Chap. 3, Sec. 3-1, it was also shown that the imaginary or reactive part of an impedance must be composed of odd-ordered terms of s such as s, s^3, s^5, etc. The reactance function can be further restricted, since $P(s)$ and $Q(s)$ of a driving-point function can only differ in degree by unity.

With these facts established, it is now useful to consider a minimum-reactance function written in the form of Eq. (6-1). (In this application minimum reactance implies that no poles or zeros lie on the $j\omega$-axis.) The real part of the impedance can be expressed as shown and expanded in terms of the coefficients of Eq. (6-1) to yield

$$Re[Z(s)]_{s=j\omega} = \frac{(A_1A_2 - B_1B_2)}{(A_2 + B_2)(A_2 - B_2)}\Bigg]_{s=j\omega}$$
$$= (a_0 - a_2\omega^2 + \cdots)(b_0 - b_2\omega^2 + \cdots)$$
$$\frac{+ \omega^2(a_1 - a_3\omega^2 + \cdots)(b_1 - b_3\omega^2 + \cdots)}{A_2{}^2 - B_2{}^2}$$

$$(6\text{-}6)$$

The denominator of Eq. (6-6) vanishes when $s = -(A_2 + B_2)$ and $s = -(A_2 - B_2)$. Suppose that s_o causes $(A_2 + B_2)$ to become zero, then $-s_o$ will have the same effect on $(A_2 - B_2)$. Hence, the denominator of Eq. (6-6) has $2n$ poles which can be divided into two groups $(A_2 + B_2)$ and $(A_2 - B_2)$, where the second group is the conjugate of the first. It is possible to select a set of poles in the left half of the s-plane

† C. Gewertz, "Synthesis of a Finite, Four-Terminal Network," *J. Math. Phys.*, vol. 12, 1932–1933, pp. 1–257.

as the poles of $Z(s)$ from $(A_2 + B_2)$ and $(A_2 - B_2)$. This procedure establishes the b coefficients of $Z(s)$ as given by Eq. (6-1). When this has been done, only the a coefficients are needed to complete $Z(s)$.

Assume that the real part of $Z(s)$ is given and can be written as an explicit expression in terms of ω as indicated in Eq. (6-2). Equations (6-2) and (6-6) must be equal; however, the b coefficients, which define the denominator of $Z(s)$, can be found according to the above discussion. Therefore, it is only necessary to equate the numerators of Eqs. (6-2) and (6-6). Equating coefficients of like powers of ω yields the following set of equations:

$$
\begin{aligned}
N_0 &= a_0 b_0 \\
N_1 &= -a_0 b_0 - a_2 b_0 + a_1 b_1 \\
N_2 &= a_0 b_4 + a_2 b_2 + a_4 b_0 - a_1 b_3 - b_1 a_3 \\
N_3 &= -a_6 b_0 - a_4 b_2 - a_2 b_4 - a_0 b_6 + a_5 b_1 + a_3 b_3 + a_1 b_5
\end{aligned}
$$
$$
\cdot \quad \cdot \quad \cdot \quad \cdot \quad \cdot \quad \cdot \quad \cdot \quad \cdot \quad \cdot \quad \cdot \tag{6-7}
$$

In this set of equations the N_i terms are known, since they are the coefficients of the numerator of the real part that is given, and the b terms can be established from the denominator of the real part. Therefore, solving for the a terms completes the process of establishing $Z(s)$.

As an example of Gewertz's procedure, assume that the real part of a driving-point impedance has been specified in terms of ω as

$$
Re[Z(j\omega)] = \frac{5\omega^4 - 8\omega^2 + 8}{\omega^4 + 4} \tag{6-8}
$$

Replacing ω by s/j in this equation yields

$$
Re[Z(j\omega)]_{\omega = s/j} = Re[Z(s)] = \frac{5s^4 - 8s^2 + 8}{s^4 + 4} \tag{6-9}
$$

Solving for the poles of this function provides

$$
Re[Z(s)] = \frac{5s^4 - 8s^2 + 8}{(s + 1 - j1)(s + 1 + j1)(s - 1 + j1)(s - 1 - j1)} \tag{6-10}
$$

The poles fall at $s_1 = -1 + j1$, $s_2 = -1 - j1$, $s_3 = 1 - j1$, and $s_4 = 1 + j1$. These poles can be plotted on the s-plane as shown in Fig. 6-1.

Because Eq. (6-8) was assumed to be derived from a real network, it must lead to a physically realizable driving-point function. The only physically realizable poles of Eq. (6-10) are those in the left half of the s-plane, namely $s_1 = -1 + j1$ and $s_2 = -1 - j1$. Because these are the only realizable poles, $Z(s)$ must be of the form

$$
Z(s) = \frac{a_0 + a_1 s + a_2 s^2}{(s + 1 + j1)(s + 1 - j1)} = \frac{a_0 + a_1 s + a_2 s^2}{s^2 + 2s + 2} \tag{6-11}
$$

If this equation is solved for its real part, the result can be equated to the real part given in Eq. (6-9).

$$Re[Z(s)]_{s=j\omega} = \frac{(2 - \omega^2)(a_0 - a_2\omega^2) + 2a_1\omega^2}{(2 - \omega^2)^2 + 4\omega^2} = \frac{5\omega^4 - 8\omega^2 + 8}{\omega^4 + 4} \quad (6\text{-}12)$$

Equating the numerators of these two forms gives

$$a_2\omega^4 - 2a_2\omega^2 - a_0\omega^2 + 2a_1\omega^2 + 2a_0 = 5\omega^4 - 8\omega^2 + 8 \quad (6\text{-}13)$$

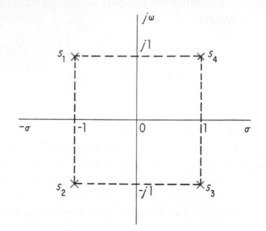

Fig. 6-1. Poles of Eq. 6-10.

Comparing terms on both sides of this equation reveals that $a_0 = 4$, $a_1 = 3$, and $a_2 = 5$. These coefficients can be placed in Eq. (6-11) to give the final driving-point impedance function.

$$Z(s) = \frac{5s^2 + 3s + 4}{s^2 + 2s + 2} \quad (6\text{-}14)$$

This impedance may be recognized as the example of Eq. (5-35), which has a Brune network as seen in Fig. 5-10, a Bott-Duffin network as seen in Fig. 5-12, and Pantell networks as seen in Figs. 5-17 and 5-18.

This concludes Gewertz's procedure for determining an impedance function if its real part is known or specified. It should be remembered that this method determines the minimum-reactive function associated with a given resistive component. Therefore, a minimum-reactance driving-point impedance is obtained. This may not be the driving-point function of the network from which the real or resistive part was measured. Gewertz's procedure, although straightforward, is not the only method for solving this problem. A second technique, credited to H. W. Bode, is based on the right half-plane analyticity of driving-point functions and insight into the position of the poles of the $Re[Z(s)]$.

The real part of a positive real function of s must be nonnegative for pure imaginary values of s. Therefore, it is possible to write

$$Re[Z(j\omega)] = \frac{1}{2}[Z(j\omega) + Z(-j\omega)] = \frac{1}{2}[Z(s) + Z(-s)]_{s=j\omega} \geq 0 \quad (6\text{-}15)$$

where $Z(-s)$ is the complex conjugate of $Z(s)$. This equation results from the fact that the sum of any complex number and its conjugate is equal to twice the real part of the number. Hence, if the real part of the function is known, by writing s for $j\omega$, or actually $(-s^2)$ for ω^2, the sum of $Z(s)$ and $Z(-s)$ are determined within a factor of two. The problem of separating $Z(s)$ and $Z(-s)$ remains. In the case of positive real functions, separation of $Z(s)$ and $Z(-s)$ is not difficult, because the $j\omega$-axis represents a boundary line. Poles of $Z(s)$ lie in one half-plane and those of $Z(-s)$ lie in the other. Unfortunately, $j\omega$-axis poles present a problem; however, as described in the previous discussion, these poles will not exist in the case of minimum-reactance functions.

Equating Eq. (6-15) to Eq. (6-2) and substituting s for $j\omega$ yields the following relationship:

$$Re[Z(s)] = \frac{1}{2}[Z(s) + Z(-s)] = \frac{N(-s^2)}{D(-s^2)}$$

$$= \frac{N_0 - N_1 s^2 + N_2 s^4 + \cdots + (-)^n N_n s^{2n}}{D_0 - D_1 s^2 + D_2 s^4 + \cdots + (-)^n D_n s^{2n}} = F(s) \quad (6\text{-}16)$$

where $F(s)$ represents a function having the left half-plane poles of $Z(s)$ and their conjugates [i.e., $F(s)$ will have poles which possess symmetry about both the σ-axis and $j\omega$-axis of the s-plane]. The denominator of $F(s)$ may be considered to represent a perfect square as indicated in Eq. (6-2), where $[D(-s^2) = (A_2 + B_2)(A_2 - B_2)]$. Therefore, a partial-fraction expansion of $F(s)$ can be made, and all terms possessing right half-plane poles can be omitted. Multiplying the remaining terms by two yields a rational function which approaches a constant k as s approaches infinity $[F(s) \to k$ as $(s \to \infty)]$. This rational function $Z(s)$ can be written in the following form when simple poles are involved, which is usually the case:

$$Z(s) = 2\left[\frac{k_1}{(s + s_1)} + \frac{k_2}{(s + s_2)} + \cdots + \frac{k_n}{(s + s_n)}\right] + k \quad (6\text{-}17)$$

In this expression conjugate poles must possess complex conjugate residues. Furthermore, Eq. (6-17) is not restricted to functions possessing simple poles. On the contrary, when poles of higher order are encountered, the partial-fraction expansion of $F(s)$ must contain the appropriate terms (See Chap. 1, Sec. 1-7) and the form of Eq. (6-17) can be modified accordingly.

An example illustrates the procedure for determining $Z(s)$ from its real part, using the technique described above. Assume that the $Re[Z(j\omega)]$ is given by

$$Re[Z(j\omega)] = \frac{10\omega^2 + 30}{\omega^6 + 7\omega^4 + 31\omega^2 + 25} \tag{6-18}$$

Substituting s for $j\omega$, factoring, and performing a partial-fraction expansion yields

$$Re[Z(s)] = \frac{-10s^2 + 30}{-s^6 + 7s^4 - 31s^2 + 25}$$

$$= \frac{\frac{1}{2}}{(s+1)} - \frac{\frac{1}{2}}{(s-1)} + \frac{j\frac{1}{4}}{(s+2+j1)} - \frac{j\frac{1}{4}}{(s+2-j1)}$$

$$+ \frac{j\frac{1}{4}}{(s-2+j1)} - \frac{j\frac{1}{4}}{(s-2-j1)} \tag{6-19}$$

Discarding terms possessing right half-plane poles and multiplying the remaining terms by two, as in Eq. (6-17), gives

$$Z(s) = 2\left[\frac{\frac{1}{2}}{(s+1)} + \frac{j\frac{1}{4}}{(s+2+j1)} - \frac{j\frac{1}{4}}{(s+2-j1)}\right] + k \tag{6-20}$$

The value of k for this example is zero since $F(s)$ approaches zero as s approaches infinity [see Eq. (6-19)]. Consequently, the minimum-reactance driving-point impedance, which possesses a real part given by Eq. (6-18), can be written as

$$Z(s) = \frac{s^2 + 5s + 6}{s^3 + 5s^2 + 9s + 5} \tag{6-21}$$

The above procedures can be extended to functions which possess $j\omega$-axis poles in the following respect. A driving-point function having $j\omega$-axis poles at $(s^2 + \omega_o{}^2)$ will possess a real part for $(s = j\omega)$ in which the corresponding terms of the form $(-\omega^2 + \omega_o{}^2)$ occur in both numerator and denominator as squared factors which cancel out. Consequently, for $j\omega$-axis poles to become evident in the driving-point function, it is necessary that appropriate common factors be included in both numerator and denominator of Eqs. (6-2) or (6-16).

Of the two procedures described above, Gewertz's method is seen to yield results directly in polynomial form. However, solution of the simultaneous equations to determine the polynomial coefficients becomes tedious when the real part of the function is of higher order. The second procedure yields a driving-point function in partial-fraction form which is often useful in subsequent realization techniques. It should be clear that the above procedure, described for driving-point impedances, may also be applied to admittance functions.†

6-2. Miyata's Synthesis Procedure

Miyata's procedure for realizing RLC driving-point functions is based on separation of the given function into the sum of several terms having properties which are more easily realized. Miyata's procedure may be stated in brief as a series of steps.

1. Remove all $j\omega$-axis poles and zeros of the given function. These roots may be realized as series and/or parallel LC networks by the procedures of Chap. 4. This step is similar to the first step of the Brune and Bott-Duffin procedures. For the sake of simplicity, the minimum-reactance function remaining after this step will be denoted by $Z(s)$.

2. The second step involves finding the real part of $Z(j\omega)$ as shown in Eq. (6-2). A check must be made of the N_i coefficients of the numerator of the $Re[Z(j\omega)]$. If any of the coefficients are negative, both numerator and denominator of $Z(s)$ must be multiplied by surplus factors of the form $(s + \beta)$. This multiplication will change both numerator and denominator of the real part of $Z(s)$, but by careful selection of the factor, β, the N_i coefficients can be made positive. It may be necessary to employ more than one surplus factor to accomplish this end.

3. When the N_i coefficients are all positive, the real part of $Z(s)$ can be broken up, as indicated in Eq. (6-3), to form the real parts of several simplified driving-point functions. The expressions for these simplified minimum-reactance driving-point functions can be determined from their respective real parts by the techniques described in Sec. 6-1.

4. Having separated the given function into a number of simplified functions, realization may be initiated by applying any of the driving-point synthesis procedures considered thus far. This yields a set of simplified networks which may be connected in series if the functions represent impedances or in parallel if they represent admittances, and the resulting structure can be combined accordingly with the LC networks derived in Step 1 to complete the realization.

The above steps may be more easily understood when applied to an example. Therefore, assume the impedance of Eq. (6-22) is given, and Miyata's procedure is to be used for its realization.

$$Z(s) = \frac{4s^2 + 6s + 1}{s^2 + 4s + 6} \tag{6-22}$$

Since this example has no $j\omega$-axis poles or zeros, Step 1 of the procedure does not apply. The second step involves determination of the real part

† A more detailed discussion of these and other procedures for determining a driving-point function when only its real part is known can be found in E. A. Guillemin, *Synthesis of Passive Networks* (New York: John Wiley & Sons, Inc., 1957), Chap. 8.

of $(Zj\omega)$. The real part for this example is given by Eq. (6-23), where it is seen that the second coefficient of the numerator is negative $(-\omega^2)$.

$$Re[Z(j\omega)] = \frac{4\omega^4 - \omega^2 + 6}{\omega^4 + 4\omega^2 + 36} \tag{6-23}$$

Because of the negative coefficient, it is impossible to break up the function as in Eq. (6-3) such that all terms are positive for all ω. Consequently it is necessary to multiply both numerator and denominator of the given function, Eq. (6-22), by surplus factors of the form $(s + \beta)$:

$$\begin{aligned} Z(s) &= \frac{(4s^2 + 6s + 1)(s + \beta)}{(s^2 + 4s + 6)(s + \beta)} \\ &= \frac{4s^3 + (6 + 4\beta)s^2 + (1 + 6\beta)s + \beta}{s^3 + (4 + \beta)s^2 + (6 + 4\beta)s + 6\beta} \end{aligned} \tag{6-24}$$

Solving for the real part of $Z(j\omega)$ yields

$$Re[Z(j\omega)] = \frac{4\omega^6 + (4\beta^2 - 1)\omega^4 + (6 - \beta^2)\omega^2 + 6\beta^2}{\omega^6 + (\beta^2 + 4)\omega^4 + (16\beta^2 + 36)\omega^2 + 36\beta^2} \tag{6-25}$$

Because the denominator of the real part is a perfect square, it is only necessary to investigate the numerator for various values of β. Clearly, β must be positive; otherwise, the impedance of Eq. (6-24) will possess a right half-plane pole and the subsequent simplified functions will not be realizable. It is seen in Eq. (6-25) that the ω^4 term will be nonnegative if $(\beta \geq 1/2)$. Similarly, for the ω^2 term to be nonnegative, it is necessary that $(\beta \leq \sqrt{6})$. Therefore, the requirement for nonnegative coefficients can be satisfied by any value of β within the limits $(1/2 \leq \beta \leq \sqrt{6})$. Using $(\beta = 1)$ might simplify the computational procedures; however, by using either $(\beta = 1/2)$ or $(\beta = \sqrt{6})$ the ω^4 or ω^2 terms respectively will be zero, thereby reducing the number of simplified networks that must be realized. Consequently $(\beta = 1/2)$ will be used as the surplus factor, in which case Eqs. (6-24) and (6-25) become

$$Z(s) = \frac{4s^3 + 8s^2 + 4s + \dfrac{1}{2}}{s^3 + \dfrac{9s^2}{2} + 8s + 3} \tag{6-26}$$

$$Re[Z(j\omega)] = \frac{4\omega^6 + \dfrac{23}{4}\omega^2 + \dfrac{3}{2}}{\omega^6 + \dfrac{17}{4}\omega^4 + 40\omega^2 + 9} = \frac{N(\omega^2)}{D(\omega^2)} \tag{6-27}$$

Splitting up the $Re[Z(j\omega)]$, as in Eq. (6-3), yields

$$Re[Z(j\omega)] = Re[Z_0(j\omega)] + Re[Z_1(j\omega)] + Re[Z_2(j\omega)]$$

where

$$Re[Z_0(j\omega)] = \frac{\frac{3}{2}}{D(\omega^2)}; \quad Re[Z_1(j\omega)] = \frac{\frac{23\omega^2}{4}}{D(\omega^2)}, \quad \text{and} \quad Re[Z_2(j\omega)] = \frac{4\omega^6}{D(\omega^2)}$$

(6-28)

Employing the techniques of Sec. 6-1, the impedances $Z_0(s)$, $Z_1(s)$, and $Z_2(s)$ can be determined from their respective real parts given by Eq. (6-28). The result of this step is given as follows:

$$Z_0(s) = \frac{\dfrac{3s^2}{44} + \dfrac{27s}{88} + \dfrac{1}{2}}{s^3 + \dfrac{9s^2}{2} + 8s + 3}$$

$$Z_1(s) = \frac{\dfrac{23s^2}{132} + \dfrac{69s}{88}}{s^3 + \dfrac{9s^2}{2} + 8s + 3}$$

$$Z_2(s) = \frac{4s^3 + \dfrac{256s^2}{33} + \dfrac{32s}{11}}{s^3 + \dfrac{9s^2}{2} + 8s + 3}$$

(6-29)

Although these impedance functions may appear more complicated than Eqs. (6-22) or (6-26), they can readily be realized by the procedure of series-parallel withdrawal (see Chap. 5, Sec. 5-1). The resulting networks which represent $Z_0(s)$, $Z_1(s)$, and $Z_2(s)$ can then be combined in series to complete the realization of Eq. (6-22), since $[Z(s) = Z_0(s) + Z_1(s) + Z_2(s)]$. The final network to complete this realization is shown in Fig. 6-2.

It is of interest to consider the effect of using suitably chosen surplus factors in the realization process, as in the above example. Multiplying both numerator and denominator of a given driving-point function by factors of the form $(s + \beta)$ increases the degree of the function, thereby increasing network complexity and the number of circuit elements required for the realization. The number of surplus factors necessary to insure nonnegative coefficients in the numerator $N(\omega^2)$ of the real part of a function depends on the problem in question. Only a first-order surplus factor was required to accomplish this end in the example biquadratic impedance of Eq. (6-22). However, a second-order surplus factor of the form $(s^2 + as + b)$, is not sufficient to insure that all N_i coefficients of the real part of the biquadratic impedance of Eq. (6-14) will be nonnegative.

The number of surplus factors required to insure nonnegative coefficients for $N(\omega^2)$ depends on the location of the zeros of the polynomial $N(-s^2)$. In other words, location of the zeros of the numerator of the real part of the given function provides a clue to the required number or order of surplus factors to be used. The closer these zeros are

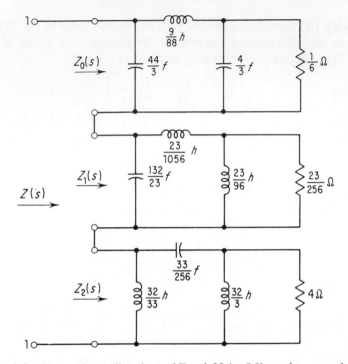

Fig. 6-2. Network realization of Eq. 6-22 by Miyata's procedure.

to the $j\omega$-axis of the s-plane the greater the number of surplus factors required. In the limit, the number or order of these factors becomes infinite when zeros of $N(-s^2)$ lie on the $j\omega$-axis. However, all N_i coefficients are guaranteed to be positive if the zeros lie within 45° regions about the σ-axis of the s-plane as indicated by the shaded areas of Fig. 6-3. This fact is probably not apparent; however, for purposes of this discussion, it can be justified on the basis of a reasoning process as described below.†

The polynomials $N(\omega^2)$ and $N(-s^2)$ are expressed in terms of their N_i coefficients in Eqs. (6-2) and (6-16), respectively. It is desired that the coefficients of these polynomials be positive and real; namely,

† A more detailed discussion of this fact can be found in the following reference. L. Kanal, "Comment on Two Papers on Miyata's Method of Synthesis," *IRE Trans. Circuit Theory*, vol. CT-4, no. 4, December 1957, pp. 340–341.

$N_0 > 0$, $N_1 > 0$, $N_2 > 0, \ldots, N_n > 0$. The polynomial $N(\omega^2)$ can be factored into a product of roots of the form $(\omega^2 - \omega_k^2)$, where zeros of the function may be expressed in polar coordinates on the ω^2-plane by $(\omega_k^2 = \rho e^{j\phi})$. First, second, third, and fourth quadrant zeros are, respectively, $(\omega_k^2 = \rho e^{j\phi})$, $[\omega_k^2 = \rho e^{j(\pi - \phi)}]$, $[\omega_k^2 = \rho e^{j(\phi - \pi)}]$, and $(\omega_k^2 = \rho e^{-j\phi})$ provided that $(\phi \leq \pi/2)$. If $N(\omega^2)$ is to possess only positive and real coefficients, zeros of the function must occur in conjugate pairs where individual zeros may be obtained by taking the square roots of the ω_k^2 roots. In other words, ω_k will be of the form $(\omega_k = \sqrt{\rho} e^{j\phi/2})$. Therefore, for positive coefficients, it is sufficient to restrict zeros of $N(\omega^2)$ on the ω-plane such that $(\phi \leq \pi/4)$, and hence, zeros of $N(-s^2)$ are restricted to the 45° regions of Fig. 6-3. It must be emphasized that this is a sufficient but not a necessary condition, since the requirement for nonzero coefficients for $N(\omega^2)$ may be satisfied when some zeros lie outside the shaded areas.

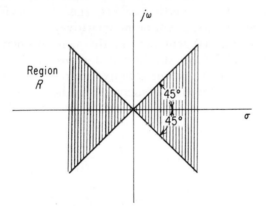

Fig. 6-3. Shaded regions for zeros of $N(-s^2)$ sufficient for non-negative N_i coefficients.

Because of the difficulties encountered when $N(\omega^2)$ possesses some negative coefficients, it would be advantageous if the real part of a given driving-point function could be broken up in a different manner, thereby eliminating the necessity for using surplus factors. For instance, the real part might be separated into only two parts such that surplus factors are not needed. If this can be accomplished, the number of subnetworks is reduced to two with a subsequent saving in circuit elements. E. S. Kuh has developed several techniques which are appropriate for many cases where the real part contains some negative coefficients.[†]

† E. S. Kuh, "Special Synthesis Techniques for Driving-Point Impedance Functions," *IRE Trans. Circuit Theory*, vol. CT-2, no. 2, December 1955, pp. 302–308.

6-3. Kuh's Procedures

As pointed out in the preceding section, it is possible to separate the real part of a function in a number of different ways, one possibility being

$$Re[Z(j\omega)] = \frac{N_0 + N_1\omega^2 + \cdots + N_k\omega^{2k}}{D(\omega^2)} + \frac{N_{k+1}\omega^{2k+2} + \cdots + N_n\omega^{2n}}{D(\omega^2)}$$

$$= Re[Z_1(j\omega)] + Re[Z_2(j\omega)] \qquad (6\text{-}30)$$

This separation will lead to a realization in which $[Z(s) = Z_1(s) + Z_2(s)]$. When all N_n coefficients are present and positive, the $Re[Z_1(j\omega)]$ has $2(n - k)$ zeros at $(\omega = \infty)$ and $Re[Z_2(j\omega)]$ has $2(k + 1)$ zeros at $(\omega = 0)$. In this case it is possible by continued-fraction expansion to realize $(n - k)$ reactive elements from $Z_1(s)$ and $(k + 1)$ reactive elements from $Z_2(s)$. Any remaining functions can be denoted as $Z_1^*(s)$ and $Z_2^*(s)$ and will be of ranks k and $(n - k - 1)$ respectively. These functions will possess the same properties as $Z(s)$ (i.e., the coefficients of the numerators of the real parts will be nonnegative).

That $Z_1^*(s)$ and $Z_2^*(s)$ will possess the same properties as $Z(s)$ is important and results from the fact that zeros of the real part of a function, except those at zero or infinity, are not changed by realizing single series or shunt reactive elements. This becomes clear when the real part of an impedance is compared with the real part of its admittance. For instance, the $Re[Y(j\omega)]$ can be written as

$$Re[Y(s)]_{s=j\omega} = \frac{A_1A_2 - B_1B_2}{A_1^2 - B_1^2}\bigg]_{s=j\omega}$$

where

$$Y(s) = \frac{1}{Z(s)} = \frac{A_2 + B_2}{A_1 + B_1} \qquad (6\text{-}31)$$

Comparing Eqs. (6-2) and (6-31), it is seen that numerators of the $Re[Y(j\omega)]$ and the $Re[Z(j\omega)]$ are identical. Therefore, realization of single series L and C elements does not change the numerator of the real part but simply reduces the rank of the denominator.

Removal of $(n - k)$ reactive terms from $Z_1(s)$ and $(k + 1)$ reactive terms from $Z_2(s)$ yields remainders $Z_1^*(s)$ and $Z_2^*(s)$ whose real parts are given by

$$Re[Z_1^*(j\omega)] = \frac{N_0 + N_1\omega^2 + \cdots + N_k\omega^{2k}}{D_0' + D_1'\omega^2 + \cdots + D_k'\omega^{2k}} \qquad (6\text{-}32)$$

$$Re[Z_2^*(j\omega)] = \frac{N_{k+1} + N_{k+2}\omega^2 + \cdots + N_n\omega^{2(n-k-1)}}{D_0'' + D_1''\omega^2 + \cdots + D_{n-k-1}''\omega^{2(n-k-1)}} \qquad (6\text{-}33)$$

In these expressions, the N_i coefficients are the same as those of the original function; however, the denominators of $Z_1^*(s)$ and $Z_2^*(s)$ have been reduced in rank to k and $(n - k - 1)$ respectively. Consequently, one cycle of this procedure will yield a network as shown in Fig. 6-4, and the procedure may be repeated on the remaining functions $Z_1^*(s)$ and $Z_2^*(s)$.

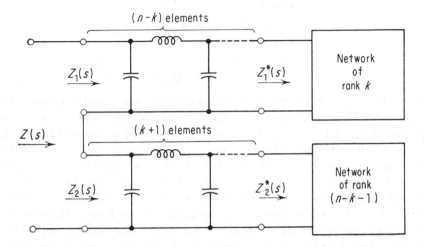

Fig. 6-4. Network for Eq. 6-30 when all N_n coefficients are positive.

In the above discussion, it was assumed that all coefficients of the real part of a function were present and positive. This condition exists when all zeros of $N(-s^2)$ are restricted to the 45° regions of the s-plane shown as shaded areas in Fig. 6-3. This condition is often satisfied when some of the zeros lie outside the region R but not on the $j\omega$-axis. In these cases the procedure described above can be applied.

A more general situation is one in which some zeros of $N(-s^2)$ lie outside the region R causing negative coefficients to arise in $N(\omega^2)$. In this case it is frequently possible to break $N(\omega^2)$ into the product of two polynomials such that $[N(\omega^2) = N'(\omega^2)N''(\omega^2)]$, where $N'(\omega^2)$ has non-negative coefficients and $N''(\omega^2)$ has some negative coefficients due to zeros of $N(-s^2)$ outside R which cannot be included in $N'(\omega^2)$. When this is accomplished, $N'(\omega^2)$ may be separated into two parts, both of which are multiplied by $N''(\omega^2)$ such that the real part of the given function assumes the following form:

$$Re[Z(j\omega)] = \frac{N'(\omega^2)N''(\omega^2)}{D(\omega^2)} = \frac{(N_0' + N_1'\omega^2 + \cdots + N_i'\omega^{2i})N''(\omega^2)}{D(\omega^2)}$$

$$+ \frac{(N_{i+1}'\omega^{2i+2} + \cdots + N_k'\omega^{2k})N''(\omega^2)}{D(\omega^2)} \qquad (6\text{-}34)$$

A special case of Eq. (6-34) exists when $N(\omega^2)$ has a pair of double real frequency zeros at $(\omega = \pm \omega_1)$. In this case if all coefficients of $N(\omega^2)/(\omega^2 - \omega_1^2)^2$ are positive, the real part of the given impedance can be decomposed along the lines of Eq. (6-34) as

$$Re[Z(j\omega)] = \frac{N'(\omega^2)N''(\omega^2)}{D(\omega^2)} = \frac{N'(\omega^2)(\omega^2 - \omega_1^2)}{D(\omega^2)}$$

$$= \frac{(\omega^2 - \omega_1^2)(N_0' + N_1'\omega^2 + \cdots + N_i'\omega^{2i})}{D(\omega^2)}$$

$$+ \frac{(\omega^2 - \omega_1^2)(N_{i+1}'\omega^{2i+2} + \cdots + N_{n-2}'\omega^{2n-4})}{D(\omega^2)} \quad (6\text{-}35)$$

When the real part is separated in this manner, it is possible to delay the realization of the real zero until the last step at which time one of the procedures of Chap. 5 can be employed to complete the realization. In other words, the subnetworks will be composed of a series of LC sections terminated by a Brune, Bott-Duffin, or Pantell circuit which realizes the zero at $(\omega = \omega_1)$. In general, this approach requires fewer elements to realize a given driving-point function than are necessary when the entire realization is accomplished by the Brune, Bott-Duffin, or Pantell procedures. If an optimum solution to the realization problem is one which requires the least number of elements, there is no known systematic approach for accomplishing the task. In many cases separation of the real part of a function requires ingenuity and may involve a trial-and-error process as the only alternative. The procedures of Chap. 3, Sec. 3-2 may be useful in checking the positiveness of the separated real parts.

As an example of the above procedure, assume the following driving-point impedance is to be realized:

$$Z(s) = \frac{s^3 + 15s^2 + 6s + 15}{s^3 + \dfrac{7}{15}s^2 + s + \dfrac{2}{15}} \quad (6\text{-}36)$$

The real part of $Z(s)$ for $(s = j\omega)$ becomes

$$Re[Z(j\omega)] = \frac{\omega^6 - 3\omega^2 + 2}{\omega^6 - \dfrac{401}{225}\omega^4 + \dfrac{197}{225}\omega^2 + \dfrac{4}{225}} = \frac{N(\omega^2)}{D(\omega^2)}$$

$$= \frac{(\omega^2 - 1)^2(\omega^2 + 2)}{D(\omega^2)} \quad (6\text{-}37)$$

Separating the $Re[Z(j\omega)]$ into two parts as suggested by Eq. (6-35) yields

$$Re[Z(j\omega)] = Re[Z_1(j\omega)] + Re[Z_2(j\omega)]$$

$$= \frac{\omega^2(\omega^2 - 1)^2}{D(\omega^2)} + \frac{2(\omega^2 - 1)^2}{D(\omega^2)} \quad (6\text{-}38)$$

Solving for $Z_1(s)$ and $Z_2(s)$ yields

$$Z(s) = Z_1(s) + Z_2(s)$$

where $Z_1(s) = \dfrac{s^3 + s}{s^3 + \dfrac{7}{15} s^2 + s + \dfrac{2}{15}} = \dfrac{1}{\dfrac{2}{15s} + 1 + \dfrac{1}{3s + \dfrac{3}{s}}}$

$$Z_2(s) = \dfrac{15s^2 + 5s + 15}{s^3 + \dfrac{7}{15} s^2 + s + \dfrac{2}{15}} = \dfrac{1}{\dfrac{s}{15} + \dfrac{1}{\dfrac{225}{2} + \dfrac{1}{\dfrac{2s}{75} + \dfrac{2}{75s}}}} \quad (6\text{-}39)$$

The impedances $Z_1(s)$ and $Z_2(s)$ can be realized by series-parallel withdrawal and combined in series, as indicated in Fig. 6-5 to complete the realization of $Z(s)$.

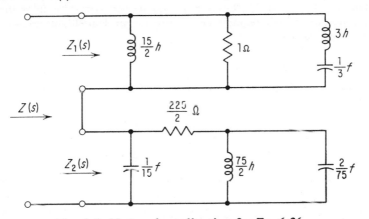

Fig. 6-5. Network realization for Eq. 6-36.

Kuh has derived a set of rules which may be useful in the realization of biquadratic driving-point functions. A biquadratic driving-point impedance was expressed in Chap. 3, Sec. 3-2, by

$$Z(s) = K \frac{s^2 + c_1 s + c_2}{s^2 + d_1 s + d_2} \quad (6\text{-}40)$$

where K, c_1, c_2, d_1, and d_2 are positive real values. The necessary and sufficient condition for $Z(s)$ to be positive real is $[c_1 d_1 \geqq (\sqrt{c_2} - \sqrt{d_2})^2]$. Once a biquadratic function has been tested and found to be positive real, it is possible to apply the following rules:

1. If any of the coefficients, c_1, c_2, d_1, or d_2, are missing, the impedance is nonminimum reactive and can be realized by Foster's procedure (see Chap. 3, Sec. 3-4).

2. $Z(s)$ can be expanded as a continued fraction if the coefficients of Eq. (6-40) satisfy the conditions:

(a) that $(c_2 > d_2)$ and $[c_1d_1 \geqq (c_2 - d_2) + d_1{}^2]$. In this case the minimum value of the $Re[Z(j\omega)]$ occurs at $(\omega = \infty)$.

(b) that $(c_2 < d_2)$ and $[c_1d_1 \geqq (d_2 - c_2) + (c_1d_1{}^2/d_2)]$. In this case the minimum value of the $Re[Z(j\omega)]$ occurs at $(\omega = 0)$.

In each of these cases a realization requiring five elements is possible.

3. Provided $[c_1d_1 \geqq |c_2 - d_2|]$, it is possible to realize a network of the form of Fig. 6-6a from the given impedance. The remaining impedance function will possess a zero at either $(\omega = 0)$ or $(\omega = \infty)$, and the given function can be realized with seven elements. Only six elements are required if $(c_1d_1 = |c_2 - d_2|)$.

4. When $(c_1d_1 \geqq c_2d_2)$, networks of the form of Fig. 6-6b or 6-6c can be realized from the given impedance. The remaining impedance will possess a zero at either $(\omega = 0)$ or $(\omega = \infty)$. The entire realization can be accomplished with seven elements or only six elements if $(c_1d_1 = c_2d_2)$.

5. If the poles of $Z(s)$ are real, it may be possible to realize the function by partial fraction expansion as a network of the form of Fig. 6-6d. If the above techniques are not successful, it is sometimes possible to apply Rule 2 or 5 to the admittance, $[Y(s) = 1/Z(s)]$. However, it may be necessary to employ the Bott-Duffin procedure which requires eight elements or Pantell's procedure which requires seven elements.

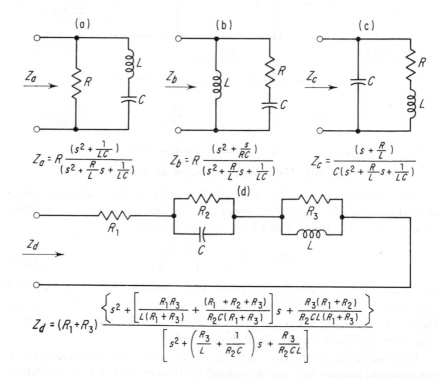

$$Z_a = R \frac{(s^2 + \frac{1}{LC})}{(s^2 + \frac{R}{L}s + \frac{1}{LC})}$$

$$Z_b = R \frac{(s^2 + \frac{s}{RC})}{(s^2 + \frac{R}{L}s + \frac{1}{LC})}$$

$$Z_c = \frac{(s + \frac{R}{L})}{C(s^2 + \frac{R}{L}s + \frac{1}{LC})}$$

$$Z_d = (R_1+R_3)\frac{\left\{ s^2 + \left[\frac{R_1 R_3}{L(R_1+R_3)} + \frac{(R_1+R_2+R_3)}{R_2 C(R_1+R_3)} \right] s + \frac{R_3(R_1+R_2)}{R_2 CL(R_1+R_3)} \right\}}{\left[s^2 + \left(\frac{R_3}{L} + \frac{1}{R_2 C} \right)s + \frac{R_3}{R_2 CL} \right]}$$

Fig. 6-6. Trial networks for satisfying the conditions of Rules 3, 4, and 5.

As an example of the realization of biquadratic functions, reconsider the driving-point impedance of Eq. (5-35) which was used to illustrate several procedures in Chap. 5. Checking the coefficients of Eq. (5-35) reveals that $(c_1 d_1 = |c_2 - d_2|)$; therefore, Rule 3 applies, and it is possible to realize a network similar to Fig. 6-6a from $Z(s)$. This network will be represented by $Z_1(s)$, and the remainder $Z_2(s)$ can be realized according to Rule 4 to yield

$$Z(s) = \frac{5s^2 + 3s + 4}{s^2 + 2s + 2} = Z_1(s) + Z_2(s)$$

$$= \frac{2(s^2 + 2)}{s^2 + 2s + 2} + \frac{3(s^2 + s)}{s^2 + 2s + 2}$$

$$= \frac{1}{\dfrac{1}{2} + \dfrac{1}{s + \dfrac{2}{s}}} + \frac{1}{\dfrac{2}{3s} + \dfrac{1}{3 + \dfrac{3}{s}}} \tag{6-41}$$

The network representation of Eq. (6-41) is shown in Fig. 6-7. This network, requiring only six elements, realizes Eq. (5-35) which has an equivalent Brune network as seen in Fig. 5-10, a Bott-Duffin network seen in Fig. 5-12, and Pantell networks seen in Figs. 5-17 and 5-18. But this is not all, since another six element configuration can be derived by expanding the biquadratic on an admittance basis according to a set of rules similar to those above. This exercise will be left to the reader.

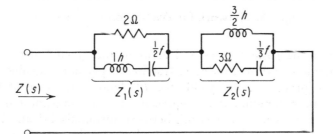

Fig. 6-7. Six element network realization of Eq. 5-35.

6-4. Darlington's Procedure

In addition to the procedures of Chap. 5 and the technique of separating a driving-point function into the summation of several simplified functions, as suggested by Miyata and Kuh, still another approach has been developed by Sidney Darlington.† In brief, Darling-

† S. Darlington, "Synthesis of Reactance 4-Poles," *J. Math. Phys.*, vol. 30, September 1939, pp. 257–353.

ton's procedure realizes the given driving-point function as a two-port reactance network terminated by a single resistor. This approach is based on a theorem by Darlington which states that a driving-point impedance or admittance can always be realized as the input driving-point function of a two-port network containing only reactive elements such as inductors, capacitors, or mutual inductance and terminated by a single resistance R. The procedure for synthesizing this network can be stated in two steps:

1. Poles and zeros of the given driving-point function on the $j\omega$-axis can be removed to form reactance structures by partial-fraction and/or continued-fraction expansions.

2. The remaining function is treated as the driving-point function of a two-port reactance network terminated in a single resistance.

As a consequence of these steps, Darlington's network takes the general form shown in Fig. 6-8.

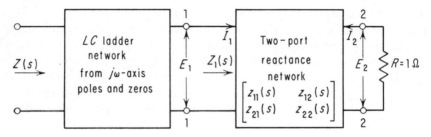

Fig. 6-8. Network for Darlington's procedure.

Removal of the $j\omega$-axis poles and zeros of the given function $Z(s)$ by partial-fraction and/or continued-fraction expansion satisfies the first step of the procedure and yields the LC ladder structure of Fig. 6-8. The remaining function $Z_1(s)$ represents the driving-point impedance of the two-port reactance network between terminals 1-1 and 2-2. This network is terminated by a resistor R which will be chosen as one ohm for the purposes of this discussion. The two-port reactive network can be characterized in terms of the voltages E_1 and E_2, currents I_1 and I_2, the open-circuit driving-point impedances $z_{11}(s)$ and $z_{22}(s)$, and transfer impedance $[z_{12}(s) = z_{21}(s)]$ as follows (see Chap. 2, Sec. 2-3):

$$E_1 = z_{11}(s)I_1 + z_{12}(s)I_2 \qquad (6\text{-}42)$$

$$E_2 = z_{21}(s)I_1 + z_{22}(s)I_2 \qquad (6\text{-}43)$$

It must be remembered that the voltages and currents may also be functions of s; therefore, solving these equations for $E_1(s)/I_1(s)$ and substituting $E_2(s) = -I_2(s)$, because of the 1-ohm load resistor, yields

$$\frac{E_1(s)}{I_1(s)} = Z_1(s) = \frac{z_{11}(s)z_{22}(s) + z_{11}(s) - z_{12}{}^2(s)}{z_{22}(s) + 1}$$

$$= z_{11}(s)\left[\frac{1 + \dfrac{z_{11}(s)z_{22}(s) - z_{12}{}^2(s)}{z_{11}(s)}}{1 + z_{22}(s)}\right] \qquad (6\text{-}44)$$

However, $Z_1(s)$ may also be expressed in the form of Eq. (6-1) in terms of A_1, A_2, B_1, and B_2, where A_1 and A_2 represent all even-ordered terms of $P(s)$ and $Q(s)$, respectively, and B_1 and B_2 represent all odd-ordered terms of $P(s)$ and $Q(s)$. Simple manipulation of Eq. (6-1) gives the following two cases:

Case 1

$$Z_1(s) = \frac{A_1}{B_2}\left[\frac{1 + \dfrac{B_1}{A_1}}{1 + \dfrac{A_2}{B_2}}\right]$$

Case 2

$$Z_1(s) = \frac{B_1}{A_2}\left[\frac{1 + \dfrac{A_1}{B_1}}{1 + \dfrac{B_2}{A_2}}\right] \qquad (6\text{-}45)$$

Equating the terms of Eqs. (6-44) and (6-45) yields

Case 1

$$z_{11}(s) = \frac{A_1}{B_2}$$

$$z_{22}(s) = \frac{A_2}{B_2}$$

$$z_{12}(s) = \frac{\sqrt{A_1 A_2 - B_1 B_2}}{B_2}$$

Case 2

$$z_{11}(s) = \frac{B_1}{A_2}$$

$$z_{22}(s) = \frac{B_2}{A_2}$$

$$z_{12}(s) = \frac{\sqrt{B_1 B_2 - A_1 A_2}}{A_2} \qquad (6\text{-}46)$$

Once $Z_1(s)$ has been determined, it can be broken up as indicated in Eq. (6-45). Using the values of A_1, A_2, B_1, and B_2, the open-circuit impedances for the two-port network between terminals 1-1 and 2-2 of Fig. 6-8 can then be obtained from either Case 1 or Case 2 of Eq. (6-46).

The real part of the driving-point impedance $Z_1(s)$ can be written in terms of real frequency as

$$Re[Z_1(s)]_{s=j\omega} = Re[Z_1(j\omega)] = \frac{A_1 A_2 - B_1 B_2}{A_2{}^2 - B_2{}^2}\bigg|_{s=j\omega} \qquad (6\text{-}47)$$

Comparing Eqs. (6-46) and (6-47), it is seen that the zeros of the $Re[Z_1(s)]$ are also the zeros of $z_{12}(s)$. These zeros are known as the transmission zeros of the two-port network. It is convenient to use Case 1 of Eq. (6-46) when $(A_1 A_2 - B_1 B_2) > 0$ and Case 2 when $(B_1 B_2 - A_1 A_2) > 0$, since this choice simplifies the determination of $z_{12}(s)$. Because $z_{12}(s)$ contains the square root of these terms, Darlington has suggested that $Z_1(s)$ be multiplied by surplus factors prior to synthesis of the two-port network such that $(A_1A_2 - B_1B_2)$ or $(B_1B_2 - A_1A_2)$ will be perfect squares. The network which realizes the open-circuit impedances will be a reactance network because of the manner in which A_1, A_2, B_1, and B_2 were determined. This network can be realized by several procedures, some of which will be investigated following a simple example of the above steps.

Assume a network is to be synthesized by Darlington's procedure to realize the driving-point impedance of Eq. (6-48).

$$Z(s) = \frac{s^4 + 2s^3 + 15s^2 + 14s + 24}{3s^3 + 2s^2 + 6s} \tag{6-48}$$

Inspection reveals that this function possesses a pole at $s = 0$; therefore, according to the first step of the procedure this pole should be removed. Performing a partial-fraction expansion yields

$$Z(s) = \frac{s^3 + 2s^2 + 3s + 6}{3s^2 + 2s + 6} + \frac{4}{s} \tag{6-49}$$

A capacitance of $1/4$ farad can be realized as a series element. The remaining function will be assumed to represent the impedance seen looking into terminals 1-1 of Fig. 6-8. In this case

$$Z_1(s) = \frac{s^3 + 2s^2 + 3s + 6}{3s^2 + 2s + 6} = \frac{A_1 + B_1}{A_2 + B_2}$$

where
$$A_1 = 2s^2 + 6 \qquad B_1 = s^3 + 3s$$
$$A_2 = 3s^2 + 6 \qquad B_2 = 2s \tag{6-50}$$

The transmission zeros of the network between terminals 1-1 and 2-2 of Fig. 6-8 are given by $(A_1A_2 - B_1B_2)$. Using Eq. (6-50), these zeros become

$$(A_1A_2 - B_1B_2) = (2s^2 + 6)(3s^2 + 6) - (s^3 + 3s)(2s) = 4(s^2 + 3)^2 \tag{6-51}$$

Since these zeros possess positive coefficients, Case 1 of Eq. (6-46) will be used to determine the open-circuit impedances. Fortunately, Eq. (6-51) is a perfect square, so $Z_1(s)$ does not need to be multiplied by surplus factors. Using A_1, A_2, B_1, and B_2 of Eq. (6-50), the open-circuit impedances of Eq. (6-46), Case 1, become

$$z_{11}(s) = \frac{A_1}{B_2} = \frac{2s^2 + 6}{2s} = s + \frac{3}{s}$$

$$z_{12}(s) = \frac{\sqrt{A_1A_2 - B_1B_2}}{B_2} = \frac{\sqrt{4(s^2 + 3)^2}}{2s} = s + \frac{3}{s}$$

$$z_{22}(s) = \frac{A_2}{B_2} = \frac{3s^2 + 6}{2s} = s + \frac{3}{s} + \frac{s}{2} \tag{6-52}$$

The fact that $z_{11}(s)$ equals $z_{12}(s)$ implies that the two-port structure between terminals 1-1 and 2-2 is an L-section. Combining the 1/4 farad capacitor determined in Eq. (6-49) with the impedances of Eq. (6-52) yields the LC network of Fig. 6-9, which must be terminated by a 1-ohm resistor to complete the realization of Eq. (6-48).

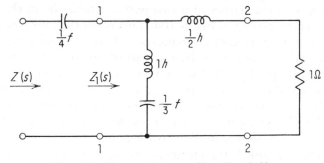

Fig. 6-9. Network to realize Eq. 6-48.

Fortunately in this example $(A_1A_2 - B_1B_2)$ is a perfect square, consequently the realization process is simplified. This condition can be accomplished in any example by multiplying both numerator and denominator of the driving-point function by suitably chosen surplus factors. However, surplus factors increase the complexity of the resulting network and require more circuit elements for the realization. It is of interest, therefore, to consider in more detail transmission zeros of various two-port reactance networks to establish conditions under which it is possible to avoid the use of surplus factors.†

As pointed out in the above discussion, zeros of the transfer impedance $z_{12}(s)$ of the two-port reactance network with its resistance termination, are identical to zeros of the real part of the driving-point impedance $Z_1(s)$. Therefore, for purposes of Darlington's procedure, it is convenient to describe the effects of realization of the two-port reactance network in terms of changes which take place in the zeros of the $Re[Z_1(s)]$. For instance, realization of series LC structures to remove $j\omega$-axis poles and zeros does not by itself affect the zeros of the $Re[Z_1(s)]$. These series structures are often called Type A sections. Realization of shunt LC structures removes real-frequency zeros from the $Re[Z_1(s)]$, and these structures are known as Type B sections. Hence, realization of alternate Type A and Type B sections not only removes excess reactance from a driving-point function but is also instrumental in removing real-frequency zeros from $Re[Z_1(s)]$.

† Techniques which avoid the use of surplus factors but introduce a gyrator, a non-reciprocal element, are described in D. Hazony, "Two Extensions of the Darlington Synthesis Procedure," *IRE Trans. Circuit Theory*, vol. CT-8, no. 3, September 1961, pp. 284–288.

Following realization of Type A and B sections, the remaining driving-point function may still possess a real part which contains real, complex, or imaginary zeros. For example, in the case of minimum-reactance functions, as encountered in Brune's procedure, the $Re[Z_1(j\omega)]$ becomes zero at ($\omega = \omega_1$), but the reactance is nonzero. Removal of the zero at ω_1 by a single Type A or B section is impossible; consequently, Brune suggested realization of a two-port reactance network, as shown in Fig. 5-6 and repeated in Fig. 6-10a. This network, known as a Type C or Brune section, accounts for removal of four imaginary zeros, two at $+j\omega_1$ and two at $-j\omega_1$, from the real part of the driving-point function.

Although Type A, B, and C sections are sufficient to remove all real and imaginary zeros of the $Re[Z_1(s)]$, a more complicated structure is required to remove complex zeros. A two-port reactance network capable of realizing complex zeros of the $Re[Z_1(s)]$ has been derived by Darlington and is shown in Fig. 6-10b. This network, which requires two perfectly coupled transformers to realize negative inductances similar to the Brune network, is known as a Type D or Darlington section.†

With Type A, B, C, and D sections it is possible to remove all zeros of the $Re[Z_1(s)]$ as two-port reactance structures. The remaining real part will be only a constant; therefore, complete realization of $Z_1(s)$ may be accomplished with a two-port reactance network terminated by a single resistor. If ideal transformers are permitted, the value of the resistor becomes arbitrary. Darlington's procedure can also be developed on an admittance basis; furthermore, Type A, B, C, and D sections are not the only two-port reactance structures that can be used in the realization process. For instance, Cauer's two-port synthesis procedure which is explained in Chap. 7, Sec. 7-2, may be useful in realizing the transmission zeros of $z_{12}(s)$.

It is not always necessary to compute the transfer and driving-point functions of the two-port reactance network in order to realize Darlington's network configuration. Driving-point functions with real parts possessing only real zeros can be realized as LC ladder structures terminated by a single resistor. In other words, alternate Type A and B sections can be realized to remove all $j\omega$-axis poles and zeros of the driving-point function until only a constant remains. By this procedure, combinations of capacitors and inductors are realized until the only remaining term can be identified as the resistor R.

In general, a driving-point function will not possess poles or zeros located on the $j\omega$-axis in such a manner that alternate Type A and B

---

† A detailed discussion of Type A, B, C, and D sections including effects of realizing these sections on the driving-point impedance of the network terminated by a resistor may be found in D. F. Tuttle, *Network Synthesis*, Vol. I (New York: John Wiley & Sons, Inc., 1958). Chap. 9.

sections can easily be realized. However, in many cases it is possible to shift zeros to more favorable positions by a technique known as zero shifting. This technique is most easily explained in terms of an example; consider the following driving-point impedance:

$$Z_1(s) = \frac{14s^3 + 10s^2 + 11s + 4}{8s^2 + 4s + 6} \tag{6-53}$$

By long division, it is possible to remove the term $14s/8$, which can be realized as an inductor of $7/4$ henrys. However, the remaining biquadratic function has no poles or zeros on the $j\omega$-axis.

$$Z_1(s) = \frac{7s}{4} + \frac{13s^2 + s + 8}{16s^2 + 8s + 12} \tag{6-54}$$

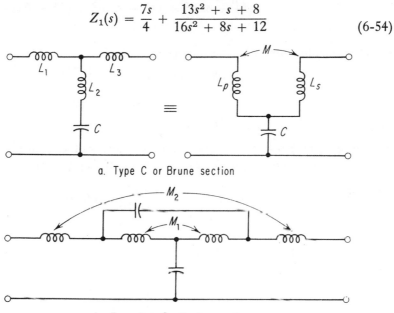

a. Type C or Brune section

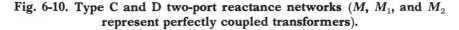

b. Type D or Darlington section

Fig. 6-10. Type C and D two-port reactance networks (M, M_1, and M_2 represent perfectly coupled transformers).

At this point it appears that it is necessary to realize a resistor from the biquadratic term of Eq. (6-54). Consider instead the possibility of realizing an inductor in the first step such that the remaining function will have a pair of zeros on the $j\omega$-axis. This can be accomplished by removing a term of the form xs from Eq. (6-53):

$$
\begin{array}{r}
xs \\
8s^2 + 4s + 6\overline{\big)14s^3 \quad + \quad 10s^2 \quad + \quad 11s \quad + \quad 4} \\
8xs^3 \quad + \quad 4xs^2 \quad + \quad 6xs \\
\hline
(14 - 8x)s^3 + (10 - 4x)s^2 + (11 - 6x)s + 4 \quad (6\text{-}55)
\end{array}
$$

This gives

$$Z_1(s) = xs + \frac{(14 - 8x)s^3 + (10 - 4x)s^2 + (11 - 6x)s + 4}{8s^2 + 4s + 6} \tag{6-56}$$

The numerator of the second term of Eq. (6-56) is a cubic in terms of s. It is desirable that this numerator contain a pair of $j\omega$-axis zeros; therefore, it can be written in the form $(as^2 + 2)(bs + 2)$. Equating this assumed form with that of Eq. (6-56) gives

$$(as^2 + 2)(bs + 2) = abs^3 + 2as^2 + 2bs + 4$$

$$= (14 - 8x)s^3 + (10 - 4x)s^2 + (11 - 6x)s + 4 \tag{6-57}$$

Equating coefficients of the various powers of s:

$$ab = (14 - 8x) \tag{6-58}$$

$$2a = (10 - 4x) \tag{6-59}$$

$$2b = (11 - 6x) \tag{6-60}$$

Solving Eqs. (6-59) and (6-60) for a and b in terms of x, multiplying the results together, and setting the product equal to Eq. (6-58),

$$ab = \left[\frac{(10 - 4x)}{2}\right]\left[\frac{(11 - 6x)}{2}\right] = (14 - 8x)$$

or

$$(110 - 104x + 24x^2) = 4(14 - 8x) \tag{6-61}$$

Solving for x yields two equal roots at $(x = 3/2)$. Substituting this value of x in Eq. (6-56)

$$Z_1(s) = \frac{3s}{2} + \frac{2s^3 + 4s^2 + 2s + 4}{8s^2 + 4s + 6}$$

$$= \frac{3s}{2} + \frac{(s^2 + 1)(s + 2)}{4s^2 + 2s + 3} \tag{6-62}$$

It is seen that the numerator of the second term contains a pair of $j\omega$-axis zeros at $s = \pm j1$ and a zero on the real axis at $s = -2$. If the second term of Eq. (6-62) is inverted to form an admittance, it is possible to perform a partial-fraction expansion as follows:

$$Z_1(s) = \frac{3s}{2} + \frac{1}{\dfrac{4s^2 + 2s + 3}{(s^2 + 1)(s + 2)}}$$

$$= \frac{3s}{2} + \frac{1}{\dfrac{s}{(s^2 + 1)} + \dfrac{3}{(s + 2)}} \tag{6-63}$$

The $s/(s^2 + 1)$ term can be recognized as the admittance of a series combination of 1 henry and 1 farad. The $3/(s + 2)$ term can be realized as a series combination of 1/3 henry and 2/3 ohm. The network of Fig. 6-11 can be identified with the impedance of Eq. (6-63).

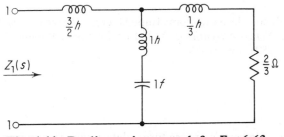

Fig. 6-11. Darlington's network for Eq. 6-63.

It should be emphasized that zero shifting and realization of the two-port reactance structure by series-parallel withdrawal are only useful techniques for realization of certain special driving-point functions. Generalized procedures for realization of two-port reactance networks will be presented in later chapters. These procedures will yield insight into methods by which a transfer impedance possessing various combinations of real and complex transmission zeros can be realized without use of surplus factors. One problem encountered with networks of the Darlington configuration is that inductors and capacitors of the reactance structure are ideal elements. Consequently, they can only be approximated by commercially available elements which possess finite resistance. In many cases this problem can be circumvented by a technique known as predistortion, which distributes a portion of the resistance of the network with each reactive element.

References

Further details on the relationship of an impedance function with its real and imaginary parts can be found in the following references.

1. E. A. Guillemin, *Synthesis of Passive Networks* (New York: John Wiley & Sons, Inc., 1957), Chap. 8.
2. S. Seshu and N. Balabanian, *Linear Network Analysis* (New York: John Wiley & Sons, Inc., 1959), Secs. 7-8 and 7-9.
3. D. F. Tuttle, *Network Synthesis*, Vol. I (New York: John Wiley & Sons, Inc., 1958), Chap. 9.

Miyata's procedure is also covered in Ref. 1, Chap. 10, and is developed in greater detail by Weinberg.

4. L. Weinberg, *Network Analysis and Synthesis* (New York: McGraw-Hill Book Co., Inc., 1962), Sec. 10-5.

Darlington's procedure is described in Secs. 9-6 through 9-10 of Ref. 1, Chap. 9 of Ref. 3, and in Sec. 10-3 of Ref. 4. This procedure is also presented in relationship to the Brune and Bott-Duffin procedures in the following reference.

5. A. B. Gierdano, "Driving-Point Impedances," *Proceedings of the Symposium on Modern Network Synthesis*, Vol. I (New York: Polytechnic Institute of Brooklyn, 1952), pp. 21–39.

Problems

6-1. Using Gewertz's procedure, determine the minimum-reactance driving-point impedances associated with each of the following real parts.

$$(a) \quad Re[Z_1(j\omega)] = \frac{2(2\omega^4 - 3\omega^2 + 5)}{\omega^4 + 6\omega^2 + 25}$$

$$(b) \quad Re[Z_1(j\omega)] = \frac{2(\omega^4 - 6\omega^2 + 17)}{\omega^4 - 30\omega^2 + 289}$$

6-2. Using the procedure outlined by Eqs. (6-15) through (6-17), determine the minimum-reactance driving-point impedances for the functions of Prob. 6-1.

6-3. Establish the minimum reactance $Im[Z(j\omega)]$ associated with each of the following real parts and write the expression for the driving-point impedance function in each case:

$$(a) \quad Re[Z(j\omega)] = \frac{2}{1 + 16\omega^2} \qquad (b) \quad Re[Z(j\omega)] = \frac{80\omega^2 + 7}{1 + 16\omega^2}$$

$$(c) \quad Re[Z(j\omega)] = \frac{\omega^4 + 35\omega^2 + 180}{\omega^4 + 29\omega^2 + 100}$$

6-4. Discuss a procedure for determining an impedance function with a minimum real part when the imaginary part or reactance is specified as a function of real frequency. Can the procedures of Sec. 6-1 be applied to this problem?

6-5. Determine an impedance function from the real part given in Prob. 6-1, Eq. (*a*), then synthesize a network to realize the resulting function by Miyata's procedure. Select a surplus factor to minimize the number of subnetworks required for the realization.

6-6. Synthesize the minimum-reactance driving-point impedances associated with the real parts given in Prob. 6-3 by Miyata's procedure.

6-7. Determine an impedance function from the real part given in Prob. 6-1, Eq. (*b*), then synthesize a network by Miyata's procedure to realize the function. Select the minimum number of surplus factors and choose values for them that minimize the number of subnetworks required for the realization.

6-8. Realize the following impedance functions by Kuh's procedure. Apply the rules for biquadratic functions where possible to minimize the number of elements required for the realization.

(a) $Z(s) = \dfrac{s^2 + 2s + 4}{s^2 + s + 1}$ (b) $Z(s) = \dfrac{s^2 + 9s + 18}{s^2 + 5s + 4}$

(c) $Y(s) = \dfrac{s^3 + 7s^2 + 6s + 2}{s^3 + 3s^2 + 8s + 4}$

6-9. Synthesize a network for the following driving-point impedance by Darlington's procedure:

$$Z_1(s) = \frac{3s^3 + 36s^2 + 24s}{s^4 + 12s^3 + 26s^2 + 72s + 48}$$

6-10. Synthesize networks for the following driving-point functions by Darlington's procedure:

(a) $Y_1(s) = \dfrac{s^3 + 8s^2 + 14s}{4s^3 + 3s^2 + 32s + 24}$

(b) $Z_1(s) = \dfrac{s^5 + 4s^4 + 38s^3 + 120s^2 + 240s}{6s^4 + 16s^3 + 126s^2 + 96s + 192}$

Chapter 7

Realization of Two-port Networks

The preceding chapters have been devoted exclusively to synthesis procedures pertaining to one-port networks, and a number of techniques have been described for realization of driving-point impedance and admittance functions. However, a large number of the synthesis problems encountered in practice are concerned with the transmission of information or energy from one set of network terminals to another. In this case two-port, or possibly multiport, networks are required to perform the desired transmission. One-port networks act as building blocks from which these two-port or multiport networks can be constructed. Therefore, the procedures developed in preceding chapters will find use in the realization of two-port networks.

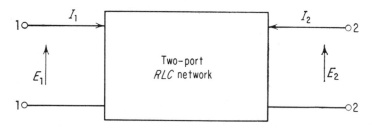

Fig. 7-1. General form of two-port networks.

A typical two-port network is shown in Fig. 7-1. If the information or energy is considered to flow from terminals 1-1 to 2-2, then terminals 1-1 represent the input and terminals 2-2 represent the output of the network. Conventional voltage and current notation is used in Fig. 7-1 with arrows indicating relative reference directions. It must be remembered that these voltages and currents may be functions of s. Because the network is assumed to be passive and arbitrary in structure, with no internal sources of energy, it is convenient for mathematical purposes to select the notation in a symmetrical manner. Behavior of the network, with respect to its transmission and/or filtering properties, can be expressed in terms of the four parameters E_1, E_2, I_1, and I_2. The relationships existing between these quantities determine the characteristics of a given two-port network, as will be seen in Sec. 7-1. The remaining sections of this chapter are devoted to synthesis procedures and techniques useful in the realization of two-port networks.

7-1. Two-port Network Functions

The properties of two-port networks are usually expressed in terms of the ratio of output to input. For instance, the ratio E_2/E_1 is known as the voltage transfer ratio and is a dimensionless function, since the units of the numerator and denominator are the same. In like manner, I_2/I_1 is spoken of as the current transfer ratio and is also dimensionless. The ratio E_2/I_1 is often called the transfer impedance and has units of ohms, whereas I_2/E_1 represents the transfer admittance. In all there are six possible relationships, three sets of two, which can be used to express the transmission characteristics of a two-port network. These relationships are:

1. $\begin{cases}\text{Specification of } E_1 \text{ and } E_2 \text{ as functions of } I_1 \text{ and } I_2 \\ \text{Specification of } I_1 \text{ and } I_2 \text{ as functions of } E_1 \text{ and } E_2\end{cases}$

2. $\begin{cases}\text{Specification of } I_1 \text{ and } E_2 \text{ as functions of } E_1 \text{ and } I_2 \\ \text{Specification of } E_1 \text{ and } I_2 \text{ as functions of } I_1 \text{ and } E_2\end{cases}$

3. $\begin{cases}\text{Specification of } E_1 \text{ and } I_1 \text{ as functions of } E_2 \text{ and } I_2 \\ \text{Specification of } E_2 \text{ and } I_2 \text{ as functions of } E_1 \text{ and } I_1\end{cases}$ (7-1)

Preliminary consideration was given to the first of these relationships in Chap. 2, Sec. 2-3. Specifically, Eq. (2-17) was derived on a simplified basis and is conveniently expressed in matrix form as follows:

$$\begin{bmatrix} E_1 \\ E_2 \end{bmatrix} = \begin{bmatrix} z_{11}(s) & z_{12}(s) \\ z_{21}(s) & z_{22}(s) \end{bmatrix} \begin{bmatrix} I_1 \\ I_2 \end{bmatrix}$$ (7-2)

The z's of Eq. (7-2) are called the open-circuit impedances of the two-port network and are defined by the following expressions:

$$z_{11}(s) = \frac{E_1}{I_1}\bigg]_{I_2=0} \qquad z_{12}(s) = \frac{E_1}{I_2}\bigg]_{I_1=0}$$

$$z_{21}(s) = \frac{E_2}{I_1}\bigg]_{I_2=0} \qquad z_{22}(s) = \frac{E_2}{I_2}\bigg]_{I_1=0}$$ (7-3)

In other words $z_{11}(s)$ and $z_{22}(s)$ represent the driving-point impedances of terminals 1-1 and 2-2 respectively, with the opposite set of terminals open-circuited. The impedances $z_{12}(s)$ and $z_{21}(s)$ are mutually shared by the input and output circuits and are known as the transfer impedances of the network. When the network consists of only passive bilateral elements such as resistors, inductors, and/or capacitors, then $z_{12}(s) = z_{21}(s)$. The transfer impedance $z_{21}(s)$ represents the voltage occurring at the open output terminals 2-2 if a current source of 1 ampere is applied to the input terminals. This fact is consistent with the general definition of the transfer impedance ratio E_2/I_1 mentioned above.

As a simple example of the relationships described above, consider the two-port network of Fig. 7-2. It will be assumed that the voltages E_1 and E_2 applied to terminals 1-1 and 2-2 respectively are both positive; and the resulting currents I_1 and I_2 flow into the network. Under these conditions, it is possible to write a pair of equations for the voltage drops around the two loops of the network as follows:

$$E_1 = [Z_a(s) + Z_c(s)]I_1 + Z_c(s)I_2$$
$$E_2 = Z_c(s)I_1 + [Z_b(s) + Z_c(s)]I_2 \tag{7-4}$$

In general, the impedances are each functions of s, since they are composed of R, L, and C elements; furthermore, the voltages and currents E_1, E_2, I_1, and I_2 may also be functions of frequency.

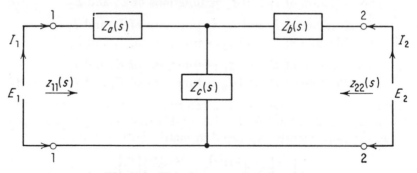

Fig. 7-2. Simple two-port network.

When terminals 1-1 and 2-2 of Fig. 7-2 are opened, the following impedance relationships can be written:

$$z_{11}(s) = Z_a(s) + Z_c(s)$$
$$z_{22}(s) = Z_b(s) + Z_c(s) \tag{7-5}$$

The impedances $z_{11}(s)$ and $z_{22}(s)$ are driving-point functions, since they are the impedances seen looking into a single pair of terminals in each case. It is also seen in Fig. 7-2 and Eq. (7-5) that the impedance $Z_c(s)$ is mutually shared by both the input and output circuits of the network.

Therefore $Z_c(s)$ represents $[z_{12}(s) = z_{21}(s)]$ and, consequently, substitution of Eq. (7-5) into Eq. (7-4) yields the more general relationships of Eq. (7-2). It should be emphasized that the characteristics of a two-port network are completely defined once the three open-circuit impedance functions $z_{11}(s)$, $z_{12}(s) = z_{21}(s)$, and $z_{22}(s)$ are known. Finally, the matrix form of Eq. (7-2) will be used in comparing the open-circuit impedance functions with short-circuit admittance functions of a two-port network.

Referring to Fig. 7-1, it is possible to apply current sources I_1 and I_2 to terminals 1-1 and 2-2 respectively. In this case equations can be written to relate the input and output currents and voltages in terms of so-called "short-circuit admittance" functions of the network. If the applied current sources are such that the magnitude and direction of current flow are identical to that assumed in Fig. 7-1, they may be considered to represent equivalent voltage sources where E_1 and E_2 are the same as used in the above discussion. Consequently the equations relating the input and output currents and voltages to the short-circuit admittance functions of the network become

$$\begin{bmatrix} I_1 \\ I_2 \end{bmatrix} = \begin{bmatrix} y_{11}(s) & y_{12}(s) \\ y_{21}(s) & y_{22}(s) \end{bmatrix} \begin{bmatrix} E_1 \\ E_2 \end{bmatrix} \tag{7-6}$$

where I_1, I_2, E_1, and E_2 are the same as those of Eq. (7-2). The short-circuit admittances are defined by the following set of relationships:

$$y_{11}(s) = \frac{I_1}{E_1}\bigg]_{E_2=0} \qquad y_{12}(s) = \frac{I_2}{E_1}\bigg]_{E_2=0}$$

$$y_{21}(s) = \frac{I_1}{E_2}\bigg]_{E_1=0} \qquad y_{22}(s) = \frac{I_2}{E_2}\bigg]_{E_1=0} \tag{7-7}$$

The admittance $y_{11}(s)$ is the driving-point admittance seen looking into terminals 1-1 with terminals 2-2 short-circuited. Similarly, $y_{22}(s)$ is the admittance seen looking into terminals 2-2 with terminals 1-1 shorted. The transfer admittance $y_{12}(s)$ equals $y_{21}(s)$ when the network contains only passive bilateral elements. Stated in a different manner, each short-circuit admittance represents the current response to a unit voltage input when the output terminals of the given network are short-circuited. In order to determine the relationships between the open-circuit impedances and short-circuit admittances, it is convenient to deal with the matrix forms of Eqs. (7-2) and (7-6). These matrix equations are inverse sets which reveal the important relationship:

$$\begin{bmatrix} z_{11}(s) & z_{12}(s) \\ z_{21}(s) & z_{22}(s) \end{bmatrix} = \begin{bmatrix} y_{11}(s) & y_{12}(s) \\ y_{21}(s) & y_{22}(s) \end{bmatrix}^{-1} \tag{7-8}$$

Solving for the open-circuit impedances in terms of the short-circuit admittances and taking into account the fact that $[z_{12}(s) = z_{21}(s)]$ yields

$$z_{11}(s) = \frac{y_{22}(s)}{|\Delta^y|} \qquad z_{22}(s) = \frac{y_{11}(s)}{|\Delta^y|} \qquad z_{12}(s) = \frac{-y_{12}(s)}{|\Delta^y|} \qquad (7\text{-}9)$$

In this set of equations, $|\Delta^y|$ is known as the short-circuit admittance determinant which can be written from Eq. (7-6) as follows:†

$$|\Delta^y| = \begin{vmatrix} y_{11}(s) & y_{12}(s) \\ y_{21}(s) & y_{22}(s) \end{vmatrix} = y_{11}(s)y_{22}(s) - y_{12}(s)y_{21}(s) \qquad (7\text{-}10)$$

For networks in which $[y_{12}(s) = y_{21}(s)]$, the short-circuit admittances can be written as functions of the open-circuit impedances as

$$y_{11}(s) = \frac{z_{22}(s)}{|\Delta^z|} \qquad y_{22}(s) = \frac{z_{11}(s)}{|\Delta^z|} \qquad y_{12}(s) = \frac{-z_{12}(s)}{|\Delta^z|} \qquad (7\text{-}11)$$

In this equation, $|\Delta^z|$ is known as the open-circuit impedance determinant which can be written from Eq. (7-2) and evaluated as follows:

$$|\Delta^z| = \begin{vmatrix} z_{11}(s) & z_{12}(s) \\ z_{21}(s) & z_{22}(s) \end{vmatrix} = z_{11}(s)z_{22}(s) - z_{12}(s)z_{21}(s) \qquad (7\text{-}12)$$

Substituting Eq. (7-10) into Eq. (7-9) and Eq. (7-12) into Eq. (7-11) yields the following general relationships between the open-circuit impedances and short-circuit admittances of a two-port network:

$$z_{11}(s) = \frac{y_{22}(s)}{y_{11}(s)y_{22}(s) - y_{12}(s)^2} \qquad y_{11}(s) = \frac{z_{22}(s)}{z_{11}(s)z_{22}(s) - z_{12}(s)^2}$$

$$z_{22}(s) = \frac{y_{11}(s)}{y_{11}(s)y_{22}(s) - y_{12}(s)^2} \qquad y_{22}(s) = \frac{z_{11}(s)}{z_{11}(s)z_{22}(s) - z_{12}(s)^2}$$

$$z_{12}(s) = \frac{-y_{12}(s)}{y_{11}(s)y_{22}(s) - y_{12}(s)^2} \qquad y_{12}(s) = \frac{-z_{12}(s)}{z_{11}(s)z_{22}(s) - z_{12}(s)^2} \qquad (7\text{-}13)$$

These relationships, which hold for any two-port network, can be used to point out some important characteristics of transfer functions.

---

† For purposes of this text, a determinant is written as a square array of coefficients (an equal number of rows and columns) set off by a pair of vertical lines enclosing the b_{ik} terms as shown below for $|\Delta^b|$. In contrast, brackets are used to indicate a matrix which is a rectangular array of coefficients (it may possess m rows and n columns) of the form shown below for $[b]$.

$$|\Delta^b| = \begin{vmatrix} b_{11} & b_{12} \ldots b_{1n} \\ b_{21} & b_{22} \ldots b_{2n} \\ \cdot & \cdot \\ b_{n1} & b_{n2} \ldots b_{nn} \end{vmatrix} \qquad [b] = \begin{bmatrix} b_{11} & b_{12} \ldots b_{1n} \\ b_{21} & b_{22} \ldots b_{2n} \\ \cdot & \cdot \\ b_{m1} & b_{m2} \ldots b_{mn} \end{bmatrix}$$

The b_{ik} terms of a determinant are variables of the function, b; therefore the determinant possesses a numerical value. A matrix may be used to identify the relative position of terms instead of writing an entire set of equations, and consequently it represents an ordered set possessing no unique value.

It is always possible to write the open-circuit impedances or short-circuit admittances of a two-port network in the form of Eq. (7-13). However, it may be necessary to multiply some or all of the impedance or admittance functions by surplus factors. For instance, the T network of Fig. 7-2 has driving-point impedances given by $[z_{11}(s) = Z_a(s) + Z_c(s)]$ and $[z_{22}(s) = Z_b(s) + Z_c(s)]$, whereas the transfer impedance is given by $[z_{12}(s) = z_{21}(s) = Z_c(s)]$. Only in the special case in which poles of $Z_a(s)$, $Z_b(s)$, and $Z_c(s)$ are identical with those of $z_{11}(s)$, $z_{12}(s)$, and $z_{22}(s)$ will the impedances have the same form as Eq. (7-13). When the poles of $Z_a(s)$, $Z_b(s)$, and $Z_c(s)$ are not identical, the impedances can be multiplied by surplus factors such that $z_{11}(s)$, $z_{12}(s)$, and $z_{22}(s)$ will have the same poles. As in all cases, the use of surplus factors does not affect the characteristics of a function. Once $z_{11}(s)$, $z_{12}(s)$, and $z_{22}(s)$ have been converted to the form of Eq. (7-13) with all impedances possessing the same poles, important characteristics of the transfer impedance $z_{12}(s)$ become apparent.

For a two-port network to be realizable in terms of passive elements, the real part of the impedance or admittance determinant must be non-negative for all real frequencies. This fact implies that the resistive part of the network must be equal to or greater than zero. For this reason the real part of the impedance determinant $|\Delta^z|$ of Eq. (7-12) can be written in terms of real frequency as

$$Re[z_{11}(j\omega)]Re[z_{22}(j\omega)] - Re[z_{12}(j\omega)]Re[z_{21}(j\omega)] \geqq 0 \qquad (7-14)$$

To evaluate this expression, it is useful to review the characteristics of driving-point functions outlined in Chap. 3. These characteristics are restated briefly as follows:

1. Driving-point functions must be rational functions of s.
2. Poles and zeros of driving-point functions are restricted to the left half of the s-plane.
3. Poles and zeros falling on the $j\omega$-axis must be simple.
4. The real part of the functions must be positive and real.
5. Complex poles or zeros must occur in conjugate pairs.

Therefore, since $z_{11}(s)$ and $z_{22}(s)$ are driving-point functions, the $Re[z_{11}(s)]$ and $Re[z_{22}(s)]$ must be greater than or equal to zero for all real frequencies. Consequently, from Eq. (7-14) it is clear that the $Re[z_{12}(s)]$, which equals the $Re[z_{21}(s)]$ for passive networks, need not be positive for all real frequencies. This fact was derived in a somewhat different manner in Chap. 2, Sec. 2-3.

If the poles of $z_{11}(s)$, $z_{12}(s)$, and $z_{22}(s)$ have been made identical, as described above, the poles of the transfer impedance $z_{12}(s)$ or admittance $y_{12}(s)$ must possess the same characteristics as the poles of the driving-point functions $z_{11}(s)$ and $z_{22}(s)$ or $y_{11}(s)$ and $y_{22}(s)$. Consequently, poles of the transfer impedance or admittance are restricted to the same areas of the s-plane as those of driving-point functions. Therefore, if the real part of the transfer impedance or admittance is to be capable of being either positive or negative, no restrictions can be placed on its zeros. As a result, the characteristics of a transfer function may be stated as follows:

1. Transfer functions must be rational functions of the complex frequency s.
2. Poles of the function are restricted to the left half of the s-plane or the $j\omega$-axis.
3. Poles of the function falling on the $j\omega$-axis must be simple.
4. Complex poles and zeros can only occur in conjugate pairs.
5. Zeros of the function are not restricted and can fall anywhere in the s-plane.

These characteristics apply to all transfer functions including the voltage and current transfer ratios E_2/E_1, I_2/I_1, E_2/I_1, and I_2/E_1. The significance of the characteristics of the transfer and driving-point functions of a two-port network will be revealed in later sections of this chapter.

Before continuing to a third matrix form, it is instructive to briefly consider certain aspects pertaining to the combination of two or more two-port networks. When a single two-port network, such as Fig. 7-1, is considered by itself, the current I_1 entering one terminal 1 equals the current emerging from the second terminal 1. In like manner, the

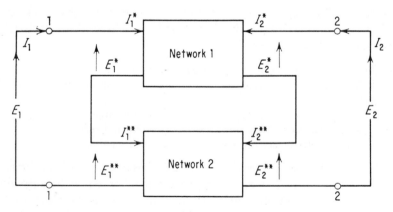

Fig. 7-3. Series combination of two-port networks.

current I_2 entering one terminal 2 equals the current emerging from the second terminal 2. However, when two or more two-port networks are interconnected, this condition is no longer assured, since there is the possibility of circulating currents between the individual networks.

Assume the following restrictions are imposed on the network of

Fig. 7-3 in order to assure that no circulating currents will exist between the two networks:

$$I_1 = I_1^* = I_1^{**} \qquad \text{and} \qquad I_2 = I_2^* = I_2^{**} \tag{7-15}$$

The impedance equations for networks 1 and 2 can be written in matrix form similar to Eq. (7-2) as

Network 1:
$$\begin{bmatrix} E_1^* \\ E_2^* \end{bmatrix} = \begin{bmatrix} z_{11}^*(s) & z_{12}^*(s) \\ z_{21}^*(s) & z_{22}^*(s) \end{bmatrix} \begin{bmatrix} I_1^* \\ I_2^* \end{bmatrix}$$

Network 2:
$$\begin{bmatrix} E_1^{**} \\ E_2^{**} \end{bmatrix} = \begin{bmatrix} z_{11}^{**}(s) & z_{12}^{**}(s) \\ z_{21}^{**}(s) & z_{22}^{**}(s) \end{bmatrix} \begin{bmatrix} I_1^{**} \\ I_2^{**} \end{bmatrix} \tag{7-16}$$

Since the two networks are in series, the input and output voltages are related such that $(E_1 = E_1^* + E_1^{**})$ and $(E_2 = E_2^* + E_2^{**})$. The matrix for the total network will be similar to Eq. (7-2); therefore, the matrices of Eq. (7-16) can be combined by addition to give

$$\begin{bmatrix} E_1 \\ E_2 \end{bmatrix} = \begin{bmatrix} E_1^* + E_2^{**} \\ E_2^* + E_2^{**} \end{bmatrix} = \begin{bmatrix} [z_{11}^*(s) + z_{11}^{**}(s)] & [z_{12}^*(s) + z_{12}^{**}(s)] \\ [z_{21}^*(s) + z_{21}^{**}(s)] & [z_{22}^*(s) + z_{22}^{**}(s)] \end{bmatrix} \begin{bmatrix} I_1 \\ I_2 \end{bmatrix} \tag{7-17}$$

It is seen that adding the two impedance matrices Z^* and Z^{**} merely adds the $z_{11}(s)$, $z_{12}(s)$, and $z_{22}(s)$ terms of each matrix together. The total impedance matrix has $z_{11}(s)$ composed of $[z_{11}^*(s) + z_{11}^{**}(s)]$, $z_{12}(s)$ of $[z_{12}^*(s) + z_{12}^{**}(s)]$, $z_{21}(s)$ of $[z_{21}^*(s) + z_{21}^{**}(s)]$, and $z_{12}(s)$ of $[z_{22}^*(s) + z_{22}^{**}(s)]$. In every case a driving-point impedance is the sum of two driving-point impedances, and the transfer impedance is the sum of two transfer impedances. In general, as in this example, the driving-point functions of a complicated network are composed of combinations of the driving-point functions of its subnetworks and must have the positive real characteristics of driving-point functions. The transfer function of a complicated network is composed of combinations of the transfer and driving-point functions of the subnetworks and will have the character-istics of a transfer function.†

The inverse matrix relationship of Eq. (7-8) reveals that a reciprocal relationship does not exist between the various open-circuit driving-point or transfer impedances and their respective short-circuit admit-tance functions for a two-port network. For instance, $z_{11}(s)$ does not equal $1/y_{11}(s)$ nor does $y_{12}(s)$ equal $1/z_{12}(s)$ since these functions are defined differently [see Eqs. (7-2) and (7-6)]. However, it is also possible to derive a third matrix form, which is often useful in synthesis problems,

---

† Other combinations of two-port networks such as parallel, series-parallel, and parallel-series interconnections are presented in E. A. Guillemin, *Communication Networks*, Vol. II (New York: John Wiley & Sons, Inc., 1935), pp. 140–151, and L. Weinberg, "Network Analysis," *Elect. Mfg.*, vol. 65, no. 1, January 1960, pp. 89–116.

by solving Eq. (7-2) for E_1 and I_1 in terms of E_2 and I_2. This third form is known as an A-matrix and can be expressed as follows:

$$\begin{bmatrix} E_1 \\ I_1 \end{bmatrix} = \begin{bmatrix} \dfrac{z_{11}(s)}{z_{12}(s)} & \dfrac{z_{12}(s)^2 - z_{11}(s)z_{22}(s)}{z_{12}(s)} \\ \dfrac{1}{z_{12}(s)} & -\dfrac{z_{22}(s)}{z_{12}(s)} \end{bmatrix} \begin{bmatrix} E_2 \\ I_2 \end{bmatrix} = \begin{bmatrix} A_{11}(s) & A_{12}(s) \\ A_{21}(s) & A_{22}(s) \end{bmatrix} \begin{bmatrix} E_2 \\ I_2 \end{bmatrix}$$

$$(7\text{-}18)$$

It should be noted that each term of the A-matrix is divided by a transfer impedance $z_{12}(s)$; therefore each term will have the characteristics of a transfer function. Furthermore, $A_{12}(s)$ does not equal $A_{21}(s)$ in the A-matrix.

Because two-port networks are generally employed for purposes of transmission, it is often convenient to assume the output current I_2 flows out of the network rather than into the network as shown in Fig. 7-1. To define the output current as flowing out of the network is particularly useful in the consideration of networks connected in a cascade arrangement as shown in Fig. 7-4. When two subnetworks are connected in cascade, the output current I_2 of the first network becomes the input current I_1^* of the second network, and obviously I_2 and I_1^* flow in the same direction.

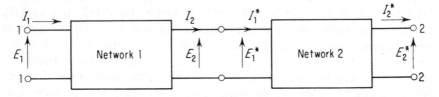

Fig. 7-4. Two networks in cascade.

Redefining the direction of output current, such that I_2 flows out of the network, causes the sign of I_2 in Eq. (7-18) to change. Consequently, the matrix form becomes

$$\begin{bmatrix} E_1 \\ I_1 \end{bmatrix} = \begin{bmatrix} \dfrac{z_{11}(s)}{z_{12}(s)} & \dfrac{z_{11}(s)z_{22}(s) - z_{12}(s)^2}{z_{12}(s)} \\ \dfrac{1}{z_{12}(s)} & \dfrac{z_{22}(s)}{z_{12}(s)} \end{bmatrix} \begin{bmatrix} E_2 \\ I_2 \end{bmatrix} = \begin{bmatrix} A(s) & B(s) \\ C(s) & D(s) \end{bmatrix} \begin{bmatrix} E_2 \\ I_2 \end{bmatrix}$$

$$(7\text{-}19)$$

This relationship is referred to as the "chain" or "transmission" matrix. The only difference between it and the A-matrix of Eq. (7-18) lies in the definition of the direction of I_2 which causes the $B(s)$ and $D(s)$ terms to possess opposite signs than their respective A-matrix terms $A_{12}(s)$ and $A_{22}(s)$. However, this difference in definition has no effect on the application of either matrix form. Therefore, the "transmission" or T-matrix will be employed in future sections of this text with the understanding that the same procedures can be applied when using the A-matrix.

It was pointed out in previous discussions that any definite RLC two-port network can be completely defined by a square matrix which relates the input voltage and current to the output voltage and current. The z-, y-, and T-matrix forms are examples of this possibility; however, because of the reciprocity property of physically realizable RLC networks, the determinant of the T-matrix equals unity. This fact can be expressed analytically as

$$\begin{vmatrix} A(s) & B(s) \\ C(s) & D(s) \end{vmatrix} = |A(s)D(s) - C(s)B(s)| = 1 \tag{7-20}$$

The relationship of Eq. (7-20) can easily be verified by substituting the various open-circuit impedance relationships of Eq. (7-19) for their respective T-matrix terms, remembering that $B(s)$ does not equal $C(s)$.

Before summarizing the various relationships which exist between the z-, y-, and T-matrices, it is instructive to consider the use of T-matrices when networks are connected in a cascade arrangement. The T-matrices for the two subnetworks of Fig. 7-4 can be written in the form of Eq. (7-19) as

$$\begin{bmatrix} E_1 \\ I_1 \end{bmatrix} = \begin{bmatrix} A(s) & B(s) \\ C(s) & D(s) \end{bmatrix} \begin{bmatrix} E_2 \\ I_2 \end{bmatrix} \quad \text{and} \quad \begin{bmatrix} E_1^* \\ I_1^* \end{bmatrix} = \begin{bmatrix} A^*(s) & B^*(s) \\ C^*(s) & D^*(s) \end{bmatrix} \begin{bmatrix} E_2^* \\ I_2^* \end{bmatrix} \tag{7-21}$$

Since the voltage E_2 of Fig. 7-4 equals E_1^* and the current I_2 equals I_1^*, the matrices of Eq. (7-21) can be combined as follows:

$$\begin{bmatrix} E_1 \\ I_1 \end{bmatrix} = \begin{bmatrix} A(s) & B(s) \\ C(s) & D(s) \end{bmatrix} \begin{bmatrix} A^*(s) & B^*(s) \\ C^*(s) & D^*(s) \end{bmatrix} \begin{bmatrix} E_2^* \\ I_2^* \end{bmatrix}$$

$$= \begin{bmatrix} [A(s)A^*(s) + B(s)C^*(s)] & [A(s)B^*(s) + B(s)D^*(s)] \\ [C(s)A^*(s) + D(s)C^*(s)] & [C(s)B^*(s) + D(s)D^*(s)] \end{bmatrix} \begin{bmatrix} E_2^* \\ I_2^* \end{bmatrix} \tag{7-22}$$

From this example it is seen that the T-matrices of cascaded networks must be multiplied together in the order in which the individual networks are arranged in order to obtain the T-matrix for the entire network. Referring to Fig. 7-5, this multiplication of T-matrices can be written as

$$\begin{bmatrix} E_1 \\ I_1 \end{bmatrix} = [T_1][T_2][T_3] \cdot \cdot \cdot [T_n]\begin{bmatrix} E_2 \\ I_2 \end{bmatrix} \qquad (7\text{-}23)$$

where T_1 is the T-matrix of the first subnetwork, T_2 is the T-matrix of the second subnetwork, etc., to the T_n subnetwork. To facilitate the mathematics of determining the overall T-matrix for a number of cascaded subnetworks, the T-matrices of several of the more common networks are tabulated in Table 7-1. All of the impedance or matrix terms of this table may be functions of s.

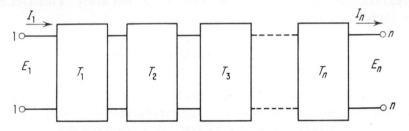

Fig. 7-5. Cascade combination of subnetworks.

The relationships existing between T-matrix and z-matrix terms are clear in Eq. (7-19). Using the z and y relationships of Eq. (7-13), it is possible to derive the relationships existing between T and y-matrices. These various relationships are summarized for convenience in Table 7-2. It should be emphasized that all terms of the table are based on voltage and current relationships shown in Fig. 7-1, with the exception of the T-matrix terms $B(s)$ and $D(s)$, which assume output current I_2 flows out of the network. It is also noted that $A(s)$ and $D(s)$ are dimensionless, whereas $B(s)$ is dimensionally an impedance and $C(s)$ is an admittance. Application of T-matrices to the realization of two-port networks will be considered in a later section.

In some analysis and synthesis problems, the concept of power is more useful in defining network characteristics than that of voltage or current. For this reason a set of parameters known as the scattering matrix has been derived and finds primary application in the design of power-transmission networks. Although scattering parameters have not been widely used as the basis of synthesis techniques, it is of interest to investigate them and their relationship to the matrices described above. Therefore, for the sake of completeness, scattering parameters will be studied briefly before describing synthesis techniques based on the characterizing functions of this section.

It is desirable to begin by considering the scattering parameters of a one-port network of the type shown in Fig. 7-6. In this configuration

TABLE 7-I
T-Matrices of Fundamental Two-Port Networks

Network title	1. Series impedance	2. Shunt impedance	3. T-Section	4. Pi-Section	5. Symmetrical lattice
Network configuration					
T-matrix terms $\begin{bmatrix} A & B \\ C & D \end{bmatrix}$	$A = 1$ $B = Z$ $C = 0$ $D = 1$	$A = 1$ $B = 0$ $C = 1/Z$ $D = 1$	$A = 1 + Z_1/Z_3$ $B = Z_1 + Z_2 + Z_1 Z_2/Z_3$ $C = 1/Z_3$ $D = 1 + Z_2/Z_3$	$A = 1 + Z_2/Z_3$ $B = Z_2$ $C = 1/Z_1 + 1/Z_3 + Z_2/Z_1 Z_3$ $D = 1 + Z_2/Z_1$	$A = (Z_A + Z_B)/(Z_B - Z_A)$ $B = 2 Z_A Z_B/(Z_B - Z_A)$ $C = 2/(Z_B - Z_A)$ $D = (Z_A + Z_B)/(Z_B - Z_A)$

Network title	6. Coupled section	7. Ideal transformer	8. Transmission line	9. Cascade of symmetric identical networks
Network configuration		 $N = n_1/n_2$	 Z = impedance/length Y = admittance/length d = length Characteristic impedance $\quad Z_o = \sqrt{Z/Y}$ Propagation constant $\quad a = \sqrt{ZY}$	 Matrix of single network $\quad T_n = \begin{bmatrix} A_n & B_n \\ C_n & D_n \end{bmatrix}$ Characteristic impedance $\quad Z_0 = \sqrt{B_n/C_n}$ Propagation constant $\quad a = \cosh^{-1} A_n$
T-matrix terms $\begin{bmatrix} A & B \\ C & D \end{bmatrix}$	$A = L_1/M$ $B = s(L_1 L_2 - M^2)/M$ $C = 1/sM$ $D = L_2/M$	$A = 1/N$ $B = 0$ $C = 0$ $D = N$	$A = \cosh(ad)$ $B = Z_o \sinh(ad)$ $C = \sinh(ad)/Z_o$ $D = \cosh(ad)$	Overall matrix of n networks $A = \cosh(an)$ $B = Z_0 \sinh(an)$ $C = \sinh(an)/Z_0$ $D = \cosh(an)$

TABLE 7-2
T-, y-, and z-matrix relationships

T-terms	z-terms	y-terms
$A(s)$	$\dfrac{z_{11}(s)}{z_{12}(s)}$	$-\dfrac{y_{22}(s)}{y_{12}(s)}$
$B(s)$	$\dfrac{z_{11}(s)z_{22}(s)-z_{12}(s)^2}{z_{12}(s)}$	$-\dfrac{1}{y_{12}(s)}$
$C(s)$	$\dfrac{1}{z_{12}(s)}$	$\dfrac{y_{11}(s)y_{22}(s)-y_{12}(s)^2}{-y_{12}(s)}$
$D(s)$	$\dfrac{z_{22}(s)}{z_{12}(s)}$	$-\dfrac{y_{11}(s)}{y_{12}(s)}$

the network to the right represents a load impedance Z on a second network which has a Thevenin equivalent circuit as shown to the left of terminals 1-1. Applying the terminology of wave propagation, the voltage V at terminals 1-1 results from an "incident" wave from the left and a "reflected" wave returning from the load. The same is true of the current I; therefore, using subscripts i and r to represent the incident and reflected waves, respectively, it is possible to write

$$V = V_i + V_r \quad \text{and} \quad I = I_i + I_r \tag{7-24}$$

If Z_o represents the "characteristic" impedance of the network to the left of terminals 1-1, the incident and reflected parameters are related such that

$$\frac{V_i}{I_i} = -\frac{V_r}{I_r} = Z_o \tag{7-25}$$

Substituting Eq. (7-25) into Eq. (7-24) and solving for V_i and V_r yields

$$V_i = \frac{V + Z_o I}{2} \quad \text{and} \quad V_r = \frac{V - Z_o I}{2} \tag{7-26}$$

The ratio of these voltages is known as the reflection coefficient ρ, or more recently as the scattering coefficient S_{11}, at terminals 1-1.

$$S_{11} = \frac{V_r}{V_i} = \frac{V - Z_o I}{V + Z_o I} = \frac{Z - Z_o}{Z + Z_o} \tag{7-27}$$

In the above derivation, Z_o was assumed to represent the equivalent or characteristic impedance of the source network. Actually, these assumptions are not necessary to support the definitions of Eqs. (7-26) and (7-27) provided Z_o is a positive real impedance. Equation (7-26) also reflects the fact that when Z_o and Z are balanced, V_i and V_r are equal; hence, the incident voltage equals half the source voltage $V_i = E_1/2$. This situation represents complete reflection or $|S_{11}| = 1$; whereas, when $|S_{11}| = 0$, there is no reflection.

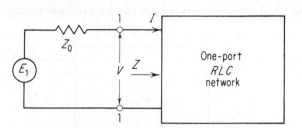

Fig. 7-6. Terminated one-port network.

Now it is possible to extend the above discussion to two-port networks. In this case it is convenient to consider the configuration of Fig. 7-7 which possesses a voltage source in series with a positive real impedance in both the input and output circuits. Incident and reflected voltages can be defined at each port of the network in a manner similar to the one-port parameters of Eq. (7-26):

$$V_{i1} = \frac{V_1 + Z_{o1}I_1}{2} \qquad V_{r1} = \frac{V_1 - Z_{o1}I_1}{2}$$

$$V_{i2} = \frac{V_2 + Z_{o2}I_2}{2} \qquad V_{r2} = \frac{V_2 - Z_{o2}I_2}{2} \tag{7-28}$$

Using these relationships, it is possible to define a scattering or S-matrix to serve the same purpose for the two-port network as the scattering coefficient serves for a one-port structure:

$$\begin{bmatrix} V_{r1} \\ V_{r2} \end{bmatrix} = \begin{bmatrix} S_{11} & S_{12} \\ S_{21} & S_{22} \end{bmatrix} \begin{bmatrix} V_{i1} \\ V_{i2} \end{bmatrix} \tag{7-29}$$

The terms of this matrix are defined specifically as follows:

$$S_{11} = \frac{V_{r1}}{V_{i1}} \bigg]_{V_{i2}=0} \qquad S_{12} = \frac{V_{r1}}{V_{i2}} \bigg]_{V_{i1}=0}$$

$$S_{21} = \frac{V_{r2}}{V_{i1}} \bigg]_{V_{i2}=0} \qquad S_{22} = \frac{V_{r2}}{V_{i2}} \bigg]_{V_{i1}=0} \tag{7-30}$$

The ratios of this equation apply when the pertinent terminals of the network are short-circuited; therefore the scattering terms are short-circuit parameters but should not be confused with the short-circuit admittances of Eq. (7-6). However, in general the scattering parameters at any point within a network can be related to the z-, y-, and T-matrix terms that represent the entire network (i.e., the network enclosed by dashed lines in Fig. 7-7).

To interpret the scattering parameters in terms of power transfer, assume for the moment that E_2 of Fig. 7-7 is zero and Z_{o1} and Z_{o2} are both one ohm resistors. In addition, let the central network be isolated by a pair of ideal transformers which can be used for voltage and current

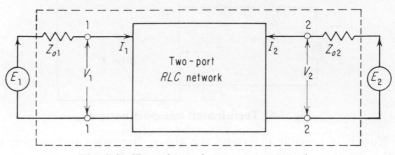

Fig. 7-7. Terminated two-port network.

normalization similar to the configuration of Fig. 2-2.† In this case the power available from the source (with $Z_{o1} = 1$ ohm) is $|E_1|^2/2$ of which half is dissipated in the unit resistance. Hence, for a balanced structure, as described in connection with Fig. 7-6, the maximum power available to the two-port network becomes

$$P_A = \frac{|E_1|^2}{4} = |V_{i1}|^2 \qquad (7\text{-}31)$$

Similarly, the power delivered to the 1-ohm load resistor Z_{o2} can be written as

$$P_L = |I_2|^2 = |V_2|^2 = |V_{i2} + V_{r2}|^2 = |V_{r2}|^2 \qquad (7\text{-}32)$$

The last step reflects the fact that $V_{i2} = E_2/2 = 0$ and the preceding step follows from the relationships of Eq. (7-28). The ratio of power delivered to that available is expressed as

$$\frac{P_L}{P_A} = \frac{|V_{r2}|^2}{|V_{i1}|^2} = |S_{21}(j\omega)|^2 \qquad (7\text{-}33)$$

Because V_{r2} and V_{i1} can be considered as phasors, S_{21} need only be evaluated in terms of real frequency $s = j\omega$. Furthermore, the power ratio expressed in terms of V_{r2} and V_{i1} remains invariant when the ideal transformers used for normalization are removed. Finally, if the transmission through the network were from right to left, the power ratio could be expressed as $|S_{12}(j\omega)|^2$.‡

† The characteristics of ideal transformers will be explained in the next section.

‡ The power relationships of scattering parameters can be used to verify the positive real characteristics of driving-point functions in addition to providing insight into the characteristics of transfer functions. *IRE Trans. Circuit Theory*, vol. CT-3, June 1956, provides several papers on this subject. In particular, a good review is given by H. J. Carlin, "The Scattering Matrix in Network Theory," pp. 88–97. These techniques have been extended to multiport networks by D. C. Youla in *IRE Trans. Circuit Theory*, vol. CT-6, December 1959, pp. 340–344.

The matrix relationships described in this section are by no means exhaustive, since so-called hybrid and image parameters are also useful in the analysis of networks. However, the z-, y-, T-, and S-matrices represent the most useful parameters for design and synthesis. For instance, when a two-port network is used to couple vacuum tubes having high input and output impedances, the open-circuit or z-matrix parameters are most appropriate. In contrast, transistor circuits having low input and output impedances and applications involving parallel combinations of networks are most easily handled in terms of short-circuit or y-matrix parameters. Similarly, when two-port networks are combined in cascade, the T-matrix parameters are most suitable. Finally, scattering parameters find their greatest application in the analysis and synthesis of microwave and transmission system problems. The relationships of this section will be referred to repeatedly in the synthesis procedures of this and later chapters.

7-2. Cauer's Two-port Reactance Synthesis Procedure

It is now of interest to investigate various procedures for realizing two-port networks for which the open-circuit impedances or short-circuit admittances have been specified. The first of these methods is a procedure developed by Cauer based on the realization of T-sections coupled by ideal transformers to step voltage up or down. It will be seen that this procedure is further limited to impedance or admittance functions possessing poles restricted to the $j\omega$-axis of the s-plane. This implies that the two-port networks to be realized will be composed of reactive elements such as inductors or capacitors. Realization of reactive two-port networks has particular importance because of the part it plays in the development of Darlington's procedure (see Chap. 6, Sec. 6-4).

It was pointed out in Sec. 7-1 that surplus factors can always be used to convert a given set of open-circuit impedance or short-circuit admittance functions to the form of Eq. (7-13), such that each function has the same poles. When this is accomplished, a specified set of impedances can be written in the following form:

$$z_{11}(s) = \frac{a_n s^n + a_{n-1} s^{n-1} + \cdots + a_0}{b_m s^m + b_{m-1} s^{m-1} + \cdots + b_0}$$

$$z_{12}(s) = \frac{c_p s^p + c_{p-1} s^{p-1} + \cdots + c_0}{b_m s^m + b_{m-1} s^{m-1} + \cdots + b_0}$$

$$z_{22}(s) = \frac{d_r s^r + d_{r-1} s^{r-1} + \cdots + d_0}{b_m s^m + b_{m-1} s^{m-1} + \cdots + b_0} \tag{7-34}$$

For a physically realizable reactance network, the poles of the driving-point impedances $z_{11}(s)$ and $z_{22}(s)$ are restricted to the $j\omega$-axis, where they must be simple with positive real residues. The poles of $[z_{12}(s) = z_{21}(s)]$ are the same as those of $z_{11}(s)$ and $z_{22}(s)$, and their residues must satisfy the requirements

$$k_{11}k_{22} - k_{12}k_{21} \geq 0 \quad \text{where} \quad k_{11} \geq 0 \quad \text{and} \quad k_{22} \geq 0 \quad (7\text{-}35)$$

This follows from the above discussion and consideration of the restrictions on the real parts of the various impedances given by Eq. (7-14).

The first step in Cauer's procedure requires that the specified equations be written in terms of partial fractions where the coefficients of the terms are the residues of the poles. Since the poles of Eq. (7-34) are restricted to the $j\omega$-axis, where they occur in conjugate pairs, it is possible to write the various impedance functions in partial-fraction form, whereupon combination of the conjugate terms yields

$$z_{11}(s) = \frac{k_{11}^0}{s} + \frac{2k_{11}^1 s}{s^2 + \omega^2} + \cdots + k_{11}^n s$$

$$z_{12}(s) = \frac{k_{12}^0}{s} + \frac{2k_{12}^1 s}{s^2 + \omega^2} + \cdots + k_{12}^n s$$

$$z_{22}(s) = \frac{k_{22}^0}{s} + \frac{2k_{22}^1 s}{s^2 + \omega^2} + \cdots + k_{22}^n s \quad (7\text{-}36)$$

The superscripts $0, 1, \ldots, n$ simply indicate the number of the term. The residues of the various poles of Eq. (7-36) must fulfill the conditions of Eq. (7-35), which can be written in a more general form as

$$k_{11}^q \geq 0; \quad k_{22}^q \geq 0; \quad \text{and} \quad k_{11}^q k_{22}^q - (k_{12}^q)^2 \geq 0 \quad (7\text{-}37)$$

where k^q indicates the residue of any pole from zero to n. Equation (7-36) can be realized as a series combination of T-sections of the form seen in Fig. 7-8. If a negative sign is needed in the synthesis process, the polarity of the ideal transformer is reversed; consequently it is useful to consider the characteristics ascribed to an ideal transformer before discussing the impedance functions which define the T-section of Fig. 7-8.

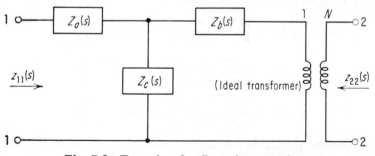

Fig. 7-8. T-section for Cauer's procedure.

The characteristics of an ideal transformer can be derived by considering two finite inductances L_1 and L_2 each with zero loss and possessing a coupling coefficient Ψ of unity. This configuration is indicated in Fig. 7-9a where the inductors are related through their turns ratio N such that $(L_2 = N^2 L_1)$. The equivalent circuit for the transformer of Fig. 7-9a is shown in Fig. 7-9b. This equivalent circuit may be expressed in terms of its open-circuit impedances or short-circuit admittances, in

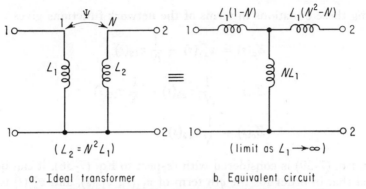

a. Ideal transformer b. Equivalent circuit

Fig. 7-9. Ideal transformer and equivalent circuit.

which case the characteristics of the ideal transformer may be obtained by investigating the behavior of the functions in the limit as L_1 approaches infinity. Consideration of Fig. 7-9b as L_1 approaches infinity reveals the following properties of an ideal transformer.

1. When the transformer secondary is open, $z_{11}(s) = \infty$.
2. When the transformer secondary is shorted, $z_{11}(s) = 0$.
3. The net reactance is zero; therefore, there is no phase shifting of signals passing through the transformer.
4. The reactive volt-amperes between primary and secondary of the transformer are conserved.
5. The output power equals the input power; therefore, power transfer is conserved.
6. When the frequency of the signal is not zero, the above characteristics are independent of frequency.
7. Periodic waveforms passing through the transformer are preserved.

The above characteristics define an ideal transformer as if it were a practical circuit element; however, it should be pointed out that the ideal transformer is different in several respects from the perfect transformer employed in Brune's procedure (see Chap. 5, Sec. 5-3).† With the above characteristics in mind, the part played by ideal transformers in Cauer's procedure is more easily understood.

† D. Rogers Crosby, "The Ideal Transformer," *IRE Trans. Circuit Theory*, vol. CT-5, no. 2, June 1958, p. 145.

Returning to Cauer's procedure, the impedance functions which represent the T-section of Fig. 7-8 can be written as follows, where N is the ratio of the output turns of the transformer to the input turns:

$$z_{11}(s) = Z_a(s) + Z_c(s)$$

$$z_{12}(s) = NZ_c(s)$$

$$z_{22}(s) = N^2[Z_b(s) + Z_c(s)] \tag{7-38}$$

Solving these equations in terms of the network functions gives

$$Z_a(s) = z_{11}(s) - \frac{1}{N} z_{12}(s)$$

$$Z_b(s) = \frac{1}{N^2} z_{22}(s) - \frac{1}{N} z_{12}(s)$$

$$Z_c(s) = \frac{1}{N} z_{12}(s) \tag{7-39}$$

When Eq. (7-39) is considered with respect to Eq. (7-36), it can be concluded that in order for the qth term of $z_{11}(s)$, $z_{12}(s)$, and $z_{22}(s)$ to yield a realizable network of the form of Fig. 7-8, the following restrictions are necessary:

1. For $Z_a(s)$ to be positive and real, it is necessary that $k_{11}^q - k_{12}^q/N^q$ be equal to or greater than zero.

2. For $Z_b(s)$ to be positive and real, $k_{22}^q/(N^q)^2 - k_{12}^q/N^q$ must be equal to or greater than zero.

3. For Z_c to be positive and real, it is necessary that N^q has the same sign as k_{12}^q.

These conditions can be combined and expressed analytically such that the magnitude of N^q is restricted by k_{11}^q, k_{22}^q, and the magnitude of k_{12}^q as follows:

$$\frac{|k_{12}^q|}{k_{11}^q} \leq |N^q| \leq \frac{k_{22}^q}{|k_{12}^q|} \tag{7-40}$$

From this equation it is seen that N^q must have the same sign as k_{12}^q, and the limits of its magnitude are restricted; however, if its value can be chosen as $+1$, the ideal transformer of the qth T-section can be removed without affecting the network.

Once the specified impedance functions have been broken into partial-fraction form, as in Eq. (7-36), individual sets of terms $z_{11}^q(s)$, $z_{12}^q(s)$, and $z_{22}^q(s)$ may be realized as T-sections of the form of Fig. 7-8. It should be emphasized that the superscript q is used only to denote a term from the 0th to the nth term in the partial-fraction expansions of $z_{11}(s)$, $z_{12}(s)$, and $z_{22}(s)$. The resulting T-sections can then be connected in series, as shown in Fig. 7-10, to complete the realization. From Eq. (7-40) and Fig. 7-10, it is seen that an infinite number of different networks can be synthesized depending on the choice of the turns ratio N for each T-section.

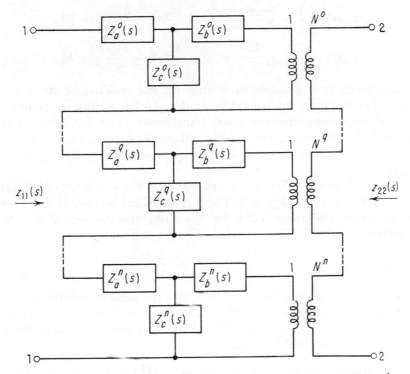

Fig. 7-10. General form for Cauer's two-port reactance network.

As an example of Cauer's procedure, assume that it is desirable to realize a reactance network with the impedance characteristics listed in Eq. (7-41). The denominators of these functions are equal; therefore surplus factors are not required to insure common poles for $z_{11}(s)$, $z_{12}(s)$, and $z_{22}(s)$. A reactance network will result, since the poles are restricted to the $j\omega$-axis:

$$z_{11}(s) = \frac{2s^4 + 16s^2 + 2}{s^3 + s}$$

$$z_{12}(s) = \frac{3s^4 + 1}{s^3 + s}$$

$$z_{22}(s) = \frac{9s^4 + 13s^2 + 2}{s^3 + s} \qquad (7\text{-}41)$$

The first step in the realization is to break the given functions into partial fractions, as follows:

$$z_{11}(s) = \frac{2}{s} + \frac{12s}{s^2 + 1} + 2s = \frac{k_{11}^0}{s} + \frac{k_{11}^1 s}{s^2 + \omega^2} + k_{11}^2 s$$

$$z_{12}(s) = \frac{1}{s} + \frac{-4s}{s^2 + 1} + 3s = \frac{k_{12}^0}{s} + \frac{k_{12}^1 s}{s^2 + \omega^2} + k_{12}^2 s$$

$$z_{22}(s) = \frac{2}{s} + \frac{2s}{s^2 + 1} + 9s = \frac{k_{22}^0}{s} + \frac{k_{22}^1 s}{s^2 + \omega^2} + k_{22}^2 s \tag{7-42}$$

In this form, it is possible to distinguish the residues of the various terms. For instance, the second term of $z_{12}(s)$ has a negative residue of -4, which means that one ideal transformer must have its polarity reversed. Furthermore, there will be three T-sections, since there are three terms in the partial-fraction expansions of $z_{11}(s)$, $z_{12}(s)$, and $z_{22}(s)$.

To synthesize the first T-section, consider the $q = 0$ set of residues, $k_{11}^0 = 2$, $k_{12}^0 = 1$, and $k_{22}^0 = 2$. These residues can be used in Eq. (7-40) to determine the turns ratio for the ideal transformer of the first T-section:

$$\frac{|1|}{2} \leq |N^0| \leq \frac{2}{|1|} \tag{7-43}$$

It is possible to choose $N^0 = 1$; therefore the ideal transformer can be removed from the first T-section. Substituting the $q = 0$ terms of Eq. (7-42) into Eq. (7-39) yields the $Z_a(s)$, $Z_b(s)$, and $Z_c(s)$ values for the first T-section for an N^0 of unity:

$$Z_a^0(s) = z_{11}^0(s) - \frac{1}{N^0} z_{12}^0(s) = \frac{2}{s} - \frac{1}{1}\left(\frac{1}{s}\right) = \frac{1}{s}$$

$$Z_b^0(s) = \frac{1}{(N^0)^2} z_{22}^0(s) - \frac{1}{N^0} z_{12}^0(s) = \frac{1}{1}\left(\frac{2}{s}\right) - \frac{1}{1}\left(\frac{1}{s}\right) = \frac{1}{s}$$

$$Z_c^0(s) = \frac{1}{N^0} z_{12}^0(s) = \frac{1}{1}\left(\frac{2}{s}\right) = \frac{2}{s} \tag{7-44}$$

Consequently, the first T-section is composed of capacitors and a transformer with a turns ratio of ($N^0 = 1$); hence the section takes the form of Fig. 7-11.

To realize the second T-section, the $q = 1$ set of residues of Eq. (7-42), $k_{11}^1 = 12$, $k_{12}^1 = -4$, and $k_{22}^1 = 2$, must be considered. These residues can be used in Eq. (7-40) to determine the transformer turns ratio for the second T-section.

$$\frac{|4|}{12} \leq |N^1| \leq \frac{2}{|4|} \quad \text{let} \quad N^1 = -\frac{1}{3} \tag{7-45}$$

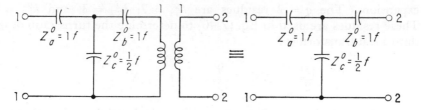

Fig. 7-11. First example T-section.

The minus sign must be used, since $z_{12}^1(s)$ is negative. Using the $q = 1$ terms of Eq. (7-42) and a turns ratio of $(N^1 = -1/3)$ in Eq. (7-39) yields

$$Z_a{}^1(s) = z_{11}^1(s) - \frac{1}{N^1} z_{12}^1(s) = \left(\frac{12s}{s^2 + 1}\right) - \frac{1}{-\frac{1}{3}}\left(\frac{-4s}{s^2 + 1}\right) = 0$$

$$Z_b{}^1(s) = \frac{1}{(N^1)^2} z_{22}^1(s) - \frac{1}{N^1} z_{12}^1(s) = \frac{1}{\frac{1}{9}}\left(\frac{2s}{s^2 + 1}\right) - \frac{1}{-\frac{1}{3}}\left(\frac{-4s}{s^2 + 1}\right)$$

$$= \frac{6s}{s^2 + 1} = \frac{1}{\frac{1}{6} s + \frac{1}{6s}}$$

$$Z_c{}^1(s) = \frac{1}{N^1} z_{12}(s) = \frac{1}{-\frac{1}{3}}\left(\frac{-4s}{s^2 + 1}\right) = \frac{12s}{s^2 + 1} = \frac{1}{\frac{1}{12} s + \frac{1}{12s}} \qquad (7\text{-}46)$$

These impedances can be realized as the second T-section as seen in Fig. 7-12. The polarity of the transformer is reversed to provide the negative turns ratio.

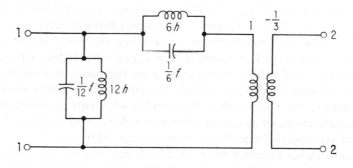

Fig. 7-12. Second example T-section.

The third and final T-section required to realize the impedances of Eq. (7-42) is found by using the $q = 2$ terms of the partial-fraction expansions. The $q = 2$ residues are $k_{11}^2 = 2$, $k_{12}^2 = 3$, and $k_{22}^2 = 9$. These residues are used in Eq. (7-40) to determine the turns ratio of the third ideal transformer:

$$\frac{|3|}{2} \leq |N^2| \leq \frac{9}{|3|} \quad \text{let} \quad N^2 = 2 \qquad (7\text{-}47)$$

Using $N^2 = 2$, the impedance terms are calculated from Eq. (7-42) as

$$Z_a{}^2(s) = z_{11}^2(s) - \frac{1}{N^2} z_{12}^2(s) = (2s) - \frac{1}{2}(3s) = \frac{1}{2}s$$

$$Z_b{}^2(s) = \frac{1}{(N^2)^2} z_{22}^2(s) - \frac{1}{N^2} z_{12}^2(s) = \frac{1}{4}(9s) - \frac{1}{2}(3s) = \frac{3}{4}s$$

$$Z_c{}^2(s) = \frac{1}{N^2} z_{12}^2(s) = \frac{1}{2}(3s) = \frac{3}{2}s \qquad (7\text{-}48)$$

These impedances represent inductors which form the third T-section as seen in Fig. 7-13. The turns ratio in this case is 2.

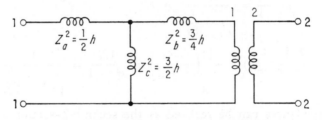

Fig. 7-13. Third example T-section.

The realization of Eq. (7-41) is completed by combining the sub-networks of Figs. 7-11, 7-12, and 7-13 in series as suggested by Eq. (7-42). Therefore, the final reactance network takes the form shown in Fig. 7-14. It is clear from this example that Cauer's procedure can yield an infinite number of solutions, depending on the turns ratios selected for the transformers of the individual T-sections. It is often possible to select turns ratios which reduce the number of circuit elements required for the realization, or cause the element values to be more realistic in terms of commercially available components. However, the procedure results in a rather complex network which can only be approximated in most cases because of the ideal transformers involved. The above technique can also be applied to realization of admittance functions in which case it is convenient to deal with Pi-sections which are combined in parallel.

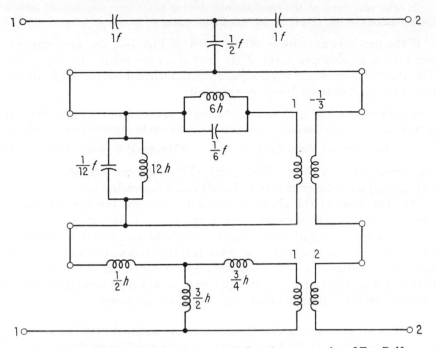

Fig. 7-14. Final reactance network for the example of Eq. 7-41.

7-3. Three-terminal *RLC* Network Synthesis

In some situations it is not only important that a two-port network possess specified transfer and driving-point characteristics, but it must also possess a terminal common to both the input and output circuits. Ladder structures, such as the Pi- and T-sections of Table 7-1 or Fig. 7-2, are typical examples of configurations that may be classified as three-terminal networks. The purpose of this section is to investigate constraints imposed on the transfer and driving-point functions of certain *RLC* three-terminal networks and techniques which can be used in their realization.

To begin this investigation, it is useful to review the properties of the three-terminal T network of Fig. 7-2. In Sec. 7-1, it was shown that a physically realizable *RLC* two-port network is insured if the transfer and driving-point functions are constrained such that:

1. Poles and zeros of the driving-point functions must lie in the left half of the s-plane or on the $j\omega$-axis. All $j\omega$-axis roots must be simple.

2. Zeros of the transfer impedance or admittance may lie anywhere on the s-plane; however, the poles have the same restrictions as those of the driving-point functions.

3. The real parts of the transfer and driving-point impedance must satisfy the conditions of Eq. (7-14) for all real frequencies.

If the two-port network is of the form of Fig. 7-2, the driving-point and branch impedances $Z_a(s)$, $Z_b(s)$, and $Z_c(s)$ are related by Eq. (7-5). The transfer impedence $z_{12}(s)$ equals the branch impedance $Z_c(s)$; therefore a fourth constraint becomes apparent.

4. The real parts of $z_{11}(s)$ and $z_{22}(s)$ must be greater than or equal to the real part of $[z_{12}(s) = z_{21}(s)]$ at all real frequencies. This can be expressed analytically as

$$Re[z_{11}(j\omega)] \geqq Re[z_{12}(j\omega)] \quad \text{and} \quad Re[z_{22}(j\omega)] \geqq Re[z_{12}(j\omega)] \quad (7\text{-}49)$$

The conditions of Eqs. (7-14) and (7-49) do not require that the $Re[z_{12}(j\omega)]$ must be nonnegative for all real frequencies.

On the basis of the above discussion, it is now possible to state a useful synthesis procedure as a series of steps. Minor variations in the procedure will be required for cases in which the real part of the transfer impedance becomes negative for some real frequency. Furthermore, the procedure outlined in the following steps is based on the assumption that $z_{11}(s)$, $z_{12}(s)$, and $z_{22}(s)$ are specified; however, a similar approach can be used if equivalent admittance functions are given.

1. Test the given functions to determine if they satisfy the four requirements stated above. If they do, the functions are realizable as a T network.
2. Synthesize the transfer impedance as the center section of the network (i.e., the section between terminals a-a and b-b of Fig. 7-15).
3. Determine the driving-point impedances $Z_{aa}(s)$ and $Z_{bb}(s)$ seen looking into the terminals of the network developed in Step 2.
4. Subtract the impedances $Z_{aa}(s)$ and $Z_{bb}(s)$ from the specified driving-point functions to determine a pair of series impedances $Z^*(s)$ and $Z^{**}(s)$.
5. Synthesize $Z^*(s)$ and $Z^{**}(s)$ and combine these networks in series with that of Step 2 to form a T network.

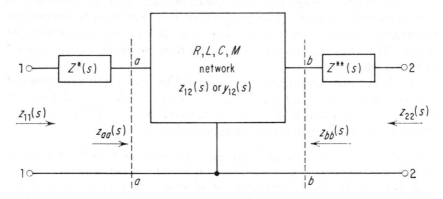
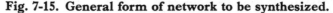

Fig. 7-15. General form of network to be synthesized.

It is of interest to first consider the case in which $z_{12}(s)$ satisfies the requirements of a driving-point function. In this case the entire network can be realized by employing the techniques of driving-point-function synthesis described in Chaps. 3 through 6. Cases in which the transfer impedance possesses right half-plane zeros or a real part that is negative will be considered in more detail later. When $z_{12}(s)$ is a driving-point function, the network of Fig. 7-15 can be redrawn in the form of Fig. 7-2. Furthermore, since $z_{11}(s)$, $z_{12}(s)$, and $z_{22}(s)$ are assumed to be specified, it is possible to determine $Z^*(s)$ and $Z^{**}(s)$ as follows:

$$z_{11}(s) - z_{12}(s) = Z^*(s)$$
$$z_{22}(s) - z_{12}(s) = Z^{**}(s) \qquad (7\text{-}50)$$

The impedances $Z^*(s)$ and $Z^{**}(s)$ are necessarily driving-point functions, since the real parts of $z_{11}(s)$, $z_{12}(s)$, and $z_{22}(s)$ are nonnegative and the real parts of $z_{11}(s)$ and $z_{22}(s)$ are larger than that of $z_{12}(s)$ [see Eq. (7-49)]. Consequently, the real parts of $Z^*(s)$ and $Z^{**}(s)$ are nonnegative for all real frequencies.

To illustrate the above procedure when $z_{12}(s)$ is a driving-point impedance satisfying the conditions of Eqs. (7-14) and (7-49), consider the example of Eq. (7-51).

$$z_{11}(s) = \frac{10s^4 + 32s^3 + 41s^2 + 34s + 16}{2s^4 + 9s^3 + 14s^2 + 8s}$$

$$z_{22}(s) = \frac{2s^4 + 33s^3 + 72s^2 + 78s + 32}{4s^3 + 10s^2 + 8s}$$

$$z_{12}(s) = \frac{3(2s^2 + 2s + 1)}{2s^2 + 5s + 4} \qquad (7\text{-}51)$$

Since these functions satisfy the requirements of three-terminal networks, it is possible to begin with Step 2 of the procedure.

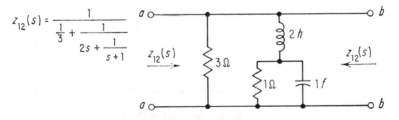

$$z_{12}(s) = \cfrac{1}{\cfrac{1}{3} + \cfrac{1}{2s + \cfrac{1}{s+1}}}$$

Fig. 7-16. Realization of $z_{12}(s)$ for the example of Eq. 7-51.

In the second step of the procedure, the transfer function is realized, and because $z_{12}(s)$ in this example is also a driving-point impedance, the one-port synthesis techniques of Chaps. 3 through 6 can be used. Applying series-parallel withdrawal of terms from $z_{12}(s)$ leads to the expansion and network of Fig. 7-16.

The third step of the procedure is to determine the impedance seen at terminals *a-a* and *b-b* of the transfer impedance network. Whenever the transfer impedance is a driving-point function and can be developed as in Fig. 7-16, $z_{aa}(s)$, $z_{bb}(s)$, and $z_{12}(s)$ are equal. The fourth step is the determination of $Z^*(s)$ and $Z^{**}(s)$, which can be accomplished for this example by substituting Eq. (7-51) into Eq. (7-50).

$$Z^*(s) = z_{11}(s) - z_{12}(s) = \frac{10s^4 + 32s^3 + 41s^2 + 34s + 16}{2s^4 + 9s^3 + 14s^2 + 8s} - \frac{3(2s^2 + 2s + 1)}{2s^2 + 5s + 4}$$

$$= \frac{2(s^2 + s + 2)}{s^2 + 2s} \tag{7-52}$$

$$Z^{**}(s) = z_{22}(s) - z_{12}(s) = \frac{2s^4 + 33s^3 + 72s^2 + 78s + 32}{4s^3 + 10s^2 + 8s} - \frac{3(2s^2 + 2s + 1)}{2s^2 + 5s + 4}$$

$$= \frac{s^2 + 8s + 8}{2s} \tag{7-53}$$

The final step in the procedure is to synthesize $Z^*(s)$ and $Z^{**}(s)$ and combine the resulting networks with that of Fig. 7-16. The networks for Eqs. (7-52) and (7-53) can be realized by series-parallel withdrawal as shown in Fig. 7-17.

$$Z^*(s) = \frac{2}{s} + \frac{1}{\frac{1}{2} + \frac{1}{s}}$$

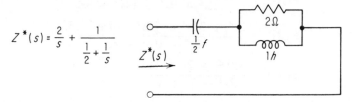

a. Realization of $Z^*(s)$

$$Z^{**}(s) = \frac{1}{2}s + 4 + \frac{4}{s}$$

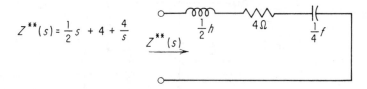

b. Realization of $Z^{**}(s)$

Fig. 7-17. Realization of Eqs. 7-52 and 7-53.

Combining the networks of Figs. 7-16 and 7-17 in the form of Fig. 7-15 results in the final network as seen in Fig. 7-18. This three-terminal *RLC* network has all the impedance characteristics specified by Eq. (7-51).

When the transfer impedance possesses a real part that is negative at some value of ω or has right half-plane zeros, the second step of the procedure must be modified. In this case even though $z_{12}(s)$ does not meet the requirements of a driving-point function, it is often possible

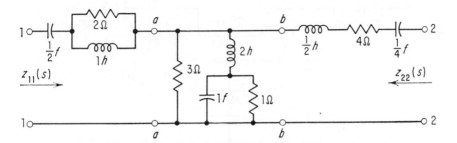

Fig. 7-18. Final network for Eq. 7-51.

to remove a portion, denoted as $z_{12}^*(s)$, which possesses driving-point characteristics. Having realized $z_{12}^*(s)$ as a one-port network, the remaining portion of the transfer impedance $z_{12}^{**}(s)$ must then be realized as a three-terminal network in series with $z_{12}^*(s)$. The decomposition of $z_{12}(s)$ can be expressed as

$$z_{12}(s) = \underbrace{z_{12}^*(s)}_{\substack{\text{driving-point} \\ \text{characteristic}}} + \underbrace{z_{12}^{**}(s)}_{\substack{\text{transfer} \\ \text{impedance}}} \tag{7-54}$$

Realization of $z_{12}^{**}(s)$ as a three-terminal structure may require an ideal transformer or a lattice structure capable of being replaced by an equivalent bridged-T or twin-T network. The general form of the network resulting from this decomposition process is shown in Fig. 7-19. The transfer impedance is contained between terminals a-a and b-b, and when $z_{12}^{**}(s)$ is realized, it must be converted to a three-terminal form to prevent the line a^*-b^* from shorting any elements.

One method for removing the driving-point function $z_{12}^*(s)$ from the transfer impedance is to determine the residues at each of the poles of $z_{12}(s)$. All poles with positive residues can be realized as $z_{12}^*(s)$. Poles with negative residues can be realized as part of $z_{12}^*(s)$ if an ideal transformer with a -1 turns ratio is employed or they can be realized as part of $z_{12}^{**}(s)$. Right half-plane zeros of $z_{12}(s)$ can be realized as a lattice network of the form shown in Table 7-1, No. 5. To prevent the line a^*-b^* from shorting part of the lattice structure, the lattice must be replaced by an equivalent three-terminal network such as a bridged or twin-T configuration. Techniques for accomplishing this step are presented in Chap. 10, Sec. 10-3.

If the transfer impedance is realized as a three-terminal network, as shown in Fig. 7-19, it is generally possible to complete the procedure according to the previously described steps. The driving-point impedances $z_{aa}(s)$ and $z_{bb}(s)$ must be determined, then $Z^*(s) = z_{11}(s) - z_{aa}(s)$

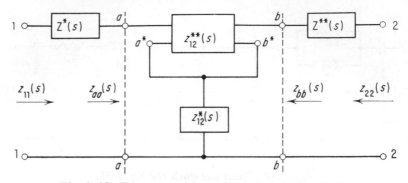

Fig. 7-19. Decomposition of $z_{12}(s)$ as in Eq. 7-54.

and $Z^{**}(s) = z_{22}(s) - z_{bb}(s)$. Because $z_{11}(s)$ and $z_{22}(s)$ are specified driving-point functions and $z_{aa}(s)$ and $z_{bb}(s)$ are the driving-point impedances seen looking into terminals a-a and b-b, respectively, $Z^*(s)$ and $Z^{**}(s)$ will be driving-point functions. Therefore, the procedures can be completed using the realization techniques of Chaps. 3 through 6. This approach will in many cases yield a realization which does not require an ideal transformer. Furthermore, an analogous approach can be accomplished on an admittance basis employing a Pi- rather than a T-network configuration.

7-4. Lucal's Procedure

Several techniques mentioned in preceding sections of this chapter have been combined by H. M. Lucal in developing a procedure to realize special classes of driving-point and transfer functions as three-terminal RC networks.† It should be pointed out that in recent literature particular emphasis has been placed on realization of RC networks. The reason for this concentration is that resistors and capacitors, which closely approximate the ideal impedance characteristics ascribed to these elements, can easily be produced at reasonable cost. In addition, a wide range of element values may be obtained having the desirable features of small physical size and low weight. Further discussion concerning the practical aspects of network synthesis as they apply to size, weight, distributed impedance losses, and element values is contained in Chap. 11.

† H. M. Lucal, "Synthesis of Three-Terminal RC Networks," *IRE Trans. Circuit Theory*, vol. CT-2, no. 4, December 1955, pp. 308–316.

Lucal's procedure involves separation of each open-circuit impedance or short-circuit admittance function into the sum of two or more component functions. It was seen in Chap. 4, Sec. 4-1, that poles and zeros of an RC driving-point function are restricted to the negative real axis of the s-plane, where they must be simple and mutually separate each other. Residues at the various poles must be real and positive. If the component impedance or admittance functions of Lucal's procedure are to be realizable in sets as component RC networks, it is necessary that restrictions be placed on them. These restrictions may be stated as follows:

1. The impedances $z_{11}(s)$ and $z_{22}(s)$ must have only finite, real, nonpositive, simple poles with real positive residues. They must also be nonnegative at infinite frequency. In the case of driving-point admittances, the functions $y_{11}(s)/s$ and $y_{22}(s)/s$, must satisfy the same conditions.

2. Residues at the poles of the various functions must satisfy the conditions of Eq. (7-37) where k_{11}^q, k_{22}^q, and k_{12}^q represent the residues at the qth pole of $z_{11}(s)$, $z_{22}(s)$, and $z_{12}(s)$ or $y_{11}(s)/s$, $y_{22}(s)/s$, and $y_{12}(s)/s$, respectively.

3. The numerator coefficients of $z_{12}(s)$ must be nonnegative and no larger than the corresponding numerator coefficients of $z_{11}(s)$ and $z_{22}(s)$. The same applies to the short-circuit admittance functions.

In addition to the above, it is also assumed that the poles of all three open-circuit impedance or short-circuit admittance functions are the same.

In general, Lucal's procedure involves decomposition of a specified set of driving-point functions into the summation of two or more component sets, each of which satisfies the conditions mentioned above. These sets represent subnetworks which may be connected in parallel if the specified functions are admittances or in series if they are impedances. A similar decomposition of the component sets, either on an impedance or admittance basis, is carried out until the resulting functions of a set are sufficiently simple to render the corresponding network obvious. For instance, a set of admittance functions may be separated into three component sets as follows:

$$
\begin{aligned}
y_{11}(s) &= \begin{bmatrix} y_{11}^a(s) \end{bmatrix} + \begin{bmatrix} y_{11}^b(s) \end{bmatrix} + \begin{bmatrix} y_{11}^c(s) \end{bmatrix} \\
y_{12}(s) &= \begin{bmatrix} y_{12}^a(s) \end{bmatrix} + \begin{bmatrix} y_{12}^b(s) \end{bmatrix} + \begin{bmatrix} y_{12}^c(s) \end{bmatrix} \\
y_{22}(s) &= \begin{bmatrix} y_{22}^a(s) \end{bmatrix} + \begin{bmatrix} y_{22}^b(s) \end{bmatrix} + \begin{bmatrix} y_{22}^c(s) \end{bmatrix}
\end{aligned}
\qquad (7\text{-}55)
$$

The brackets of this equation simply emphasize the component sets which represent three subnetworks connected in parallel. Inspection should reveal all component sets that can be realized as Pi networks of the form seen in Fig. 7-20. The remaining sets are then transformed, using the relationships of Eq. (7-13), to form a set of impedances which in turn are separated into two sets. Impedance functions are always separated into just two sets—one representing a T network which may degenerate into an L-section or a one-port structure. This is necessary because the series combination of two three-terminal subnetworks is also a three-terminal network only if one of the subnetworks is a T.

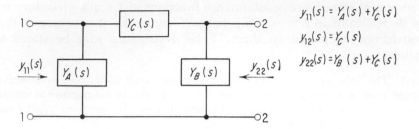

Fig. 7-20. General Pi-network on admittance basis.

To illustrate the above discussion, assume the admittances of Eq. (7-55) bearing superscripts a are transformed and separated as follows:

$$z_{11}^a(s) = \frac{y_{22}^a(s)}{y_{11}^a(s)y_{22}^a(s) - y_{12}^a(s)^2} = \left[z_{11}^{a'}(s)\right] + \left[z_{11}^{a''}(s)\right]$$

$$z_{12}^a(s) = \frac{-y_{12}^a(s)}{y_{11}^a(s)y_{22}^a(s) - y_{12}^a(s)^2} = \left[z_{12}^{a'}(s)\right] + \left[z_{12}^{a''}(s)\right]$$

$$z_{22}^a(s) = \frac{y_{11}^a(s)}{y_{11}^a(s)y_{22}^a(s) - y_{12}^a(s)^2} = \left[z_{22}^{a'}(s)\right] + \left[z_{22}^{a''}(s)\right] \quad (7\text{-}56)$$

Series connection of the subnetworks represented by the primed and double-primed impedances of Eq. (7-56) will take the form shown in Fig. 7-21. Admittance functions are not restricted in this manner since the parallel combination of any number of three-terminal subnetworks always yields a three-terminal network. It is clear that care must be taken during each step of the procedure to insure that the combination of subnetworks will result in a final three-terminal configuration.

It is a simple matter to establish whether or not a component set of admittance functions satisfies the necessary requirements once each component function is separated so that it contains only a few terms in its expansion. For instance, when the component sets are written in partial-fraction form, inspection is usually sufficient to establish whether or not the second and third requirements are satisfied. To be realizable in the form of an RC Pi network, $y_{12}(s)$ must be negative or zero and not larger than $y_{11}(s)$ or $y_{22}(s)$ at either zero or infinite frequencies. If the admittances have poles at $(s = \infty)$ or vanish at $(s = 0)$, the above statement applies to the coefficient of s in the asymptotic expression as s approaches either extreme.

The problem of separating specified functions into physically realizable sets containing only a few terms each is, in general, a trial-and-error process which may not always be possible. However, with practice

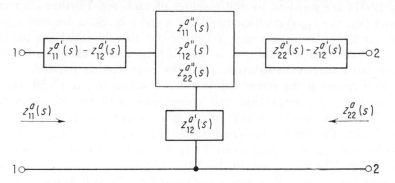

Fig. 7-21. Series combination of *T*-network and "double-primed" network.

it is not a difficult task to quickly reveal whether such a separation can be achieved. For example, consider the following set of short-circuit admittance functions:

$$y_{11}(s) = \frac{2s^3 + 18s^2 + 38s}{s^2 + 6s + 8} = \frac{2s(s + 5.618)(s + 3.382)}{(s + 2)(s + 4)}$$

$$y_{12}(s) = \frac{s^3 + 5s^2 + 2s}{s^2 + 6s + 8} = \frac{s(s + 4.562)(s + 0.438)}{(s + 2)(s + 4)}$$

$$y_{22}(s) = \frac{s^3 + 13s^2 + 28s}{s^2 + 6s + 8} = \frac{s(s + 10.275)(s + 2.725)}{(s + 2)(s + 4)} \qquad (7\text{-}57)$$

The poles and zeros of $y_{11}(s)$ and $y_{22}(s)$ are simple and lie on the negative real axis where they mutually separate each other. The poles and zeros of $y_{12}(s)$ are simple and lie on the negative real axis but do not separate one another; consequently $y_{12}(s)$ cannot be treated as a driving-point function as in the procedure of Sec. 7-3. However, the functions of Eq. (7-57) satisfy the first requirement mentioned above; therefore an attempt will be made to separate them. Performing a partial-fraction expansion yields:

$$y_{11}(s) = \overbrace{\left[2s \right.}^{a} + \overbrace{\left. \frac{5s}{(s + 2)} \right.}^{b} + \overbrace{\left. \frac{s}{(s + 4)} \right]}^{c}$$

$$y_{12}(s) = \left[s \right] + \left[\frac{-2s}{(s + 2)} \right] + \left[\frac{s}{(s + 4)} \right]$$

$$y_{22}(s) = \left[s \right] + \left[\frac{3s}{(s + 2)} \right] + \left[\frac{4s}{(s + 4)} \right] \qquad (7\text{-}58)$$

In this expansion, terms with like poles are grouped into component sets distinguished by brackets labeled a, b, and c. Inspection of the poles of $y_{11}(s)/s$, $y_{12}(s)/s$, and $y_{22}(s)/s$ reveals that the conditions of Eq. (7-37) are satisfied by the residues of each set. Further inspection shows that the $y_{12}(s)$ coefficients in the a and c brackets are nonnegative and not larger than those of $y_{11}(s)$ and $y_{22}(s)$, thereby satisfying the third requirement. As a result, it is possible to realize these two sets of bracketed functions as subnetworks to be connected in parallel.

Realization of the terms within the a brackets of Eq. (7-58) may be accomplished by inspection and comparison with the Pi network of Fig. 7-20. The network which results is a reverse L-section as shown in Fig. 7-22a. The terms contained within the c brackets of Eq. (7-58) can also be realized as a degenerate Pi (a forward L-section) as shown in Fig. 7-22b. The terms within the b brackets are not readily realized on an admittance basis; therefore employing Eq. (7-13) to transform to an impedance basis gives

$$z_{11}^b(s) = \frac{\dfrac{3s}{(s+2)}}{\left[\dfrac{5s}{(s+2)}\right]\left[\dfrac{3s}{(s+2)}\right] - \left[\dfrac{-2s}{(s+2)}\right]^2} = \frac{3}{11} + \frac{6}{11s}$$

$$z_{12}^b(s) = \frac{\dfrac{2s}{(s+2)}}{\left[\dfrac{5s}{(s+2)}\right]\left[\dfrac{3s}{(s+2)}\right] - \left[\dfrac{-2s}{(s+2)}\right]^2} = \frac{2}{11} + \frac{4}{11s}$$

$$z_{22}^b(s) = \frac{\dfrac{5s}{(s+2)}}{\left[\dfrac{5s}{(s+2)}\right]\left[\dfrac{3s}{(s+2)}\right] - \left[\dfrac{-2s}{(s+2)}\right]^2} = \frac{5}{11} + \frac{10}{11s} \tag{7-59}$$

The impedances of Eq. (7-59) can be realized by inspection as a simple T network as shown in Fig. 7-22c. The complete realization of the admittance functions specified in Eq. (7-57) is accomplished by connecting the subnetworks of Figs. 7-22a, b, and c in parallel to yield the composite network of Fig. 7-22d.

The configuration of Fig. 7-22d is not the only two-port RC network which can be synthesized to realize the functions of Eq. (7-57), nor is it necessarily the configuration requiring the fewest elements or most desirable element values. Separation of the functions of Eq. (7-57) in a different manner could conceivably lead to a more satisfactory solution. To reduce the number of elements, it is generally desirable to separate the given functions so that one or both driving-point functions of a given set equal the transfer function of the set. In this case the set can be realized as a degenerate T or Pi network. It is also desirable that each component set of admittance functions be capable of transformation

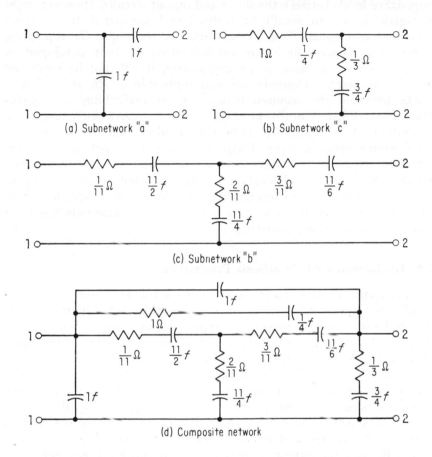

Fig. 7-22. Composite and subnetworks for realization of Eq. 7-57.

to yield realizable impedance functions. In many cases this is a hopeless task, since

1. There are no straightforward techniques for separating $y_{12}(s)$ into two or more functions each with negative numerator coefficients and having residues at the poles which satisfy Eq. (7-37) when considered along with the residues of the driving-point functions of each set.

2. There is no way of insuring that numerator coefficients of $y_{12}^q(s)$ will be smaller than the corresponding numerator coefficients of $y_{11}^q(s)$ and $y_{22}^q(s)$.

3. Even though the separation may be successful in the first cycle of the procedure, there is no insurance that it can be achieved successfully in subsequent cycles.

Finding an acceptable separation becomes increasingly difficult when $y_{12}(s)$ has right half-plane zeros and there is a large difference in impedance levels between the input and output circuits. However, right half-plane zeros can usually be realized with associated driving-point functions as parallel T or Pi networks. A technique for separating $y_{12}(s)$ when all zeros lie in the left half-plane has been developed by Ozaki; however, because of its complexity, it will not be explained here.† The above techniques are also applicable to *RL* and *LC* networks provided the required conditions for realizability are appropriately modified. Lucal's procedure can be particularly useful in realization of two-port *LC* networks required for the solution of Darlington's procedure (see Chap. 6, Sec. 6-4). Furthermore, ideal transformers and mutual inductance are not required by this procedure. Finally, *R*, *L*, and *C* elements can often be used advantageously to reduce the number of elements required to realize a specific set of functions. However, the procedure is not general in that only restricted classes of functions are realizable.

7-5. Guillemin's *RC* Synthesis Procedure

The characteristics of a two-port network are completely established if all three open-circuit impedances or short-circuit admittances are specified. In many instances the input and/or output driving-point functions do not play an important part in the anticipated employment of the network. However, to synthesize a two-port network it is imperative that the transfer function be specified. Therefore, it is often convenient to set one of the two driving-point functions equal to the transfer function such that $[z_{22}(s) = z_{12}(s)]$ or $[z_{11}(s) = z_{12}(s)]$.

The characteristics of a two-port network can also be specified in terms of the voltage and current transfer ratios [see Eqs. (7-3) and (7-7)]. Because the output terminals of the network are generally connected to a load impedance across which the voltage E_2 is measured, it is often desirable to consider the load impedance along with the transfer function. For example, the *RLC* two-port network of Fig. 7-23 is terminated by a load impedance $Z_L(s)$. The two-port structure between terminals 1-1 and 2-2 can be represented in terms of the voltages, currents, and open-circuit impedance functions of the network by Eq. (7-2). Furthermore, using the current directions of Fig. 7-23, the output voltage and current are related such that $E_2 = -I_2 Z_L(s)$. Substituting E_2 in Eq. (7-2) yields

$$E_2 = -I_2 Z_L(s) = z_{21}(s)I_1 + z_{22}(s)I_2 \qquad (7\text{-}60)$$

---

† H. Ozaki, "Synthesis of RC Three-Terminal Networks Without Ideal Transformers," *Technology Reports*, Osaka University, vol. 3, 1953.

Solving for the ratio of output to input current:

$$\frac{-I_2}{I_1} = \frac{z_{21}(s)}{Z_L(s) + z_{22}(s)} = \frac{z_{12}(s)}{Z_L(s) + z_{22}(s)} \tag{7-61}$$

Substituting $E_2/Z_L(s)$ for $-I_2$ back in Eq. (7-61) gives:

$$\frac{E_2}{I_1} = \frac{Z_L(s)z_{12}(s)}{Z_L(s) + z_{22}(s)} = G_1(s) \tag{7-62}$$

The results of Eq. (7-62) are seen to be the ratio of output voltage to input current and will be denoted as the transfer ratio $G_1(s)$. Similarly, using the short-circuit admittance functions of Eq. (7-7) and the load admittance $Y_L(s)$, the transfer ratio $G_2(s)$ is determined as follows:

$$\frac{I_2}{E_1} = \frac{Y_L(s)y_{12}(s)}{Y_L(s) + y_{22}(s)} = G_2(s) \tag{7-63}$$

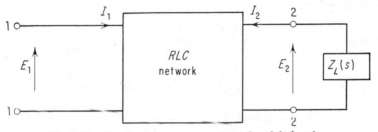

Fig. 7-23. Typical two-port network with load.

It is of interest to note that the characteristics of a two-port network are not completely defined by the transfer ratios $G_1(s)$ or $G_2(s)$, since the input driving-point functions $z_{11}(s)$ or $y_{11}(s)$ do not appear in either expression. Consequently, it is convenient to assume, for purposes of realization, that $[z_{11}(s) = z_{12}(s)]$ or $[y_{11}(s) = y_{12}(s)]$. In future discussions when only one driving-point function and the transfer function for a network are specified, it will be understood that the remaining driving-point function equals the transfer function. For example, if $y_{12}(s)$ and $y_{22}(s)$ are the only specified functions, it will be assumed that $[y_{11}(s) = y_{12}(s)]$. It should also be clear that it is possible to derive a similar set of transfer ratios which relate $z_{12}(s)$ and $z_{11}(s)$ or $y_{12}(s)$ and $y_{11}(s)$ to the load impedance.

To carry this discussion one step further, consider the case in which the load impedance is a 1-ohm resistor. In this case Eqs. (7-62) and (7-63) become

$$G_1(s) = \frac{z_{12}(s)}{1 + z_{22}(s)} \quad \text{and} \quad G_2(s) = \frac{y_{12}(s)}{1 + y_{22}(s)} \tag{7-64}$$

On the other hand, the transfer ratio of a two-port network can be expressed in general terms as the ratio of two polynomials $P(s)$ and $Q(s)$:

$$G_1(s) \text{ or } G_2(s) = \frac{a_0 + a_1 s + \cdots + a_n s^n}{b_0 + b_1 s + \cdots + b_m s^m} = \frac{P(s)}{Q(s)} \qquad (7\text{-}65)$$

The denominator polynomial $Q(s)$ can be broken into the sum of two polynomials $Q_1(s) + Q_2(s)$, in which case Eq. (7-65) can be written as

$$G_1(s) \text{ or } G_2(s) = \frac{P(s)}{Q(s)} = \frac{P(s)}{Q_1(s) + Q_2(s)} = \frac{\dfrac{P(s)}{Q_1(s)}}{1 + \dfrac{Q_2(s)}{Q_1(s)}} \qquad (7\text{-}66)$$

Comparison of Eqs. (7-64) and (7-66) reveals that both functions are of the same form; consequently it is possible to equate the various terms. Hence it follows that:

From $G_1(s)$: $\quad z_{12}(s) = \dfrac{P(s)}{Q_1(s)} \quad$ and $\quad z_{22}(s) = \dfrac{Q_2(s)}{Q_1(s)}$

From $G_2(s)$: $\quad y_{12}(s) = \dfrac{P(s)}{Q_1(s)} \quad$ and $\quad y_{22}(s) = \dfrac{Q_2(s)}{Q_1(s)} \qquad (7\text{-}67)$

Several interesting facts become clear upon inspection of Eqs. (7-66) and (7-67). Because $G_1(s)$ and $G_2(s)$ are transfer ratios, there are no restrictions on the zeros of either function; therefore $P(s)$ may have zeros anywhere in the s-plane. These zeros are transferred intact to the transfer functions $z_{12}(s)$ and $y_{12}(s)$. The poles of $G_1(s)$ or $G_2(s)$ form $Q(s)$ and are restricted to the left half of the s-plane. Consequently, if $Q(s)$ can be separated into $Q_1(s) + Q_2(s)$ such that $z_{22}(s)$ or $y_{22}(s)$ of Eq. (7-67) meet the requirements of driving-point functions, it may be possible to realize a two-port network terminated by a 1-ohm resistor which possesses the specified transfer ratio characteristics.

Guillemin's procedure makes it possible to realize a transfer ratio, within a constant multiplier, by an RC network terminated in a 1-ohm resistor.† The constant multiplier can then be compensated for with a series amplifier or attenuator to give the desired results. Because the procedure is somewhat complicated, its explanation will be done on an admittance basis, although the same techniques can be used for realizing impedance functions. Furthermore, the specified transfer ratio will be denoted simply as $G(s)$ rather than differentiating between $G_1(s)$ and $G_2(s)$ as in the above discussion.

† E. A. Guillemin, "Synthesis of RC-Networks," *J. Math. Phys.*, vol. 28, no. 1, 1949, pp. 22–42.

To be realizable in the form of an *RC* network by Guillemin's procedure, a transfer ratio $G(s)$ must be restricted such that:

1. Its poles are simple and lie on the negative real axis.
2. The degree of the numerator cannot be greater than that of the denominator.

Zeros of $G(s)$ are arbitrary and can be located anywhere on the s-plane. Therefore, the given transfer ratio can be written as

$$G(s) = \frac{P(s)}{Q(s)} = \frac{a_0 + a_1 s + a_2 s^2 + \cdots + a_n s^n}{b_0 + b_1 s + b_2 s^2 + \cdots + b_m s^m} \Bigg]_{m \geq n} \qquad (7\text{-}68)$$

In this discussion, it will be assumed that $(m = n)$; however, functions for which $(m < n)$ can be synthesized by the same procedure.

The first step of Guillemin's procedure requires that the transfer ratio be converted to the form of Eq. (7-66) or (7-67). Therefore it is necessary that $Q(s)$ of the transfer ratio be broken into $Q_1(s) + Q_2(s)$. The denominator of Eq. (7-68) can be written in factored form as

$$G(s) = \frac{P(s)}{Q(s)} = \frac{a_0 + a_1 s + a_2 s^2 + \cdots + a_n s^n}{b_n(s + \sigma_1)(s + \sigma_3)(s + \sigma_5) \cdots (s + \sigma_{2n-1})}$$

where $\qquad 0 < \sigma_1 < \sigma_3 < \sigma_5 \cdots \sigma_{2n-1}$ $\qquad (7\text{-}69)$

The poles of Eq. (7-69) lie on the negative real axis at $s = -\sigma_1, s = -\sigma_3$, $s = -\sigma_5, \ldots, s = -\sigma_{2n-1}$. These poles have been purposely defined with odd-numbered subscripts and are shown in Fig. 7-24a. The denominator can be split into $Q_1(s) + Q_2(s)$ by forming a polynomial $Q_1(s)$ in which values are chosen for $\sigma_2, \sigma_4, \sigma_6, \ldots, \sigma_{2n}$ such that they mutually separate the poles at $\sigma_1, \sigma_3, \sigma_5, \ldots, \sigma_{2n-1}$. This is illustrated in Fig. 7-24b. The reason for choosing the terms with even-numbered subscripts such that they mutually separate the poles of $G(s)$ is that this selection will insure the network can be realized with only *RC* elements. The even-numbered values of σ form the zeros of $Q_1(s)$, and the odd-numbered values form the zeros of $Q_2(s)$. Referring to Eq. (7-67), it is seen that $[y_{22}(s) = Q_2(s)/Q_1(s)]$; therefore, if this function is to be realized as an *RC* network, its poles and zeros [i.e., zeros of $Q_1(s)$ and $Q_2(s)$] must mutually separate each other. Because $Q(s)$ represents the poles of the transfer ratio and $[Q(s) = Q_1(s) + Q_2(s)]$, the zeros of $Q(s)$ and $Q_2(s)$ are denoted in Fig. 7-24 by X's.

The polynomial $Q_1(s)$ can be written as

$$Q_1(s) = d(s + \sigma_2)(s + \sigma_4)(s + \sigma_6) \cdots (s + \sigma_{2n})$$

where $\qquad 0 < \sigma_1 < \sigma_2 < \sigma_3 < \sigma_4 < \sigma_5 < \sigma_6 \cdots \sigma_{2n-1} < \sigma_{2n}$ $\qquad (7\text{-}70)$

The constant multiplier d must be restricted such that

$$d(\sigma_2)(\sigma_4)(\sigma_6) \cdots (\sigma_{2n}) < b_0 = b_n(\sigma_1)(\sigma_3)(\sigma_5) \cdots (\sigma_{2n-1}) \qquad (7\text{-}71)$$

Selection of d such that this condition is satisfied completes the determination of $Q_1(s)$. It is then a simple matter to compute $Q_2(s)$ since

$$Q_2(s) = Q(s) - Q_1(s) \tag{7-72}$$

Once $Q_2(s)$ has been determined, $P(s)$, $Q_1(s)$, and $Q_2(s)$ can be used to establish $y_{12}(s)$ and $y_{22}(s)$ from Eq. (7-67). It should be noted that

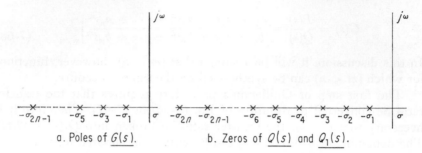

a. Poles of $G(s)$. b. Zeros of $Q(s)$ and $Q_1(s)$.

Fig. 7-24. Separation of the poles of $G(s)$.

$Q_1(s)$ is the denominator of both $y_{12}(s)$ and $y_{22}(s)$. Furthermore, $y_{22}(s)$ is a driving-point admittance and $y_{12}(s)$ is a transfer admittance.

The admittance $y_{12}(s)$ can be broken up as indicated in Eq. (7-73).

$$
\begin{aligned}
y_{12}(s) &= \frac{P(s)}{Q_1(s)} = \frac{a_0 + a_1 s + a_2 s^2 + \cdots + a_n s^n}{Q_1(s)} \\
&= \frac{a_0}{Q_1(s)} + \frac{a_1 s}{Q_1(s)} + \frac{a_2 s^2}{Q_1(s)} + \cdots + \frac{a_n s^n}{Q_1(s)} \\
&= y_{12}^0(s) + y_{12}^1(s) + y_{12}^2(s) + \cdots + y_{12}^n(s)
\end{aligned}
\tag{7-73}
$$

Hence the transfer admittance has been broken into the sum of a number of admittances which are denoted by the superscripts $0, 1, 2, \ldots, n$. Likewise, $y_{22}(s)$ can be expanded in n different ways, and these expansions will be denoted as $y_{22}^0(s), y_{22}^1(s), y_{22}^2(s), \ldots, y_{22}^n(s)$. The expansions of $y_{22}(s)$ must be performed in such a manner that each expansion realizes the form of one of the $y_{12}^n(s)$ terms. For instance, the form of $y_{12}^0(s)$ and $y_{22}^0(s)$ is realized by one subnetwork, whereas the form of $y_{12}^1(s)$ and $y_{22}^1(s)$ is realized by another, etc., until the designer has n different subnetworks, each with the desired $y_{22}(s)$ and a portion of the desired $y_{12}(s)$. To complete the realization, the n subnetworks must be adjusted in terms of admittance levels and combined in parallel. Consequently, the procedure leads to a network of the form of Fig. 7-25; however, it can also be developed on an impedance basis, in which case the resulting network will be a series combination of subnetworks.

When combining the n subnetworks, the resulting $y_{22}(s)$ will differ from its desired value by a constant multiplying factor unless admittance level adjustments are made before the subnetworks are combined. However, the transfer admittance $y_{12}(s)$ will differ from its desired value by a constant multiplying factor if this is done. It is desirable to obtain the proper $y_{22}(s)$, since the constant multiplying factor associated with

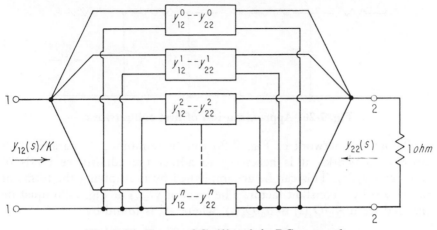

Fig. 7-25. Form of Guillemin's *RC* network.

the resulting $y_{12}(s)$ can be corrected for by using amplification or attenuation networks in series with the synthesized network. The details of the adjustment procedure will be investigated later and will be demonstrated in an example.

It is now possible to consider in detail the manner in which the various subnetworks can be realized. Inspection of Eq. (7-73) reveals that $y_{12}(s)$ has been broken into n parts, and therefore n subnetworks must be realized. Consequently, $y_{22}(s)$ must be expanded in n different ways, and each of these expansions must realize one of the $y_{12}(s)$ terms. For example, if $y_{22}(s)$ is written as

$$y_{22}(s) = \frac{Q_2(s)}{Q_1(s)} = \frac{p_0 + p_1 s + p_2 s^2 + \cdots + p_n s^n}{h_0 + h_1 s + h_2 s^2 + \cdots + h_n s^n} \qquad (7\text{-}74)$$

then the first method of expansion is to perform a complete forward continued-fraction expansion of $1/y_{22}(s)$. This expansion can be written as follows and will be denoted by $y_{22}^0(s)$, because it will realize the form of the $y_{12}^0(s)$ term.

$$y_{22}^0(s) = \frac{1}{y_{22}(s)} = r_1 + \cfrac{1}{C_1 s + \cfrac{1}{r_2 + \cfrac{1}{C_2 s \cdots \cfrac{}{\ddots \cfrac{1}{r_{n+1}}}}}}$$

where $r_1 = h_n/p_n$ $(7\text{-}75)$

This expansion has a network of the form shown in Fig. 7-26. The $y_{12}^0(s)$ term is realized by this form of network, since $[y_{12}^0(s) = a_0/Q_1(s)]$. Furthermore, the network realizes the desired $y_{22}(s)$.

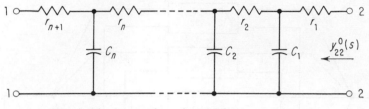

Fig. 7-26. Approximation of first subnetwork.

Before the network of Fig. 7-26 can be combined in parallel with other subnetworks, it is necessary to adjust the admittance levels of $y_{22}^0(s)$ and $y_{12}^0(s)$. This can be accomplished by multiplying the terms of Eq. (7-75) by a constant factor. The level of $y_{12}^0(s)$ of Fig. 7-26 must be changed from $A_0/Q_1(s)$ to $a_0/Q_1(s)$, where A_0 is found by

$$A_0 = \frac{Q_1 \text{ with } s \text{ equal to zero}}{r_1 + r_2 + \cdots + r_{n+1}} \tag{7-76}$$

Multiplying $y_{12}^0(s)$ of Fig. 7-26 by a constant factor a_0/A_0K yields

$$y_{12}^0(s) = \left[\frac{A_0}{Q_1(s)}\right]\frac{a_0}{A_0K} = \frac{1}{K}\left[\frac{a_0}{Q_1(s)}\right] \tag{7-77}$$

This is seen to be $1/K$ times the desired $y_{12}^0(s)$, but the same multiplication must be done to $y_{22}^0(s)$:

$$y_{22}^0(s) = \left[\frac{Q_2(s)}{Q_1(s)}\right]\frac{a_0}{A_0K} \tag{7-78}$$

This forms a new $y_{22}^0(s)$ which is a_0/A_0K of the total or desired $y_{22}(s)$. The relationships of Eqs. (7-77) and (7-78) represent an adjusted network similar to Fig. 7-26 in which all of the shunt terms are multiplied by a_0/A_0K and all of the series terms are divided by the same factor.

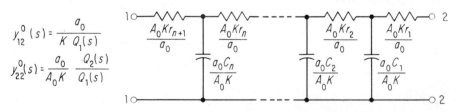

$$y_{12}^0(s) = \frac{a_0}{K\,Q_1(s)}$$

$$y_{22}^0(s) = \frac{a_0}{A_0K}\frac{Q_2(s)}{Q_1(s)}$$

Fig. 7-27. First subnetwork of Guillemin's procedure.

This completes the first subnetwork, which takes the form of Fig. 7-27, and the problem of establishing the value of K will be explained shortly. To realize the form of $y_{12}^1(s)$, one cycle of backward continued-fraction expansion is practiced on $y_{22}(s)$ of Eq. (7-74), and the process is completed in the forward direction. This technique yields an expansion of the following form:

$$y_{22}^1(s) = g_1 + \cfrac{1}{\cfrac{1}{C_1}s^{-1} + r_2 + \cfrac{1}{C_2 s \cdot \cdot \cdot \cdot \cfrac{1}{r_{n+1}}}}$$

where
$$g_1 = p_0/h_0 \qquad\qquad (7\text{-}79)$$

This expansion gives the network of Fig. 7-28, thereby realizing $y_{22}^1(s)$ and $y_{12}^1(s)$ which is of the form $[y_{12}^1(s) = a_1 s/Q_1(s)]$. As in the first case,

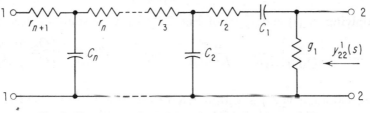

Fig. 7-28. Approximation of second subnetwork.

the network must be adjusted to represent the desired admittance functions. For instance, $y_{12}^1(s)$ of Fig. 7-28 equals $A_1 s/Q_1(s)$ rather than $a_1 s/Q_1(s)$, where A_1 is given by

$$A_1 = \frac{Q_1 \text{ with } s \text{ equal to zero}}{\dfrac{1}{C_1}} \qquad\qquad (7\text{-}80)$$

Multiplying $y_{12}^1(s)$ and $y_{22}^1(s)$ of Fig. 7-28 by a constant, $a_1/A_1 K$ yields:

$$y_{12}^1(s) = \left[\frac{A_1 s}{Q_1(s)}\right]\frac{a_1}{A_1 K} = \frac{a_1 s}{K Q_1(s)} \quad \text{and} \quad y_{22}^1(s) = \left[\frac{Q_2(s)}{Q_1(s)}\right]\frac{a_1}{A_1 K}$$

$$(7\text{-}81)$$

The new $y_{12}^1(s)$ is again $1/K$ times its desired value and $y_{22}^1(s)$ is a fraction $a_1/A_1 K$ of the desired $y_{22}(s)$. Furthermore, all shunt terms in the network of Fig. 7-28 are multiplied by $a_1/A_1 K$, and all series terms are divided by the same factor.

The third subnetwork is obtained by expanding $y_{22}(s)$ using two cycles of backward expansion and the remainder of the function by forward expansion:

$$y_{22}^2(s) = g_1 + \cfrac{1}{\cfrac{s^{-1}}{C_1} + \cfrac{1}{g_2 + \cfrac{1}{\cfrac{s^{-1}}{C_2} + r_3 + \cfrac{1}{C_3 s \cdots \cfrac{\cdot\cdot}{\cdot} \cfrac{1}{r_{n+1}}}}}}$$

where $\qquad\qquad g_1 = p_0/h_0 \qquad\qquad$ (7-82)

This expansion represents the network shown in Fig. 7-29, which realizes $y_{22}^2(s)$ and the form of $y_{12}^2(s)$. The level of $y_{12}^2(s)$ must be adjusted from $A_2 s^2/Q_1(s)$ to $a_2 s^2/Q_1(s)$ using the factor

$$A_2 = \frac{Q_1 \text{ with } s \text{ equal to zero}}{\dfrac{g_2}{C_1 C_2}}$$

(7-83)

Multiplying $y_{12}^2(s)$ and $y_{22}^2(s)$ of Fig. 7-29 by a constant $a_2/A_2 K$ gives

$$y_{12}^2(s) = \left[\frac{A_2 s^2}{Q_1(s)}\right]\frac{a_2}{A_2 K} = \frac{a_2 s^2}{K Q_1(s)} \quad \text{and} \quad y_{22}^2(s) = \left[\frac{Q_2(s)}{Q_1(s)}\right]\frac{a_2}{A_2 K}$$

(7-84)

In this equation $y_{12}^2(s)$ is within $1/K$ of the desired value, and the new $y_{22}^2(s)$ is a fraction $a_2/A_2 K$ of the desired $y_{22}(s)$. To complete the adjustment of the third subnetwork, the shunt terms of Fig. 7-29 must be multiplied by $a_2/A_2 K$ and the series terms must be divided by the same factor.

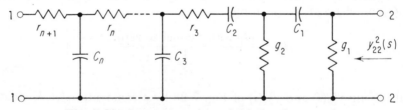

Fig. 7-29. Approximation of third subnetwork.

This procedure is continued until the nth subnetwork is obtained. In the determination of the nth subnetwork, n cycles of backward expansion are practiced and no forward expansion. The adjustment factor for the nth network will be of the form

$$A_n = \frac{Q_1 \text{ with } s \text{ equal to zero}}{(g_2 g_3 \cdots g_n)\left[\dfrac{1}{C_1 C_2 \ldots C_n}\right]}$$

(7-85)

Multiplying $y_{12}^n(s)$ and $y_{22}^n(s)$ by a_n/A_nK gives

$$y_{12}^n(s) = \frac{a_n s^n}{KQ_1(s)} \quad \text{and} \quad y_{22}^n(s) = \left[\frac{Q_2(s)}{Q_1(s)}\right]\frac{a_n}{A_nK} \quad (7\text{-}86)$$

The $y_{22}^n(s)$ driving-point admittances of the adjusted subnetworks are fractions of the desired $y_{22}(s)$. In addition, each adjusted subnetwork realizes one of the $y_{12}^n(s)$ terms within a constant $1/K$ of the desired value. Therefore, when all the A values have been determined and since $a_0, a_1, a_2, \ldots, a_n$ are known, it is possible to combine the subnetworks in parallel and then determine K such that the desired $y_{22}(s)$ is realized. When this is done, it is possible to write the following equation for $y_{22}(s)$ based on the adjusted $y_{22}^n(s)$ terms:

$$\begin{aligned}
y_{22}(s) &= y_{22}^0(s) + y_{22}^1(s) + y_{22}^2(s) + \cdots + y_{22}^n(s) \\
&= \frac{a_0}{KA_0}\frac{Q_2(s)}{Q_1(s)} + \frac{a_1}{KA_1}\frac{Q_2(s)}{Q_1(s)} + \frac{a_2}{KA_2}\frac{Q_2(s)}{Q_1(s)} + \cdots + \frac{a_n}{KA_n}\frac{Q_2(s)}{Q_1(s)} \\
&= \frac{1}{K}\frac{Q_2(s)}{Q_1(s)}\left(\frac{a_0}{A_0} + \frac{a_1}{A_1} + \frac{a_2}{A_2} + \cdots + \frac{a_n}{A_n}\right) \quad (7\text{-}87)
\end{aligned}$$

Since $y_{22}(s)$ must equal $Q_2(s)/Q_1(s)$, then

$$K = \left(\frac{a_0}{A_0} + \frac{a_1}{A_1} + \frac{a_2}{A_2} + \cdots + \frac{a_n}{A_n}\right) \quad (7\text{-}88)$$

In this relationship, the a's and A's are known; therefore K can be computed such that when the subnetworks are combined the desired $y_{22}(s) = Q_2(s)/Q_1(s)$ is obtained. The new or adjusted transfer admittances $y_{12}^n(s)$ add to give the overall transfer admittance $y_{12}(s)$ as follows:

$$\begin{aligned}
y_{12}(s) &= \frac{a_0}{KQ_1(s)} + \frac{a_1 s}{KQ_1(s)} + \frac{a_2 s^2}{KQ_1(s)} + \cdots + \frac{a_n s^n}{KQ_1(s)} \\
&= \frac{1}{K}\left(\frac{a_0 + a_1 s + a_2 s^2 + \cdots + a_n s^2}{Q_1(s)}\right) = \frac{1}{K}\frac{P(s)}{Q_1(s)} \quad (7\text{-}89)
\end{aligned}$$

The overall transfer ratio of the synthesized network, which is terminated in a 1-ohm resistor, can be written in terms of the adjusted admittance functions in the form of Eq. (7-66) as follows:

$$G(s) = \frac{y_{12}(s)}{1 + y_{22}(s)} = \frac{\dfrac{1}{K}\dfrac{P(s)}{Q_1(s)}}{1 + \dfrac{Q_2(s)}{Q_1(s)}} = \frac{1}{K}\frac{P(s)}{Q(s)}$$

where $$Q(s) = Q_1(s) + Q_2(s) \quad (7\text{-}90)$$

This shows that the resultant transfer ratio will be within a constant $1/K$ of the desired function.

As an example of Guillemin's procedure, assume that it is desirable to synthesize an RC two-port network with the following transfer-ratio characteristics:

$$G(s) = \frac{I_2}{E_1} = \frac{2s + 3}{s^2 + 8s + 15} = \frac{P(s)}{Q(s)} \tag{7-91}$$

The first step in the procedure is the separation of $Q(s)$ into two polynomials. Therefore, writing $Q(s)$ in factored form and denoting the roots as σ_1 and σ_3 gives

$$Q(s) = s^2 + 8s + 15 = (s + 3)(s + 5)$$

where $\quad s = -\sigma_1 = -3 \quad$ and $\quad s = -\sigma_3 = -5 \tag{7-92}$

It is now possible to write a polynomial $Q_1(s)$ in the form of Eq. (7-70) by choosing σ_2 and σ_4 such that these roots alternate with those of Eq. (7-92) along the negative real axis. For this example, choose the new roots at $(s = -\sigma_2 = -4)$ and $(s = -\sigma_4 = -6)$.

$$Q_1(s) = d(s + 4)(s + 6) = d(s^2 + 10s + 24) \tag{7-93}$$

The value of d must satisfy the conditions of Eq. (7-71); hence, for this example, $[d(4)(6) \leq (3)(5)]$. Choosing a value for d of $1/2$ and substituting it in Eq. (7-93) yields

$$Q_1(s) = \frac{1}{2}(s^2 + 10s + 24) = \frac{s^2}{2} + 5s + 12 \tag{7-94}$$

Using Eqs. (7-92) and (7-94), the expression for $Q_2(s)$ can be determined as follows:

$$Q_2(s) = Q(s) - Q_1(s)$$

$$= (s^2 + 8s + 15) - \left(\frac{s^2}{2} + 5s + 12\right)$$

$$= \frac{s^2}{2} + 3s + 3 \tag{7-95}$$

It is now possible to write $y_{12}(s)$ and $y_{22}(s)$ using $P(s)$, $Q_1(s)$, and $Q_2(s)$ as in Eq. (7-67).

$$y_{12}(s) = \frac{3 + 2s}{\dfrac{s^2}{2} + 5s + 12} = \frac{a_0}{Q_1(s)} + \frac{a_1 s}{Q_1(s)}$$

$$y_{22}(s) = \frac{\dfrac{s^2}{2} + 3s + 3}{\dfrac{s^2}{2} + 5s + 12} = \frac{s^2 + 6s + 6}{s^2 + 10s + 24} \tag{7-96}$$

Both these admittances possess the same denominator, and because $y_{12}(s)$ has been broken into two factors, there will be two subnetworks. The first of these subnetworks will be the $y_{22}^0(s)$ network, which realizes $[y_{12}^0(s) = a_0/Q_1(s)]$. This network is found by expanding $1/y_{22}^0(s)$ in a complete forward expansion similar to Eq. (7-75):

$$y_{22}^0(s) = \frac{1}{y_{22}(s)} = 1 + \cfrac{1}{\cfrac{s}{4} + \cfrac{1}{\cfrac{8}{3} + \cfrac{1}{3s + \cfrac{1}{1}{3}}}}$$

(7-97)

This expansion yields the network of Fig. 7-30 which must be adjusted before combining it with the second subnetwork.

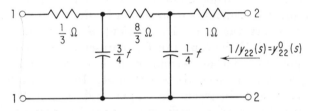

Fig. 7-30. **First unadjusted subnetwork.**

Before computing adjustment factors, it is desirable to determine the second subnetwork for $y_{22}^1(s)$ which realizes $[y_{12}^1(s) = a_1 s/Q_1(s)]$. This network is determined by making one cycle of backward expansion before the forward expansion of $y_{22}(s)$ similar to Eq. (7-79):

$$y_{22}^1(s) = \frac{1}{4} + \cfrac{1}{\cfrac{48}{7}s^{-1} + \cfrac{4}{3} + \cfrac{1}{\cfrac{63s}{16} + \cfrac{1}{\cfrac{8}{147}}}}$$

(7-98)

This expansion gives the second unadjusted network as seen in Fig. 7-31.

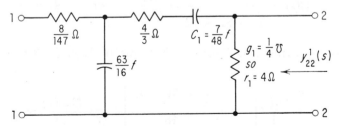

Fig. 7-31. **Second unadjusted subnetwork.**

Now that the unadjusted networks have been determined, the adjustment factors for each subnetwork can be computed. Two methods can be used to obtain the values of A_0 and A_1. One method is based on the fact that A is the multiplying coefficient of the unadjusted network's transfer function $y_{12}^n(s)$. For example, $y_{12}^0(s)$ for the unadjusted network of Fig. 7-30 can be written as

$$y_{12}^0(s) = \frac{3}{\dfrac{s^2}{2} + 5s + 12} = \frac{A_0}{Q_1(s)} \qquad \text{or} \qquad A_0 = 3 \tag{7-99}$$

The second method is to use Eq. (7-85) or its special cases which are based on the fact that the transfer coefficient of an RC network can be determined with reasonable accuracy at low frequencies. This point deserves further explanation; therefore, consider the network of Fig. 7-30. In this case the major admittance between the input and output terminals at low frequencies is represented by the series resistors; hence Eq. (7-76) provides the desired coefficient A_0 as s approaches zero. Similarly, in Fig. 7-31 the capacitor C_1 represents the major admittance between input and output terminals at low frequencies; therefore Eq. (7-80) provides the desired coefficient A_1. In like manner, as series capacitors are added between the input and output terminals, the expression for the transfer coefficient approaches that of Eq. (7-85). However, this equation is only an approximation made at low frequencies and can lead to results that are not precise.

As an example of the application of Eq. (7-85), the appropriate terms of Eqs. (7-96) and (7-97) can be used to compute A_0:

$$A_0 = \left. \frac{Q_1(s)}{r_1 + r_2 + r_3} \right]_{s=0} = \left. \frac{\dfrac{s^2}{2} + 5s + 12}{\dfrac{1}{3} + \dfrac{8}{3} + 1} \right]_{s=0} = \frac{12}{4} = 3 \tag{7-100}$$

The value of A_1 can be determined by solving for $y_{12}^1(s)$ of the second unadjusted network, Fig. 7-31:

$$y_{12}^1(s) = \frac{\dfrac{7s}{4}}{\dfrac{s^2}{2} + 5s + 12} = \frac{A_1 s}{Q_1(s)} \qquad \text{or} \qquad A_1 = \frac{7}{4} \tag{7-101}$$

Similarly, applying Eq. (7-85) with terms of Eqs. (7-96) and (7-98) yields

$$A_1 = \left. \frac{Q_1(s)}{\dfrac{1}{C_1}} \right]_{s=0} = \left. \frac{\dfrac{s^2}{2} + 5s + 12}{\dfrac{48}{7}} \right]_{s=0} = \frac{(12)(7)}{48} = \frac{7}{4} \tag{7-102}$$

Having determined A_0 and A_1, it is possible to compute the constant K. From Eq. (7-96) it is seen that $a_0 = 3$ and $a_1 = 2$. Equations (7-99) through (7-102) reveal that $A_0 = 3$ and $A_1 = 7/4$; consequently, substituting these terms into Eq. (7-88) gives

$$K = \left[\frac{a_0}{A_0} + \frac{a_1}{A_1} \right] = \left[\frac{3}{3} + \frac{2}{\frac{7}{4}} \right] = \frac{15}{7}$$

$$(7\text{-}103)$$

The two adjustment factors $a_0/A_0 K$ and $a_1/A_1 K$ can then be determined from the above parameters as

$$\frac{a_0}{A_0 K} = \frac{7}{15} \quad \text{and} \quad \frac{a_1}{A_1 K} = \frac{8}{15} \qquad (7\text{-}104)$$

The subnetworks of Figs. 7-30 and 7-31 are adjusted by multiplying all shunt elements and dividing all series elements by the appropriate form of Eq. (7-104). The admittance functions of the resulting subnetworks are also adjusted by the same factors. The $a_0/A_0 K$ and $a_1/A_1 K$ factors are related to the subnetworks of Figs. 7-30 and 7-31 respectively. The adjusted subnetworks take the form seen in Fig. 7-32a and b. These subnetworks must be combined in parallel and terminated by a 1-ohm resistor to complete the final network which is within a constant $(1/K = 7/15)$ of the desired result specified by Eq. (7-91). The final network is shown in Fig. 7-32c.

Several checks can be made to determine whether or not the final network is correct. For instance, it is noted that the subnetwork of Fig. 7-32a realizes 7/15 and that of Fig. 32b realizes the remaining 8/15 of $y_{22}(s)$. A check can also be made to determine if the ratio I_2/E_1 is $1/K$ of the desired value given by Eq. (7-91). Figure 7-32c reveals that there is only one path for direct current to flow from the input to the output. The resistance of this path to ground is

$$R = \frac{5}{7} + \frac{40}{7} + \frac{15}{7} + \frac{\frac{15}{2}}{1 + \frac{15}{2}} = \frac{(75)(15)}{(7)(17)} \quad \text{ohms}$$

$$(7\text{-}105)$$

The output voltage appears across 15/17 of this, so at zero frequency:

$$\left. \frac{I_2}{E_1} \right]_{s=0} = \frac{\frac{15}{17}}{\frac{(75)(15)}{(7)(17)}} = \frac{7}{75}$$

$$(7\text{-}106)$$

Substituting $s = 0$ in Eq. (7-91) and multiplying the result by $1/K = 7/15$ gives $I_2/E_1 = 7/75$ which is in agreement with Eq. (7-106).

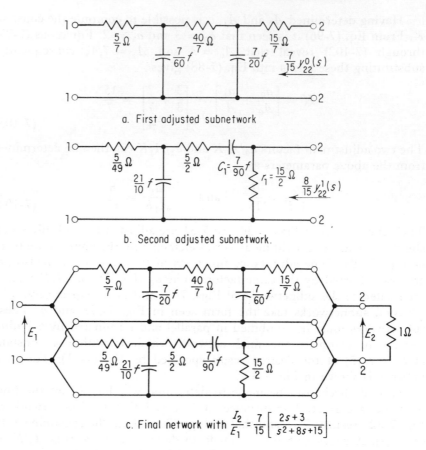

a. First adjusted subnetwork

b. Second adjusted subnetwork.

c. Final network with $\dfrac{I_2}{E_1} = \dfrac{7}{15}\left[\dfrac{2s+3}{s^2+8s+15}\right]$.

Fig. 7-32. Adjusted subnetworks and final configuration for the example of Eq. 7-91.

Guillemin's procedure can be used to obtain a simplified network of the same form and still within a constant of the desired result if the equation for $y_{12}(s)$ is written as

$$y_{12}(s) = \frac{P(s)}{Q_1(s)} = \frac{a_0 + a_1 s}{Q_1(s)} + \frac{a_2 s^2 + a_3 s^3}{Q_1(s)} + \cdots + \frac{a_{n-1}s^{n-1} + a_n s^n}{Q_1(s)}$$

$$(7\text{-}107)$$

In this case the number of ladder networks needed to synthesize the result is cut in half, and each of the $y_{12}^q(s)$ terms must be realized by one of the expansions of $y_{22}(s)$. Depending on whether n is odd or even, the last term will have a numerator containing one or two component terms. If only one term is present, the last $y_{12}(s)$ term can be determined in the manner described in the previous example. The subnetworks representing the $y_{12}(s)$ terms must be adjusted, as before, by a constant multiplier. These multipliers can be denoted by $B_1, B_2, B_3, \ldots, B_q$, where the subscripts indicate the individual ladder networks. The admittance level $y_{22}^q(s)$ of each ladder is adjusted by multiplying by factors $H_1, H_2, H_3, \ldots, H_q$, and these factors are chosen such that

$$H_1 + H_2 + H_3 + \cdots + H_q = 1 \qquad (7\text{-}108)$$

Each element of each ladder is adjusted by the factor H for that ladder, and if the overall $y_{12}(s)$ of the network is to be adjusted, then

$$B_1 H_1 = B_2 H_2 = B_3 H_3 = \cdots = B_q H_q \qquad (7\text{-}109)$$

This equation is solved for the values of H, and the final network is formed by combining the subnetworks in parallel and terminating them in a 1-ohm resistor as in Fig. 7-25.† It is not necessary that the load impedance be a 1-ohm resistor. For instance, Eqs. (7-62) and (7-63) give the transfer ratio in terms of the two-port transfer and driving-point functions as well as the load impedance or admittance. Using these equations, the procedure can often be modified to take into account the desired load impedance.

7-6. Dasher's *RC* Synthesis Procedure

This section is devoted to an explanation of Dasher's procedure which is based on the series connection of individual *RC* ladder and bridged-T or twin-T sections to realize a given driving-point and transfer admittance.‡ As in Guillemin's procedure, Dasher's technique also yields a network which realizes the desired functions within a constant multiplier. The driving-point and transfer admittance may be derived from a specified transfer ratio in the manner described for Guillemin's procedure. Furthermore, the functions must satisfy the same set of restrictions if they are to be realizable as an *RC* two-port network. Namely, the poles and zeros of the driving-point admittance must lie on the negative real axis where they mutually separate each other. The poles of the transfer admittance must be the same as those of the driving-point function, although zeros of the transfer admittance may lie anywhere in the *s*-plane.

† J. G. Truxal, *Automatic Feedback Control System Synthesis* (New York: McGraw-Hill Book Co., Inc., 1955), pp. 203–206.

‡ B. J. Dasher's procedure was originally presented in (1) Research Laboratory of Electronics (MIT), *Technical Report*, No. 215 (November 20, 1951), and (2) Professional Group on Circuit Theory, *IRE Trans.*, December 1952.

In Dasher's procedure, the real zeros of the transfer admittance are realized as a ladder network, then all complex zeros are realized in pairs to form ladder sections with some negative RC terms. These ladder sections are later replaced by a bridged-T or twin-T section which is equivalent and contains only positive elements. It will be assumed, for the sake of discussion, that $y_{11}(s)$ and $y_{12}(s)$ are specified, in which case the procedure can be explained as a series of steps.

Step 1. All poles of $y_{11}(s)$ not present in $y_{12}(s)$ are removed as a shunt admittance which can be denoted as $Y_1(s)$. The remaining admittance represents $Y_2(s)$, and the network takes the form seen to the left of Fig. 7-33.

Step 2. Part of $Y_2(s)$ is synthesized as a ladder network to realize the real zeros of $y_{12}(s)$. An RC remainder function $Y_3(s)$ results which contains the conjugate complex zeros of $y_{12}(s)$. The center portion of Fig. 7-33 illustrates this step of the procedure.

Step 3. As a third step, one pair of conjugate complex zeros of $y_{12}(s)$ are considered and can be denoted as

$$s_o = -a_o + jb_o = \omega_o \underline{/\phi_o} \qquad \text{and} \qquad s_o = -a_o - jb_o = \omega_o \underline{/-\phi_o}$$
$$(7\text{-}110)$$

The values of a_o, b_o, and ω_o must be determined for future use.

Step 4. In Step 4 part of a pole of $Y_3(s)$ is removed to create the first portion of a zero-producing Pi-section. The Pi-section may possess negative elements; therefore, this step must be restricted in the following manner if the structure is to be replaced later by an equivalent bridged-T or twin-T network possessing only positive elements.

(a) If $Y_3(s)$ is the ratio of a quadratic function to a linear function, then enough of a pole of $Y_3(s)$ must be removed to make the product of the zeros of $Y_3(s)$ equal ω_o^2.

(b) If $Y_3(s)$ is more complicated, then $Y_4(s)$ must satisfy the following condition.

$$Y_4(s) = k_0 + \sum_{q=1}^{n} \frac{k_q s}{(s + \sigma_q)} + k_\infty s$$

where

$$k_\infty \sum_{q=1}^{n} \frac{k_q \sigma_q}{\varphi_q^4} - k_0 \sum_{q=1}^{n} \frac{k_q \sigma_q^2}{\varphi_q^4 \varphi_o^2} + \frac{1}{2} \sum_{q=1}^{n} \sum_{\mu=1}^{n} \frac{k_q k_\mu (\sigma_q - \sigma_\mu)^2 (\sigma_q \sigma_\mu - \omega_o^2)}{\varphi_q^4 \varphi_\mu^4} = 0$$

and
$$\varphi_q^2 = b_o^2 + (\sigma_q - s_o)^2 \qquad (7\text{-}111)$$

If this condition is not satisfied by reducing the residues of $Y_3(s)$, it can be satisfied by removing part of a pole of $s/Y_3(s)$ which is the same as inserting a series element in the network. The completion of this step is represented by the right-hand portion of Fig. 7-33, and $Y_4(s)$ is now prepared for the realization of the zero-producing section.

Step 5. This step of the procedure is based on the realization of a Pi-section of the type seen in Fig. 7-34. The stars on the admittance functions indicate that they express the characteristics of the section

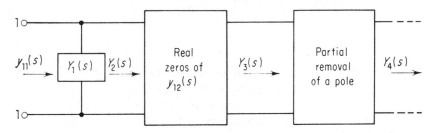

Fig. 7-33. Network prepared for zero-producing section.

but are not the final result. The values for these admittance functions are determined such that

$$y_{11}^* = c_0\left[s + \frac{\omega_0^2}{\sigma_0} + \beta\left(\sigma_0 + \frac{\omega_0^2}{\sigma_0} - 2a_0\right)\frac{s}{s + \sigma_0}\right]$$

$$y_{12}^* = c_0\left[s + \frac{\omega_0^2}{\sigma_0} - \left(\sigma_0 + \frac{\omega_0^2}{\sigma_0} - 2a_0\right)\frac{s}{s + \sigma_0}\right]$$

$$y_{22}^* = c_0\left[s + \frac{\omega_0^2}{\sigma_0} + \frac{1}{\beta}\left(\sigma_0 + \frac{\omega_0^2}{\sigma_0} - 2a_0\right)\frac{s}{s + \sigma_0}\right] \qquad (7\text{-}112)$$

In these equations ω_0^2 and s_0 are known from Step 3, and the values of c_0, β, and σ_0 must still be determined.

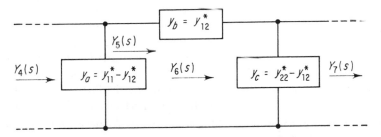

Fig. 7-34. Zero-producing Pi-section.

If the Pi-section is to have a zero at s_0 in the series branch $y_b(s)$, then $Y_5(s)$ must also contain this zero. This implies that $y_a(s_0) = Y_4(s)$. The value of $y_a(s_0)$ can also be determined from y_{11}^* and y_{12}^* of Eq. (7-112) as seen in Fig. 7-34.

$$y_a(s_0) = y_{11}^* - y_{12}^* = c_0(\beta + 1)\left(\sigma_0 + \frac{\omega_0^2}{\sigma_0} - 2a_0\right)\frac{s_0}{s_0 + \sigma_0} \qquad (7\text{-}113)$$

However, if $y_a(s_o)$ and $Y_4(s_o)$ are to be equal, they must be equal in both amplitude and phase. Consequently, it follows that

$$|Y_4(s_o)| = c_o(\beta + 1)\left(\sigma_o + \frac{\omega_o{}^2}{\sigma_o} - 2a_o\right)\left|\frac{s_o}{s_o + \sigma_o}\right|$$

and

$$\underline{/Y_4(s_o)} = \underline{/\frac{s_o}{s_o + \sigma_o}} \tag{7-114}$$

The phase of $Y_4(s_o)$ can be used to obtain the value of σ_o. This value can then be used in the magnitude of $Y_4(s_o)$ along with $\omega_o{}^2$ and s_o to find $c_o(\beta + 1)$. Finally, these constants can be substituted back in Eq. (7-113) to obtain $y_a(s_o)$ which can be realized as the section on the left of Fig. 7-35.

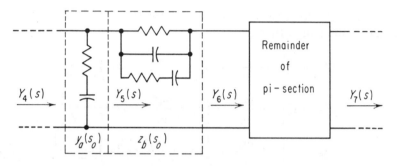

Fig. 7-35. Realization of the zero at s_o.

Step 6. In this step $y_a(s_o)$ can be subtracted from $Y_4(s)$ to yield $Y_5(s)$ from which the remainder of the Pi-section can be obtained. Since $Y_5(s)$ has a zero at s_o, by inverting the function, the impedance $z_b(s_o)$ can be realized as the center section of Fig. 7-35.

Step 7. The value of c_o can now be determined, since $z_b(s_o)$ equals $1/y_{12}^*$ according to Fig. 7-34. The value of $c_o(1 + \beta)$ was found in Step 5, so using c_o it is possible to find the value of β. This is the last of the constants which must be found for the first cycle of the procedure. Usually only one cycle is needed, since in most cases there is only one pair of conjugate complex zeros.

Step 8. An admittance $y_c(s)$ similar in form to $y_a(s)$ can be removed from $Y_6(s)$, since y_{12}^* is known and $[y_c(s) = y_{22}^* - y_{12}^*]$. If a remainder $Y_7(s)$ exists, it can be realized as an RC driving-point admittance. This completes one cycle of the procedure, and the zero-producing Pi-section takes the form of Fig. 7-36. Generally the Pi-section will contain some negative elements; consequently, the procedure must be carried one step further to replace this section with an equivalent bridged-T or twin-T section containing only positive elements.

Step 9. Using the desired zero s_0 and the parameters c_0, σ_0, a_0, β, and $\omega_0{}^2$, a bridged-T or twin-T section of the form seen in Fig. 7-37

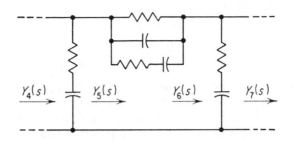

Fig. 7-36. **Final zero-producing Pi-section.**

can be substituted for the Pi-section with the same values of y_{11}^*, y_{12}^*, and y_{22}^*.

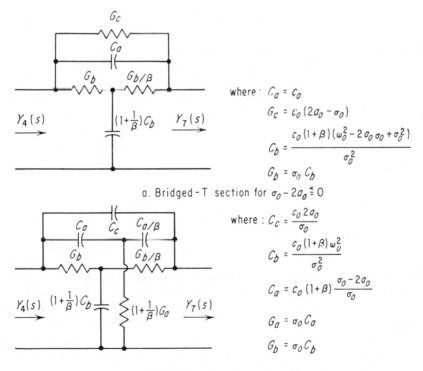

where: $C_a = C_0$

$G_c = C_0 (2a_0 - \sigma_0)$

$C_b = \dfrac{c_0 (1 + \beta)(\omega_0^2 - 2 a_0 \sigma_0 + \sigma_0^2)}{\sigma_0^2}$

$G_b = \sigma_0 C_b$

a. Bridged-T section for $\sigma_0 - 2a_0 \gtreqless 0$

where: $C_c = \dfrac{c_0 \, 2 a_0}{\sigma_0}$

$C_b = \dfrac{c_0 (1 + \beta) \omega_0^2}{\sigma_0^2}$

$C_a = c_0 (1 + \beta)\dfrac{\sigma_0 - 2 a_0}{\sigma_0}$

$G_a = \sigma_0 C_a$

$G_b = \sigma_0 C_b$

b. Twin-T section for $\sigma_0 - 2a_0 \gtreqless 0$

Fig. 7-37. **Bridged-T and twin-T equivalent of Fig. 7-36.**

As an example of Dasher's procedure, assume the following driving-point and transfer admittances are to be realized as a two-port RC network.

$$y_{11}(s) = \frac{s^2 + 6s + 8}{s^2 + 8s + 15} = \frac{(s + 2)(s + 4)}{(s + 3)(s + 5)}$$

$$y_{12}(s) = \frac{s^2 + s + 1}{s^2 + 8s + 15} = \frac{(2s + 1 + j\sqrt{3})(2s + 1 - j\sqrt{3})}{4(s + 3)(s + 5)} \qquad (7\text{-}115)$$

Steps 1 and *2*. In the first step all poles of $y_{11}(s)$ not present in $y_{12}(s)$ are removed. For this example, $y_{11}(s)$ contains no poles not present in $y_{12}(s)$. This will be the case whenever the functions are determined from a specified transfer ratio by the separation technique outlined in Guillemin's procedure. The real zeros of $y_{12}(s)$ are realized in the second step, but for this example $y_{12}(s)$ contains no real zeros.

Step 3. The complex transmission zeros of $y_{12}(s)$ are determined in Step 3 in order to obtain the value of a_o and ω_o. The complex zeros of $y_{12}(s)$, Eq. (7-115), are at

$$s_o = \frac{-1}{2} \pm j\frac{\sqrt{3}}{2} = 1\underline{/\pm 60°} \qquad (7\text{-}116)$$

Referring to Eq. (7-110), it is seen that $a_o = 1/2$ and $\omega_o = 1$.

Step 4. According to Step 4, the procedure is simplified if $y_{11}(s)$ is the ratio of a quadratic to a linear function. Both the numerator and denominator of $y_{11}(s)$, Eq. (7-115), are quadratics; however, it is possible to reduce the order of the denominator by inverting $y_{11}(s)$ and removing a series impedance. This impedance can be chosen as a resistance equal to the value of $1/y_{11}(s)$ at infinite frequency. In this example as s approaches infinity $1/y_{11}(s)$ approaches 1 ohm. Therefore, it follows that:

$$Z_2(s) = \frac{1}{y_{11}(s)} - 1 = \frac{s^2 + 8s + 15}{s^2 + 6s + 8} - 1$$

$$= \frac{2s + 7}{s^2 + 6s + 8} \quad \text{or} \quad Y_2(s) = \frac{(s + 2)(s + 4)}{2s + 7} \qquad (7\text{-}117)$$

The admittance $Y_2(s)$ is seen to be the ratio of a quadratic to a linear function and can be prepared for the removal of the zero-producing Pi-section. To complete this preparation the product of the zeros must equal ω_o^2; however, $\omega_o^2 = 1$ and the product of the zeros is $[(2)(4) = 8]$. The product of the zeros can be reduced by realizing an admittance $Y_3(s)$. In this example it is possible to realize a 1-ohm resistor as $Y_3(s)$ leaving a remainder $Y_4(s)$.

$$Y_2(s) = \frac{s^2 + 6s + 8}{2s + 7} = \frac{s^2 + 4s + 1}{2s + 7} + 1 = Y_4(s) + Y_3(s) \qquad (7\text{-}118)$$

Step 5. At this point a series and shunt 1-ohm resistor have been realized from $y_{11}(s)$, and $Y_4(s)$ is prepared for computing the parameters of the zero-producing section. Therefore it is possible to expand $Y_4(s)/s$ and then multiply through by s to give a form similar to y_{11}^* of Eq. (7-112).

$$y_{11}^* = Y_4(s) = \frac{1}{2}\left(s + \frac{2}{7} + \frac{3}{14} \frac{s}{s + \frac{7}{2}} \right) \tag{7-119}$$

Comparing the terms of this expansion with Eq. (7-112) and remembering that $a_o = 1/2$ and $\omega_o{}^2 = 1$ from Step 3, it is seen that $c_o = 1/2$, $\sigma_o = 7/2$, and $\beta = 1/13$.

Steps 6, 7, and 8. It is not necessary to determine the Pi-section, since all of the constants have been determined; therefore, Steps 6 through 8 can be skipped.

Step 9. Before the zero-producing network is realized, it is necessary to determine the value of $(\sigma_o - 2a_o)$. This will determine whether a bridged-T or twin-T network as seen in Fig. 7-37 must be used. For this example, a twin-T section is appropriate since $(\sigma_o - 2a_o = 5/2)$ is greater than zero. Using the values of ω_o, a_o, c_o, and β, the element values can be determined as

$$C_c = \frac{c_o 2a_o}{\sigma_o} = \frac{1}{7}f \qquad\qquad G_a = \sigma_o C_a = \frac{35}{26}\,\mho$$

$$C_b = \frac{c_o(1 + \beta)\omega_o{}^2}{\sigma_o{}^2} = \frac{4}{91}f \qquad\qquad G_b = \sigma_o C_b = \frac{2}{13}\,\mho$$

$$C_a = \frac{c_o(1 + \beta)(\sigma_o - 2a_o)}{\sigma_o} = \frac{5}{13}f \qquad \frac{1}{\beta}C_a = 5f$$

$$\frac{1}{\beta}G_b = 2\mho \tag{7-120}$$

With these values and the 1-ohm resistors of Step 4, the final network can be drawn as in Fig. 7-38.

Two simple checks can be made on this network to establish how well it matches the specified functions. For instance, it is possible to short-circuit terminals 2-2 and compute the resistance looking into terminals 1-1. In this case the resistance becomes

$$R = 1 + \frac{\left(\frac{25}{4} + \frac{3}{4}\right)1}{1 + \frac{25}{4} + \frac{3}{4}} = \frac{15}{8}\,\Omega \tag{7-121}$$

Converting this to a conductance of 8/15 mhos, it is seen that this agrees with the admittance $y_{11}(s)$ of Eq. (7-115) with $s = 0$. Therefore, this network is an exact duplication of the desired driving-point function at zero frequency. The transfer admittance can easily be checked at infinite frequency, since capacitors short-circuit the twin-T section, leaving

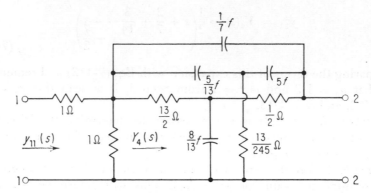

Fig. 7-38. Final network for Eq. 7-115 by Dasher's procedure.

only the series 1-ohm resistor which agrees with $y_{12}(s)$ of Eq. (7-115) when $s = \infty$. The transmittance of the twin-T section has a value of 1/2 at low frequencies, due primarily to the capacitors across the top. These checks are not sufficient to insure that the network is an exact duplication of the specified functions of Eq. (7-115). Complete verification is left to the reader.

References

The following references provide further detail concerning the functions that can be used to characterize two-port networks.

1. E. A. Guillemin, *Communication Networks*, Vol. II (New York: John Wiley & Sons, Inc., 1935), Chaps. 4 and 5.
2. E. S. Kuh and D. O. Pederson, *Principles of Circuit Synthesis* (New York: McGraw-Hill Book Co., Inc., 1959), Chaps. 4 and 5.
3. M. E. Van Valkenburg, *Introduction to Modern Network Synthesis* (New York: John Wiley & Sons, Inc., 1960), Chap. 2.

Transmission matrices are described in Ref. 1 and a detailed presentation is provided in the following:

4. L. A. Pipes, "Certain Applications of Matrices to Circuit Theory," *Trans. AIEE Communications and Electronics*, May 1958, pp. 251–256.

Scattering parameters are defined in Ref. 3 and described in detail in Chap. 14 of Ref. 2. Cauer's reactance procedure is considered in Secs. 11.2 and 11.4 of Ref. 3; however, extensive coverage is provided in the following:

5. W. Cauer, *Synthesis of Linear Communication Networks*, Vols. I and II (New York: McGraw-Hill Book Co., Inc., 1958), Chaps. 3, 5, and 8.

Guillemin's procedure is covered briefly in Sec. 11.5 of Ref. 3 and in Secs. 3.5 through 3.7 of Ref. 6. Dasher's procedure is also presented in Sec. 3.7 of Ref. 6.

6. J. G. Truxal, *Automatic Feedback Control System Synthesis* (New York: McGraw-Hill Book Co., Inc., 1955), Chap. 3.

Problems

7-1. Determine the open-circuit impedances $z_{11}(s)$, $z_{12}(s) = z_{21}(s)$, and $z_{22}(s)$ for the networks of Fig. 7-39. Also determine the short-circuit admittances $y_{11}(s)$, $y_{12}(s) = y_{21}(s)$, and $y_{22}(s)$ for each network. Using these functions show that the conversions of Eq. (7-13) are true.

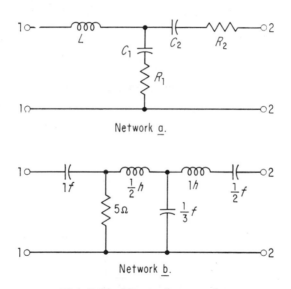

Fig. 7-39. Networks **a** and **b**.

7-2. Using Table 7-1 of typical T-matrices, determine the values of $A(s)$, $B(s)$, $C(s)$, and $D(s)$ for the networks of Prob. 7-1. Use any convenient combination of the forms of Table 7-1.

7-3. Determine the T-matrix for the network of Fig. 7-40. Use any convenient combination of the forms of Table 7-1.

7-4. Prove that the terms to the right of Fig. 7-41 are the T-matrix terms for the bridged-T network. This can be accomplished by determining the y- or z-matrix for the network and using the conversions of Table 7-2.

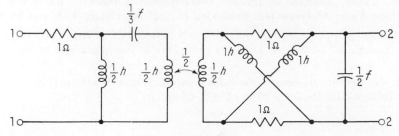

Fig. 7-40

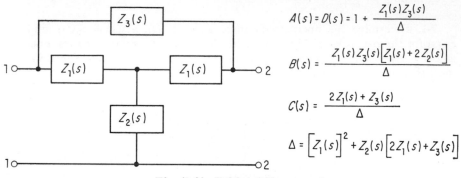

$$A(s) = D(s) = 1 + \frac{Z_1(s)Z_3(s)}{\Delta}$$

$$B(s) = \frac{Z_1(s)Z_3(s)\left[Z_1(s)+2Z_2(s)\right]}{\Delta}$$

$$C(s) = \frac{2Z_1(s)+Z_3(s)}{\Delta}$$

$$\Delta = \left[Z_1(s)\right]^2 + Z_2(s)\left[2Z_1(s)+Z_3(s)\right]$$

Fig. 7-41. Bridged-T network.

7-5. Determine the open-circuit impedances for the twin-T network of Fig. 7-42. Using the values of $z_{11}(s)$, $z_{12}(s)$, and $z_{22}(s)$, determine the T-matrix terms for the twin-T.

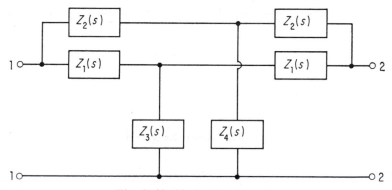

Fig. 7-42. Twin-T network.

7-6. Using Cauer's procedure of Sec. 7-2, synthesize a network for the following impedance functions (use ideal transformers with turns ratios of 1 and -1):

$$z_{11}(s) = \frac{10s^2 + 16}{s^3 + 4s} \qquad z_{12}(s) = \frac{-3s^2 + 4}{s^3 + 4s} \qquad z_{22}(s) = \frac{7s^2 + 12}{s^3 + 4s}$$

7-7. Using Cauer's procedure, synthesize a network for the following impedances. Use ideal transformers with turns ratios of 1 for the ks terms, 1 for the $k/2s$ terms, 2 for the $ks/(s^2 + 1)$ terms, and $-1/3$ for the $ks/(s^2 + 3)$ terms.

$$z_{11}(s) = \frac{15s^6 + 89s^4 + 87s^2 + 9}{2s^5 + 8s^3 + 6s} \qquad z_{12}(s) = \frac{19s^6 + 91s^4 + 97s^2 + 9}{2s^5 + 8s^3 + 6s}$$

$$z_{22}(s) = \frac{8s^6 + 30s^4 + 36s^2 + 6}{2s^5 + 8s^3 + 6s}$$

7-8. Determine the surplus factors necessary to make the denominators of the following impedances equivalent. Synthesize an RLC network to realize these functions.

$$z_{11}(s) = \frac{s + 4}{s + 1} \qquad z_{12}(s) = \frac{s + 3}{s^2 + 3s + 2} \qquad z_{22}(s) = \frac{s^3 + 5s^2 + 8s + 6}{s^4 + 5s^3 + 10s^2 + 10s + 4}$$

7-9. Synthesize an RLC network for the following impedance functions (insure that the driving-point as well as the transfer impedance characteristics are realized):

$$z_{11}(s) = \frac{s^4 + 49s^3 + 285s^2 + 477s + 108}{3s^3 + 39s^2 + 36s}$$

$$z_{12}(s) = \frac{s^2 + 7s + 18}{3(s + 1)} \qquad z_{22}(s) = \frac{8s^3 + 38s^2 + 195s + 105}{15s(s + 1)}$$

7-10. Synthesize an RLC network to realize the driving-point as well as the transfer-impedance characteristics of the following functions:

$$z_{11}(s) = \frac{52s^2 + 207s + 162}{3(4s + 3)} \qquad z_{12}(s) = \frac{6 - \dfrac{2s}{s + 4}}{2} + \frac{4s^2 + 3s + 36}{3(4s + 3)}$$

$$z_{22}(s) = \frac{56s^2 + 186s + 144}{3(4s + 3)}$$

7-11. Realize the following admittance functions as an RC two-port network, using Lucal's procedure:

$$y_{11}(s) = \frac{5s^2 + 9s + 1}{5s^2 + 15s + 10} \qquad y_{12}(s) = \frac{1}{5s^2 + 15s + 10} \qquad y_{22}(s) = \frac{3s^2 + 7s + 3}{15s^2 + 45s + 30}$$

7-12. Realize the following admittance functions as an RC two-port network, using Lucal's procedure:

$$y_{11}(s) = \frac{K(16s^4 + 130s^3 + 335s^2 + 281s + 24)}{3Q(s)} \qquad y_{12}(s) = \frac{K(s^2 + 5s + 8)}{Q(s)}$$

$$y_{22}(s) = \frac{K(8s^4 + 70s^3 + 205s^2 + 227s + 72)}{9Q(s)}$$

where $K = 3/16$ and $Q(s) = s^4 + 10s^3 + 35s^2 + 50s + 24$.

7-13. Break the following transfer ratio into admittances $y_{22}(s)$ and $y_{12}(s)$ to form an RC network terminated by a 1-ohm resistor. In breaking $Q(s)$ into $Q_1(s) + Q_2(s)$, choose the most logical roots for $Q_1(s)$ and use a value of $d = 1/4$.

$$\frac{I_2}{E_1} = \frac{s^2 + 2s + 2}{(s + 1)(s^2 + 8s + 15)} = \frac{P(s)}{Q(s)}$$

7-14. Determine the transfer ratio for a network having the following admittances and terminated by a 4-ohm resistor:

$$y_{22}(s) = \frac{s^2 + 8s + 15}{s^2 + 6s + 8} \quad \text{and} \quad y_{12}(s) = \frac{s + 3}{s^2 + 6s + 8}$$

7-15. Synthesize an RC network by Guillemin's procedure for the following admittance functions (determine the adjustment factors, the gain factor, and draw the network):

$$y_{22}(s) = \frac{s^2 + 2s}{s^2 + 4s + 3} \quad \text{and} \quad y_{12}(s) = \frac{2}{s^2 + 4s + 3}$$

7-16. Synthesize an RC network for the functions of Prob. 7-14, and terminate it in a 4-ohm resistor. How closely does the network approximate the transfer ratio determined in Prob. 7-14?

7-17. Synthesize a network for the following admittance functions by Dasher's procedure:

$$y_{11}(s) = \frac{s^2 + 6s + 5}{s^2 + 9s + 14} \quad \text{and} \quad y_{12}(s) = \frac{s^2 + 2s + 5}{s^2 + 9s + 14}$$

7-18. Synthesize a network for the following admittance functions by Dasher's procedure:

$$y_{11}(s) = \frac{2(s^2 + 7s + 6)}{s^3 + 9s^2 + 30s + 40} \quad \text{and} \quad y_{12}(s) = \frac{s^2 + 2s + 4}{s^2 + 12s + 20}$$

Chapter 8

Additional Procedures for Realization
of Two-port Ladder Networks

Several procedures have been presented in Chap. 7 for realization of two-port networks possessing specified driving-point and transfer characteristics. In general these procedures pertain to ladder or three-terminal networks, the only exception being Cauer's procedure of Sec. 7-2 which requires ideal transformers and cannot always be reduced to a form possessing a common ground between input and output circuits. Although techniques for synthesis of RLC networks were described, emphasis was placed on procedures yielding RC networks. The purpose of this chapter is to investigate additional procedures which can be used for the realization of a desired transfer ratio by RC and RLC ladder networks. The first of these techniques to be considered was developed by Louis Weinberg and is based in part on the parallel-ladder structure of Guillemin's procedure.†

8-1. Weinberg's RC Ladder Synthesis Procedure

For Weinberg's procedure, the transfer ratio is permitted to possess zeros anywhere within the s-plane except on the positive real axis. Poles of the function are restricted to the negative real axis, and it is necessary that the number of poles be greater than or equal to the number of zeros. These conditions are necessary to insure a physically realizable RC network. Hence, the voltage transfer ratio can be written as

$$\frac{E_2}{E_1} = \frac{P(s)}{Q(s)} = \frac{a_n s^n + a_{n-1} s^{n-1} + \cdots + a_1 s + a_0}{b_m s^m + b_{m-1} s^{m-1} + \cdots + b_1 s + b_0} \bigg]_{m \geq n} \quad (8\text{-}1)$$

A preliminary step of Weinberg's procedure requires that all coefficients of $P(s)$ must be positive. So-called minimum-phase functions (i.e.,

† L. Weinberg, "Synthesis of Transfer Functions with Poles Restricted to the Negative Real Axis," *J. Appl. Phys.*, vol. 24, no. 2, February 1953, pp. 207–216.

functions possessing no right half-plane zeros), will have a numerator with only positive coefficients. Functions with right half-plane zeros may have negative coefficients for $P(s)$ in which case it is necessary to multiply both $P(s)$ and $Q(s)$ by surplus factors until positive coefficients are obtained for all terms.

The polynomial $P(s)$ may contain both negative real and complex conjugate zeros; whereas $Q(s)$ contains only negative real zeros. But $Q(s)$ must be associated with an RC driving-point function; consequently, separation of $P(s)$ such that its negative real zeros are realized with zeros of $Q(s)$ will reduce the number of ladder sections required for the realization. In other words, $P(s)$ can be separated so that $[P(s) = P_1(s)P_2(s)]$, where $P_2(s)$ is formed by some or all of the negative real zeros and $P_1(s)$ is formed by the remaining zeros of $P(s)$. It is also possible to divide both $P(s)$ and $Q(s)$ by a suitably chosen polynomial $W(s)$ which is selected such that its zeros alternate with those of $Q(s)$. The degree of $W(s)$ should be one less than that of $Q(s)$, and its zeros should cancel as many zeros of $P_2(s)$ as possible. Consequently, $W(s)$ may be considered to be represented by two polynomials $[W(s) = W_1(s)W_2(s)]$ where $W_2(s)$ contains all zeros that cancel with those of $P_2(s)$, and $W_1(s)$ contains the remaining zeros. In this case if it is assumed that it is desirable to realize a specified voltage transfer ratio within a constant multiplier K of the desired function, Eq. (8-1) can be rewritten as

$$G(s) = K\frac{E_2}{E_1} = K\frac{\dfrac{P(s)}{W(s)}}{\dfrac{Q(s)}{W(s)}} = K\frac{\left[\dfrac{P_1(s)}{W_1(s)}\right]\left[\dfrac{P_2(s)}{W_2(s)}\right]}{W_1(s)W_2(s)} \qquad (8\text{-}2)$$

The denominator of Eq. (8-2) may be separated by partial fractions to yield

$$G(s) = K\frac{\left[\dfrac{P_1(s)}{W_1(s)}\right]\left[\dfrac{P_2(s)}{W_2(s)}\right]}{\left[\dfrac{Q_1(s)}{W_1(s)}\right] + \left[\dfrac{Q_2(s)}{W_2(s)}\right]} \qquad (8\text{-}3)$$

This set of terms can be associated with the driving-point and transfer admittances of two cascaded two-port RC networks.

Consider the cascaded networks of Fig. 8-1a. Applying Norton's theorem (i.e., substitution of an equivalent current source and shunt admittance) to network N_a converts the configuration to that of Fig. 8-1b. The following definitions and relationships then become evident from Fig. 8-1:

$$\frac{I_2}{E_1} \equiv y_{12}(s); \qquad \frac{I_2}{E} \equiv y_{12}^b(s); \qquad \frac{I_{sc}}{E_1} \equiv y_{12}^a(s)$$

$$\frac{E_2}{E_1} = \frac{Z_L(s)I_2}{E_1} = Z_L(s)y_{12}(s); \qquad \frac{E_2}{E} = \frac{Z_L(s)I_2}{E} = Z_L(s)y_{12}^b(s) \qquad (8\text{-}4)$$

The driving-point admittances of the output and input circuits of networks N_a and N_b are defined in Fig. 8-1a as $Y_a(s)$ and $Y_b(s)$ respectively, where $Y_a(s)$ is equivalent to $y_{22}^a(s)$. The short-circuit current I_{sc} in Fig. 8-1b flows through the parallel admittances $Y_a(s)$ and $Y_b(s)$ yielding the voltage E; therefore

$$E = \frac{I_{sc}}{Y_a(s) + Y_b(s)} = \frac{E_1 y_{12}^a(s)}{y_{22}^a(s) + Y_b(s)} \qquad (8\text{-}5)$$

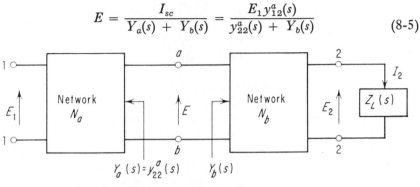

a. Cascaded two-port networks

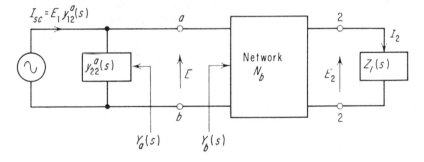

b. Network N_a replaced by equivalent current source

Fig. 8-1. Cascaded two-port networks transformed by Norton's theorem.

It is possible to express the output current of Fig. 8-1 as $[I_2 = E y_{12}^b(s)]$; consequently Eq. (8-5) becomes

$$\frac{I_2}{E_1} = \frac{y_{12}^a(s) y_{12}^b(s)}{y_{22}^a(s) + Y_b(s)} \qquad (8\text{-}6)$$

Multiplying both sides by the load impedance gives

$$\frac{I_2 Z_L(s)}{E_1} = \frac{E_2}{E_1} = \frac{y_{12}^a(s) y_{12}^b(s) Z_L(s)}{y_{22}^2(s) + Y_b(s)} \qquad (8\text{-}7)$$

If network N_b and the load impedance $Z_L(s)$ consist of simply a 1-ohm resistor, Eq. (8-7) reduces to the familiar form of Eq. (7-64) used in Guillemin's procedure. It is also important to note that Eq. (8-7) is of the same general form as Eq. (8-3), making it possible to equate similar terms of both equations. For instance, the following relationships may be derived:

$$y_{12}^a(s) = \frac{P_1(s)}{W_1(s)}; \qquad y_{22}^a(s) = \frac{Q_1(s)}{W_1(s)}; \qquad y_{12}^b(s)Z_L(s) = \frac{P_2(s)}{W_2(s)};$$

and
$$Y_b(s) = \frac{Q_2(s)}{W_2(s)} \tag{8-8}$$

In this equation $P_1(s)$ contains complex conjugate and all negative real zeros not used in $P_2(s)$, and $W_1(s)$ contains only negative real zeros. Because $Q_1(s)$ was formed by partial-fraction expansion of a positive real function, it is possible to realize $y_{12}^a(s)$ and $y_{22}^a(s)$ within a constant by Guillemin's procedure. The polynomials $P_2(s)$, $Q_2(s)$, and $W_2(s)$ contain only negative real zeros. Since $Y_b(s)$ is the driving-point admittance of network N_b, it is possible to remove a portion of the positive real function $Q_2(s)/W_2(s)$ as a shunt branch; then by a technique known as zero-shifting the remainder of $Y_b(s)$ is realized to yield the proper transfer and load relationship $y_{12}^b(s)Z_L(s)$ simultaneously. In this manner network N_b is realized as a single-ladder structure. Adjustment of the admittance levels of the various ladder sections must be performed, as in Guillemin's procedure, before the sections are combined to yield the final network configuration.

To illustrate Weinberg's procedure, assume it is desirable to realize the following voltage transfer ratio by an RC two-port network:

$$\frac{E_2}{E_1} = \frac{2(s^2 + 5s + 7)(s + 2)}{(s + 1)(s + 3)(s + 5)(s + 7)} = \frac{P(s)}{Q(s)} \tag{8-9}$$

This function may be decomposed in several ways; however, the following separation of $P(s)$ will be used.

$$P(s) = P_1(s)P_2(s) = 2(s^2 + 5s + 7)(s + 2)$$

where $\qquad P_1(s) = (s^2 + 5s + 7) \quad$ and $\quad P_2(s) = 2(s + 2) \tag{8-10}$

It is also possible to select a polynomial $W(s)$ such that its zeros alternate with those of $Q(s)$. Because $Q(s)$ is fourth-order, $W(s)$ can be chosen as third-order, and its zeros should cancel as many zeros of $P_2(s)$ as possible. Let $W(s)$ be given by

$$W(s) = W_1(s)W_2(s) = (s + 2)(s + 4)(s + 6)$$

where $\qquad W_1(s) = (s + 4)(s + 6) \quad$ and $\quad W_2(s) = (s + 2) \tag{8-11}$

Insight into the procedure indicates that some separations of $P(s)$ and

$W(s)$ are more optimum than others in reducing the number of ladder structures and elements required for the realization. For instance, if $P_1(s)$ were chosen as $(s^2 + 5s + 7)(s + 2)$, then with a third-order function for $W_1(s)$, as many as four ladder sections might be required to realize the resulting $y_{12}^a(s)$. Usually it is desirable to realize as many poles and zeros of the transfer ratio as possible by the single-ladder section represented by $y_{12}^b(s)Z_L(s)$ and $Y_b(s)$.

Returning to the problem at hand, Eqs. (8-10) and (8-11) can be combined in the form of Eq. (8-2) to yield

$$G(s) = \frac{\left[\dfrac{s^2 + 5s + 7}{(s + 4)(s + 6)}\right]\left[\dfrac{2(s + 2)}{(s + 2)}\right]}{\left[\dfrac{(s + 1)(s + 3)(s + 5)(s + 7)}{(s + 2)(s + 4)(s + 6)}\right]} \tag{8-12}$$

Performing a partial-fraction expansion of the denominator gives

$$G(s) = \frac{\left[\dfrac{s^2 + 5s + 7}{(s + 4)(s + 6)}\right](2)}{\left[s + \dfrac{105}{48} + \dfrac{0.9375s}{(s + 2)} + \dfrac{0.5625s}{(s + 4)} + \dfrac{0.3125s}{(s + 6)}\right]} \tag{8-13}$$

Using Eqs. (8-3) and (8-7), it is possible to identify terms of Eq. (8-13) with the driving-point and transfer admittances of networks N_a and N_b. An additional degree of freedom can be obtained by the following choice:

$$\text{Network } N_a \begin{cases} y_{12}^a(s) = \dfrac{(s^2 + 5s + 7)}{(s + 4)(s + 6)} \\[2ex] y_{22}^a(s) = \beta\,\dfrac{105}{48} + \dfrac{0.5625s}{(s + 4)} + \dfrac{0.3125s}{(s + 6)} \end{cases}$$

$$\text{Network } N_b \begin{cases} y_{12}^b(s)Z_L(s) = 2 \\[2ex] Y_b(s) = (1 - \beta)\left(\dfrac{105}{48}\right) + s + \dfrac{0.9375s}{(s + 2)} \end{cases} \quad (0 \leq \beta \leq 1)$$

$$\tag{8-14}$$

The constant β is inserted in the denominator of Eq. (8-13) such that $y_{22}^a(s)$ and $Y_b(s)$ can be selected in a more optimum manner. Proper selection of β may make it possible to simplify the realization by duplicating zeros of $y_{12}^a(s)$ or $y_{12}^b(s)$ in $y_{22}^a(s)$ or $Y_b(s)$. This technique is known as zero-shifting in that zeros of $y_{22}^a(s)$ or $Y_b(s)$ may be shifted to more desirable positions. Inspection of Eq. (8-14) reveals that it is easier to realize $y_{12}^b(s)Z_L(s)$ and $Y_b(s)$ if β is chosen as $(\beta = 0.0857)$ in which case

$$y_{12}^b(s)Z_L(s) = 2 \quad \text{and} \quad Y_b(s) = 2 + s + \frac{0.9375s}{(s + 2)} \tag{8-15}$$

These admittances are readily realized as a single-ladder structure, and if a specific load impedance is desired, it must be taken into account at this time. The load will not be defined for this example; consequently, the admittances of Eq. (8-15) are realized by the network of Fig. 8-2.

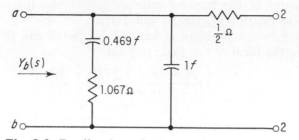

Fig. 8-2. Realization of network N_b for Eq. 8-15.

It is also possible to write the expressions for $y_{12}^a(s)$ and $y_{22}^a(s)$ from Eq. (8-14) using ($\beta = 0.0857$). These functions represent network N_a and may be realized by Guillemin's procedure as parallel RC ladder structures:

$$y_{12}^a(s) = \frac{s^2 + 5s + 7}{(s + 4)(s + 6)}$$

$$y_{22}^a(s) = \frac{1.0625s^2 + 6.5s + 4.5}{(s + 4)(s + 6)} = \frac{1.0625(s + 0.786)(s + 5.389)}{(s + 4)(s + 6)} \qquad (8\text{-}16)$$

The details of Guillemin's procedure for the realization of Eq. (8-16) will not be repeated, since a description of the procedure appears in Chap. 7, Sec. 7-5. In brief, $y_{22}^a(s)$ may be expanded in three different ways to yield three-ladder structures, each of which realizes one term in the numerator of $y_{12}^a(s)$. These ladders are then adjusted and connected in parallel to complete network N_a which realizes $y_{22}^a(s)$ exactly and $y_{12}^a(s)$ within a constant $K = 0.0255$ of that specified by Eq. (8-16).

Network N_a must be connected in cascade with N_b of Fig. 8-2 to complete the realization; therefore the final configuration is shown in Fig. 8-3. For this example, network N_b did not require adjustment; consequently the network of Fig. 8-3 realizes the desired transfer ratio of Eq. (8-9) within a multiplying factor of ($K = 0.0255$). This fact becomes apparent when the admittances of Fig. 8-3 are recombined in the form of Eq. (8-7). If Guillemin's procedure had been applied, by itself, to the realization of Eq. (8-9) and the terms of $P(s)$ were taken one at a time, as many as four complicated ladder sections would have been required.

Although zero-shifting is fairly simple, it is sometimes advantageous to employ a more sophisticated procedure to simplify the resulting realization. Weinberg is credited with a technique which can often be used to decompose functions having complex conjugate left half-plane zeros and a single negative real axis pole.† Because this technique is useful in the present discussion and in later sections, it is worthwhile to investigate it in more detail.

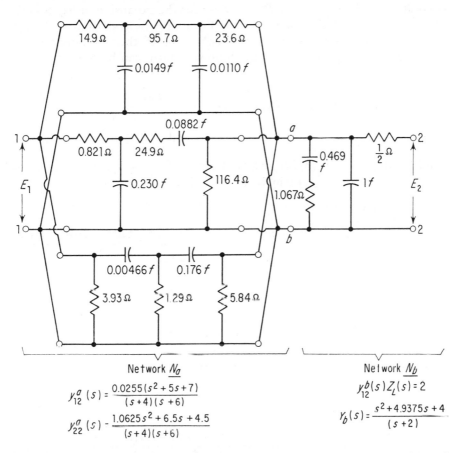

Network N_a

$$y_{12}^a(s) = \frac{0.0255(s^2 + 5s + 7)}{(s+4)(s+6)}$$

$$y_{22}^a(s) = \frac{1.0625s^2 + 6.5s + 4.5}{(s+4)(s+6)}$$

Network N_b

$$y_{12}^b(s)Z_L(s) = 2$$

$$Y_b(s) = \frac{s^2 + 4.9375s + 4}{(s+2)}$$

Fig. 8-3. Final network to realize E_2/E_1 within a constant ($K = 0.0255$) of Eq. 8-9.

Consider the following general form containing a pair of left half-plane complex conjugate zeros and a negative real axis pole:

$$Y_1(s) = \frac{(s + b + jc)(s + b - jc)}{(s + a)} \tag{8-17}$$

† Louis Weinberg, "Synthesis of Unbalanced RLC Networks," *J. Appl. Phys.*, vol. 24, no. 3, March 1953, pp. 300–306.

Multiplying out the numerator and dividing by the denominator gives

$$Y_1(s) = \frac{s^2 + 2bs + b^2 + c^2}{(s + a)} = s + (2b - a) + \frac{a^2 + b^2 + c^2 - 2ab}{(s + a)}$$

$$(8\text{-}18)$$

In order to yield a realizable RC network for the expansion of Eq. (8-18), it is necessary that the coefficients of Eq. (8-17) be restricted such that $(2b - a) \geq 0$ and $(a^2 + b^2 + c^2 - 2ab) \geq 0$. If these conditions are satisfied, an admittance $y(s)$ of the following form can be removed from $Y_1(s)$:

$$y(s) = (1 - d)s + (1 - e)(2b - a) + \frac{(1 - f)(a^2 + b^2 + c^2 - 2ab)}{(s + a)}$$

where $0 \leq d \leq 1;$ $0 \leq e \leq 1;$ and $0 \leq f \leq 1$ (8-19)

Multiplying out Eq. (8-19) and subtracting the result from Eq. (8-18) leaves a remainder $Y_2(s)$ which can be written as

$$Y_2(s) = Y_1(s) - y(s)$$

$$= \frac{d\left\{ s^2 + \dfrac{(2be + ad - ae)s}{d} + \dfrac{[f(a^2 + b^2 + c^2 - 2ab) - ae(a - 2b)]}{d} \right\}}{(s + a)}$$

$$(8\text{-}20)$$

If it is desired that the complex conjugate zeros of $Y_2(s)$ be at $s = -g + jh$ and $s = -g - jh$, then the numerator of $Y_2(s)$ must be of the form $(s^2 + 2gs + g^2 + h^2)$. Equating the coefficients of this quadratic with those of the numerator of Eq. (8-20) gives

$$2g = \frac{(2be + ad - ae)}{d}$$

$$g^2 + h^2 = \frac{[f(a^2 + b^2 + c^2 - 2ab) - ae(a - 2b)]}{d} \qquad (8\text{-}21)$$

Since a, b, and c are known from the original function $Y_1(s)$ and g and h are known from the positions of the desired zeros, it is usually possible to choose values of d, e, and f which satisfy the conditions of Eqs. (8-19) and (8-21). Once d, e, and f have been established it is possible to use Eqs. (8-19) and (8-20) to find $y(s)$ and $Y_2(s)$, where $Y_2(s)$ has the desired complex conjugate zeros and the same pole as $Y_1(s)$ of Eq. (8-17).

Although zero-shifting of the type described above can often be useful in simplifying a realization procedure, several other approaches can be used to reduce the number of ladder sections and circuit elements required for the realization. For instance, terms in the numerator of $y_{12}^a(s)$ of network N_a can be realized by Guillemin's procedure in pairs rather than individually, thereby reducing the number of ladder sections by nearly 50 percent. Actually, if $P_1(s)$ is of pth degree and there are r right half-plane zeros, the number of ladder sections t needed for realization of N_a when terms of $y_{12}^a(s)$ are taken in pairs is given by the largest integer satisfying $[t = (p - r + 1)/2]$ when $(p - r)$ is odd or $[t = (p - r + 2)/2]$ when $(p - r)$ is even. However, Malti and Sun have extended the procedure such that it is possible to realize N_a by only two RC ladder sections coupled by an ideal transformer.† This method also applies to more generalized transfer ratios in that no restrictions are placed on the zeros of the function.

The procedure proposed by Malti and Sun follows the same basic steps as Weinberg's procedure. The polynomial $P(s)$ is separated such that some or all of its negative real zeros are included in $P_2(s)$, which is realized by network N_b and remaining zeros form $P_1(s)$. The second step in the procedure involves selection of a polynomial $W(s)$ and separation of the various functions as shown in Eqs. (8-2) through (8-8). Network N_b is realized as a single-ladder section; however, a somewhat different approach is used in the realization of network N_a. The polynomial $P_1(s)$ forms the numerator of $y_{12}^a(s)$ as indicated in Eq. (8-8) and may contain zeros located anywhere within the s-plane. Malti and Sun, as well as I. Howowitz,‡ have shown that it is possible to separate $P_1(s)$ into the summation of two polynomials, $P_1'(s)$ plus $P_1''(s)$, each of which possess only negative real zeros. This separation can be accomplished as follows:

1. Divide $P_1(s)$ by a polynomial $D(s)$ which is at least the same degree as $P_1(s)$ and contains only simple negative real zeros.

2. Perform a partial-fraction expansion of $P_1(s)/D(s)$. All residues of this expansion will be real; therefore, it is possible to collect all terms with positive residues to form a set which is denoted as $F'(s)$. Terms possessing negative residues form a second set, $F''(s)$, such that

$$\frac{P_1(s)}{D(s)} = F'(s) - F''(s) \tag{8-22}$$

where $F'(s)$ and $F''(s)$ are each composed of a series of terms with poles on the negative real axis and positive real residues.

3. Multiplying both sides of Eq. (8-22) by $D(s)$ yields

$$P_1(s) = F'(s)D(s) - F''(s)D(s) = P_1'(s) + P_1''(s) \tag{8-23}$$

In this equation $[P_1'(s) = F'(s)D(s)]$ and $[-P_1''(s) = F''(s)D(s)]$ are polynomials with negative real zeros, since the poles of $F'(s)$ and $F''(s)$

† M. G. Malti and Hun Hsuan Sun, "Synthesis of Transfer Functions with Poles Restricted to the Negative Real Axis into Two Parallel R-C Ladders and an Ideal Transformer," *AIEE Trans. Communications and Electronics*, May 1956, pp. 165–171.

‡ *Ibid.*, p. 171.

are cancelled by zeros of $D(s)$. Consequently, with exception of the negative sign associated with $P_1''(s)$, both polynomials can be used to represent the numerators of parallel RC transfer admittances. In other words, $y_{12}^a(s)$ of Eq. (8-8) may be separated as follows:

$$y_{12}^a(s) = \frac{P_1(s)}{W_1(s)} = y_{12}^{a'}(s) + y_{12}^{a''}(s)$$

where

$$y_{12}^{a'}(s) = \frac{P_1'(s)}{W_1(s)} = \frac{F'(s)D(s)}{W_1(s)} \quad \text{and} \quad y_{12}^{a''}(s) = \frac{P_1''(s)}{W_1(s)} = \frac{-P''(s)D(s)}{W_1(s)} \quad (8\text{-}24)$$

By proper selection of $D(s)$, the transfer admittances $y_{12}^{a'}(s)$ and $y_{12}^{a''}(s)$ may be constrained such that their poles and zeros alternate along the negative real axis. Consequently they can be realized as parallel RC ladder sections, and the minus sign associated with $P''(s)D(s)$ or $y_{12}^{a''}(s)$ can be accounted for by employing an ideal transformer with a turns ratio of (-1). Part of $y_{22}^a(s)$ is realized with each of the transfer admittances such that all of $y_{22}^a(s)$ is realized when the ladder sections are combined in parallel. Adjustment of the two ladder sections can be accomplished by Guillemin's technique, and the multiplying constant or gain error associated with the transfer admittances may be corrected by using a transformer turns ratio other than unity. By this method, the realization of the desired transfer ratio takes the form shown in Fig. 8-4, where network N_a' realizes $y_{12}^{a'}(s)$ and part of $y_{22}^a(s)$, and network N_a'' realizes $y_{12}^{a''}(s)$ and the remainder of $y_{22}^a(s)$.

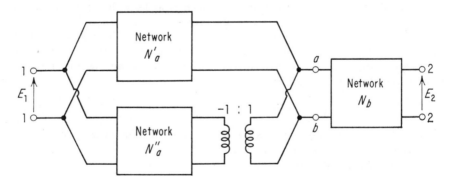

Fig. 8-4. Network configuration for Malti and Sun's procedure.

It should be pointed out that it is often possible to reduce the number of circuit elements required for a given realization by applying Dasher's procedure in the synthesis of networks N_a and/or N_b. In this case, once the specified transfer ratio has been separated in the manner previously described the realization can be accomplished by two ladder structures in cascade. Finally, it should be clear that the above techniques and procedures can be accomplished in a similar manner on an impedance basis.

8-2. Kuh's *RC* Ladder Synthesis Procedure

The various two-port *RC* synthesis procedures considered in previous sections have been based on the implied assumption that the source impedance for the network is zero. Furthermore, the gain or constant multiplier of the transfer ratio and practical load impedance have been assigned only secondary importance. These aspects of the *RC*-synthesis problem are given primary attention in a procedure developed by Kuh.[†] Particular emphasis is placed on realizing a specified voltage transfer ratio with maximum possible gain when source and load resistances for the network are prescribed.

Kuh's procedure is concerned with a network of the form shown in Fig. 8-5, where in addition to the resistances R_S and R_L shunt capacitors appear in both the input and output circuits. These capacitors cause the network to be a low-pass structure (i.e., it passes only low frequencies); however, situations in which the capacitors do not appear will be considered later. Because of the capacitors, two transmission zeros must be provided for at infinite frequency in the specification of the voltage transfer ratio. In other words, if the voltage transfer ratio is written as $[E_2/E_1 = KP(s)/Q(s)]$, $P(s)$ must be at least two degrees lower than $Q(s)$. Furthermore, to be realizable as an *RC* network, the poles of the function [i.e., zeros of $Q(s)$] must be simple and restricted to the negative real axis. Two cases will be considered—one in which the zeros of $P(s)$ are restricted to the negative real axis, and the other in which the zeros may lie anywhere in the left half-plane including the $j\omega$-axis. In both cases the problem is to realize the given transfer ratio such that the gain constant K is maximized.

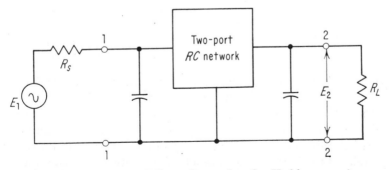

Fig. 8-5. Two-port *RC* configuration for Kuh's procedure.

† E. S. Kuh, "Synthesis of RC Grounded Two-Ports," *IRE Trans. Circuit Theory*, vol. CT-5, no. 1, March 1958, pp. 55–61.

Case 1. The first case to be considered is that of a voltage transfer ratio possessing simple poles and zeros restricted to the negative real axis. The function may be written in the following form:

$$\frac{E_2}{E_1} = K\frac{P(s)}{Q(s)} = K\frac{(s + b_1)(s + b_2)\cdots(s + b_m)}{(s + a_1)(s + a_2)\cdots(s + a_n)}\bigg]_{n \geq m+2} \quad (8\text{-}25)$$

The first step in the procedure is to absorb the termination resistances R_S and R_L of Fig. 8-5 into the two-port network. These resistors represent boundary conditions that must be satisfied; consequently it is possible to write

$$\frac{E_2}{E_1} = \frac{I_2 R_L}{E_1} = y_{12}(s)R_L \quad (8\text{-}26)$$

Substituting Eq. (8-25) for E_2/E_1 gives

$$y_{12}(s) = \frac{K}{R_L}\left[\frac{(s + b_1)(s + b_2)\cdots(s + b_m)}{(s + a_1)(s + a_2)\cdots(s + a_n)}\right] \quad (8\text{-}27)$$

In this form the voltage transfer ratio and short-circuit transfer admittance $y_{12}(s)$ are related through the load resistance R_L. Performing a partial-fraction expansion of $y_{12}(s)/s$ yields

$$\frac{y_{12}(s)}{s} = \frac{K}{R_L}\left[\frac{k_{12}^0}{s} + \frac{k_{12}^1}{(s + a_1)} + \frac{k_{12}^2}{(s + a_2)} + \cdots + \frac{k_{12}^n}{(s + a_n)}\right] \quad (8\text{-}28)$$

In this expansion k_{12}^q represents the residue at the pole $(s = -a_q)$.

The two-port network to be realized must also possess short-circuit driving-point admittances $y_{11}(s)$ and $y_{22}(s)$ which can arbitrarily be assumed to be of the same form as $y_{12}(s)$:

$$\frac{y_{11}(s)}{s} = \frac{K}{R_L}\left[\frac{k_{11}^0}{s} + \frac{k_{11}^1}{(s + a_1)} + \frac{k_{11}^2}{(s + a_2)} + \cdots + \frac{k_{11}^n}{(s + a_n)}\right]$$

$$\frac{y_{22}(s)}{s} = \frac{K}{R_L}\left[\frac{k_{22}^0}{s} + \frac{k_{22}^1}{(s + a_1)} + \frac{k_{22}^2}{(s + a_2)} + \cdots + \frac{k_{22}^n}{(s + a_n)}\right] \quad (8\text{-}29)$$

The residues at each pole k_{11}^q, k_{22}^q, and k_{12}^q of Eqs. (8-28) and (8-29) must satisfy the residue conditions stated in Chap. 7, Sec. 7-2 and given by Eq. (7-32). The number of elements required for the realization is reduced if at any pole $[k_{11}^q k_{22}^q = (k_{12}^q)^2]$. The network is said to be "compact" if this condition holds at all poles with possible exception of those related to the first series branch of the network on an impedance basis, or the first shunt branch on an admittance basis.

Because the desired network begins with a series resistance R_S the expansions of Eqs. (8-28) and (8-29), when multiplied through by s, must each possess constant terms sufficiently large to satisfy the termination. In this respect it is useful to assume that

$$k_{11}^0 = k_{22}^0 = |k_{12}^0| = c_0 \tag{8-30}$$

At this point the k_{12}^q residues of Eq. (8-28) are known from the expansion of the desired transfer ratio of Eq. (8-27); however, k_{11}^q and k_{22}^q have not yet been established. If the requirement for a compact network is imposed, the condition $k_{11}^q k_{22}^q = (k_{12}^q)^2$ relates the residues of Eq. (8-29) to those of Eq. (8-28). Therefore, Eq. (8-29) can be rewritten as

$$\frac{y_{11}(s)}{s} = \frac{K}{R_L}\left[\frac{c_0}{s} + \frac{d_1}{(s + a_1)} + \frac{d_2}{(s + a_2)} + \cdots + \frac{d_n}{(s + a_n)}\right]$$

$$\frac{y_{22}(s)}{s} = \frac{K}{R_L}\left[\frac{c_0}{s} + \frac{c_1^2/d_1}{(s + a_1)} + \frac{c_2^2/d_2}{(s + a_2)} + \cdots + \frac{c_n^2/d_n}{(s + a_n)}\right]$$

where $\qquad c_q = |k_{12}^q| \qquad$ and $\qquad d_q = k_{11}^q \tag{8-31}$

To fulfill the desired boundary conditions, $y_{11}(s)$ and $y_{22}(s)$ may be evaluated at infinite frequency. In this case the expansions of Eq. (8-31) become

$$\frac{1}{R_S} = y_{11}(s)\Big]_{s = \infty} = \frac{K}{R_L}[c_0 + d_1 + d_2 + \cdots + d_n]$$

$$\frac{1}{R_L} = y_{22}(s)\Big]_{s = \infty} = \frac{K}{R_L}\left[c_0 + \frac{c_1^2}{d_1} + \frac{c_2^2}{d_2} + \cdots + \frac{c_n^2}{d_n}\right] \tag{8-32}$$

These relationships reveal that the unknown residues of Eq. (8-31) and the terminating resistances must satisfy the following condition:

$$u = f(d_1, d_2, \ldots, d_n) = \left[c_0 + \sum_{q=1}^{n} d_q\right] - \frac{R_L}{R_S}\left[c_0 + \sum_{q=1}^{n} \frac{c_q^2}{d_q}\right] = 0 \tag{8-33}$$

It is now possible to select the coefficients d_q [the c_q coefficients are known from Eqs. (8-28) and (8-31)] such that the gain K will be maximized. Furthermore, all of the d_q coefficients must be nonnegative; therefore, solving the first relationship of Eq. (8-32) for K yields

$$K = \frac{\dfrac{R_L}{R_S}}{\left[c_0 + \displaystyle\sum_{q=1}^{n} d_q\right]} \tag{8-34}$$

This equation reveals that for a specified R_L and R_S, the maximum K is obtained when $1/(c_0 + \sum_1^n d_q)$ is maximized.

The maximum value of K that satisfies Eq. (8-33) can be determined by use of Lagrange's multiplier rule, which may be stated briefly as follows: If u is a function of n parameters $[u = f(x_1, x_2, \ldots, x_n)]$ and there are $(h < n)$ other conditions of the form $\Psi_1(x_1, x_2, \ldots, x_n) = 0$; $\Psi_2(x_1, x_2, \ldots, x_n) = 0$; $\ldots$, $\Psi_h(x_1, x_2, \ldots, x_n) = 0$, it is possible to select h constants L_h called Lagrange multipliers to form an equation $[F = f + L_1\Psi_1 + L_2\Psi_2 + \cdots + L_h\Psi_h]$. Letting the n partial derivatives of F vanish (i.e., $\partial F/\partial x_1 = 0$; $\partial F/\partial x_2 = 0$; $\ldots \partial F/\partial x_n = 0$), together with the h conditions of the form $(\Psi_h = 0)$, it is possible to determine the $(h + n)$ variables such that a suitable value of u results. Applying the above rule to Eqs. (8-33) and (8-34) yields

$$F = K + L_1 u = \frac{\dfrac{R_L}{R_S}}{\left[c_0 + \displaystyle\sum_{q=1}^{n} d_q\right]} + L_1 f(d_1, d_2, \ldots, d_n) \tag{8-35}$$

Setting the partial derivative of F with respect to each of the d_q coefficients and L_1 equal to zero yields the following simple relationships:

$$\frac{d_1}{c_1} = \frac{d_2}{c_2} = \cdots \frac{d_n}{c_n} = M \tag{8-36}$$

where M is a constant. The value of M is readily determined by substituting Eq. (8-36) into Eq. (8-33) gives

$$M - \frac{R_L}{R_S M} + \frac{c_0\left(1 - \dfrac{R_L}{R_S}\right)}{\displaystyle\sum_{q=1}^{n} c_q} = 0 \tag{8-37}$$

Lagrange's procedure assures the positive realness of M required for physical realizability; hence, using M and Eq. (8-34), the maximum gain becomes[†]

$$K = \frac{\dfrac{R_L}{R_S}}{c_0 + M \displaystyle\sum_{q=1}^{n} c_q} \tag{8-38}$$

Having established the gain and residue values for Eqs. (8-28) and (8-29), it is possible by zero-shifting to realize the desired network, working with either $y_{11}(s)$ or $y_{22}(s)$.

As an example of the above procedure, assume that the following voltage transfer ratio has been specified to couple a load resistance of

† The sufficient condition for positive network element values can be shown to be $[b_q > a_{q+2}$ for $q = 1, 2, \ldots, n]$.

6 ohms and a source resistance of 2 ohms. The gain K is to be maximized.

$$\frac{E_2}{E_1} = \frac{K}{(s + 2)(s + 5)} \tag{8-39}$$

Writing Eq. (8-39) in the form of Eq. (8-27) where $(R_L = 6)$ and performing a partial-fraction expansion of $y_{12}(s)/s$ gives

$$\frac{y_{12}(s)}{s} = \frac{K}{6}\left[\frac{\frac{1}{10}}{s} + \frac{-\frac{1}{6}}{(s + 2)} + \frac{\frac{1}{15}}{(s + 5)}\right]$$

where

$$c_0 = |k_{12}^0| = \frac{1}{10} \qquad c_1 = |k_{12}^1| = \frac{1}{6} \qquad c_2 = |k_{12}^2| = \frac{1}{15} \tag{8-40}$$

It is possible to construct $y_{11}(s)/s$ and $y_{22}(s)/s$ from Eq. (8-31) as

$$\frac{y_{11}(s)}{s} = \frac{K}{6}\left[\frac{\frac{1}{10}}{s} + \frac{d_1}{(s + 2)} + \frac{d_2}{(s + 5)}\right]$$

$$\frac{y_{22}(s)}{s} = \frac{K}{6}\left[\frac{\frac{1}{10}}{s} + \frac{\frac{1}{36d_1}}{(s + 2)} + \frac{\frac{1}{225d_2}}{(s + 5)}\right] \tag{8-41}$$

At this point the d_q coefficients and K must be determined. These parameters can be computed directly from Eqs. (8-36) and (8-37), since the c_q coefficients are known.

$$\frac{d_1}{\frac{1}{6}} = \frac{d_2}{\frac{1}{15}} = M \qquad \text{where} \qquad M - \frac{6}{2M} + \frac{\left(1 - \frac{6}{2}\right)}{10\left(\frac{1}{6} + \frac{1}{15}\right)} = 0$$

or

$$M = 2.213 \quad \text{and} \quad -1.356 \tag{8-42}$$

For positive real coefficients, M must be chosen as $(M = 2.213)$; consequently $(d_1 = 0.369)$ and $(d_2 = 0.148)$. With these parameters, the maximum gain can be obtained from Eq. (8-38).

$$K = \frac{3}{\frac{1}{10} + 2.213\left(\frac{1}{6} + \frac{1}{15}\right)} = 4.868 \tag{8-43}$$

Substituting the values established in Eqs. (8-42) and (8-43) into Eqs. (8-40) and (8-41) leads to the following set of admittance functions:

$$y_{11}(s) = \frac{4.868}{6}\left[\frac{1}{10} + \frac{0.369s}{(s+2)} + \frac{0.148s}{(s+5)}\right] = \frac{\dfrac{s^2}{2} + 2.303s + 0.8113}{(s^2 + 7s + 10)}$$

$$y_{12}(s) = \frac{4.868}{6}\left[\frac{1}{10} - \frac{\dfrac{s}{6}}{(s+2)} + \frac{\dfrac{s}{15}}{(s+5)}\right] = \frac{0.8113}{(s^2 + 5s + 10)}$$

$$y_{22}(s) = \frac{4.868}{6}\left[\frac{1}{10} + \frac{0.0753s}{(s+2)} + \frac{0.03s}{(s+5)}\right] = \frac{\dfrac{s^2}{6} + 0.922s + 0.8113}{(s^2 + 7s + 10)}$$

$$(8\text{-}44)$$

The desired network can be obtained by performing a continued-fraction expansion of either $y_{11}(s)$ or $y_{22}(s)$. Expanding $y_{11}(s)$ yields

$$y_{11}(s) = \cfrac{1}{2 + \cfrac{1}{0.209s + \cfrac{1}{4.325 + \cfrac{1}{0.113s + \cfrac{1}{6}}}}} \qquad (8\text{-}45)$$

The network which realizes Eq. (8-45) is shown in Fig. 8-6. This network satisfies the desired source and load resistances ($R_S = 2$ ohms and $R_L = 6$ ohms) as well as the specified voltage transfer ratio of Eq. (8-39) such that the gain is maximized ($K = 4.868$).

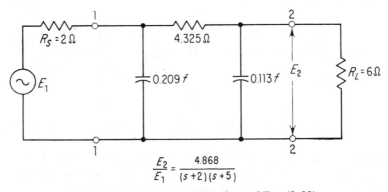

$$\frac{E_2}{E_1} = \frac{4.868}{(s+2)(s+5)}$$

Fig. 8-6. Network realization of Eq. (8-39).

When the voltage transfer ratio is of higher order, possessing zeros as well as poles, the realization is generally simplified by removing R_S plus the first shunt capacitor from $y_{11}(s)$ and R_L plus the first shunt capacitor from $y_{22}(s)$. At this point the network takes the form of Fig. 8-5, and the remaining driving-point admittances can be denoted as $y_{11}^*(s)$ and $y_{22}^*(s)$. Each of the functions will possess the same poles; consequently, using the zeros of $y_{12}(s)$, it is possible to construct $y_{12}^*(s)$. Having established the three admittances $y_{11}^*(s)$, $y_{12}^*(s)$, and $y_{22}^*(s)$ the center section of the network can be realized by Lucal's procedure of Chap. 7, Sec. 7-4.

Case 2. When the voltage transfer ratio possesses complex conjugate zeros in the left half-plane or on the $j\omega$-axis, the procedure is similar to that described above but must be modified to insure that the functions fulfill the conditions required for Lucal's procedure. It can be shown that the gain K can be maximized while satisfying these conditions in cases where the terminating resistors are equal, ($R_S = R_L$). It can also be maximized in a restricted sense when the terminating resistors are not equal.

When ($R_S = R_L$), the admittance functions of Eq. (8-31) are related by the coefficients determined from Eqs. (8-36) and (8-37) such that M becomes unity. Therefore, it follows from Eq. (8-36) that $d_q = c_q$, and the maximum gain, given by Eq. (8-38), reduces to

$$K = \frac{1}{c_0 + \sum_{q=1}^{n} c_q} \tag{8-46}$$

Applying these facts to Eq. (8-31) and interpreting the results with respect to Eqs. (8-28), (8-29), and (8-46) reveal that the maximum value of K results when

$$k_{11}^q = k_{22}^q = |k_{12}^q| \tag{8-47}$$

This relationship at each pole insures that $y_{11}(s)$ equals $y_{22}(s)$ and all of the k_{11}^q and k_{22}^q residues are positive real terms, whereas the k_{12}^q terms may be negative.

To show that a network of the form of Fig. 8-5 can be realized by employing Lucal's procedure when ($R_S = R_L$), the admittance functions are first converted to open-circuit impedance functions using the transformations of Eq. (7-9). For the conditions stated above

$$z_{11}(s) = z_{22}(s) = \frac{y_{11}(s)}{|\Delta^y|} = \frac{y_{22}(s)}{|\Delta^y|} \quad \text{and} \quad z_{12}(s) = \frac{-y_{12}}{|\Delta^y|}$$

where
$$\Delta^y = y_{11}(s)y_{22}(s) - y_{12}(s)^2 \tag{8-48}$$

If $y_{11}(s)$, $y_{12}(s)$, and $y_{22}(s)$ are derived from a transfer ratio having a denominator of degree n and numerator of degree $(n - 2)$, the partial-fraction expansions of $[y_{11}(s) = y_{22}(s)]$ will be of degree (n/n) [see Eqs. (8-25) through (8-29)]. Also because the residues at all poles must satisfy Eq. (8-47), $|\Delta^y|$ will have only simple poles of degree (n/n). Therefore, following the transformation of Eq. (8-48), $[z_{11}(s) = z_{22}(s)]$ is of degree (n/n), whereas $z_{12}(s)$ will be of degree $(n-2)/n$. Removing a resistance $(R = R_S = R_L)$ and expanding the impedance functions in partial fractions yields

$$z_{11}(s) = z_{22}(s) = R + z_{11}^*(s) = R + z_{22}^*(s) = R + \sum_{q=1}^{n} \frac{\beta_q}{(s + b_q)}$$

$$z_{12}^*(s) = \sum_{q=1}^{n} \frac{(k_{12}^q)^*}{(s + b_q)} \tag{8-49}$$

where $z_{12}^*(s)$ is of degree $(n-2)/n$. Applying the transformation of Eq. (7-11), the $|\Delta^{z*}|$ determinant will be of degree $(n-2)/n$. The corresponding admittance functions are given by

$$y_{11}^*(s) = y_{22}^*(s) = \frac{z_{11}^*(s)}{|\Delta^{z*}|} = \frac{z_{22}^*(s)}{|\Delta^{z*}|} \quad \text{and} \quad y_{12}^*(s) = \frac{-z_{12}^*(s)}{|\Delta^{z*}|}$$

where
$$\Delta^{z*} = z_{11}^*(s)z_{22}^*(s) - z_{12}^*(s)^2 \tag{8-50}$$

The admittances $y_{11}^*(s)$ and $y_{22}^*(s)$ are of degree $(n-1)/(n-2)$ and $y_{12}^*(s)$ is of degree $(n-2)/(n-2)$. Consequently, poles can be removed from $y_{11}^*(s)$ and $y_{22}^*(s)$ at $(s = \infty)$ to realize the shunt capacitances, and the remaining admittance functions still satisfy the conditions required for Lucal's procedure. The same argument applies when the degree of the numerator of the voltage transfer ratio is more than two orders less than that of the denominator.

When the terminating resistors are not equal, the partial-fraction expansion of $y_{12}(s)/s$ given by Eq. (8-28) can be separated into two parts:

$$\frac{y_{12}(s)}{s} = \frac{y_{12}'(s)}{s} - \frac{y_{12}''(s)}{s} = \frac{K}{R_L}\left[\frac{c_0}{s} + \sum_{q=1}^{i} \frac{c_q}{(s + a_q)}\right] - \frac{K}{R_L}\left[\sum_{i+1}^{n} \frac{c_q}{(s + a_q)}\right] \tag{8-51}$$

where $y_{12}'(s)/s$ is composed of all poles having positive real residues and $y_{12}''(s)/s$ represents all poles possessing negative residues. Then, to insure that Lucal's procedure can be used, $y_{11}(s)$ and $y_{22}(s)$ are selected such that

$$\frac{y_{11}(s)}{s} = \frac{y_{11}'(s)}{s} + \frac{y_{11}''(s)}{s} = \frac{K}{R_L}\left[\frac{c_0}{s} + \sum_{q=1}^{i} \frac{c_q}{(s + a_q)}\right] + \frac{K}{R_L}\left[\sum_{i+1}^{n} \frac{d_q}{(s + a_q)}\right]$$

$$\frac{y_{22}(s)}{s} = \frac{y_{22}'(s)}{s} + \frac{y_{22}''(s)}{s} = \frac{K}{R_L}\left[\frac{c_0}{s} + \sum_{q=1}^{i} \frac{c_q}{(s + a_q)}\right] + \frac{K}{R_L}\left[\sum_{i+1}^{n} \frac{\frac{c_q^2}{d_q}}{(s + a_q)}\right] \tag{8-52}$$

The terms of $y'_{11}(s)/s$ and $y'_{22}(s)/s$ are selected to match those of $y'_{12}(s)/s$, thereby, satisfying Eq. (8-47) as though R_S and R_L were equal. However, to satisfy the actual terminations, $y_{11}(s)$ and $y_{22}(s)$ must be evaluated at infinite frequency:

$$R_S = \left.\frac{1}{y_{11}(s)}\right]_{s=\infty} \quad \text{and} \quad R_L = \left.\frac{1}{y_{22}(s)}\right]_{s=\infty} \tag{8-53}$$

As a result of this step, the gain factor K is partially fixed since the c_q coefficients associated with $y'_{11}(s)$ and $y'_{22}(s)$ are fixed. However, K can be optimized in a restricted sense while selecting the d_q coefficients associated with $y''_{11}(s)$ and $y''_{22}(s)$ to satisfy the conditions necessary for $y''_{11}(s)$, $y''_{12}(s)$, and $y''_{22}(s)$ to be realizable by Lucal's procedure.

The above procedure can be modified to realize networks which have terminating resistors that are not shunted by capacitors as in Fig. 8-5. For instance, assume the voltage transfer ratio is specified by a function of the form of Eq. (8-25), but the degree of the numerator and denominator polynomials is simply restricted such that $(m \leq n)$. To satisfy the terminating resistors, $y_{11}(s)$ and $y_{22}(s)$ must be evaluated at the first and last transmission zeros of the function $(s = -b_r)$ and $(s = -b_t)$ where the zeros are assumed to be arranged in order such that $b_1 \leq b_2 \leq \cdots \leq b_m$. Lagrange's multiplier rule can be used to maximize K; however, the equations become somewhat more complicated. For example, if d_q represents the residues of $y_{11}(s)/s$ and c_q represents the absolute values of the residues of $y_{12}(s)/s$, the relationships, similar to Eqs. (8-36) and (8-37), that relate c_q, d_q, R_S, and R_L become

$$\frac{d_1}{c_1}\sqrt{\frac{b_r - a_1}{b_t - a_1}} = \frac{d_2}{c_2}\sqrt{\frac{b_r - a_2}{b_t - a_2}} = \cdots \frac{d_q}{c_q}\sqrt{\frac{b_r - a_q}{b_t - a_q}} = M$$

and

$$b_t M - \frac{R_L b_r}{R_S M} + \frac{c_0\left(1 - \dfrac{R_L}{R_S}\right)}{\displaystyle\sum_{q=1}^{n} \frac{c_q}{\sqrt{(b_r - a_q)(b_t - a_q)}}} = 0 \tag{8-54}$$

From these relationships it becomes clear that the poles and zeros of the specified function must be restricted such that $[a_{q-1} < b_r < a_q]$ and $[a_{q-1} < b_t < a_q]$, otherwise the positive realness of the d_q coefficients cannot be insured. Using the value of M determined from Eq. (8-54), the optimum value of K becomes

$$K = \frac{\dfrac{R_L}{R_S}}{c_0 + b_t M \displaystyle\sum_{q=1}^{n} \frac{c_q}{\sqrt{(b_r - a_q)(b_t - a_q)}}} \tag{8-55}$$

This value represents the maximum gain for the specified terminating resistances evaluated at $(s = -b_r)$ and $(s = -b_t)$.

The maximum K for any set of terminating resistors requires that various combinations of transmission zeros be inspected within the restrictions defined by Eq. (8-54). Having established K, the three admittance functions may be determined as previously explained and transformed into open-circuit impedance functions. The terminating resistors are realized from $z_{11}(s)$ and $z_{22}(s)$, after which Lucal's procedure is applied to complete the realization. The network which results from this approach will generally be of the form shown in Fig. 8-7a. However,

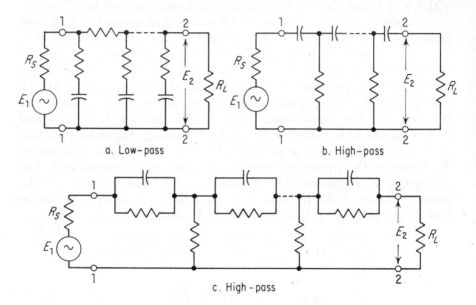

Fig. 8-7. Additional network forms realizable by Kuh's procedure.

if the procedure outlined by Eqs. (8-25) through (8-38) is performed on an impedance basis, a high-pass network (i.e., one that passes high frequencies more readily than low frequencies) will result. In general, this network will be of the form shown in Fig. 8-7b. Similarly, on an impedance basis, the high-pass configuration of Fig. 8-7c can be realized by applying the techniques described above, but these are not the only configurations realizable by Kuh's procedure. Because Lucal's procedure is used to complete the realizations of the center section of the two-port network, a number of varied configurations such as twin-T or bridged-T structures are possible.

8-3. Maximum Gain of a Two-port RC Network

The maximum gain that can be achieved by a two-port network has a direct bearing on the RC synthesis procedures described thus far in Chaps. 7 and 8; therefore, this subject deserves further investigation. In particular, attention will be focused on the maximum voltage transfer ratio gain that can be realized by a two-port RC network in the absence of terminating impedances. Surprising to many is the fact, reported by Longmire and later by Epstein, that voltage transfer ratios having gains greater than unity can be realized within restricted bands of frequency by RC networks.[†]

Consider the simple network of Fig. 8-8 which has a voltage transfer ratio given by

$$\frac{E_2}{E_1} = \frac{As + 1}{Bs^2 + As + 1}$$

where $A = (R_1 C_1 + R_2 C_1 + R_2 C_2)$ and $B = R_1 C_1 R_2 C_2$ (8-56)

Inspection reveals that this function is unity at $(s = j\omega = 0)$; furthermore, A and B must be positive real coefficients since they represent combinations of passive elements. The magnitude of Eq. (8-56) can be written in terms of real frequency as

$$\left|\frac{E_2}{E_1}\right| = \left|\frac{jA\omega + 1}{-B\omega^2 + jA\omega + 1}\right| = \frac{1}{\left|1 - \dfrac{B\omega^2}{1 + jA\omega}\right|}$$ (8-57)

Because A and B are positive real numbers, some finite values of ω will cause the denominator of Eq. (8-57) to have a magnitude less than unity. Hence the magnitude of E_2/E_1 will be greater than unity throughout this range of frequencies. The problem that remains is to determine how great the voltage transfer ratio gain can be made such that the network will still be realizable by RC elements.

The maximum gain realizable by a two-port RC network, such as that described above, has been studied extensively by Fialkow and Gerst.[‡] Results indicate that, contrary to popular belief, it is possible to achieve any desired gain at a particular frequency by an RC network of sufficient complexity. This fact becomes apparent by considering the cascaded combination of a series of two-port sections of the form described above provided suitable impedance level separation is maintained between adjacent sections. Consequently it is desirable that the relationships between complexity of the network, as measured by the

† C. L. Longmire, "An R-C Circuit Giving Over Unity Gain," *Tele-Tech*, vol. 6, April 1947, pp. 40–41; and H. Epstein, "Synthesis of Passive RC Networks with Gains Greater than Unity," *Proc. IRE*, vol. 39, no. 7, July 1951, pp. 833–835.

‡ A. D. Fialkow and I. Gerst, "The Maximum Gain of an RC Network," *Proc. IRE*, vol. 41, no. 3, March 1953, pp. 392–395.

degree of its voltage transfer ratio and maximum realizable gain, be established.

The voltage transfer ratio for a general two-port network can be written as

$$\frac{E_2}{E_1} = \frac{a_n s^n + a_{n-1} s^{n-1} + \cdots + a_1 s + a_0}{b_m s^m + b_{m-1} s^{m-1} + \cdots + b_1 s + b_0} = \frac{P(s)}{Q(s)} \qquad (8\text{-}58)$$

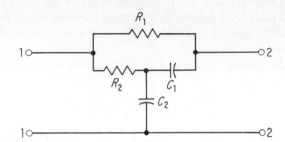

Fig. 8-8. Example network for the transfer ratio of Eq. (8-56).

The transfer ratio must be restricted in the following respects in order that it be realizable by *RC* elements:

1. Zeros of $Q(s)$ must be simple and lie on the negative real axis.
2. The degree of $P(s)$ must be less than or equal to that of $Q(s)$ (i.e., $m \geq n$).
3. The leading coefficients of $Q(s) + P(s)$ and $Q(s) - P(s)$ are positive.

The highest values of gain for E_2/E_1 most likely occur when $P(s)$ and $Q(s)$ are of equal degree, since $P(s)$ cannot be of higher degree than $Q(s)$; therefore it will be assumed that $(n = m)$.

It can be shown that any rational function satisfying the above restrictions will possess the following property.†

$$0 \leq |a_i| \leq b_i \qquad (i = 0, 1, 2, \ldots, n) \qquad (8\text{-}59)$$

This condition requires that E_2/E_1 be normalized such that $(b_m = 1)$ where $m = n$. The negative real poles may be denoted by $(s = -\beta_1)$, $(s = -\beta_2), \ldots, (s = -\beta_n)$; hence $Q(s)$ can be written as

$$Q(s) = \sum_{k=0}^{n} b_k s^k = \prod_{k=1}^{n} (s + \beta_k) \qquad (8\text{-}60)$$

It is desirable to find the coefficients, a_i and b_i, for Eq. (8-58) such that the magnitude of E_2/E_1 will be a maximum at some real frequency $(s = -j\omega_o)$. Because the particular frequency has no direct bearing on

† The first two restrictions have been mentioned in Sec. 7-4 of Chap. 7. The third and fourth restrictions and the relationship of Eq. (8-59) are readily demonstrated by examples. For a thorough discussion of these properties see A. Fialkow and I. Gerst, "The Transfer Function of General Two-Terminal-Pair RC Networks," *Quart. Appl. Math.*, vol. 10, July 1952, pp. 113–127.

the maximum value, it is convenient to let ($\omega_o = 1$). The square of the magnitude of Eq. (8-58) can then be written in terms of ($s = j\omega_o = j1$) as

$$\left|\frac{E_2}{E_1}\right|^2_{s=j1} = \frac{(a_n - a_{n-2} + \cdots)^2 + (a_{n-1} - a_{n-3} + \cdots)^2}{\prod_{k=1}^{n}(1 + \beta_k^2)} \tag{8-61}$$

If the denominator is considered fixed, the numerator is maximized in keeping with Eq. (8-59) when ($a_n = \pm b_n$), ($a_{n-2} = \mp b_{n-2}$), ..., and ($a_{n-1} = \pm b_{n-1}$), ($a_{n-3} = \mp b_{n-3}$), ...; consequently, Eq. (8-61) becomes

$$\left|\frac{E_2}{E_1}\right|^2 = \frac{(b_n + b_{n-2} + \cdots)^2 + (b_{n-1} + b_{n-3} + \cdots)^2}{\prod_{k=1}^{n}(1 + \beta_k^2)} \tag{8-62}$$

The value of $|E_2/E_1|$ derived from this expression represents the maximum value at ($\omega_o = 1$) for all transfer functions of the form of Eq. (8-58) possessing the poles $Q(s)$. However, to obtain a true maximum, an optimum choice of the poles must be made. Therefore, performing calculations based on Eq. (8-60) yields

$$\left|\frac{E_2}{E_1}\right|^2 = \frac{1}{2}\frac{\left[\prod_{k=1}^{n}(1 + \beta_k)^2 + \prod_{k=1}^{n}(-1 + \beta_k)^2\right]}{\prod_{k=1}^{n}(1 + \beta_k^2)} \tag{8-63}$$

The numerator of this expression can be replaced by the inequality

$$\left[\prod_{k=1}^{n}(1 + \beta_k)^2 + \prod_{k=1}^{n}(-1 + \beta_k)^2\right] \leq \prod_{k=1}^{n}[(1 + \beta_k)^2 + (-1 + \beta_k)^2]$$

$$= 2^n \prod_{k=1}^{n}(1 + \beta_k^2) \tag{8-64}$$

As a result, it can be concluded that

$$\left|\frac{E_2}{E_1}\right|^2_{max} \leq 2^{(n-1)} \quad \text{or} \quad \left|\frac{E_2}{E_1}\right|_{max} \leq 2^{(n-1)/2} \tag{8-65}$$

Four possible transfer functions of the form $[E_2/E_1 = (\pm s \pm \beta_1)/(s + \beta_1)]$ occur when ($n = 1$); each form yielding a maximum magnitude for E_2/E_1 of unity. When ($n > 1$), the equal sign of Eq. (8-65) holds only if ($\beta_k = 1$). This represents an unlikely situation; therefore the maximum gain to be obtained by a practical two-port RC network will simply approach $2^{(n-1)/2}$ as an upper limit, although physically realizable networks can be realized at ($s = j\omega_o = j1$) with gains as close to this limit as desired.

A detailed discussion of the maximum gain limits for three-terminal RC networks will not be included because of its complexity. However,

Fialkow and Gerst have demonstrated by a technique similar to the above that the maximum gain of a three-terminal RC network asymptotically approaches $2^{(n-3)/2}$ for voltage transfer ratios of higher degree. In other words, the ratio of maximum realizable gain of a three-terminal RC network to $2^{(n-3)/2}$ tends towards unity for large values of n. For small values of n the maximum gain limits depend on whether n is even or odd, and as in the case of general two-port networks, the maximum gain is unity for $(n = 1)$.

An interesting technique for the synthesis of three-terminal RC networks with gains greater than unity has been suggested by Epstein. The procedure is based on consideration of a general three-terminal structure of the form shown in Fig. 8-9. In this figure the input voltage E_1 is applied to terminals 1-1', and the customary output voltage E_2 is observed between terminals 2-2'. However, a second output voltage denoted by E_2^* may be observed between terminals 1'-2'. In the case of the voltage E_2 a common ground occurs between the input and output circuits by virtue of the connection between terminals 1-2, whereas in the case of E_2^* the common ground is represented by terminal 1'.

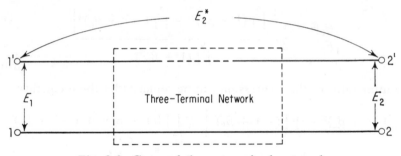

Fig. 8-9. General three-terminal network.

The transfer ratio relating the input and output voltages E_1 and E_2 of Fig. 8-9 can be written in the form of Eq. (8-58). This function must satisfy the restrictions described following Eq. (8-58) if the network is to be realizable as an RC structure. However, the voltage E_2^* is, in effect, the difference between E_1 and E_2 and can be expressed as

$$E_2^* = E_1 - E_2 \qquad (8\text{-}66)$$

If the network between terminals 1-1' and 2-2' produces a phase shift of $180°$ at some real frequency $(s = j\omega_o)$, the input and output voltages are related such that $E_2 = -\lambda E_1$ where λ is a gain factor greater than zero. In other words, the network is such that at any instant the polarity of the voltage between the input and output circuits is reversed. Substituting $E_2 = -\lambda E_1$ into Eq. (8-66) yields

$$E_2^* = (1 + \lambda)E_1 \qquad \text{where} \qquad \lambda > 0 \qquad (8\text{-}67)$$

Consequently, a gain greater than unity is obtained at the frequency ω_o by a three-terminal structure in which terminal $1'$ is the common ground. The voltage transfer ratio for this network can be expressed directly in terms of $P(s)$ and $Q(s)$ from Eqs. (8-58) and (8-66):

$$\frac{E_2^*}{E_1} = 1 - \frac{P(s)}{Q(s)} = \frac{Q(s) - P(s)}{Q(s)} \tag{8-68}$$

It should be noted that the denominators of E_2/E_1 and E_2^*/E_1, given by Eqs. (8-58) and (8-68), are identical; whereas, in general the numerator of E_2^*/E_1 is of higher degree than that of E_2/E_1. It is now possible to apply Eq. (8-68) to the synthesis of a three-terminal network possessing a gain greater than unity at some real frequency. Assume that a desired voltage transfer ratio $E_2'/E_1 = P'(s)/Q(s)$ has been specified. Setting this function equal to Eq. (8-68) yields

$$\frac{E_2'}{E_1} = \frac{E_2^*}{E_1} = \frac{P'(s)}{Q(s)} = \frac{Q(s) - P(s)}{Q(s)} \quad \text{or} \quad P(s) = Q(s) - P'(s) \tag{8-69}$$

Since $P'(s)$ and $Q(s)$ are known from the specified function, $P(s)$ can be computed from Eq. (8-69), and the transfer ratio $[E_2/E_1 = P(s)/Q(s)]$ may be established. This transfer ratio E_2/E_1 can then be realized by one of the two-port RC synthesis procedures described in the preceding sections to yield the network between terminals $1-1'$ and $2-2'$ of Fig. 8-9. The desired transfer ratio E_2'/E_1 is then realized between terminals $1-1'$ and $1'-2'$, and terminal $1'$ represents the common ground.

As an example of the procedure, consider the following transfer ratio which has a gain of 1.0926 at $\omega_o = 1/2$.

$$\frac{E_2'}{E_1} = \frac{12s + 4}{5s^2 + 12s + 4} = \frac{P'(s)}{Q(s)} \tag{8-70}$$

Substituting this function in Eq. (8-69) and solving for $P(s)$ yields

$$P(s) = Q(s) - P'(s) = 5s^2 + 12s + 4 - 12s - 4 = 5s^2$$

therefore

$$\frac{E_2}{E_1} = \frac{P(s)}{Q(s)} = \frac{5s^2}{5s^2 + 12s + 4} = \frac{s^2}{(s + 2/5)(s + 2)} \tag{8-71}$$

This transfer ratio E_2/E_1 can be realized as a two-port RC network by one of the procedures previously described. For instance, it may readily be realized by Guillemin's procedure, in which case $Q(s)$ must first be separated into $Q_1(s)$ plus $Q_2(s)$. For this example, the separation will be chosen as follows:

$$Q(s) = s^2 + \frac{12s}{5} + \frac{4}{5} = Q_1(s) + Q_2(s)$$

where

$$Q_1(s) = \frac{4(s + 1)(s + 3)}{15} \quad \text{and} \quad Q_2(s) = \frac{11s^2 + 20s}{15} \tag{8-72}$$

Equation (8-71) can then be written as

$$\frac{E_2}{E_1} = \frac{P(s)}{Q_1(s) + Q_2(s)} = \frac{\dfrac{P(s)}{Q_1(s)}}{1 + \dfrac{Q_2(s)}{Q_1(s)}} = \frac{y_{12}(s)}{1 + y_{22}(s)}$$

where

$$y_{12}(s) = \frac{P(s)}{Q_1(s)} = \frac{15s^2}{4s^2 + 16s + 12} \quad \text{and} \quad y_{22}(s) = \frac{Q_2(s)}{Q_1(s)} = \frac{11s^2 + 20s}{4s^2 + 16s + 12} \tag{8-73}$$

Expanding $y_{22}(s)$ in a reverse manner gives

$$y_{22}(s) = \cfrac{1}{\cfrac{4}{11} + \cfrac{3}{5s} + \cfrac{1}{\cfrac{1100}{117} + \cfrac{605s}{117}}} \tag{8-74}$$

This expansion leads to the network of Fig. 8-10a. In this example the driving-point admittance is of secondary importance, but the transfer admittance $y_{12}(s)$ of Eq. (8-73) must be satisfied. Fortunately, the element values for a single-ladder section such as Fig. 8-10a do not require adjustment; however, the network must be terminated by a 1-ohm resistor [see Eq. (8-73) or Chap. 7, Sec. (7-5)] to complete the realization. The resistors in the output circuit may be combined, and the resulting network can be redrawn with terminal 1' as the common ground, thereby completing the realization of the transfer ratio given by Eq. (8-70). The final network is shown in Fig. 8-10b where ζ is any positive real multiplying constant. To verify that the network of Fig. 8-10b realizes the transfer ratio of Eq. (8-70) for any value of ζ, it is possible to substitute the element values of the figure into the transfer ratio of Eq. (8-56).

A special case of the three-terminal RC configuration described above is the ladder network composed of a cascaded combination of L-sections. Space does not permit a complete discussion of the maximum gain possibilities of such networks; however, a few significant points deserve mention. For instance, the voltage transfer ratio can be written from Eq. (8-58) in terms of its poles β_k and zeros α_i as

$$\frac{E_2}{E_1} = K \left. \frac{\prod\limits_{i=1}^{m} (s + \alpha_i)}{\prod\limits_{k=1}^{n} (s + \beta_k)} \right]_{m \leq n} \tag{8-75}$$

This function must satisfy the following conditions if it is to be realizable as a two-port RC ladder network.

1. The poles must be simple and restricted to the negative real axis, excluding the origin and infinity (i.e., β_k must be real, positive, and distinct).

2. The zeros may be of any order but must be restricted to the negative real axis, including the origin and infinity (i.e., α_i must be real and nonnegative).

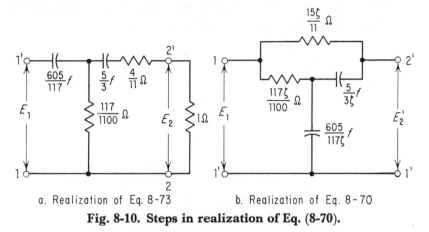

a. Realization of Eq. 8-73   b. Realization of Eq. 8-70

Fig. 8-10. Steps in realization of Eq. (8-70).

In addition to establishing the sufficiency of these conditions, Fialkow and Gerst have proved that the maximum gain of a two-port RC ladder network is unity.[†] This fact follows since the maximum gain of a single RC L-section is unity at any particular frequency. Consequently, the cascaded combination of several such L-sections forms a ladder network having a gain of unity.

A question remains concerning the transfer ratio of Eq. (8-75) as to the maximum value of K that can be realized by a two-port RC ladder network. Paige and Kuh investigated this problem for three variations of the transfer ratio, leading to low-pass, high-pass, and bandpass networks.[‡] Results indicate that the maximum realizable gain factor K_{max} is dependent on the poles and zeros of the transfer ratio and is given accordingly for each of the three cases studied.

Case 1. When m and n are related such that $[(r + 1) \leqq m \leqq n]$, where $r \geqq 0$, the maximum gain factor is given by

$$K_{max} = \frac{\prod\limits_{k=(r+1)}^{n} \beta_k}{\prod\limits_{i=(r+1)}^{m} \alpha_i} \tag{8-76}$$

[†] A. D. Fialkow and I. Gerst, "The Transfer Function of an RC Ladder Network," *J. Math. Phys.*, vol. 30, January 1952, pp. 49–71.

[‡] A. Paige and K. S. Kuh, "Maximum Gain Realization of an RC Ladder Network," *IRE Trans. Circuit Theory*, vol. CT-7, no. 1, March 1960, pp. 32–40.

These conditions can be satisfied by the transfer ratio of a low-pass, high-pass, or bandpass network; consequently, this relationship represents a general case. When ($r = 0$), Eqs. (8-75) and (8-76) lead to a low-pass network possessing a gain variation with real frequency of the form shown in Fig. 8-11a. The maximum voltage transfer ratio of unity is achieved at zero frequency, in which case all of the shunt arms and none of the series arms of the network are open-circuited. The resulting configuration is illustrated in Fig. 8-11b.

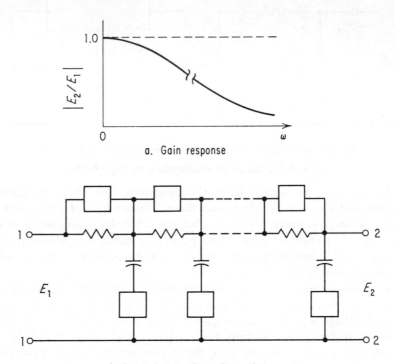

a. Gain response

b. General network configuration

Fig. 8-11. Low-pass RC ladder network and gain versus frequency response.

A straightforward procedure has been suggested by Paige and Kuh for the realization of transfer ratios satisfying the above conditions. The procedure can be stated briefly as follows:

1. The voltage transfer ratio for the ladder network can be expressed as

$$\frac{E_2}{E_1} = \frac{z_{21}(s)}{z_{11}(s)} = \frac{-y_{12}(s)}{y_{22}(s)} \qquad (8\text{-}77)$$

Consequently, $z_{11}(s)$ [or $y_{22}(s)$] can be chosen as a realizable RC driving-point function of the form

$$z_{11}(s) = \frac{\prod\limits_{k=1}^{n}(s + \beta_k)}{s \prod\limits_{i=1}^{n-1}(s + \alpha_i)} \tag{8-78}$$

The poles of the function must be simple and alternate with the zeros along the negative real axis; however, because $z_{11}(s)$ is of secondary importance, the values of α_i may be selected arbitrarily.

2. Evaluate $z_{11}(s)$ at each of its transmission zeros, including those at $(s = 0)$ and $(s = \infty)$. The smallest positive value obtained in this evaluation will be denoted as R_o, and its transmission zero will be β_o.

3. Form the function $z_{11}^{*}(s) = z_{11}(s) - R_o$, then remove the pole of $1/z_{11}^{*}(s)$ at β_o to form an admittance function $y_{11}^{**}(s)$.

$$y_{11}^{**}(s) = \frac{1}{z_{11}^{*}(s)} - \frac{k_o s}{(s + \beta_o)} \tag{8-79}$$

4. Repeat Steps 2, 3, and 4 until the function is fully expanded. The network resulting from this expansion will be of the form of Fig. 8-11b where each of the unlabeled blocks represents resistors.

Case 2. When m and n of Eq. (8-75) are related such that $[m < (r + 1) < n]$, the maximum gain factor is given by

$$K_{\max} = \prod\limits_{k=(r+1)}^{n} \beta_k \tag{8-80}$$

A special case of this relationship exists when $(r = 0)$, since all of the zeros of the voltage transfer ratio are at $(s = \infty)$ and Eq. (8-75) becomes

$$\frac{E_2}{E_1} = \frac{K}{\prod\limits_{k=1}^{n}(s + \beta_k)} \tag{8-81}$$

This transfer ratio represents a low-pass network which has a maximum gain of unity at zero frequency when K is given by Eq. (8-80). Voltage transfer ratios satisfying these conditions are readily realized by selecting a driving-point impedance $z_{11}(s)$ as in Step 1 of Case 1 [see Eq. (8-78)] and expanding the function in one of Cauer's canonic forms.

Case 3. When $(m = n = r)$, the transfer ratio of Eq. (8-75) represents a high-pass RC ladder network. The maximum gain factor of unity is achieved in a high-pass network at infinite frequency if all the series arms and none of the shunt arms are effectively short-circuited. This can be accomplished by a network of the form shown in Fig. 8-12a. The magnitude or gain variation with real frequency of a high-pass network is of the form shown in Fig. 8-12b.

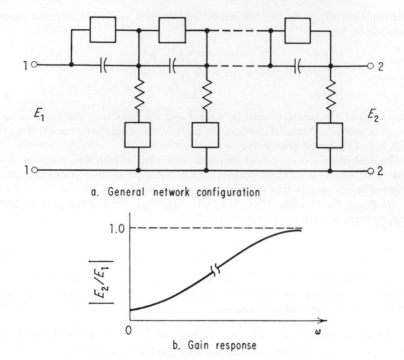

a. General network configuration

b. Gain response

Fig. 8-12. High-pass RC ladder network and gain versus frequency response.

A special case of the high-pass ladder network exists when all of the zeros of the voltage transfer ratio occur at the origin. In this case Eq. (8-75) becomes

$$\frac{E_2}{E_1} = \frac{Ks^n}{\prod\limits_{k=1}^{n}(s + \beta_k)} \qquad (8\text{-}82)$$

This transfer ratio can be realized by choosing an admittance function $y_{22}(s)$ and expanding it in the manner described in Case 1. The driving-point admittance can be written as

$$y_{22}(s) = \frac{\prod\limits_{k=1}^{n}(s + \beta_k)}{\prod\limits_{i=1}^{n-1}(s + \alpha_i)} \qquad (8\text{-}83)$$

When the voltage transfer ratio is of the form

$$\frac{E_2}{E_1} = K \frac{s^m \prod\limits_{i=(m+1)}^{n} (s + \alpha_i)}{\prod\limits_{k=1}^{n} (s + \beta_k)} \tag{8-84}$$

where $(\alpha_k < \beta_k$ for $k = 1, 2, \ldots, n)$ a high-pass RC ladder network can be realized by choosing a driving-point admittance of the form of Eq. (8-83) and using the procedure of Steps 1 through 5 of Case 1 on an admittance basis. The resulting network will be of the form of Fig. 8-12a where each of the unlabeled blocks represents resistors.

The maximum gain of unity can only be achieved in a low-pass RC ladder network at $(s = 0)$ and in a high-pass structure at $(s = \infty)$. Consequently, since a bandpass ladder network can be considered as the cascaded combination of low-pass and high-pass L-sections possessing gains less than unity at intermediate frequencies, the maximum gain of the bandpass network can only approach unity at any particular frequency. The maximum gain factor in this case is given by Eq. (8-76), and the magnitude or gain of the transfer ratio varies as a function of real frequency as shown in Fig. 8-13.

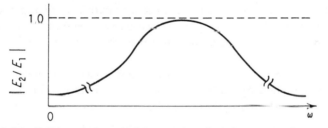

Fig. 8-13. RC band-pass ladder network gain versus frequency.

Realization of a bandpass voltage transfer ratio can be achieved by separating it into the product of two functions which represent the cascaded combination of a low-pass and a high-pass ladder structure. For instance, the bandpass transfer ratio can be written as

$$\frac{E_2}{E_1} = \frac{-y_{21}^a(s)z_{21}^b(s)}{1 + y_{22}^a(s)z_{11}^b(s)} = \left[\frac{-y_{21}^a(s)z_{21}^b(s)}{y_{22}^a(s)z_{11}^b(s)}\right] \frac{1}{1 + \dfrac{1}{y_{22}^a(s)z_{11}^b(s)}}$$

$$= \left(\frac{E_2}{E_1}\right)^a \left(\frac{E_2}{E_1}\right)^b \frac{1}{1 + \dfrac{1}{y_{22}^a(s)z_{11}^b(s)}} \tag{8-85}$$

If the given bandpass transfer ratio is separated according to Eq. (8-85), $[(E_2/E_1)^a = -y_{21}^a(s)/y_{22}^a(s)]$ can be realized as a high-pass ladder network by the methods described in Case 3. Similarly, $[(E_2/E_1)^b = z_{21}^b(s)/z_{11}^b(s)]$ represents a low-pass ladder network which may be realized by the procedures of Case 1. Networks (a) and (b) are then combined in cascade to complete the realization. Note that in the separation process of Eq. (8-85), $y_{22}^a(s)$ of the high-pass section and $z_{11}^b(s)$ of the low-pass section are completely specified. Bandpass transfer ratios not readily separated in this form can be realized as ladder networks by one of the previously described techniques such as Guillemin's, Dasher's, or Weinberg's procedure.

8-4. Ho's Procedure

Thus far the synthesis procedures of this chapter have been restricted to realization techniques requiring only resistors and capacitors. Similar procedures can be derived for RL and LC network realization; however, from the standpoint of efficient design, it is generally useful to employ resistors, inductors, and capacitors in the realization. Unfortunately, the added degree of freedom in the RLC case sometimes obscures a preferable procedure and may cause the designer to lose insight into the realization process. A procedure which avoids this difficulty has been developed by E. C. Ho and is based on a matrix factorization technique.†
Although this technique does not lead to a network requiring a minimum number of elements, it does permit arbitrary selection of the load and source resistances and does not require the use of ideal or perfect transformers.

In Chap. 7, Sec. 7-1, it was shown that a two-port network can be completely specified by its transmission or T-matrix. The T-matrix for the ladder network of Fig. 8-14 can be written as

$$\begin{bmatrix} E_1 \\ I_1 \end{bmatrix} = \begin{bmatrix} A(s) & B(s) \\ C(s) & D(s) \end{bmatrix} \begin{bmatrix} E_2 \\ I_2 \end{bmatrix}$$

where

$$\begin{bmatrix} A(s) & B(s) \\ C(s) & D(s) \end{bmatrix} = \begin{bmatrix} 1 & Z_1 \\ 0 & 1 \end{bmatrix} \begin{bmatrix} 1 & 0 \\ Y_2 & 1 \end{bmatrix} \begin{bmatrix} 1 & Z_3 \\ 0 & 1 \end{bmatrix} \cdots \begin{bmatrix} 1 & Z_{n-1} \\ 0 & 1 \end{bmatrix} \begin{bmatrix} 1 & 0 \\ Y_n & 1 \end{bmatrix} \quad (8\text{-}86)$$

The current I_2 in Fig. 8-14 is assumed to flow out of the network. Furthermore, the T-matrix for the entire structure is expressed simply as the product of the T-matrices of the individual series and shunt arms of the network [see Eq. (7-23) and Table 7-1]. This relationship suggests that if a prescribed T-matrix can be factored in the form of Eq. (8-86), it can be realized by the reverse process of the analysis approach used above.

† E. C. Ho, "A General Matrix Factorization Method," *IRE Trans. Circuit Theory,* vol. CT-2, June 1955, pp. 146–153.

Before discussing possible factorization techniques, it should be noted that the transmission functions of the T-matrix are related to the network voltages and currents as follows:

$$A(s) = \left.\frac{E_1}{E_2}\right]_{I_2 = 0} \qquad B(s) = \left.\frac{E_1}{I_2}\right]_{E_2 = 0}$$

$$C(s) = \left.\frac{I_1}{E_2}\right]_{I_2 = 0} \qquad D(s) = \left.\frac{I_1}{I_2}\right]_{E_2 = 0} \qquad (8\text{-}87)$$

These relationships are readily obtained from the open-circuit impedances of Eq. (7-3) or short-circuit admittances of Eq. (7-7) and their equivalent T-matrix terms of Table 7-2. In the majority of synthesis problems, one of the transfer ratios E_2/E_1, I_2/E_1, E_2/I_1, or I_2/I_1 is given, thereby

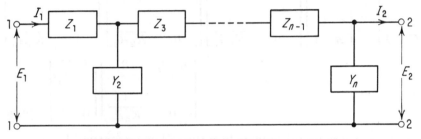

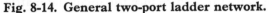

Fig. 8-14. General two-port ladder network.

completely establishing one of the four transmission functions of Eq. (8-87). Specification of only one T-matrix function is not sufficient to completely define a particular network; however, in most cases realization of the desired transfer ratio is the primary requirement. Satisfying terminating conditions such as source and/or load impedances or desired input and/or output driving-point characteristics is generally of secondary importance. Fortunately, specification of one of the four transmission functions does not rule out matrix factorization as a realization technique, nor does it prevent the satisfaction of arbitrary source and load impedances. However, it may be possible to realize the transfer ratio only within a constant multiplying factor of the desired function.

A given nonsingular T-matrix can be factored into three component matrices by a series of linear transformations. This factorization can be written as follows where it is understood that each of the A, B, C, and D terms may be functions of s.

$$\begin{bmatrix} A & B \\ C & D \end{bmatrix} = \begin{bmatrix} 1 & 0 \\ \dfrac{C}{A} & 1 \end{bmatrix} \begin{bmatrix} A & 0 \\ 0 & \dfrac{1}{A} \end{bmatrix} \begin{bmatrix} 1 & \dfrac{B}{A} \\ 0 & 1 \end{bmatrix} \qquad (8\text{-}88)$$

The factorization of Eq. (8-88) takes advantage of the fact that, for a physically realizable RLC network, the determinant of the matrix must equal unity [see Eq. (7-20)].

If the desired voltage transfer ratio E_2/E_1 for a network is specified, the transmission function A is known from Eq. (8-87) and can be considered to represent the product of several factors.

$$A = (K_1 A_1)(K_2 A_2)(K_3 A_3) \cdots (K_n A_n) \qquad (8\text{-}89)$$

In this expression, the K's are constant multipliers, and the A's are simplified transmission functions. Substituting Eq. (8-89) into the center diagonal matrix of Eq. (8-88) leads to further expansion:

$$\begin{bmatrix} A & B \\ C & D \end{bmatrix} = \begin{bmatrix} 1 & 0 \\ \dfrac{C}{A} & 1 \end{bmatrix} \begin{bmatrix} K_1 A_1 & 0 \\ 0 & \dfrac{1}{K_1 A_1} \end{bmatrix} \begin{bmatrix} K_2 A_2 & 0 \\ 0 & \dfrac{1}{K_2 A_2} \end{bmatrix} \begin{bmatrix} K_3 A_3 & 0 \\ 0 & \dfrac{1}{K_3 A_3} \end{bmatrix}$$

$$\cdots \begin{bmatrix} K_n A_n & 0 \\ 0 & \dfrac{1}{K_n A_n} \end{bmatrix} \begin{bmatrix} 1 & \dfrac{B}{A} \\ 0 & 1 \end{bmatrix} \qquad (8\text{-}90)$$

At this point it is useful to introduce the following matrix identity:

$$\begin{bmatrix} A_g & 0 \\ 0 & \dfrac{1}{A_g} \end{bmatrix} \equiv \begin{bmatrix} 1 & 0 \\ \left(-1 + \dfrac{1}{A_g}\right) & 1 \end{bmatrix} \begin{bmatrix} 1 & 1 \\ 0 & 1 \end{bmatrix} \begin{bmatrix} 1 & 0 \\ (A_g - 1) & 1 \end{bmatrix} \begin{bmatrix} 1 & \dfrac{-1}{A_g} \\ 0 & 1 \end{bmatrix}$$

$$(8\text{-}91)$$

It is important to note that multiplication to the right of a series of diagonal a-matrices of the form of Eq. (8-91) by a triangular b-matrix modifies the triangular b-matrix as follows:

$$\begin{bmatrix} 1 & b \\ 0 & 1 \end{bmatrix} \begin{bmatrix} a_1 & 0 \\ 0 & \dfrac{1}{a_1} \end{bmatrix} \begin{bmatrix} a_2 & 0 \\ 0 & \dfrac{1}{a_2} \end{bmatrix} \cdots \begin{bmatrix} a_n & 0 \\ 0 & \dfrac{1}{a_n} \end{bmatrix}$$

$$\equiv \begin{bmatrix} a_1 & 0 \\ 0 & \dfrac{1}{a_1} \end{bmatrix} \begin{bmatrix} a_2 & 0 \\ 0 & \dfrac{1}{a_2} \end{bmatrix} \cdots \begin{bmatrix} a_n & 0 \\ 0 & \dfrac{1}{a_n} \end{bmatrix} \begin{bmatrix} 1 & \dfrac{b}{(a_1 a_2 \ldots a_n)^2} \\ 0 & 1 \end{bmatrix} \qquad (8\text{-}92)$$

Successive substitution of Eq. (8-91) into the diagonal matrices of Eq. (8-90) and application of the triangular matrix modification of Eq.

(8-92) plus multiplying together similar adjacent matrices leads to the following expanded form.

$$\begin{bmatrix} A & B \\ C & D \end{bmatrix} = \begin{bmatrix} 1 & 0 \\ \left[\dfrac{C}{A}-1+\dfrac{1}{K_1A_1}\right] & 1 \end{bmatrix}\begin{bmatrix} 1 & 1 \\ 0 & 1 \end{bmatrix}\begin{bmatrix} 1 & 0 \\ \left[K_1A_1-2+\dfrac{1}{K_2A_2}\right] & 1 \end{bmatrix}$$

$$\times \begin{bmatrix} 1 & 1 \\ 0 & 1 \end{bmatrix}\cdots\begin{bmatrix} 1 & 0 \\ \left[K_2A_2-2+\dfrac{1}{K_3A_3}\right] & 1 \end{bmatrix}\begin{bmatrix} 1 & 1 \\ 0 & 1 \end{bmatrix}$$

$$\cdots\begin{bmatrix} 1 & 0 \\ \left[K_{n-1}A_{n-1}-2+\dfrac{1}{K_nA_n}\right] & 1 \end{bmatrix}\begin{bmatrix} 1 & 1 \\ 0 & 1 \end{bmatrix}\begin{bmatrix} 1 & 0 \\ (K_nA_n-1) & 1 \end{bmatrix}$$

$$\cdots\begin{bmatrix} 1 & \left[\dfrac{B}{A}-\left(\dfrac{1}{K_1K_2{}^2K_3{}^2\ldots K_n{}^2A_1A_2{}^2A_3{}^2\ldots A_n{}^2}+\cdots\right.\right. \\ 0 & \\ & \left.\left.+\dfrac{1}{K_{n-1}K_n{}^2A_{n-1}A_n{}^2}+\dfrac{1}{K_nA_n}\right)\right] \\ & 1 \end{bmatrix} \quad (8\text{-}93)$$

This matrix represents a particular physically realizable RLC ladder network when all four of the transmission functions are specified. However, if only E_2/E_1 is given such that A is the only transmission function known, the first and last matrices on the right-hand side of Eq. (8-93) can be deleted. The resulting expression represents the physically realizable ladder network required to realize the prescribed function A; however, B^*, C^*, and D^* are new functions and not necessarily equal to B, C, and D of Eq. (8-93).

$$\begin{bmatrix} A & B^* \\ C^* & D^* \end{bmatrix} = \begin{bmatrix} 1 & 1 \\ 0 & 1 \end{bmatrix}\begin{bmatrix} 1 & 0 \\ \left[K_1A_1-2+\dfrac{1}{K_2A_2}\right] & 1 \end{bmatrix}\begin{bmatrix} 1 & 1 \\ 0 & 1 \end{bmatrix}\cdots$$

$$\cdots\begin{bmatrix} 1 & 0 \\ \left[K_{n-1}A_{n-1}-2+\dfrac{1}{K_nA_n}\right] & 1 \end{bmatrix}\begin{bmatrix} 1 & 1 \\ 0 & 1 \end{bmatrix}\begin{bmatrix} 1 & 0 \\ (K_nA_n-1) & 1 \end{bmatrix} \quad (8\text{-}94)$$

Comparison of this matrix with that of Eq. (8-86) reveals that Eq. (8-94) represents a two-port ladder network of the form shown in Fig. 8-14 where each of the series impedances $Z_1, Z_3, \ldots, Z_{n-1}$, is a 1-ohm resistor. Furthermore, resistive terminations are readily achieved, since the first matrix on the right-hand side of Eq. (8-94) represents a 1-ohm resistor and the last matrix represents a nonminimum conductive admittance. Hence, arbitrary selection of the source and load resistances can be obtained by adjusting the impedance level of the network by a constant R_S for the source resistance, and choosing an appropriate value of K_n to satisfy the desired load resistance R_L. With this modification, Eq. (8-94) becomes

$$
\begin{bmatrix} A & B^* \\ C^* & D^* \end{bmatrix} = \begin{bmatrix} 1 & R_S \\ 0 & 1 \end{bmatrix} \begin{bmatrix} 1 & 0 \\ \dfrac{1}{R_S}\left[K_1 A_1 - 2 + \dfrac{1}{A_2 K_2}\right] & 1 \end{bmatrix} \begin{bmatrix} 1 & R_S \\ 0 & 1 \end{bmatrix} \cdots
$$

$$
\cdots \begin{bmatrix} 1 & 0 \\ \dfrac{1}{R_S}\left[K_g A_g - 2 + \dfrac{1}{A_h K_h}\right] & 1 \end{bmatrix} \begin{bmatrix} 1 & R_S \\ 0 & 1 \end{bmatrix} \cdots
$$

$$
\cdots \begin{bmatrix} 1 & 0 \\ \dfrac{1}{R_S}(K_n A_n - 1) - R_L & 1 \end{bmatrix} \begin{bmatrix} 1 & 0 \\ R_L & 1 \end{bmatrix} \tag{8-95}
$$

Because of the impedance-level adjustment, this matrix factorization realizes A (i.e., the specified voltage transfer ratio) within a constant multiplier, while at the same time satisfying prescribed terminating resistances. The resulting network is illustrated in Fig. 8-15.

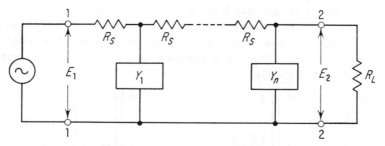

Fig. 8-15. Ladder network realization for Eq. (8-95).

The synthesis procedure, based on the above factorization technique, varies somewhat depending on whether the given function is a minimum or nonminimum phase transfer ratio. In the case of minimum-phase transfer ratios (i.e., rational functions of s with all poles and zeros restricted to the left half of the s-plane or the $j\omega$-axis), the procedure begins by writing the inverse of the specified voltage transfer ratio as A.

Then A must be factored into the product of a finite number of nonminimum-resistive positive real functions. This can be accomplished as indicated in Eq. (8-89); however, the factorization may require the selection of a set of positive real numbers $d_1, d_2, \ldots, d_n$. When the transfer ratio $E_2/E_1 = P(s)/KQ(s)$ is such that $P(s)$ and $Q(s)$ are of equal degree, the resulting factorization can be written as

$$
A = \frac{E_1}{E_2} = K \frac{s^p + a_{p-1}s^{p-1} + \cdots + a_1 s + a_0}{s^m + b_{m-1}s + \cdots + b_1 s + b_0} \bigg]_{p=m}
$$

$$
= K \frac{(s^2 + e_1 s + f_1)(s + e_3)(s + e_5) \cdots}{(s^2 + e_2 s + f_2)(s^2 + e_4) \cdots}
$$

$$
= \left[K_1 \frac{(s^2 + e_1 s + f_1)}{(s + d_1)(s + d_2)} \right] \left[K_2 \frac{(s + d_3)(s + d_4)}{(s^2 + e_2 s + f_2)} \right] \left[K_3 \frac{(s + d_1)}{(s + d_3)} \right] \left[K_4 \frac{(s + d_2)}{(s + d_4)} \right] \cdots
$$

$$
\cdots \left[K_5 \frac{(s^2 + s + e_4)}{(s_2 + e_4)} \right] \left[K_6 \frac{(s + d_5)(s + d_6)}{(s^2 + s + e_4)} \right] \left[K_7 \frac{(s + e_3)}{(s + d_5)} \right] \left[K_8 \frac{(s + e_5)}{(s + d_6)} \right] \cdots
$$

$$
= (K_1 A_1)(K_2 A_2)(K_3 A_3)(K_4 A_4) \ldots (K_n A_n) \tag{8-96}
$$

where $A_1, A_2, \ldots, A_n$ represent nonminimum-resistive positive real functions, and $K_1, K_2, \ldots, K_n$ are constant multipliers which can be chosen later to give the value of K as $(K = K_1 K_2, \ldots, K_n)$. For cases in which $(p > m)$, factors of the form $K_i(s + d_i)$ must also be included in Eq. (8-96). It is possible to multiply E_1/E_2 by surplus factors when necessary; however, this should be avoided if possible since they cause redundant elements to be added to the realization.

The success of the factorization of A into a product such as Eq. (8-96) is assured by the following lemmas:

1. For a given second degree polynomial $(s^2 + es + f)$ where $(e > 0)$ and $(f > 0)$, it is always possible to determine two positive real numbers d_1 and d_2 such that for all values of s on the $j\omega$-axis the real part of the rational function,

$$
\frac{s^2 + es + f}{(s + d_1)(s + d_2)} \tag{8-97}
$$

will be bounded between two real, finite, positive, nonzero numbers. The real part of Eq. (8-97) reveals that the lemma will be satisfied for all values of ω if d_1 and d_2 are chosen such that

$$
(d_1 e + d_2 e - d_1 d_2) \gtrless 0 \tag{8-98}
$$

2. If $(e > 0)$, then $(s^2 + s + e)/(s^2 + e)$ is a positive real function of the complex variable s. Furthermore, the real part of this function is bounded from below by a positive nonzero number for all values of s on the $j\omega$-axis.

As a result of these lemmas, the transmission function A of a minimum-phase transfer ratio can be separated in a manner similar to Eq. (8-96). Once this separation has been accomplished, it is possible to realize A within a constant multiplier of the desired function by substituting its separated terms and the desired terminating resistances into Eq. (8-95) and choosing appropriate multiplying factors K_1, K_2, ..., K_n. The resulting network will be of the form shown in Fig. 8-15.

As an example of the above procedure, assume the following minimum-phase transfer ratio is given along with desired source and load resistances of $R_S = 3$ ohms and $R_L = 9$ ohms.

$$\frac{E_2}{E_1} = \frac{(s + 1)}{(s^3 + 6s^2 + 14s + 15)} \tag{8-99}$$

To synthesize a network which is within a constant K of Eq. (8-99) and satisfying the desired source and load impedances, it is first necessary to determine a factored form for A. This can be accomplished as follows:

$$A = \frac{E_1}{E_2} = K \frac{(s^3 + 6s^2 + 14s + 15)}{(s + 1)}$$

$$= \left[K_1 \frac{(s^2 + 3s + 5)}{(s + 1)} \right] [K_2(s + 3)] = (K_1 A_1)(K_2 A_2) \tag{8-100}$$

Substituting the A_1 and A_2 factors of Eq. (8-100), $R_S = 3$, and $R_L = 9$ into Eq. (8-95) yields

$$\begin{bmatrix} A & B^* \\ C^* & D^* \end{bmatrix} = \begin{bmatrix} 1 & 3 \\ 0 & 1 \end{bmatrix} \begin{bmatrix} 1 & 0 \\ \frac{1}{3} \left[\frac{K_1(s^2 + 3s + 5)}{(s + 1)} - 2 + \frac{1}{K_2(s + 3)} \right] & 1 \end{bmatrix} \cdots$$

$$\cdots \begin{bmatrix} 1 & 3 \\ 0 & 1 \end{bmatrix} \begin{bmatrix} 1 & 0 \\ \frac{1}{3}[K_2(s + 3) - 1] - 9 & 1 \end{bmatrix} \begin{bmatrix} 1 & 0 \\ 9 & 1 \end{bmatrix} \tag{8-101}$$

The form of the network is almost immediately apparent; however, K_1 and K_2 must be properly chosen such that no negative elements result. Fortunately, they can also be chosen in such a manner that the total number of elements is reduced. Combining the last two matrices of Eq. (8-101) gives

$$\begin{bmatrix} 1 & 0 \\ \frac{1}{3}[K_2(s+3)-1]-9 & 1 \end{bmatrix} \begin{bmatrix} 1 & 0 \\ 9 & 1 \end{bmatrix} = \begin{bmatrix} 1 & 0 \\ \frac{1}{3}[K_2(s+3)-1] & 1 \end{bmatrix} = \begin{bmatrix} 1 & 0 \\ Y_2 & 1 \end{bmatrix} \tag{8-102}$$

The admittance of the last subnetwork and load resistor becomes

$$Y_2 = \frac{1}{3}[K_2(s + 3) - 1] \tag{8-103}$$

The load resistor must be 9 ohms; therefore, K_2 can be chosen as $K_2 = 4/9$, in which case Eq. (8-103) yields

$$Y_2 = \frac{1}{3}\left[\frac{4}{9}(s + 3) - 1\right] = \frac{4s}{27} + \frac{1}{9} \qquad (8\text{-}104)$$

Substituting K_2 in the second matrix of the right-hand side of Eq. (8-101), it becomes possible to select a realizable value for K_1. Choosing $(K_1 = 1)$, the admittance of this matrix can be written and expanded as

$$Y_1 = \frac{1}{3}\left[\frac{(s^2 + 3s + 5)}{(s + 1)} - 2 + \frac{9}{4(s + 3)}\right] = \frac{4s^3 + 16s^2 + 33s + 45}{12(s + 1)(s + 3)}$$

$$= \frac{1}{3}s + \frac{1}{(s + 1)} + \frac{\frac{3}{4}}{(s + 3)} \qquad (8\text{-}105)$$

The entire T-matrix of Eq. (8-101) can then be written in terms of the parameters established above as

$$\begin{bmatrix} A & B^* \\ C^* & D^* \end{bmatrix} = \begin{bmatrix} 1 & 3 \\ 0 & 1 \end{bmatrix}\begin{bmatrix} 1 & 0 \\ \dfrac{s}{3} + \dfrac{1}{(s + 1)} + \dfrac{3}{4(s + 3)} & 1 \end{bmatrix} \cdots$$

$$\cdots \begin{bmatrix} 1 & 3 \\ 0 & 1 \end{bmatrix}\begin{bmatrix} 1 & 0 \\ \dfrac{4s}{27} + \dfrac{1}{9} & 1 \end{bmatrix} \qquad (8\text{-}106)$$

This factorization yields the network of Fig. 8-16, which realizes the transfer ratio of Eq. (8-99) within a multiplying factor $(1/K = 1/K_1K_2 = 9/4)$ of the desired value.

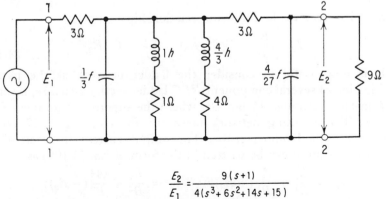

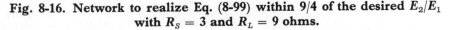

Fig. 8-16. Network to realize Eq. (8-99) within 9/4 of the desired E_2/E_1 with $R_S = 3$ and $R_L = 9$ ohms.

It should be pointed out that proper selection of the gain factors K_1, $K_2, \ldots, K_n$ not only can reduce the number of elements required for the realization but can also be useful in associating resistance with the reactive elements (e.g., resistors can be realized in series with inductors). It is also possible to maximize the transfer gain by carefully selecting the gain factors. Finally, if one of the other transmission functions B, C, or D is prescribed, it is possible to factor it and expand the T-matrix in equivalent matrices similar to that described above for the A function. A second approach, which may be easier in many instances, is to convert the specified transfer ratio into an equivalent A function, after which realization can be accomplished by a straightforward application of the above techniques.

The realization of nonminimum-phase transfer ratios is similar in many respects to that of the minimum-phase case. However, it is necessary to restrict the transfer ratio such that no zeros fall on the positive real axis of the s-plane. The poles of E_2/E_1 may lie anywhere within the left half-plane, but the function must be regular at ($s = \infty$). Consider the possibility of terminating an RLC two-port ladder network such as Fig. 8-14 by a 1-ohm resistor. If this is done, $(E_2/I_2 = 1)$, and since one of the equations characterizing the network in terms of T-matrices is given by $[E_1 = AE_2 + BI_2]$ [see Eq. (8-86)], the inverse of the transfer ratio becomes

$$\frac{E_1}{E_2} = \frac{E_1}{I_2} = A + B \tag{8-107}$$

It is possible by proper selection of A and B to realize a nonminimum-phase transfer ratio as a two-port network terminated by a 1-ohm resistor. One suitable choice of A and B is

$$A = B = \frac{1}{2}\frac{E_1}{E_2} = \frac{1}{2}K\frac{Q(s)}{P(s)} \tag{8-108}$$

This choice leads to the following relationship:

$$I_2 = \frac{E_1}{B} + \frac{A}{B}(-E_2) = \frac{E_1}{B} + (-E_2) \tag{8-109}$$

It is now useful to consider the ladder network as the parallel combination of several component RLC ladder sections each represented by T-matrix functions A^q and B^q, where the superscript q ranges from 1 to m. The resulting network takes the form of Fig. 8-17 and is terminated by a 1-ohm resistor. The output current for each of the component sections can be written in the form of Eq. (8-109) as

$$I_2{}^1 = \frac{E_1}{B^1} + \frac{A^1}{B^1}(-E_2); \qquad I_2{}^2 = \frac{E_1}{B^2} + \frac{A^2}{B^2}(-E_2);$$

$$\cdots I_2{}^m = \frac{E_1}{B^m} + \frac{A^m}{B^m}(-E_2) \tag{8-110}$$

The total current I_2 flowing through the 1-ohm terminating resistor must equal the summation of all the currents of Eq. (8-110), ($I_2 = \sum_{q=1}^{m} I_2{}^q$). Consequently, from Eqs. (8-109) and (8-110), it follows that

$$\frac{A}{B} = 1 = \frac{A^1}{B^1} + \frac{A^2}{B^2} + \cdots + \frac{A^m}{B^m} \tag{8-111}$$

$$\frac{1}{B} = \frac{2P(s)}{KQ(s)} = \frac{1}{B^1} + \frac{1}{B^2} + \cdots + \frac{1}{B^m} \tag{8-112}$$

A solution for Eq. (8-111) is given by ($A^q/B^q = 1/m$) for ($q = 1, 2, \ldots, m$); however, the solution of Eq. (8-112) requires that the physical realizability of parallel ladder networks be investigated. Fortunately, one condition can be stated immediately. The polynomials $P(s)$ and $Q(s)$ which define the specified transfer ratio must possess only positive coefficients. The poles of E_2/E_1 are given by $Q(s)$ which is a Hurwitz polynomial, hence $Q(s)$ has no negative coefficients. However, $P(s)$ is permitted to possess zeros in the right half-plane and may have negative coefficients. In this case it is necessary to multiply $P(s)/Q(s)$ by surplus factors $U(s)/U(s)$ until positive coefficients are obtained. This approach is satisfactory provided $P(s)$ contains no zeros on the positive real axis; therefore, positive real axis zeros must be ruled out in the specification of the desired transfer ratio.

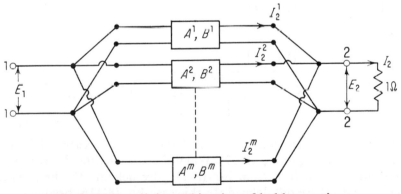

Fig. 8-17. Parallel combination of ladder sections.

Let the polynomial $P^*(s)$ represent the product of $P(s)$ and a surplus factor $U(s)$. In this case it is possible to divide $P^*(s)$ into the summation of several groups of terms. For instance, taking terms three at a time yields

$$\begin{aligned}
P^*(s) = P(s)U(s) &= (a_n s^n + a_{n-1} s^{n-1} + a_{n-2} s^{n-2}) \\
&\quad + (a_{n-3} s^{n-3} + a_{n-4} s^{n-4} + a_{n-5} s^{n-5}) + \cdots \\
&\quad + (a_2 s^2 + a_1 s + a_0) \\
&= P^1(s) + P^2(s) + \cdots + P^m(s) \tag{8-113}
\end{aligned}$$

Likewise, if the product $Q(s)U(s)$ is denoted by $Q^*(s)$, it is possible to rewrite Eq. (8-112) as follows:

$$\frac{1}{B} = \frac{2P^*(s)}{KQ^*(s)} = \frac{2P^1(s)}{KQ^*(s)} + \frac{2P^2(s)}{KQ^*(s)} + \cdots + \frac{2P^m(s)}{KQ^*(s)} \quad (8\text{-}114)$$

Each of these terms is a minimum-phase transmission function by virtue of the surplus factor and separation process described above. Consequently, E_2/E_1 can be realized by m parallel ladder networks terminated by a 1-ohm resistor, where each of the component structures is represented by the two transmission functions:

$$A^q = \frac{KQ^*(s)}{2mP^q(s)} \quad \text{and} \quad B^q = \frac{KQ^*(s)}{2P^q(s)} \quad (q = 1, 2, \ldots, m) \quad (8\text{-}115)$$

The pairs of minimum-phase functions A^q and B^q can be realized by the previously described procedure; however, modification of the matrix expansion is required.

A general matrix factorization similar to that of Eq. (8-93) can be developed by linear transformation in a reverse direction. This expansion can be written as

$$\begin{bmatrix} A & B \\ C & D \end{bmatrix} = \begin{bmatrix} 1 & 0 \\ \left[\dfrac{C}{A} - \dfrac{1}{K_1{}^2K_2{}^2\ldots K_nA_2{}^2\ldots A_n} + \cdots\right] & 1 \end{bmatrix}$$

$$\times \begin{bmatrix} 1 & (K_1A_1 - 1) \\ 0 & 1 \end{bmatrix} \begin{bmatrix} 1 & 0 \\ 1 & 1 \end{bmatrix} \cdots$$

$$\begin{bmatrix} 1 & \left[K_nA_n - 2 + \dfrac{1}{K_{n-1}A_{n-1}}\right] \\ 0 & 1 \end{bmatrix} \begin{bmatrix} 1 & 0 \\ 1 & 1 \end{bmatrix} \begin{bmatrix} 1 & \left[\dfrac{B}{A} - 1 + \dfrac{1}{K_nA_n}\right] \\ 0 & 1 \end{bmatrix} \quad (8\text{-}116)$$

The transmission function A^q of Eq. (8-115) can be expanded for each value of q according to Eq. (8-97). When this is done, the desired matrix factorization is obtained from Eq. (8-116) by deleting the first matrix, since C^q and D^q are not defined. In this case Eq. (8-116) becomes

$$\begin{bmatrix} A^q & B^q \\ C^{*q} & D^{*q} \end{bmatrix} = \begin{bmatrix} 1 & (K_1{}^qA_1{}^q - 1) \\ 0 & 1 \end{bmatrix} \begin{bmatrix} 1 & 0 \\ 1 & 1 \end{bmatrix} \cdots$$

$$\cdots \begin{bmatrix} 1 & \left[K_n{}^qA_n{}^q - 2 + \dfrac{1}{K_{n-1}^qA_{n-1}^q}\right] \\ 0 & 1 \end{bmatrix} \begin{bmatrix} 1 & 0 \\ 1 & 1 \end{bmatrix} \begin{bmatrix} 1 & \left[m - 1 + \dfrac{1}{K_n{}^qA_n{}^q}\right] \\ 0 & 1 \end{bmatrix}$$

$$(8\text{-}117)$$

The constants $K_1{}^q$, $K_2{}^q$, $\ldots$, $K_n{}^q$ must be chosen such that all m ladder networks are physically realizable (m is an integer equal to or greater than unity). It is noted in Eq. (8-117) that the shunt arms of each ladder structure will be 1-ohm resistors (i.e., referring to Fig. 8-14, $Y_2 = Y_4 = \cdots = Y_m = 1$ ohm); whereas, the series arms of each ladder may be RLC sections. To complete the realization, the individual ladder structures must be combined in parallel as shown in Fig. 8-17. The 1-ohm terminating resistor is generated during the realization process; however, the procedure can be extended to provide prescribed source and load resistors by proper selection of the gain factors associated with each component ladder structure.

8-5. Matthaei's Procedure for Constant-resistance Ladder Synthesis

A synthesis technique based on the cascade combination of constant-resistance ladder sections has been developed by G. I. Matthaei for the realization of specified voltage transfer ratios.† Although this procedure is developed by logical consideration of the poles and zeros of the transfer ratio, it will be seen that the resulting network is related to the ladder structures obtained by Ho's procedure. Matthaei's procedure is most easily understood by investigating the effects of poles and zeros of the transfer ratio on network design. Clearly, poles of E_2/E_1 represent points of infinite gain, whereas zeros are points of infinite loss between the input and output circuits. The zeros of E_2/E_1 are generated physically in a network by three methods.

1. When a network has more than one path of transmission from its input to output, infinite loss (i.e., zeros of E_2/E_1) occurs at frequencies for which the outputs from the different paths cancel.

2. Zeros of series impedances, such as Z_1 of Fig. 8-14, prevent transmission from the input to the output. Consequently they are also zeros of E_2/E_1, provided impedances to the right, such as $Z_3, \ldots, Z_{n-1}$, do not possess zeros at the same frequencies. If impedances to the right have the same zeros, they act as voltage dividers and transmission is maintained.

3. Zeros of the shunt admittances, such as Y_2 of Fig. 8-14, short the signal transmission, provided admittances to the right, such as $Y_4, \ldots, Y_n$, do not have the same zeros, in which case they act as current dividers and transmission is maintained.

Bridged-T, lattice, and parallel-ladder networks provide zeros of E_2/E_1 primarily by virtue of the first method; whereas, a single-ladder structure generates infinite loss strictly by the second and third methods.

† G. I. Matthaei, "Some Techniques for Network Synthesis," *Proc. IRE*, vol. 42, no. 7, July 1954, pp. 1126–1137.

In Chap. 7, Sec. 7-1, it was mentioned that the poles of the open-circuit impedance functions, $z_{11}(s)$, $z_{12}(s)$, and $z_{22}(s)$, will in general be the same, except for possible pole-zero cancellations. Likewise, consideration of Eq. (8-87) and the impedance to T-matrix transformations of Table 7-2 leads to the conclusion that zeros of the transmission function $A(s)$ (poles of the transfer ratio E_2/E_1) will be the same as the poles of the input and output driving-point impedances, except for possible cancellations. Poles of E_2/E_1 which do not appear as poles of the input and/or output driving-point impedances, indicate the presence of natural modes of resonance within branches of the network unrelated to those generating the driving-point functions. Consequently the poles of E_2/E_1 are completely defined in most cases when a driving-point impedance for the network is specified.

Assume the problem has been posed of realizing a specified voltage transfer ratio while satisfying given source and load resistance conditions. Matthaei's approach to this problem is based on construction of a driving-point impedance function which has the same poles as the transfer ratio. This function can be separated into the summation of three impedances, one which represents the source resistance, a second to satisfy the desired load resistance, and a third to realize the zeros of the transfer ratio. These three impedances are then realized in the form of an L-section. If the second and third impedances are denoted by $Z_a(s)$ and $Z_b(s)$ respectively, the L-section formed by these impedances takes the form shown in Fig. 8-18.

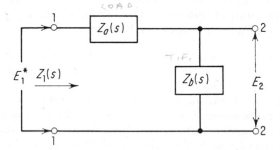

Fig. 8-18. Simple L-section.

For optimum coupling between the voltage source and network of Fig. 8-18 it is desirable that the input impedance $Z_1(s)$ be equal to the source resistance. Analytically, this can be expressed as $[Z_1(s) = Z_a(s) + Z_b(s) = R_S]$, where R_S is the source resistance. To satisfy the desired transfer ratio, the poles of $[E_2/E_1 = KP(s)/Q(s)]$ are chosen as the poles of $Z_a(s)$ and $Z_b(s)$, and zeros of E_2/E_1 are produced by selecting $Z_b(s)$ as

$$Z_b(s) = \frac{K_1 R_S P(s)}{Q(s)} \tag{8-118}$$

Therefore, the transfer ratio for the L-section of Fig. 8-18 becomes

$$\frac{E_2}{E_1^*} = \frac{Z_b(s)}{Z_a(s) + Z_b(s)} = \frac{\dfrac{K_1 R_S P(s)}{Q(s)}}{R_S} = \frac{K_1 P(s)}{Q(s)} \qquad (8\text{-}119)$$

Having established $Z_b(s)$, $Z_a(s)$ can be computed from $[Z_a(s) + Z_b(s) = R_S]$.

$$Z_a(s) = R_S - \frac{K_1 R_S P(s)}{Q(s)} = R_S \left[\frac{Q(s) - K_1 P(s)}{Q(s)} \right] \qquad (8\text{-}120)$$

Consequently, $Z_a(s)$ and $Z_b(s)$ both possess the same poles as E_2/E_1; however, the value of K_1 must be chosen judicially to insure that $Z_a(s)$ will be physically realizable. Assume for the moment that E_2/E_1 is a nonminimum real-part positive real function of s. In this case it follows that

$$Re\left[\frac{P(j\omega)}{Q(j\omega)}\right]_{min} > 0 \quad \text{and} \quad Re\left[\frac{Q(j\omega)}{P(j\omega)}\right]_{max} > 0 \qquad (8\text{-}121)$$

The real part of $Z_a(s)$ must be greater than zero for all real frequencies; consequently, selection of K_1 for Eq. (8-120) to satisfy this condition also insures that $Z_b(s)$ will be physically realizable because of the manner in which $Z_a(s)$ and $Z_b(s)$ were formed.

It is now possible to expand $Z_b(s)$ of Eq. (8-118) to satisfy the desired terminating conditions. This can be accomplished as follows:

$$Z_b(s) = \frac{1}{\dfrac{Q(s)}{K_1 R_S P(s)}} = \frac{1}{Y_b^*(s) + \dfrac{1}{R_L}}$$

where $\quad Y_b^*(s) = \dfrac{Q(s) - K_2 P(s)}{K_1 R_S P(s)} \quad$ and $\quad R_L = \dfrac{K_1 R_S}{K_2} \qquad (8\text{-}122)$

The value of K_2 must be chosen such that $Y_b^*(s)$ is physically realizable while simultaneously satisfying, as nearly as possible, the desired load resistance R_L. It may be necessary to apply an iterative process in the selection of K_1 and K_2 to satisfy R_L. At this point the input impedance $Z_1(s)$ can be written in terms of Eqs. (8-120) and (8-122) as

$$Z_1(s) = Z_a(s) + Z_b(s) = R_S \left[\frac{Q(s) - K_1 P(s)}{Q(s)} \right] + \frac{1}{\left[\dfrac{Q(s) - K_2 P(s)}{K_1 R_S P(s)} \right] + \dfrac{1}{\dfrac{K_1 R_S}{K_2}}}$$

$$(8\text{-}123)$$

This function represents a constant-resistance L-section [i.e., $Z_1(s) = R_S$] of the form shown to the right of terminals 1-1 in Fig. 8-19. When E_1^*

of Fig. 8-18 is replaced by a voltage source comprised of E_1 and R_S, as shown to the left of terminals 1-1 in Fig. 8-19, the transfer ratio becomes

$$\frac{E_2}{E_1} = \frac{Z_b(s)}{Z_a(s) + Z_b(s) + R_S} = \frac{\dfrac{K_1 R_S P(s)}{Q(s)}}{R_S + R_S} = \frac{K_1 P(s)}{2Q(s)} \qquad (8\text{-}124)$$

Hence the network of Fig. 8-19 realizes E_2/E_1 within a constant multiplier $(K = K_1/2)$ of the desired function while at the same time satisfying the prescribed terminating resistances.

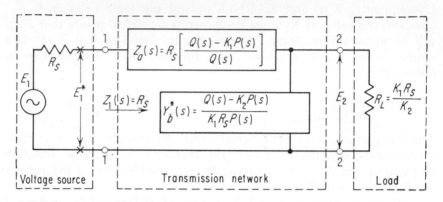

Fig. 8-19. Constant-resistance ladder for Matthaei's procedure.

Because the input impedance of the L-section $Z_1(s)$ is a constant resistance for all values of s, it can serve as the load resistance for a similar preceding section. A complicated voltage transfer ratio can therefore be realized by separating it into the product of several component transfer ratios, each of which can be realized as an L-section. The realization is completed by connecting the component L-sections in cascade, such that one L-section acts as the load resistance for the preceding. Although the transfer ratio for each component L-section must be a nonminimum real-part positive real function, it is not necessary that the overall transfer ratio satisfy this requirement. Separation of the desired transfer ratio into the product of nonminimum real-part positive real functions may require the use of surplus factors; however, it is possible to realize any minimum-phase transfer ratio within a constant multiplying factor by this technique.

As an example of Matthaei's procedure, assume the voltage transfer ratio of Eq. (8-125) is to be realized as a two-port RLC network to couple source and load resistances of $(R_S = 2\text{ ohms})$ and $(R_L = 4\text{ ohms})$.

$$\frac{E_2}{E_1} = \frac{(s^2 + s + 8)}{(s^2 + 2s + 2)} = \frac{P(s)}{Q(s)} \qquad (8\text{-}125)$$

Equation (8-125) is a minimum real-part function which does not satisfy Eq. (8-121) {e.g., $Re[P(j\omega)/Q(j\omega)] = 0$ at $\omega = 2$}; therefore, it is impossible to proceed directly with the realization. However, multiplying both $P(s)$ and $Q(s)$ by surplus factors of the form $(s^2 + as + b)$ makes it possible to perform the following separation:

$$\frac{E_2}{E_1} = \frac{(s^2 + s + 8)(s^2 + as + b)}{(s^2 + 2s + 2)(s^2 + as + b)} = \left(\frac{E_2}{E_1}\right)' \left(\frac{E_2}{E_1}\right)''$$

where

$$\left(\frac{E_2}{E_1}\right)' = \frac{(s^2 + s + 8)}{(s^2 + as + b)} = \frac{P'(s)}{Q'(s)}$$

$$\left(\frac{E_2}{E_1}\right)'' = \frac{(s^2 + as + b)}{(s^2 + 2s + 2)} = \frac{P''(s)}{Q''(s)} \tag{8-126}$$

Both $(E_2/E_1)'$ and $(E_2/E_1)''$ can be forced to satisfy the conditions of Eq. (8-121) by proper selection of a and b. For this example these parameters will be chosen as $(a = 10)$ and $(b = 2)$. It is then possible to proceed with the realization of $(E_2/E_1)'$ and $(E_2/E_1)''$ as individual L-sections which will later be combined in cascade.

Beginning with the realization of $(E_2/E_1)'$, the impedance $Z_a'(s)$ can be expressed in the form of Eq. (8-120) as

$$Z_a'(s) = R_S \left[\frac{Q'(s) - K_1'P'(s)}{Q'(s)}\right]$$

$$= 2 \left[\frac{(s^2 + 10s + 2) - K_1'(s^2 + s + 8)}{(s^2 + 10s + 2)}\right] \tag{8-127}$$

The value of K_1' must be selected such that $Z_a'(s)$ is a realizable driving-point impedance. Using a value of $(K_1' = 1/4)$, $Z_a'(s)$ and $Z_b'(s)$ can be written from Eqs. (8-127) and (8-118), respectively, as

$$Z_a'(s) = \frac{3(s^2 + 13s)}{2(s^2 + 10s + 2)}$$

and

$$Z_b'(s) = \frac{K_1'R_SP'(s)}{Q'(s)} = \frac{2(s^2 + s + 8)}{4(s^2 + 10s + 2)} \tag{8-128}$$

The continued-fraction expansions of these functions are given by

$$Z_a'(s) = \cfrac{1}{\cfrac{4}{39s} + \cfrac{1}{\cfrac{3}{2} + \cfrac{1}{\cfrac{26s}{123} + \cfrac{256}{123}}}} \quad \text{and} \quad Z_b'(s) = \cfrac{1}{\cfrac{1}{2} + \cfrac{1}{\cfrac{16}{39s} + \cfrac{1}{\cfrac{3}{2} + \cfrac{1}{\cfrac{13s}{246} + \cfrac{5}{246}}}}}$$

$$\tag{8-129}$$

The networks which realize $Z'_a(s)$ and $Z'_b(s)$ are connected to form an L-section similar to Fig. 8-18. This L-section represents the completion of the first part of the problem and is shown as the network between terminals 1-1 and a-a of Fig. 8-20. There is one notable exception in Fig. 8-20; the 2-ohm resistor represented by the first term in the expansion of $Z'_b(s)$ of Eq. (8-129) has been omitted. This resistor should bridge the gap between terminals a-a; however, it has been replaced by the second L-section, which will now be considered.

The second L-section must possess an input resistance of 2 ohms, $[Z''_1(s) = R''_S = 2 \text{ ohms}]$, if it is to replace the 2-ohm resistor of $Z'_b(s)$. In addition, it must realize $(E_2/E_1)''$ of Eq. (8-126) within a constant multiplying factor. Consequently, $Z''_a(s)$ is written in the form of Eq. (8-120) as

$$Z''_a(s) = R''_S\left[\frac{Q''(s) - K''_1 P''(s)}{Q''(s)}\right] = 2\left[\frac{(s^2 + 2s + 2) - K''_1(s^2 + 10s + 2)}{(s^2 + 2s + 2)}\right]$$

$$(8\text{-}130)$$

The value of K''_1 must be selected such that $Z''_a(s)$ is a realizable driving-point impedance. In this case $(K''_1 = 1/10)$ will be used, after which Eq. (8-130) can be expanded as follows:

$$Z''_a(s) = \frac{(9s^2 + 10s + 18)}{5(s^2 + 2s + 2)} = \cfrac{1}{\cfrac{5}{9} + \cfrac{1}{\cfrac{81s}{40} + \cfrac{9}{4} + \cfrac{81}{20s}}} \qquad (8\text{-}131)$$

The impedance $Z''_b(s)$, can be written in the form of Eq. (8-118); however, at this point it becomes necessary to consider the desired load resistance $(R_L = 4 \text{ ohms})$. Using the load resistance, as in Eq. (8-122), the value of K''_2 becomes

$$R_L = \frac{K''_1 R''_S}{K''_2} = \frac{(1/10)(2)}{K''_2} = 4 \qquad \text{or} \qquad K''_2 = \frac{1}{20} \qquad (8\text{-}132)$$

This value must also cause $Y_b^{*''}(s)$ to be physically realizable; otherwise, it is necessary to return to the selection of K''_1 and by an iterative process attempt to satisfy both conditions. In this example, $(K''_2 = 1/20)$ is satisfactory; therefore, $Y_b^{*''}(s)$ can be written in the form of Eq. (8-122) and expanded as follows:

$$Y_b^{*''}(s) = \left[\frac{Q''(s) - K''_2 P''(s)}{K''_1 R''_S P''(s)}\right] = \frac{(19s^2 + 30s + 38)}{4(s^2 + 10s + 2)} = \cfrac{1}{\cfrac{4}{19} + \cfrac{1}{\cfrac{361}{320s} + \cfrac{57}{64} + \cfrac{361s}{640}}}$$

$$(8\text{-}133)$$

Combining the networks which represent Eqs. (8-131) and (8-133) in an *L*-section similar to Fig. 8-19 leads to the structure between terminals *a-a* and 2-2 of Fig. 8-20. The realization is completed by adding a load resistance of 4 ohms across terminals 2-2 and a source resistance of 2 ohms in series with terminals 1-1. The resulting network satisfies the desired transfer ratio of Eq. (8-125) within a multiplying factor of $(K = K_1'K_1''/2 = 1/400)$. A simple check can be made on the realization by computing the input impedance of terminals 1-1 at zero and infinite frequencies to show that $(Z_1' = 2 \text{ ohms})$.

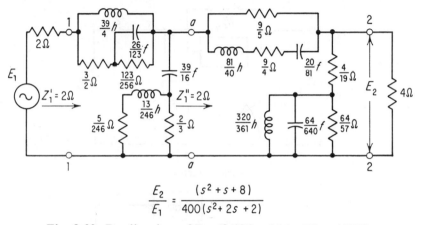

$$\frac{E_2}{E_1} = \frac{(s^2 + s + 8)}{400(s^2 + 2s + 2)}$$

Fig. 8-20. Realization of Eq. (8-125) within $(K = 1/400)$.

When Matthaei's procedure is developed on an admittance basis, a constant-resistance reverse *L*-section of the form shown in Fig. 8-21 results. This structure is analogous to that of Fig. 8-19 and also is useful in the realization of a specified voltage transfer ratio to within a multiplying factor.

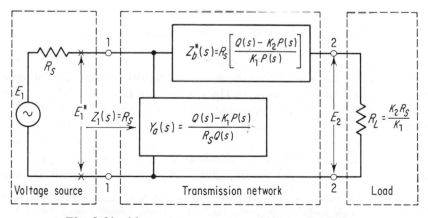

Fig. 8-21. Alternate constant-resistance *L*-section.

The constant-resistance L-sections of Figs. 8-19 and 8-21 are easily transformed to so-called "classical" constant-resistance ladder networks of the forms shown in Fig. 8-22. For example, substituting $(R_x = R_S)$, $(K_1 = K_2)$, and $\{Z_y(s) = R_S[Q(s) - K_1 P(s)]/K_1 P(s)\}$ in the L-section of Fig. 8-19 yields the constant-resistance network of Fig. 8-22a. Likewise, the network of Fig. 8-22b represents a special case of the L-section of Fig. 8-21. Therefore, the L-sections of Matthaei's procedure represent generalizations of the classical constant-resistance structures of Fig. 8-22.

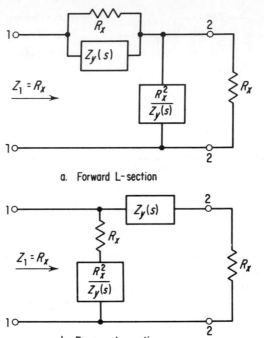

a. Forward L-section

b. Reverse L-section

Fig. 8-22. Classical constant-resistance networks.

Leo Storch has shown that the networks resulting from the elaborate matrix factorization technique of Ho's procedure (see Sec. 8-4) can also be derived from the constant-resistance structures of Fig. 8-22.† For instance, the constant-resistance network of Fig. 8-23 can be obtained from Fig. 8-22b by interchanging R_x and $Z_y(s)$ in the output circuit. Choosing R_x as 1 ohm, the admittance $Y_y(s)$ becomes $[Y_y(s) = R_x^2/Z_y(s) = 1/Z_y(s)]$; and the impedance $Z_y(s)$ across terminals 2-2 can

† Leo Storch, "Realization of Minimum-Phase and Nonminimum-Phase Transfer Functions by RLC Ladder-Type Networks," *IRE Trans. Circuit Theory*, vol. CT-7, no. 2, June 1960, pp. 137–150.

be separated into a 1-ohm load resistor and a parallel admittance of $[Y_y(s) - 1]$. Because Ho's procedure does not require a constant-resistance structure, the shunt arm between terminals a-a of Fig. 8-23 can be omitted. In this case the remaining forward L-section possesses a transmission matrix similar in form to the individual sections of the matrix factorization of Eq. (8-94) provided the shunt admittance $[Y_y(s) - 1]$ is chosen as $(K_n A_n - 2)$. Consequently, the matrix factorization suggested by Ho can be derived from Matthaei's procedure. Furthermore, the interchange of R_x and $Z_y(s)$ in the development of Fig. 8-23 tends to reduce the number of reactive elements required for the realization by Ho's procedure. However, Ho's procedure requires redundant isolation resistors between sections, and both procedures suffer in terms of the number of elements required when surplus factors are introduced.

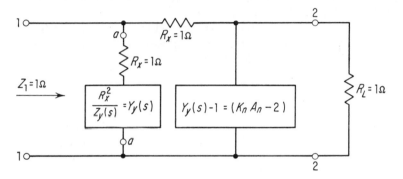

Fig. 8-23. Constant-resistance section for interpretation of Ho's procedure.

This completes the discussion of two-port ladder network synthesis procedures. It has been seen that the problem of maintaining insight into the realization process becomes complicated, especially in the case of RLC networks. Furthermore, the procedures of Chaps. 7 and 8 are representative but by no means an exhaustive review of all possible techniques. In fact, they are not necessarily optimum in one sense or another. For instance, Storch has made an extensive study of techniques to reduce the number of elements required for the realization of RLC networks.† His approach is based on equivalent circuits and is capable of producing comparable network configurations to those of Ho and Matthaei, but with fewer elements. Several of the RC synthesis techniques can also be generalized, making it possible to realize RLC networks with fewer elements. This possibility was suggested by

† *Ibid.*

Weinberg for the procedure of Sec. 8-1.† Some of these techniques and other approaches to the problem of synthesizing two-port RLC ladder networks will be mentioned in later chapters.

References

Most of the procedures of this chapter have not yet been covered extensively in text books of this type. Therefore, the reader is directed to the references mentioned in the footnotes for further details concerning specific procedures. Weinberg's recent book includes his own procedures in Chap. 12 in addition to topics dealing with the maximum gain of two-port networks in Sec. 8-2, and constant-resistance networks in Sec. 1-10.

1. L. Weinberg, *Network Analysis and Synthesis* (New York: McGraw-Hill Book Co., Inc., 1962).

   Kuh's procedure is presented in Chap. 11 of his book and constant-resistance networks are covered in Chap. 12.

2. E. S. Kuh and D. O. Pederson, *Principles of Circuit Synthesis* (New York: McGraw-Hill Book Co., Inc., 1959).

   An extension of Ho's procedure is outlined in the following reference:

3. E. C. Ho, "RLC Transfer Function Synthesis," *IRE Trans. Circuit Theory*, vol. CT-3, September 1956, pp. 188–190.

Problems

8-1. Decompose the following voltage transfer ratio into admittance functions such that a realization can be accomplished by Weinberg's procedure in the form of parallel RC ladder networks terminated by a single RC ladder section. Select the most logical zeros for $W(s)$ as suggested by the separation of Eqs. (8-2) through (8-8).

$$\frac{E_2}{E_1} = \frac{s(s + 4)(s^2 + 4s + 5)}{(s + 1)(s + 3)(s + 5)(s + 7)}$$

8-2. Using the following sets of admittance functions, realize a network by Weinberg's procedure. Select β to minimize the number of parallel RC sections required for the realization. Compute the resulting voltage transfer ratio, then discuss the possibility of simplifying the design by applying an ideal transformer.

$$\begin{cases} y^a_{12}(s) = \dfrac{(s^2 + 6s + 9)}{(s + 5)} \\[2mm] y^a_{22}(s) = s + \beta\left(\dfrac{384}{105}\right) + \dfrac{0.465s}{(s + 5)} \end{cases}$$

and

$$\begin{cases} Y_b(s) = (1 - \beta)\left(\dfrac{384}{105}\right) + \dfrac{0.625s}{(s + 3)} + \dfrac{0.257s}{(s + 7)} \\[2mm] Y^b_{12}(s)Z_L(s) = \dfrac{s}{(s + 7)} \end{cases}$$

† L. Weinberg, "Synthesis of Unbalanced RLC Networks," *J. Appl. Phys.*, vol. 24, no. 3, March 1953, pp. 300–306.

8-3. An RC network is to be realized to connect a source impedance of $R_S = 2$ ohms with a load impedance of $R_L = 6$ ohms. Construct a set of driving-point and transfer admittances for the network using Kuh's procedure such that the gain constant K of the following voltage transfer ratio is maximized.

$$\frac{E_2}{E_1} = \frac{K}{(s + 2)(s + 3)(s + 5)}$$

8-4. Repeat the requirements of Prob. 8-3 for a source impedance of $R_S = 1$ ohm and a load impedance of $R_L = 4$ ohms such that the following voltage transfer ratio is satisfied:

$$\frac{E_2}{E_1} = \frac{K(s^2 + 2s + 2)}{(s + 1)(s + 2)(s + 3)(s + 4)}$$

8-5. Realize the admittance functions of Prob. 7-12 by Kuh's procedure as an RC ladder network to couple a source impedance of $R_S = 1$ ohm and a load impedance of $R_L = 6$ ohms. Show that these admittance functions satisfy the following voltage transfer ratio with a maximum value of K.

$$\frac{E_2}{E_1} = \frac{K(s^2 + 5s + 8)}{(s + 1)(s + 2)(s + 3)(s + 4)}$$

8-6. Realize a two-port RC ladder network by the procedures of Sec. 8-3 to satisfy the following voltage transfer ratio, and determine the maximum realizable gain factor for the network:

$$\frac{E_2}{E_1} = K\frac{(s + 3)(s + 6)}{(s + 4)(s + 5)}$$

8-7. Determine the maximum realizable gain factors for two-port RC ladder networks possessing the following voltage transfer ratios:

(a) $\dfrac{E_2}{E_1} = \dfrac{K(s + 4)}{(s + 3)(s + 5)}$ (b) $\dfrac{E_2}{E_1} = \dfrac{Ks}{(s + 6)(s + 8)}$

(c) $\dfrac{E_2}{E_1} = \dfrac{K(s + 3)}{(s + 2)(s + 4)(s + 6)}$ (d) $\dfrac{E_2}{E_1} = \dfrac{Ks(s + 3)(s + 6)}{(s + 2)(s + 7)(s + 8)}$

8-8. Synthesize a network using Ho's procedure to realize the following voltage ratio transfer function within a constant K and having a load impedance of 4 ohms and a source impedance of 1 ohm:

$$\frac{E_2}{E_1} = \frac{s + 2}{(s^2 + 4s + 5)(s + 4)}$$

8-9. Realize the voltage transfer ratio of Prob. 8-4 as an RLC network by Ho's procedure such that K is maximized. Use the source and load impedances defined in Prob. 8-4. How does the gain factor of Ho's network compare with the maximum value possible for an RC network?

8-10. Realize the following voltage transfer ratio by Matthaei's procedure to satisfy a source impedance of $R_S = 1$ ohm and a load impedance of $R_L = 5$ ohms.

$$\frac{E_2}{E_1} = \frac{(s^2 + 3s + 2)}{(s^2 + 2s + 2)}$$

8-11. Realize the following voltage transfer ratio by Matthaei's procedure to satisfy a source impedance of $R_S = 2$ ohms and a load impedance of $R_L = 6$ ohms. Surplus factors may be necessary.

$$\frac{E_2}{E_1} = \frac{(s^2 + 4s + 1)}{(s^2 + s + 9)}$$

Chapter 9

Synthesis of Symmetrical

Lattice Networks

A number of procedures have been investigated in Chaps. 7 and 8 for realization of two-port ladder networks. One point each of these procedures had in common was a decided increase in network complexity whenever nonminimum-phase transfer characteristics were desired. This added complexity results from the fact that right half-plane zeros of a transfer function can be realized only by a signal-cancellation process requiring more than one path of transmission between the input and output circuits. This can only be achieved in ladder networks by parallel or bridged structures. If the common ground between the input and output circuits can be dispensed with, right half-plane zeros are readily realized by a bridge structure of the form shown in Fig. 9-1.

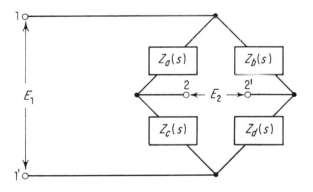

Fig. 9-1. General two-port bridge network.

When a voltage source of frequency ω_o is applied to terminals 1-1' of Fig. 9-1 and the impedances are related such that $[Z_a(j\omega_o)Z_d(j\omega_o) = Z_b(j\omega_o)Z_c(j\omega_o)]$, the voltages at terminals 2 and 2' will be identical. Therefore, there is no voltage drop across terminals 2-2', resulting in

279

zero transmission or a zero of the voltage transfer ratio at $(s = j\omega_o)$. A bridge network satisfying these conditions is said to be balanced. If opposite arms of the bridge possess the same impedances $[Z_A(s) = Z_a(s) = Z_d(s)]$ and $[Z_B(s) = Z_b(s) = Z_c(s)]$, the network is said to be symmetrical. In this case twisting the bridge leads to the configuration of Fig. 9-2 which is known as a symmetrical lattice. Although unsymmetrical lattice networks may be employed in isolated applications, primary interest lies in the symmetrical form which is particularly useful in balanced or push-pull circuits. Furthermore, symmetrical lattice networks are easier to deal with mathematically and are capable of realizing a wide variety of transfer functions. Consequently, this chapter is devoted exclusively to synthesis procedures which lead to symmetrical lattice networks. Restrictions on the prescribed transfer functions necessary to insure physically realizable symmetrical lattice networks will be considered in greater detail in Sec. 9-1.

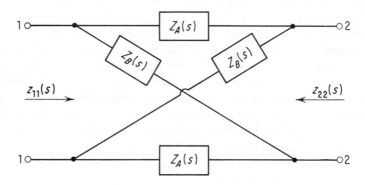

Fig. 9-2. Symmetrical lattice network.

The open-circuit impedance or short-circuit admittance functions are readily obtained for the network of Fig. 9-2. For instance, the open-circuit driving-point impedances represent the parallel combination of two series connections of $Z_A(s)$ and $Z_B(s)$; whereas the transfer impedance can be considered as the parallel combination of the difference in $Z_B(s)$ and $Z_A(s)$. Because the structure is symmetrical, the following relationships are obtained:

$$z_{11}(s) = z_{22}(s) = \frac{[Z_A(s) + Z_B(s)][Z_A(s) + Z_B(s)]}{[Z_A(s) + Z_B(s)] + [Z_A(s) + Z_B(s)]} = \frac{Z_A(s) + Z_B(s)}{2}$$

$$z_{12}(s) = z_{21}(s) = \frac{[Z_B(s) - Z_A(s)][Z_B(s) - Z_A(s)]}{[Z_B(s) - Z_A(s)] + [Z_B(s) - Z_A(s)]} = \frac{Z_B(s) - Z_A(s)}{2}$$

$$(9\text{-}1)$$

Similarly, by short circuiting the opposing sets of terminals and replacing the impedances by admittances, the short-circuit admittance functions become

$$y_{11}(s) = y_{22}(s) = \frac{Y_A(s) + Y_B(s)}{2}$$

and
$$y_{12}(s) = y_{21}(s) = \frac{Y_B(s) - Y_A(s)}{2} \tag{9-2}$$

Conversely, from Eqs. (9-1) and (9-2), it is seen that

$$Z_A(s) = z_{11}(s) - z_{12}(s) = z_{22}(s) - z_{12}(s)$$
$$Z_B(s) = z_{11}(s) + z_{12}(s) = z_{22}(s) + z_{12}(s)$$
$$Y_A(s) = y_{11}(s) - y_{12}(s) = y_{22}(s) - y_{12}(s)$$
$$Y_B(s) = y_{11}(s) + y_{12}(s) = y_{22}(s) + y_{12}(s) \tag{9-3}$$

Equations (9-1) through (9-3) are the basic functions of a symmetrical lattice. Unsymmetrical lattice networks can be solved in the same manner. The functions $z_{12}(s)$ and $y_{12}(s)$ of Eqs. (9-1) and (9-2) illustrate why lattice networks are ideally suited for realizing transfer functions possessing right half-plane zeros of the form $(s - a)$. Several procedures, based on the decomposition of a given transfer ratio to yield $Z_A(s)$ and $Z_B(s)$, have been developed for the synthesis of symmetrical lattice networks. Some of these procedures will be investigated, after which it will be shown in Chap. 10 that it is often possible to transform the lattice into an equivalent unsymmetrical form or even a ladder network.

9-1. Transfer Functions of Symmetrical Lattice Networks

Although any physically realizable transfer function can be synthesized in the form of an unsymmetrical *RLC* lattice network, a symmetrical lattice partially restricts the scope of realizable functions. In particular, certain physically realizable transfer functions possessing poles on the $j\omega$-axis cannot be synthesized as symmetrical lattice structures. Furthermore, a symmetrical lattice is also limited, as compared to a general two-port network, in its maximum attainable gain constant.†These facts will be proved in the following discussion.

In Chap. 7, Sec. 7-1, it was shown that the transfer function of a general *RLC* two-port network will have poles restricted to the left half of the s-plane or the $j\omega$-axis. Poles on the $j\omega$-axis must be simple with purely imaginary residues. These constraints are also necessary when considering the transfer function of a symmetrical lattice; however, additional constraints are also required. Before considering these constraints, it is useful to consider the voltage transfer ratio of a symmetrical

† A. D. Fialkow and I. Gerst, "RLC Lattice Transfer Functions," *Proc. IRE*, vol. 43, no. 4, April 1955, pp. 462–469.

lattice network. Using the open-circuit impedances of Eq. (9-1), the voltage transfer ratio for the network of Fig. 9-2 can be expressed as

$$\frac{E_2}{E_1} = \frac{z_{12}(s)}{z_{22}(s)} = \frac{Z_B(s) - Z_A(s)}{Z_B(s) + Z_A(s)} = K\frac{P(s)}{Q(s)} \tag{9-4}$$

The impedances of Eq. (9-4) can be replaced by new functions $Z_A^*(s)$ and $Z_B^*(s)$ of the form

$$Z_A^*(s) = \left(\frac{1+\lambda}{2}\right)Z_A(s) + \left(\frac{1-\lambda}{2}\right)Z_B(s)$$

$$Z_B^*(s) = \left(\frac{1-\lambda}{2}\right)Z_A(s) + \left(\frac{1+\lambda}{2}\right)Z_B(s) \tag{9-5}$$

where λ is a positive real constant satisfying the conditions $(0 < \lambda \leqq 1)$. In this case, Eq. (9-4) becomes

$$\frac{E_2^*}{E_1^*} = \frac{Z_B^*(s) - Z_A^*(s)}{Z_B^*(s) + Z_A^*(s)} = \lambda\frac{Z_B(s) - Z_A(s)}{Z_B(s) + Z_A(s)} = \lambda K\frac{P(s)}{Q(s)} \tag{9-6}$$

Substituting a new multiplying constant $K^* = \lambda K$ where $(0 < K^* \leqq K)$, it follows from Eq. (9-6) that

$$\frac{Z_A^*(s)}{Z_B^*(s)} = \frac{Q(s) - K^*P(s)}{Q(s) + K^*P(s)} \tag{9-7}$$

The impedances $Z_A^*(s)$ and $Z_B^*(s)$ must be driving-point functions; therefore, ruling out common zeros of the polynomials $Q(s) - K^*P(s)$ and $Q(s) + K^*P(s)$ it is possible to conclude that zeros of these polynomials must lie in the left half of the s-plane or on the $j\omega$-axis.

The sufficiency of the above statement can be demonstrated by showing that the rational function formed by the ratio of the polynomials $Q(s) - KP(s)$ and $Q(s) + KP(s)$ cannot have a negative real value in the right half-plane. To accomplish this end, consider the ratio

$$T(s) = \frac{Q(s) - KP(s)}{Q(s) + KP(s)} \tag{9-8}$$

If a value $s = s_o$ exists in the right half-plane such that the $Re[T(s_o)]$ is negative and the $Im[T(s_o)]$ is zero, then it follows from Eq. (9-8) that

$$Re[T(s_o)] = \frac{|Q(s_o)|^2 - K^2|P(s_o)|^2}{|Q(s_o) + KP(s_o)|^2} < 0 \tag{9-9}$$

$$Im[T(s_o)] = \frac{K|\overline{P(s_o)}Q(s_o) - P(s_o)\overline{Q(s_o)}|}{j|Q(s_o) + KP(s_o)|^2} = 0 \tag{9-10}$$

The bars in this expression denote conjugate complex values. For a nonzero value of $Q(s_o)$, it can be concluded from Eq. (9-10) that

$[P(s_o)/Q(s_o) = \overline{P(s_o)}/\overline{Q(s_o)}]$, in which case $P(s_o)/Q(s_o)$ must be real. Therefore, it follows from Eq. (9-9) that

$$1 - K^2 \left[\frac{P(s_o)}{Q(s_o)}\right]^2 < 0 \tag{9-11}$$

Consequently, for the new constant $K^* = |Q(s_o)/P(s_o)|$ the inequalities $(0 < K^* \leq K)$ still hold; however, the fact that $[Q^2(s_o) - K^{*2}P^2(s_o) = 0]$ contradicts the original statement. As a result, $T(s)$ cannot be negative real in the right half-plane. Hence, for Eq. (9-4) to be the transfer ratio of a symmetric lattice, it is both necessary and sufficient that $Q(s) - K^*P(s) = 0$ and $Q(s) + K^*P(s) = 0$ have no zeros in the right half-plane for all $0 < K^* \leq K$.

The polynomial $Q(s)$ must be Hurwitz, since it represents the poles of the transfer function. If K^* is sufficiently small, the zeros of the polynomials $Q(s) \pm K^*P(s)$ will be essentially the same as those of $Q(s)$. Therefore, in general there is no problem unless the zeros of $Q(s)$ lie on the $j\omega$-axis, in which case a small value of K^* may cause the zeros of either $Q(s) + K^*P(s)$ or $Q(s) - K^*P(s)$ to move into the right half-plane. This would contradict the requirement that both of these poly-nomials can only possess left half-plane or $j\omega$-axis zeros. Consequently for a transfer function to be realizable as a symmetrical lattice, con-straints must be placed on the location of its poles and zeros $Q(s)$ and $P(s)$ and on the gain constant K.

A complete derivation of the required constraints is both complicated and lengthy; however, Fialkow and Gerst have summarized the results neatly in terms of two conditions.† These conditions can be stated as follows:

1. The expression $X_h(s)$ is written to relate the real part of the derivatives of the reciprocal transfer function $1/T(s)$.

$$X_h(s) = Re\left\{j^h \frac{d}{ds}\left[\frac{1}{T(s)}\right]\frac{d}{ds^h}\left[\frac{1}{T(s)}\right]\right\} \text{ for } h = 2, 3, \ldots \tag{9-12}$$

Then at each pole of $T(s)$ on the $j\omega$-axis, either all values of $X_h(j\omega)$ must be zero or the first nonzero value occurs for an even value of h and must be negative.

2. The gain constant K must be restricted such that $(-K_o \leq K \leq K_o)$, where K_o is the smallest real positive value of K^* chosen such that $Q(s) - (K^* + \delta)P(s)$ or $Q(s) + (K^* + \delta)P(s)$ has a zero in the right half-plane for all small positive value of δ. The determination of K_o can be accomplished by the following steps:

(a) Solve Eq. (9-13) for all pairs of roots and gains, $s = j\omega_i$ and $K^* = K_i^*$, where ω_i is real and nonzero and K_i^* is greater than zero.

$$Q_e(s) \pm K^*P_e(s) = 0 \quad \text{and} \quad Q_o(s) \pm K^*P_o(s) = 0 \tag{9-13}$$

The subscripts e and o denote even and odd power terms, respectively, of $Q(s)$ and $P(s)$. The values of $s = j\omega_i$ are readily determined by eliminating

† *Ibid.*, pp. 463–466.

K^* from Eq. (9-13) to obtain the zeros of the polynomial $[P_e(s)Q_o(s) - P_o(s)Q_e(s)]$. The K_i^* factors are found by substituting $s = j\omega_i$ back in Eq. (9-13).

(b) Let K_i' represent those values of K_i^* for which $s = j\omega_i$ is either a double root of $Q(s) \pm K^*P(s)$ or is an odd order zero of $[P_e(s)Q_o(s) - P_o(s)Q_e(s)]$.

(c) Then K_o will be the minimum of $[1, K_i', \text{ or } |b_m/a_n|]$ where b_m is the coefficient of the highest order term of $Q(s)$ and a_n is the coefficient of the highest order term of $P(s)$ and $(n = m)$. For $(n < m)$, K_o is the minimum of $[K_i' \text{ or } |b_m/a_n|]$.

Transfer functions satisfying the above conditions pertaining to pole-zero locations and maximum gain can be realized as symmetrical lattice networks. However, before investigating synthesis procedures, it is of value to apply the above conditions to some example transfer functions. For instance, consider the following physically realizable transfer function:

$$T(s) = \frac{K(s + 1)}{(s^2 + 4)} = \frac{KP(s)}{Q(s)} \tag{9-14}$$

Applying Condition 1 to this function, it is found that for $(h = 2)$, Eq. (9-12), when evaluated at the pole $(s = j2)$, becomes

$$X_2(j2) = Re\left\{-1\left[\frac{s^2 + 2s - 4}{K(s + 1)^2}\right]\left[\frac{10}{K(s + 1)^3}\right]\right\}_{s=j2}$$

$$= Re\left[\frac{8(24 + j7)}{125K^2}\right] = \frac{192}{125K^2} > 0 \tag{9-15}$$

Since this value is positive for any finite K, Eq. (9-14) cannot be realized as a symmetrical lattice. The same conclusion is easily reached by substituting $[Q(s) = s^2 + 4]$ and $[P(s) = (s + 1)]$ into the polynomial $[Q(s) - K^*P(s)]$. In this case to be realizable, $[s^2 - K^*s + 4 + K^*]$ can have no right half-plane zeros; however, any finite value of K^* greater than zero will cause at least one right half-plane zero.

As a second simple example, consider the function $[T(s) = K/(s^2 + 4)]$. In this case application of Eq. (9-12) for $(h = 2)$ and evaluation at the pole $(s = j2)$ yields

$$X_2(j2) = Re\left\{-1\left[\frac{-2s}{K}\right]\left[\frac{2s}{K}\right]\right\}_{s=j2} = \frac{-4}{K^2} < 0 \tag{9-16}$$

Because $X_2(j2)$ is negative for all values of K, this transfer function satisfies the first condition. However, it is still necessary to check the range of K that will permit $T(s)$ to be realizable as a symmetrical lattice. Since $[P(s) = 1]$ and $[Q(s) = s^2 + 4]$, the polynomials $[Q(s) \pm K^*P(s)]$ become $(s^2 + 4 \pm K^*)$ and can have no right half-plane zeros. This condition is satisfied for all values of K^* when the plus sign is used;

however, when the minus sign is used, a right half-plane zero exists for $K^* > 4$. Therefore, for $T(s)$ to be realizable as a symmetrical lattice, it is necessary that $(0 < K \leq 4)$. A symmetrical lattice realization of this transfer function with the maximum gain $(K = 4)$ is given in the form of Eq. (9-4) by

$$T(s) = \frac{E_2}{E_1} = \frac{4}{s^2 + 4} = \frac{Z_B(s) - Z_A(s)}{Z_B(s) + Z_A(s)}$$

where $\qquad Z_A(s) = s \qquad$ and $\qquad Z_B(s) = s + \dfrac{8}{s} \qquad$ (9-17)

In summary, certain realizable transfer functions cannot be synthesized (even within a multiplying constant) by a symmetrical lattice network. These functions always possess $j\omega$-axis poles which do not satisfy the conditions described above. Therefore, before an attempt is made to realize a specified transfer ratio possessing $j\omega$-axis poles it is useful to test the function first to establish its realizability and the range of realizable gain factors. With this background, it is now possible to proceed with the discussion of realization procedures.

9-2. Weinberg's Procedure for *RLC* Lattice Network Synthesis

The first procedure is based on a technique originally suggested by Bower and Ordung for the realization of *RC* lattice structures.† The procedure was later generalized by Louis Weinberg and involves equating the transfer ratio E_2/I_1 with $z_{12}(s)$, which is then decomposed by partial-fraction expansion such that $Z_A(s)$ and $Z_B(s)$ are separately positive real functions.‡ The open-circuit transfer impedance of a symmetrical lattice network can be written from Eq. (9-1) as

$$\frac{E_2}{I_1} = K \frac{P(s)}{Q(s)} = z_{12}(s) = \frac{Z_B(s) - Z_A(s)}{2}$$

$$= K \frac{s^n + a_{n-1}s^{n-1} + \cdots + a_1 s + a_0}{s^m + b_{m-1}s^{m-1} + \cdots + b_1 s + b_0}$$

$$= K \frac{(s + s_1^*)(s + s_2^*) \cdots (s + s_n^*)}{(s + s_1)(s + s_2) \cdots (s + s_m)} \qquad (9\text{-}18)$$

For realizability as an *RLC* network, it is necessary that the zeros of $Q(s)$, $s_1, s_2, \ldots, s_m$, lie in the left half of the *s*-plane or on the $j\omega$-axis. Zeros of $P(s)$, denoted by $s_1^*, s_2^*, \ldots, s_n^*$, may lie anywhere in the *s*-plane;

---

† J. L. Bower and P. R. Ordung, "The Synthesis of Resistor-Capacitor Networks," *Proc. IRE*, vol. 38, no. 3, March 1950, pp. 263–269.

‡ L. Weinberg, "RLC Lattice Networks," *Proc. IRE*, vol. 41, no. 9, September 1953, pp. 1139–1144.

however, it is also required that $(m + 1 \geq n)$. Additional restrictions for realization as a symmetrical lattice have been described in Sec. 9-1.

Even though E_2/I_1 may not be a positive real function, it is possible to perform a partial-fraction expansion, after which the poles can be identified with $Z_A(s)$ and $Z_B(s)$. The residues of these poles can be distributed such that both impedance functions are positive real. This can always be accomplished by adding sufficient real part to each function that both become positive real. In the case of Eq. (9-18) this can be achieved by adding a resistance R to both $Z_A(s)$ and $Z_B(s)$ without changing the value of $z_{12}(s)$.

Consider the case in which a given impedance function is separated by partial-fraction expansion into only simple poles. Typically, the results can be expressed in alternate forms as indicated in the following example:

$$
\begin{aligned}
Z(s) &= \frac{k_1}{(s + \sigma_1 - j\omega_1)} + \frac{\bar{k}_1}{(s + \sigma_1 + j\omega_1)} + \frac{k_2}{(s + \beta)} \\
&= \frac{a_1 + jb_1}{(s + \sigma_1 - j\omega_1)} + \frac{a_1 - jb_1}{(s + \sigma_1 + j\omega_1)} + \frac{k_2}{(s + \beta)} \\
&= \frac{2a_1\left(s + \sigma_1 - \dfrac{b_1\omega_1}{a_1}\right)}{s^2 + 2\sigma_1 s + (\sigma_1^2 + \omega_1^2)} + \frac{k_2}{(s + \beta)} \\
&= Z_1(s) + Z_2(s)
\end{aligned}
\tag{9-19}
$$

The parameters k_2 and β must both be positive if the impedance $Z_2(s)$ associated with the real pole is to be realizable. Similarly, realizability of $Z_1(s)$ requires that a_1 be positive and

$$
\frac{|b_1|}{a_1} \leq \frac{\sigma_1}{\omega_1}
\tag{9-20}
$$

where σ_1 and ω_1 are assumed to be real positive numbers. The complex poles of Eq. (9-19) can be plotted as shown in Fig. 9-3. When the condition of Eq. (9-20) is imposed, for $Z_1(s)$ to be a positive real function, a_1 must be positive and the angle of a particular pole to the $j\omega$-axis must be greater than or equal to the angle of its residue. Analytically, this can be expressed as

$$
(\delta \gtreqless \phi)
$$

where $\delta = \tan^{-1}(\sigma_1/\omega_1)$ and $\phi = \tan^{-1}(b_1/a_1)$ (9-21)

The limiting case exists when $(\delta = \phi)$ in which case $(\gamma = 90°)$. Consequently, for $Z_1(s)$ to be realizable, the residues $a_1 \pm jb_1$ of the complex poles must lie somewhere within the cross-hatched region of Fig. 9-3 where $(\gamma = 90°)$.

The transfer function of Eq. (9-18) can be expanded in partial fractions to yield

$$\frac{E_2}{I_1} = z_{12}(s) = K\frac{P(s)}{Q(s)} = \sum_{q=1}^{m}\frac{k_q}{(s + s_q)} \tag{9-22}$$

where m is the degree of $Q(s)$. In this case

$$k_q = a_q + jb_q \quad \text{and} \quad s_q = \sigma_q + j\omega_q = |s_q|e^{j\Psi_q} \tag{9-23}$$

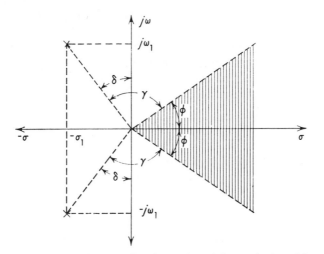

Fig. 9-3. Illustration of pole and residue relationship.

Likewise, the undetermined impedances $Z_A(s)$ and $Z_B(s)$ can be expressed in partial-fraction form as

$$\frac{Z_A(s)}{2} = \sum_{q=1}^{m}\frac{k_q^A}{(s + s_q)} \quad \text{and} \quad \frac{Z_B(s)}{2} = \sum_{q=1}^{m}\frac{k_q^B}{(s + s_q)}$$

where

$$\begin{cases} k_q^A = a_q^A + jb_q^A = |k_q^A|e^{j\phi_q^A} \\ k_q^B = a_q^B + jb_q^B = |k_q^B|e^{j\phi_q^B} \end{cases} \tag{9-24}$$

Substituting Eqs. (9-22) and (9-24) into Eq. (9-18) and relating the residues of like poles, it can be concluded that $k_q = k_q^B - k_q^A$. It is then possible to apply the results of the discussion pertaining to Eqs. (9-19) through (9-21) (provided no multiple order poles exist) to each term of $Z_A(s)/2$ and $Z_B(s)/2$ in Eq. (9-24). Consequently, if s_q is real, k_q must be either positive or negative real, and the following distribution of residues results:

$$k_q^A = 0 \quad \text{and} \quad k_q^B = k_q \quad \text{when} \quad k_q > 0$$

$$k_q^A = q \quad \text{and} \quad k_q^A = 0 \quad \text{when} \quad k_q < 0 \tag{9-25}$$

When dealing with complex poles, the conditions that must be satisfied for $Z_A(s)$ and $Z_B(s)$ to be positive real can be stated in terms of the angles defined in Eqs. (9-23) and (9-24).

$$|\phi_q^A| \leq |\Psi_q| - \frac{\pi}{2} \quad \text{and} \quad |\phi_q^B| \leq |\Psi_q| - \frac{\pi}{2} \tag{9-26}$$

This condition can be verified analytically or graphically to show that for values of k_q located anywhere within the s-plane, a solution will exist within a bounded region about the real axis. The residues $|k_q^A|$ and $|k_q^B|$ have a minimum value when $|\phi_q^A| = |\phi_q^B| = |\Psi_q| - \pi/2$ and $|\Psi_q| - \pi/2 \leq \pi/4$.

If the specified function possesses higher-order real or complex conjugate poles, it becomes necessary to modify the approach. Consider the case of a real pole of order i at the point $(s = -\beta)$. The partial-fraction expansion of this function can be written as

$$T(s) = \frac{t(s)}{(s + \beta)^i} = \frac{k_1}{(s + \beta)} + \frac{k_2}{(s + \beta)^2} + \cdots + \frac{k_i}{(s + \beta)^i} \tag{9-27}$$

In general, the terms of this expansion will not be positive real; however, if the minimum real part of $T(s)$ is positive there is no problem since the function can be realized as part of $Z_B(s)/2$ or $Z_A(s)/2$. If the smallest real part is negative, addition of a resistance R which is equal in magnitude to the minimum real part makes the resulting function $[T(s) + R]$ positive real. This function can be realized as $[Z_B(s)/2 = T(s) + R]$, and the impedance $[Z_A(s)/2 + R]$ completes the realization. The final transfer function can be expressed from Eq. (9-18) as

$$z_{12}(s) = \frac{Z_B(s)}{2} - \frac{Z_A(s)}{2} = [T(s) + R] - R = T(s) \tag{9-28}$$

Although the above discussion pertains to higher-order poles on the negative real axis, the same procedure can be used for higher-order complex poles once the conjugate poles of like order are combined to form a single term.

As an example of Weinberg's procedure, consider the nonminimum phase function of Eq. (9-29).

$$\frac{E_2}{I_1} = z_{12}(s) = \frac{2s^3 + 6s^2 + 4s - 20}{(s^2 + 4s + 8)(s + 2)^2} \tag{9-29}$$

This function is readily expressed in the following form:

$$z_{12}(s) = \frac{a_1 - jb_1}{(s + 2 + j2)} + \frac{a_1 + jb_1}{(s + 2 - j2)} + \frac{(cs + d)}{(s + 2)^2} \tag{9-30}$$

The complex poles of $z_{12}(s)$ occur at $(\sigma_1 = 2)$ and $(\omega_1 = 2)$; therefore, if a realizable function is to be derived to represent this combination of poles, a_1 and b_1 must be chosen within the restrictions of Eq. (9-20). Selecting $(a_1 = 1/2)$ and $(b_1 = 1/4)$, the expansion of Eq. (9-30) becomes

$$z_{12}(s) = z'_{12}(s) + z''_{12}(s)$$

where $z'_{12}(s) = \dfrac{(s + 1)}{(s^2 + 4s + 8)}$ and $z''_{12}(s) = \dfrac{(s - 3)}{(s + 2)^2}$ (9-31)

Consequently, $z'_{12}(s)$ is positive real and can be realized as part of $Z_B(s)/2$; however, $z''_{12}(s)$ requires further consideration.

The real part of $z''_{12}(s)$ is given by the following expression which is negative for all values of ω from $(\omega = 0)$ to $(\omega = \sqrt{12/7})$:

$$Re[z''_{12}(j\omega)] = \dfrac{7\omega^2 - 12}{\omega^4 + 8\omega^2 + 16}$$ (9-32)

The minimum value occurs at $(\omega = 0)$ where $\{Re[z''_{12}(j\omega)] = -3/4\}$. To make $z''_{12}(s)$ a positive real function, it is necessary to add a resistance $(R \geq 3/4)$ to $z''_{12}(s)$ and subtract an equal amount from $z_{12}(s)$. If R is chosen greater than 3/4, more resistance than necessary is added to the network; consequently, redundant elements will result. This may be a desirable feature from the standpoint of approximating commercially available components such as inductors which possess distributed resistance. However, for this example $(R = 3/4)$ will be used, causing $z''_{12}(s)$ to be a minimum real part function at $(\omega = 0)$. Functions of this type are readily realized by the procedures of Chap. 5. With this selection of R, Eq. (9-31) can be rewritten as

$$z_{12}(s) = \dfrac{(s + 1)}{(s^2 + 4s + 8)} + \dfrac{(s - 3)}{(s + 2)^2} + \dfrac{3}{4} - \dfrac{3}{4}$$

$$= \dfrac{(s + 1)}{(s^2 + 4s + 8)} + \dfrac{3s^2 + 16s}{4(s + 2)^2} - \dfrac{3}{4}$$

$$= \dfrac{Z_B(s)}{2} - \dfrac{Z_A(s)}{2}$$ (9-33)

The impedance $Z_A(s)$ can be identified as $[Z_A(s) = 3/2]$, and all remaining terms are combined to yield $Z_B(s)/2$. It is then possible to expand $Z_B(s)$ as

$$Z_B(s) = \cfrac{1}{\dfrac{s}{2} + \dfrac{3}{2} + \cfrac{1}{2s + \dfrac{2}{5}}} + \cfrac{1}{\dfrac{1}{2s} + \cfrac{1}{\dfrac{32}{13} + \dfrac{6s}{13}} + \cfrac{1}{\dfrac{8}{s} + \dfrac{3}{2}}}$$ (9-34)

The realization of Eq. (9-29) is completed by combining the impedances determined above in the form of Fig. 9-4. In this figure the dashed lines represent elements of the opposite arms of the lattice such that the configuration is symmetrical as in Fig. 9-2.

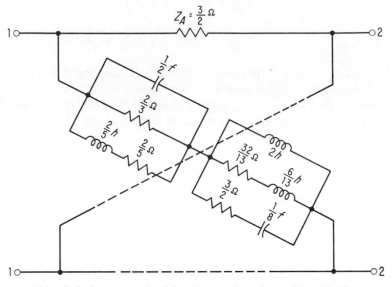

Fig. 9-4. Symmetrical lattice realization of Eq. (9-29).

Lattice networks synthesized by the above technique require no transformers, and by proper selection of parameters it is possible to associate resistance with each reactive element. Furthermore, the procedure is easily applied to realization of RC networks by imposing additional constraints. For instance, it is necessary that the poles of the transfer ratio of an RC network be simple and lie on the negative real axis; however, there are no restrictions on the zeros. Residues of the simple real poles must be real numbers; hence the impedances $Z_A(s)$ and $Z_B(s)$ can be computed using the approach of Eqs. (9-22) through (9-25). In this case realization of $Z_A(s)$ and $Z_B(s)$ can be accomplished by Foster's procedure. Finally, the techniques described above can also be applied on an admittance basis to provide analogous symmetrical lattice structures.

Although the above procedure is adequate for realization of most transfer ratios, Weinberg is credited with a more general approach which can be used to realize a specified voltage transfer ratio as an open-circuited symmetrical lattice with an optimized gain factor.† A distinction must be made between optimized and maximum gain. Weinberg's procedure attempts to maximize the gain but is not always successful

† L. Weinberg, "A General RLC Synthesis Procedure," *Proc. IRE*, vol. 42, no. 2, February 1954, pp. 428–438.

in obtaining the maximum realizable gain factor described in Sec. 9-1. Assume a transfer ratio is given by $[E_2/E_1 = KP(s)/Q(s) = P(s)/HQ(s)]$ where the gain factor is denoted by $(K = 1/H)$. For the highest possible gain, the minimum value of H is desired. If the transfer ratio is written in the form of Eq. (9-4), $Z_A(s)$ and $Z_B(s)$ must be determined such that H is minimized. In Weinberg's procedure, this is accomplished by first separating $Q(s)$ into two polynomials such that

$$Q(s) = Q'(s) + GQ''(s) \qquad (9\text{-}35)$$

where $Q'(s)$ possesses zeros only in the left-half plane, $Q''(s)$ is the derivative of $Q'(s)$, and G is a suitable positive real number. Proof that this separation is always possible is based on a theorem of algebra which states that roots of a polynomial are continuous functions of the coefficients.†

Consider the case in which $Q(s)$ is a polynomial of the form

$$Q(s) = s^m + c_{m-1}s^{m-1} + c_{m-2}s^{m-2} + \cdots + c_1 s + c_0 \qquad (9\text{-}36)$$

where all the c coefficients are known. It is possible to choose $Q'(s)$ in the same form:

$$Q'(s) = s^m + d_{m-1}s^{m-1} + d_{m-2}s^{m-2} + \cdots + d_1 s + d_0 \qquad (9\text{-}37)$$

where the d coefficients must be determined. Taking G times the derivative of Eq. (9-37) yields

$$GQ''(s) = G[ms^{m-1} + d_{m-1}(m-1)s^{m-2} + d_{m-2}(m-2)s^{m-3} + \cdots + d_1]$$
$$(9\text{-}38)$$

Adding Eqs. (9-37) and (9-38) according to Eq. (9-35) and equating coefficients with those of like powers of s in Eq. (9-36) gives

$$d_{m-1} + mG = c_{m-1}$$
$$d_{m-2} + d_{m-1}(m-1)G = c_{m-2}$$
$$d_{m-2} + d_{m-2}(m-2)G = c_{m-3}$$

. . . .

$$d_0 + d_1 G = c_0 \qquad (9\text{-}39)$$

These equations can be solved one at a time for the d coefficients once a suitable value of G is found. For high gain, G should be chosen as large as possible; however, as G increases, complex roots of $Q'(s)$ move closer to the $j\omega$-axis, resulting in a realization requiring higher reactance. Therefore, a compromise in the choice of G may be desired. The maximum realizable value of G results when the zeros of $Q'(s)$ reach the $j\omega$-axis, since $Q'(s)$ can have no right half-plane zeros.

† L. Weinberg, "Synthesis of Unbalanced RLC Networks," *J. Appl. Phys.*, March 1953, pp. 300–306.

Once $Q(s)$ has been separated, both numerator and denominator of the transfer ratio can be divided by $Q'(s)$ to give

$$\frac{E_2}{E_1} = \frac{P(s)}{HQ(s)} = \frac{\dfrac{P(s)}{Q'(s)}}{H\left[1 + \dfrac{GQ''(s)}{Q'(s)}\right]} \tag{9-40}$$

It is now possible to perform partial-fraction expansions of $P(s)/Q'(s)$ and $GQ''(s)/Q'(s)$. Residues of the poles of $P(s)/Q'(s)$ will be positive or negative real values for real poles and complex for complex poles. The expansion of the denominator of Eq. (9-40) can be written as

$$H\left[1 + \frac{GQ''(s)}{Q'(s)}\right] = H\left[k_0^D + \frac{k_1^D}{(s + s_1)} + \frac{k_2^D}{(s + s_2)} + \cdots + \frac{k_q^D}{(s + s_q)}\right] \tag{9-41}$$

where $(k_0^D = 1)$, and all the remaining residues k_q^D equal G. This useful fact, based on the relationship of a polynomial and its derivative, is readily verified by the so-called "cancellation" technique for determining residues as described in Chap. 1, Sec. 1-7.

If the numerator of Eq. (9-4) is thought of as a partial-fraction expansion, the residues of like terms of $P(s)/Q(s)$ of Eq. (9-40) can be equated with those of $[Z_B(s) - Z_A(s)]$. Similarly, if $[Z_B(s) + Z_A(s)]$ of Eq. (9-4) is assumed to represent a partial-fraction expansion, its residues can be equated with those of like terms of Eq. (9-41). When this is done, it becomes apparent that

$$k_q^B - k_q^A = k_q^N \qquad \text{and} \qquad k_q^B + k_q^A = Hk_q^D \tag{9-42}$$

where the superscripts A, B, N, and D refer to $Z_A(s)$, $Z_B(s)$, and the numerator and denominator of E_2/E_1, respectively. The subscript q denotes poles [i.e., zeros of $Q'(s)$] at $(s_q = -\sigma_q + j\omega_q)$, $(s_q = -\sigma_q - j\omega_q)$, or $(s_q = -\sigma_q)$ for which σ_q and ω_q are positive. Solving Eq. (9-42) for the unknown residues of $Z_A(s)$ and $Z_B(s)$ yields

$$k_q^A = \frac{(Hk_q^D - k_q^N)}{2} \qquad k_q^B = \frac{(Hk_q^D + k_q^N)}{2}$$

$$k_q^A = a_q^A + jb_q^A = \frac{(Hk_q^D - a_q^N - jb_q^N)}{2} \qquad k_q^B = a_q^B + jb_q^B = \frac{(Hk_q^D + a_q^N + jb_q^N)}{2}$$

for $\qquad\qquad q = 0, 1, 2, \ldots, m \tag{9-43}$

Further reduction gives

$$k_0^A = \frac{(H - k_0^N)}{2} \qquad \text{and} \qquad k_0^B = \frac{(H + k_0^N)}{2} \qquad \text{for} \qquad (q = 0)$$

and $\qquad a_q^A = \dfrac{(GH - a_q^N)}{2} \qquad a_q^B = \dfrac{(GH + a_q^N)}{2}$

$$b_q^A = -\frac{b_q^N}{2} \qquad \text{and} \qquad b_q^B = \frac{b_q^N}{2} \qquad \text{for} \qquad (q \neq 0) \tag{9-44}$$

Residues k_q^A and k_q^B of negative real axis poles must be real and positive; therefore, when $(q \neq 0)$ in Eq. (9-44), it is necessary that

$$-1 \leq \frac{k_q^N}{GH} \leq 1 \tag{9-45}$$

These conditions arise in the realization of RC lattice structures, since the poles must all lie on the negative real axis.

For RLC networks, complex poles must also be provided for in which case the real part of the residues must, in addition to being positive, satisfy the condition of Eq. (9-20). Therefore, complex poles of $Z_A(s)$ must possess residues that are constrained such that

$$\frac{|b_q^A|}{a_q^A} \leq \frac{\sigma_q}{\omega_q} \quad \text{or} \quad a_q^A \geq \frac{|b_q^A|\omega_q}{\sigma_q} \geq \frac{|b_q^N|\omega_q}{2\sigma_q} = F_q \tag{9-46}$$

where F_q is a positive constant. The same conditions hold for complex poles of $Z_B(s)$, in which case the A superscripts of Eq. (9-46) can be replaced by B. When F_q is substituted in the relationships of Eq. (9-44) for $(q \neq 0)$, it becomes apparent that

$$1 \geq \frac{2F_q - a_q^N}{GH} \quad \text{and} \quad 1 \geq \frac{2F_q + a_q^N}{GH} \tag{9-47}$$

It is only necessary to satisfy the stronger of these conditions for any particular complex pole. If a_q^N is positive, the first condition is stronger and must be used to minimize H, whereas if a_q^N is negative, the second condition is used. Consequently, when complex poles are encountered, it is necessary to determine F_q for each pole after which the minimum value of H is chosen to satisfy the stronger of the two conditions of Eq. (9-47).

Using the above approach, the minimum values of H required to satisfy Eq. (9-45) for each of the real poles and Eq. (9-47) for each of the complex poles can be tabulated. Any value of H equal to or greater than the largest of these tabulated values guarantees the satisfaction of the required condition for each pole. The larger H is chosen, the greater is the real part of $Z_A(s)$ and $Z_B(s)$. Having selected a suitable value of H, the residues k_q^A and k_q^B can be computed from Eq. (9-43) and the impedances can be written as

$$Z_A(s) = k_0^A + \frac{k_1^A}{(s + s_1)} + \frac{k_2^A}{(s + s_2)} + \cdots + \frac{k_m^A}{(s + s_m)}$$

$$Z_B(s) = k_0^B + \frac{k_1^B}{(s + s_1)} + \frac{k_2^B}{(s + s_2)} + \cdots + \frac{k_m^B}{(s + s_m)} \tag{9-48}$$

Complex conjugate poles are combined, then $Z_A(s)$ and $Z_B(s)$ can be realized by expansion of the resulting terms.

As an example of this procedure, consider the following voltage transfer ratio:

$$\frac{E_2}{E_1} = \frac{KP(s)}{Q(s)} = \frac{(s-3)}{H(s^4 + 12s^3 + 54s^2 + 108s + 80)}$$

where
$$K = 1/H \qquad (9\text{-}49)$$

The first step in the procedure is to separate $Q(s)$ according to Eq. (9-35). To maximize the gain K, this step should be accomplished such that G is as large as possible without permitting any zeros of $Q'(s)$ to move into the right half-plane. However, to demonstrate considerations pertaining to both, real and complex poles, the value of G will not be maximized. Instead, it will be selected as $(G = 0.2)$.

Comparing Eqs. (9-36) and (9-49), it is seen that $(m = 4)$, $(c_3 = 12)$, $(c_2 = 54)$, $(c_1 = 108)$, and $(c_0 = 80)$. Substituting these parameters into Eq. (9-39) and using $(G = 0.2)$, the d coefficients of Eq. (9-37) are readily evaluated:

$$Q'(s) = s^4 + 11.2s^3 + 47.28s^2 + 89.09s + 62.18$$
$$= (s + 1.85)(s + 3.72)(s + 2.82 + j1.05)(s + 2.82 - j1.05)$$
$$(9\text{-}50)$$

It follows from Eq. (9-38) that the derivative $Q''(s)$ is given by
$$Q''(s) = 4s^3 + 33.6s^2 + 94.56s + 89.09 \qquad (9\text{-}51)$$

It is now possible to perform partial-fraction expansions of $P(s)/Q'(s)$ and $Q''(s)/Q'(s)$ to yield

$$\frac{P(s)}{Q'(s)} = \frac{-1.27}{(s + 1.85)} + \frac{1.88}{(s + 3.72)}$$
$$+ \frac{-0.30 + j1.40}{(s + 2.82 + j1.05)} + \frac{-0.30 - j1.40}{(s + 2.82 - j1.05)}$$

$$\frac{Q''(s)}{Q'(s)} = \frac{0.99}{(s + 1.85)} + \frac{1.01}{(s + 3.72)}$$
$$+ \frac{1.00}{(s + 2.82 + j1.05)} + \frac{1.00}{(s + 2.82 - j1.05)} \qquad (9\text{-}52)$$

Because of the relationship between $Q'(s)$ and $Q''(s)$, the residues of the second expansion must all be unity (except for round off errors). Consequently, when this expansion is written in the form of Eq. (9-41), all k_q^D residues equal G for $(q \neq 0)$.

$$H\left[1 + \frac{GQ''(s)}{Q'(s)}\right] = H\left[1 + \frac{0.20}{(s + 1.85)} + \frac{0.20}{(s + 3.72)}\right.$$
$$\left. + \frac{0.20}{(s + 2.82 + j1.05)} + \frac{0.20}{(s + 2.82 - j1.05)}\right]$$
$$(9\text{-}53)$$

From the above two equations, the residues at the various poles and other pertinent parameters can be summarized as follows:

$(q = 0)$: $k_0^N = 0$ and $k_0^D = 1$

$(q = 1)$: $\sigma_1 = -1.85$ $k_1^N = -1.27$ $\qquad$ $k_1^D = 0.20$

$(q = 2)$: $\sigma_2 = -3.72$ $k_a^N = 1.88$ $\qquad$ $k_2^D = 0.20$

$(q = 3)$: $\sigma_3 = -2.82$ $k_3^N = a_3^N \pm jb_3^N$ $\qquad$ $k_3^D = a_3^D = 0.20$

$\qquad\qquad$ $\omega_3 = \pm 1.05$ $\quad = -0.30 \pm j1.40$ $\qquad$ (9-54)

At this point, the permissible range of H for each pole can be investigated. For the $q = 0$ terms of Eq. (9-54), it follows from consideration of Eq. (9-44) that any positive value of H will yield positive constants for k_0^B and k_0^A; therefore, $(H_0 > 0)$. The values of H for the real poles must satisfy the conditions of Eq. (9-45). Therefore, using $(G = 0.2)$ and the parameters of Eq. (9-54) for $(q = 1)$ and $(q = 2)$, the permissible range of H in each case becomes

$$-1 \leq \frac{-1.27}{0.2H_1} \leq 1 \quad \text{so} \quad H_1 \leq -6.35 \quad \text{and} \quad H_1 \geq 6.35$$

$$\text{and} \quad -1 \leq \frac{1.88}{0.2H_2} \leq 1 \quad \text{so} \quad H_2 \leq -9.40 \quad \text{and} \quad H_2 \geq 9.40$$

$$\text{(9-55)}$$

For the complex poles, H must satisfy the stronger of the two conditions of Eq. (9-47) at each pole. At $(s = -2.82 - j1.05)$, the value of F_3, computed from Eq. (9-46) using the data of Eq. (9-54), becomes

$$F_3 = \frac{|1.40|(-1.05)}{2(-2.82)} = 0.26 \qquad \text{(9-56)}$$

Hence from Eq. (9-47) it follows that

$$1 \geq \frac{2(0.26) - 0.30}{0.2H_3} \quad \text{and} \quad 1 \geq \frac{2(0.26) + 0.30}{0.2H_3}$$

or $H_3 \geq 1.05$ and $H_3 \geq 4.15$ $\qquad$ (9-57)

Similar results are obtained for the pole at $(s = -2.82 + j1.05)$.

To maximize the gain K, a single value of H must be chosen equal to or greater than the largest of the required values H_0, H_1, H_2, and H_3 given by Eqs. (9-55) and (9-57). Consequently, $H \geq 9.40$ will lead to a realizable solution. The maximum possible value of K cannot be achieved in this example, since G was not maximized. For instance, a choice of $(G = 1)$ leads to a realizable solution in which $Q'(s)$ possesses two pairs of complex poles and a subsequently higher value of K. Using

($H = 9.40$) and the parameters of Eq. (9-54), the residues at the poles of $Z_A(s)$ and $Z_B(s)$ can be computed from Eq. (9-44).

$$(q = 0): \quad k_0^A = k_0^B = \frac{H}{2} = 4.70 \qquad (q = 2): \quad \begin{cases} k_2^A = 0 \\ k_2^B = 1.88 \end{cases}$$

$$(q = 1): \quad \begin{cases} k_1^A = 1.58 \\ k_1^B = 0.31 \end{cases} \qquad (q = 3): \quad \begin{cases} k_3^A = 1.09 - j0.70 \\ k_3^B = 0.79 + j0.70 \end{cases}$$

$$(9\text{-}58)$$

The residues of Eq. (9-58) can be used with their respective poles to construct the impedance functions $Z_A(s)$ and $Z_B(s)$ in the form of Eq. (9-48):

$$Z_A(s) = 4.70 + \frac{1.58}{(s+1.85)} + \frac{1.09 - j0.70}{(s+2.82+j1.05)} + \frac{1.09 + j0.70}{(s+2.82-j1.05)}$$

$$Z_B(s) = 4.70 + \frac{0.31}{(s+1.85)} + \frac{1.88}{(s+3.72)} + \frac{0.79+j0.70}{(s+2.82+j1.05)} + \frac{0.79-j0.70}{(s+2.82-j1.05)}$$

$$(9\text{-}59)$$

Combining the conjugate poles and expanding the terms individually yields

$$Z_A(s) = 4.70 + \cfrac{1}{0.63s + \cfrac{1}{0.85}} + \cfrac{1}{0.46s + \cfrac{1}{1.75} + \cfrac{1}{1.50s + 3.23}}$$

$$Z_B(s) = 4.70 + \cfrac{1}{3.23s + \cfrac{1}{0.17}} + \cfrac{1}{0.53s + \cfrac{1}{0.51}} + \cfrac{1}{0.63s + \cfrac{1}{0.83} + \cfrac{1}{0.81s + 3.04}}$$

$$(9\text{-}60)$$

The symmetrical lattice network which represents these impedance functions is shown in Fig. 9-5. This network realizes Eq. (9-49) within a gain factor of ($K = 1/9.40 = 0.106$). Although K was not maximized in this example due to the choice of G, the discussion should adequately reveal the technique to be used. Furthermore, selection of H such that the residue at one of the poles vanishes, as k_2^A does at ($s = -3.72$) in Eq. (9-58), reduces the number of required elements. Higher than required values of H add resistance to the network; consequently, a trade-off is often possible between an acceptable gain factor and the amount of resistance to be used in the realization.

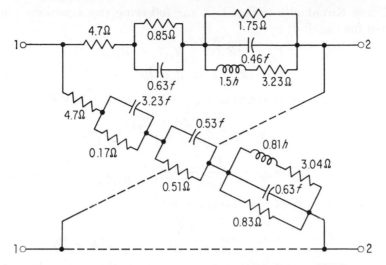

Fig. 9-5. Realization of Eq. (9-49) where (K = 0.106).

9-3. Realization of Resistance-terminated Lattice Networks

In addition to the procedures described in the preceding section, a wide variety of specified transfer ratios can be realized as resistance-terminated symmetrical lattice networks. The lattice with its load resistance R_L can be drawn in bridge form as shown in Fig. 9-6. In this figure the two currents I_a are equal because of the symmetry of the bridge. The same applies to the two currents I_b. The input current is denoted by I_1 and the output or load current by I_2.

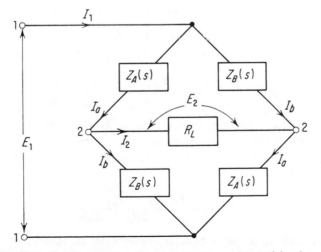

Fig. 9-6. Bridge form of resistance-terminated lattice.

Using Kirchhoff's voltage law, the following two equations can be written for Fig. 9-6:

$$E_1 = [2Z_A(s) + R_L]I_a - R_L I_b$$
$$E_1 = Z_A(s)I_a + Z_B(s)I_b \qquad (9\text{-}61)$$

Solving for I_a and I_b in terms of E_1, $Z_A(s)$, $Z_B(s)$, and R_L yields

$$I_a = \frac{E_1[Z_B(s) + R_L]}{Z_B(s)[2Z_A(s) + R_L] + R_L Z_A(s)}$$

$$I_b = \frac{E_1[Z_A(s) + R_L]}{Z_B(s)[2Z_A(s) + R_L] + R_L Z_A(s)} \qquad (9\text{-}62)$$

The load current I_2 of Fig. 9-6 is given by

$$I_2 = I_a - I_b = \frac{E_1[Z_B(s) - Z_A(s)]}{Z_B(s)[2Z_A(s) + R_L] + R_L Z_A(s)} \qquad (9\text{-}63)$$

The voltage E_2 equals $R_L I_2$; therefore, using Eq. (9-63) the voltage transfer ratio becomes

$$\frac{E_2}{E_1} = \frac{I_2 R_L}{E_1} = \frac{R_L[Z_B(s) - Z_A(s)]}{2Z_A(s)Z_B(s) + R_L Z_B(s) + R_L Z_A(s)}$$

$$= \frac{[Z_B(s) - Z_A(s)]}{\dfrac{2Z_A(s)Z_B(s)}{R_L} + [Z_B(s) + Z_A(s)]} \qquad (9\text{-}64)$$

This expression will be of the same form as the voltage transfer ratio of an open-circuited lattice network [See Eq. (9-40)] provided the term $2Z_A(s)Z_B(s)/R_L$ can be reduced to a constant. This end can be accomplished by introducing the following useful relationship:

$$Z_A(s)Z_B(s) = R_L^2 \qquad (9\text{-}65)$$

Imposing this condition on Eq. (9-64) yields

$$\frac{E_2}{E_1} = \frac{Z_B(s) - Z_A(s)}{2R_L + Z_B(s) + Z_A(s)} = \frac{R_L - Z_A(s)}{R_L + Z_A(s)} \qquad (9\text{-}66)$$

It is easily shown that Eq. (9-66) represents the voltage transfer ratio of a constant-resistance symmetrical lattice network. For instance, the input impedance of the resistance terminated lattice of Fig. 9-6 can be determined from Eq. (9-62) as

$$\frac{E_1}{I_1} = \frac{E_1}{I_a + I_b} = Z_1(s) = \frac{[Z_A(s) + Z_B(s)]R_L + 2Z_A(s)Z_B(s)}{2R_L + Z_A(s) + Z_B(s)} \qquad (9\text{-}67)$$

If the network is to be a constant-resistance structure, its input impedance $Z_1(s)$ must equal the load resistance R_L for all values of s.

Equating Eq. (9-67) to R_L and solving for R_L in terms of $Z_A(s)$ and $Z_B(s)$ gives $[R_L = \sqrt{Z_A(s)Z_B(s)}]$, which is identical to the condition chosen in Eq. (9-65). Consequently, satisfaction of Eq. (9-65) insures that the lattice will be a constant-resistance network possessing the voltage transfer ratio given by Eq. (9-66).

Further inspection of Eq. (9-66) reveals that the first expression is of the same general form as the voltage transfer ratio of Eq. (9-40). Therefore, one technique for realization of a constant-resistance lattice structure is provided by appropriate modification of Weinberg's procedure. For instance, the specified voltage transfer ratio may be separated in the manner described by Eqs. (9-35) through (9-40). The results of this separation can then be expanded by partial fractions and equated to a similar expansion of Eq. (9-66). The second expression of Eq. (9-66) reveals that for a constant-resistance structure it is only necessary to deal with R_L and $Z_A(s)$. Furthermore, G and H provide an added degree of freedom for satisfying the constraint of Eq. (9-65) in addition to optimizing the gain. After establishing R_L and a realizable function for $Z_A(s)$, the expression for $Z_B(s)$ can be computed from Eq. (9-65). The networks derived by this approach can be obtained more easily by application of the reciprocity theorem and well-known lattice transformations. In other words, the prescribed voltage transfer ratio can be realized as an open-circuited lattice according to the procedures of Sec. 9-2. Shunt resistance is then removed from the lattice by an appropriate transformation to satisfy the desired load resistance. Inasmuch as these techniques and transformations will be considered in greater detail in Chap. 10, it is not considered necessary to expand Eq. (9-66) or dwell on the required modifications of Weinberg's procedure.

A second approach to the realization of a prescribed voltage transfer ratio as a constant-resistance symmetrical lattice is to select R_L and $Z_A(s)$ in the form

$$R_L = \frac{Q(s) + KP(s)}{M(s)} \quad \text{and} \quad Z_A(s) = \frac{Q(s) - KP(s)}{M(s)} \tag{9-68}$$

where $M(s)$ is a polynomial chosen to satisfy the desired load resistance. This choice of R_L and $Z_A(s)$ follows directly from consideration of Eq. (9-66), since

$$\frac{E_2}{E_1} = \frac{R_L - Z_A(s)}{R_L + Z_A(s)} = \frac{\left[\dfrac{Q(s) + KP(s)}{M(s)}\right] - \left[\dfrac{Q(s) - KP(s)}{M(s)}\right]}{\left[\dfrac{Q(s) + KP(s)}{M(s)}\right] + \left[\dfrac{Q(s) - KP(s)}{M(s)}\right]} = \frac{KP(s)}{Q(s)}$$

$$\tag{9-69}$$

Solving Eq. (9-68) for $Z_A(s)$ in terms of R_L, K, $P(s)$, and $Q(s)$ yields

$$Z_A(s) = R_L \frac{Q(s) - KP(s)}{Q(s) + KP(s)} \tag{9-70}$$

If the voltage transfer ratio is to be realizable as a symmetrical lattice, then according to the discussion of Sec. 9-1, it is required that $Q(s) - KP(s)$ and $Q(s) + KP(s)$ possess no right half-plane zeros. This condition is also necessary if $Z_A(s)$, given by Eq. (9-70), is to be physically realizable as a driving-point function; however, this condition is not sufficient. It is also required that the real part of $Z_A(j\omega)$ be equal to or greater than zero for all real frequencies:

$$Re[Z_A(j\omega)] = Re\left[R_L \frac{Q(j\omega) - KP(j\omega)}{Q(j\omega) + KP(j\omega)}\right] \geq 0 \quad \text{for} \quad 0 \leq \omega \leq \infty \tag{9-71}$$

Provided $Q(s) \pm KP(s)$ have no right half-plane zeros and Eq. (9-71) is satisfied, the transfer ratio will lead to a realizable impedance $Z_A(s)$ in the form of Eq. (9-70). Once $Z_A(s)$ has been established, $Z_B(s)$ can be determined from Eqs. (9-65) and (9-70) as follows:

$$Z_B(s) = \frac{R_L^2}{Z_A(s)} = R_L \frac{Q(s) + KP(s)}{Q(s) - KP(s)} \tag{9-72}$$

Since $Z_A(s)$ and $Z_B(s)$ are related by the square of a positive real value R_L, $Z_B(s)$ will also be physically realizable.

The synthesis procedure resulting from the discussion of Eqs. (9-68) through (9-72) is probably apparent; however, an example should serve to illustrate the details of this technique. Consider the following voltage transfer ratio:

$$\frac{E_2}{E_1} = K \frac{P(s)}{Q(s)} = \frac{1}{2} \frac{(s^2 + 2s - 8)}{(s^2 + 4s + 5)} \tag{9-73}$$

This function will be realized as a constant-resistance symmetrical lattice terminated by a load resistance of $R_L = 4$ ohms. The first step in the procedure is to test the polynomials $Q(s) \pm KP(s)$ for right half-plane zeros. For this example, the polynomials become

$$Q(s) - KP(s) = (s^2 + 4s + 5) - \frac{1}{2}(s^2 + 2s - 8)$$

$$= \frac{s^2}{2} + 3s + 9 = \frac{(s + 3 + j3)(s + 3 - j3)}{2}$$

$$Q(s) + KP(s) = (s^2 + 4s + 5) + \frac{1}{2}(s^2 + 2s - 8)$$

$$= \frac{3s^2}{2} + 5s + 1 = \frac{3(s + 1.67 + j1.45)(s + 1.67 - j1.45)}{2} \tag{9-74}$$

Clearly, both polynomials have no right half-plane zeros; therefore, it is possible to write the expression for $Z_A(s)$ in the form of Eq. (9-70) as

$$Z_A(s) = \frac{4\left(\dfrac{s^2}{2} + 3s + 9\right)}{\left(\dfrac{3s^2}{2} + 5s + 1\right)} = \frac{4s^2 + 24s + 72}{3s^2 + 10s + 2} \qquad (9\text{-}75)$$

This function must satisfy Eq. (9-71) to be realizable; a simple check reveals that

$$Re[Z_A(j\omega)] = \frac{12\omega^4 + 16\omega^2 + 144}{9\omega^4 + 88\omega^2 + 4} \geq 0 \qquad \text{for} \qquad 0 \leq \omega \leq \infty \qquad (9\text{-}76)$$

Since the condition of Eq. (9-71) is also satisfied, $Z_A(s)$ is realizable as a driving-point function.

If perchance the tests of Eqs. (9-74) and (9-76) had failed, it might still be possible to realize the prescribed transfer ratio within a constant multiplier by adjusting the value of K to satisfy both conditions. For this example, values of K up to 5/8 are realizable, but zeros of $Q(s) + KP(s)$ move into the right half-plane for $K > 5/8$. Returning to the realization, $Z_B(s)$ can be written in the form of Eq. (9-72) as

$$Z_B(s) = \frac{4\left(\dfrac{3s^2}{2} + 5s + 1\right)}{\left(\dfrac{s^2}{2} + 3s + 9\right)} = \frac{12s^2 + 40s + 8}{s^2 + 6s + 18} \qquad (9\text{-}77)$$

The real part of $Z_B(j\omega)$ is given by

$$Re[Z_B(j\omega)] = \frac{12\omega^4 + 16\omega^2 + 144}{\omega^4 + 324} \geq 0 \qquad \text{for} \qquad 0 \leq \omega \leq \infty \qquad (9\text{-}78)$$

Hence, $Z_B(s)$ is also realizable, as could be predicted from $Z_A(s)$ and Eq. (9-65). It is now possible to expand Eqs. (9-75) and (9-77) as follows:

$$Z_A(s) = \cfrac{1}{\cfrac{1}{36} + \cfrac{1}{\cfrac{54}{7s} + \cfrac{9}{49} + \cfrac{1}{\cfrac{686}{255s} + \cfrac{183}{765}}}}$$

$$Z_B(s) = \frac{4}{9} + \cfrac{1}{\cfrac{27}{56s} + \cfrac{9}{784} + \cfrac{1}{\cfrac{10976}{175s} + \cfrac{4420}{441}}} \qquad (9\text{-}79)$$

The network which represents the impedances of Eq. (9-79) is shown in

Fig. 9-7. The load resistance (R_L = 4 ohms) is added across terminals 2-2 to complete the realization of Eq. (9-73).

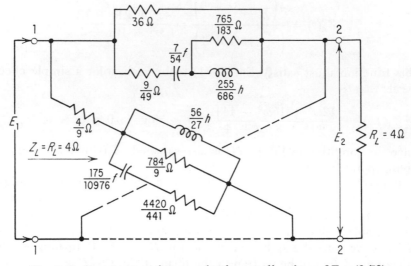

Fig. 9-7. Constant-resistance lattice realization of Eq. (9-73).

Although the above example is not particularly complicated, it demonstrates a procedure that can be used for the realization of constant-resistance symmetrical lattice networks. This technique and Matthaei's procedure of Chap. 8, Sec. 8-5, combine to suggest a method for realization of more complicated transfer ratios. For instance, a complicated transfer ratio can be separated into the product of several functions of lower order. Each of these simplified functions is then realized as a constant-resistance ladder or symmetrical lattice section such that one section satisfies the desired load resistance. This section also serves as the load resistance of the preceding section and so forth, such that the cascaded combination of all the sections realizes the prescribed transfer ratio.

9-4. Additional Considerations Pertaining to Lattice-network Realization

It was mentioned in the preceding section that lattice transformations exist which make it possible to remove resistance from a lattice to satisfy desired load resistance conditions. These transformations, described in detail in Chap. 10, can also be used in many cases to remove inductance and/or capacitance from the lattice. Consequently in many practical situations it is possible to satisfy more complicated load impedances. Furthermore, part or all of the impedance removed from a lattice can be associated with the input circuit to satisfy a desired source impedance. It is sometimes possible, by the same transformations, to unbalance a symmetrical lattice to yield an equivalent grounded structure. For this reason, the procedures of lattice-network synthesis are often used as an intermediate step in the realization of ladder or three-terminal networks. For the conversion process from a lattice to a ladder network to succeed it is necessary that the transfer function satisfy the conditions for a ladder network in addition to the constraints of a symmetrical lattice. The effect of these combined constraints on pole-zero locations and maximum realizable gain are not considered here, since these topics have already been described in Chaps. 7 and 8.

In the case of constant-resistance lattice networks, the transfer ratio of Eq. (9-66) can be converted, according to Eq. (9-65), to the following form:

$$\frac{E_2}{E_1} = \frac{R_L - Z_A(s)}{R_L + Z_A(s)} = \frac{Z_B(s) - R_L}{Z_B(s) + R_L} \tag{9-80}$$

This conversion suggests that separation of the transfer ratio, described in the preceding section, can be accomplished in a manner such as to yield $Z_B(s)$ directly rather than $Z_A(s)$. Applying the frequency transformations of Chap. 13 to Eq. (9-80) reveals that it is possible to convert a high-pass network (i.e., a network which passes only high frequencies) to a low-pass structure by simply interchanging $Z_A(s)$ and $Z_B(s)$. A bandpass filter can be transformed to a band-rejection network by the same procedure. Although the procedures of this chapter do not generally realize a transfer function as a lattice possessing a minimum number of elements or maximum gain, they do avoid the use of ideal or perfect transformers. In many cases the redundant elements serve a useful purpose. For instance, resistance may be associated with the reactive elements of the network, thereby making it possible to more accurately approximate these elements with commercially available components.

References

Further details concerning the procedures of this chapter are provided in the references given in the footnotes. However, general background information concerning lattice networks is provided in the following references.

1. E. A. Guillemin, *Communication Networks*, Vol. II (New York: John Wiley & Sons, Inc., 1935), Chap. 10, Secs. 1 through 4.
2. M. E. Van Valkenburg, *Introduction to Modern Network Synthesis* (New York: John Wiley & Sons, Inc., 1960), Chap. 12, Secs. 1, 2, 3, and 6.

Weinberg's procedures and transfer functions of lattice networks are covered in Secs. 7-8, 12-3, and 12-4 of his book.

3. L. Weinberg, *Network Analysis and Synthesis* (New York: McGraw-Hill Book Co., Inc., 1962).

Additional lattice synthesis procedures related to those described in this chapter are presented in the following journals:

4. H. J. Orchard, "The Synthesis of *RC* Networks to Have Prescribed Transfer Functions," *Proc. IRE*, vol. 39, no. 4, April, 1951, pp. 428–432.

5. L. Weinberg, "Synthesis of Unbalanced *RLC* Networks," *Proc. National Electronic Conference*, vol. 8, January 1953, pp. 598–608.

Problems

9-1. Determine the maximum value of gain K for the following voltage transfer ratios such that each function will be realizable as an RLC symmetrical lattice network.

(a) $\dfrac{E_2}{E_1} = \dfrac{KP(s)}{Q(s)} = \dfrac{K(s^2 + 4s - 5)}{(s^3 + 8s^2 + 25s + 26)}$

(b) $\dfrac{E_2}{E_1} = \dfrac{KP(s)}{Q(s)} = \dfrac{K(3s^3 + 5s^2 + 5s + 3)}{(4s^4 + 5s^3 + 11s^2 + 7s + 5)}$

9-2. A knowledge of root-locus techniques, borrowed from control system theory, is useful in determining the maximum realizable gain for problems such as 9-1. Sketch the locus of the roots of $[KP(s)/Q(s) = -1]$ and $[KP(s)/Q(s) = 1]$ for the transfer ratios of Prob. 9-1 as K varies from zero to six. Show that the locus for each function crosses the $j\omega$-axis when the maximum realizable gain is achieved.

9-3. Realize the first voltage transfer ratio (a) of Prob. 9-1 by Weinberg's procedure of Sec. 9-2, Eqs. (9-19) through (9-28). Use a gain factor of ($K = 3$) for this problem. Can the maximum realizable value of K, determined in Prob. 9-1, be achieved by this synthesis technique?

9-4. Repeat the requirements of Prob. 9-3 for the second voltage transfer ratio (b) of Prob. 9-1. Use a gain factor of ($K = 1$).

9-5. Separate the following polynomials into the sum of two polynomials, $Q(s) = Q'(s) + GQ''(s)$, such that $Q'(s)$ is a Hurwitz polynomial, G is a real positive constant, and $Q''(s)$ is the derivative of $Q'(s)$. Determine the maximum value for G that satisfies these conditions in each case.

(a) $Q(s) = s^4 + 6s^3 + 13s^2 + 14s + 6$

(b) $Q(s) = s^5 + 8s^4 + 30s^3 + 60s^2 + 64s + 32$

9-6. Decompose the following voltage transfer ratio according to Weinberg's procedure of Eqs. (9-35) through (9-48). Determine the impedances, $Z_A(s)$ and $Z_B(s)$, such that H is minimized. Complete the realization of the voltage transfer ratio and draw the resulting lattice network.

$$\frac{E_2}{E_1} = \frac{P(s)}{HQ(s)} = \frac{(s^2 + 4s + 5)}{H(s^3 + 5s^2 + 8s + 6)}$$

9-7. Realize the first voltage transfer ratio (a) of Prob. 9-1 by Weinberg's procedure as outlined in Eqs. (9-35) through (9-48). Optimize the gain factor, K, by minimizing H. Is it possible to realize the maximum realizable gain factor for this problem?

9-8. Realize the following voltage transfer ratio as a symmetrical lattice terminated by a load resistance of $R_L = 10$ ohms. Use the procedures of Sec. 9-3. This function has a real part that is negative at $\omega = 1$; consequently, use sufficient surplus factors to make the impedances, $Z_A(s)$ and $Z_B(s)$, realizable.

$$\frac{E_2}{E_1} = \frac{2s^2 + 3s + 7}{2(2s^2 + s + 1)}$$

9-9. Realize the following voltage transfer ratio as a resistance terminated symmetrical lattice network. Satisfy a load resistance of $R_L = 4$ ohms.

$$\frac{E_2}{E_1} = \frac{s^4 + 2s^3 + 3s^2 + s + 1}{s^4 + s^3 + 3s^2 + 2s + 1}$$

9-10. Replace the load resistor of Fig. 9-6 by an impedance, $Z_L(s)$, then determine the expression for the voltage transfer ratio in terms of $Z_A(s)$, $Z_B(s)$, and $Z_L(s)$. Realize the voltage transfer ratio of Prob. 9-9 for a load impedance of 1 farad.

Chapter 10

Equivalent-network

Configurations

A number of procedures have been presented thus far and in several cases it has been seen that different networks can be synthesized to realize a given driving-point or transfer function. For instance, a number of equivalent one-port structures were obtained by the driving-point synthesis techniques of Chaps. 5 and 6. Furthermore, it was mentioned in Chap. 9 that symmetrical lattice networks can often be transformed into equivalent unbalanced or ladder configurations. Consequently, the purpose of this chapter is to investigate various equivalent-network configurations and the transformations which make it possible to convert from one form to another. Specifically, three simplified one-port conversions will be considered after which attention will be turned to equivalent two-port networks. In this respect simple ladder networks will be studied followed by a discussion of Bartlett's bisection theorem and a number of lattice conversion techniques. A final section is devoted to impedance-level transformations which are also useful in developing equivalent-network configurations by replacing specific element values with combinations of elements which produce the same net result.

10-1. Equivalent One-port Networks

A number of equivalent one-port networks can be derived by the procedures of Chaps. 3 through 6, or by employing terminated two-port networks which possess equivalent input driving-point characteristics. However, rather than consider these more complicated possibilities, the purpose of this section is to investigate three simplified one-port network conversions. These conversions will be considered individually and were originally derived by Zobel.† The equivalence of any particular conversion is easily established by comparing terms of the driving-point functions of the networks in question.

A. Conversion of a Series and Parallel Network Combination.
The network of Fig. 10-1b is equivalent to the configuration of Fig. 10-1a provided the conditions of Eq. (10-1) are satisfied. The A, B, C, and D terms must be real positive numbers, and the impedances $Z_a(s)$ and $Z_b(s)$ are assumed to be physically realizable.

$$Z_1(s) = \frac{Z_a(s)Z_b(s)}{Z_a(s) + Z_b(s)} + AZ_a(s) = \frac{DZ_a(s)[BZ_a(s) + CZ_b(s)]}{(B + D)Z_a(s) + CZ_b(s)}$$

or $\quad B = A(1 + A) \quad\quad C = (1 + A)^2 \quad$ and $\quad D = (1 + A)$ (10-1)

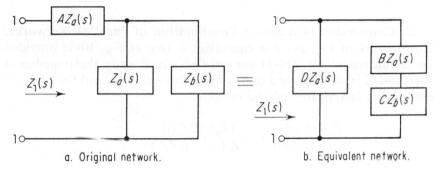

a. Original network. b. Equivalent network.

Fig. 10-1. Equivalent networks for the conditions of Eq. (10-1).

B. Conversion of a Parallel Combination of Series Networks.
The network of Fig. 10-2b is equivalent to the configuration of Fig. 10-2a provided the conditions of Eq. (10-2) are satisfied. As in the above case A, B, C, D, E, and F must be real positive numbers, and $Z_a(s)$ and $Z_b(s)$ are assumed to be physically realizable.

$$Z_1(s) = \frac{[Z_a(s) + Z_b(s)][AZ_a(s) + BZ_b(s)]}{(1 + A)Z_c(s) + (1 + B)Z_b(s)}$$

$$= \frac{CZ_a(s)DZ_b(s)}{CZ_a(s) + DZ_b(s)} + EZ_a(s) + FZ_b(s)$$

or

$$C = \frac{(A - B)^2}{(1 + A)(1 + B)^2} \quad\quad D = \frac{(A - B)^2}{(1 + A)^2(1 + B)}$$

$$E = \frac{A}{(1 + A)} \quad \text{and} \quad F = \frac{B}{(1 + B)}$$ (10-2)

† Otto J. Zobel, "Theory and Design of Uniform and Composite Electric Wave-Filters," *Bell System Technical Journal*, January 1923, Appendix III.

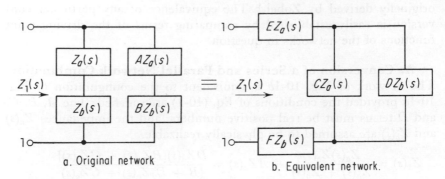

a. Original network

b. Equivalent network.

Fig. 10.2. Equivalent networks for the conditions of Eq. (10-2).

C. Conversion of a Series Combination of Parallel Networks. The network of Fig. 10-3*b* is equivalent to that of Fig. 10-3*a* provided the conditions of Eq. (10-3) are satisfied. Once again the impedances $Z_a(s)$ and $Z_b(s)$ are assumed to be physically realizable, and the constant multiplying factors are real and positive.

$$Z_1(s) = \frac{Z_a(s)Z_b(s)}{Z_a(s) + Z_b(s)} + \frac{AZ_a(s)BZ_b(s)}{AZ_a(s) + BZ_b(s)}$$

$$= \frac{CDZ_a(s)Z_b(s)[EZ_a(s) + FZ_b(s)]}{CDZ_a(s)Z_b(s) + [CZ_a(s) + DZ_b(s)][EZ_a(s) + FZ_b(s)]}$$

or

$$C = (1 + A) \qquad D = (1 + B)$$

$$E = \frac{A(1 + A)(1 + B)^2}{(A - B)^2} \quad \text{and} \quad F = \frac{B(1 + A)^2(1 + B)}{(A - B)^2} \tag{10-3}$$

A number of equivalent one-port networks can be derived by simply equating the driving-point functions of various configurations and solving for the required conditions. In this approach care must be taken to establish all constraints necessary to insure a physically realizable conversion. Furthermore, the three network conversions described above can also be applied in a reverse sense. However, this is most easily accomplished by assigning new notation to the structures and solving for the conditions required for equivalence. Finally, simplified conversions such as these are often useful in the manipulation of two-port networks to be considered in the following sections.

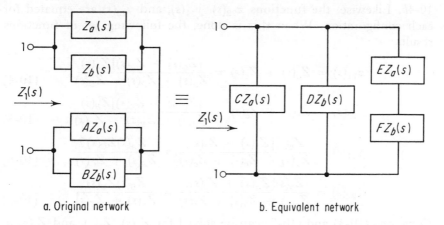

a. Original network   b. Equivalent network

Fig. 10-3. Equivalent networks for the conditions of Eq. (10-3).

10-2. Equivalent T and Pi Ladder Networks

The most common ladder network transformation is that between T- and Pi-sections of the forms shown in Fig. 10-4. The reason for this is the widespread use of T- and Pi-sections, and the fact that many two-port networks can be realized as equivalent T- or Pi-sections. The possibility of a transformation between T and Pi configurations at a single frequency is well known; however, an exact transformation for networks operating over a range of frequencies is not always possible.

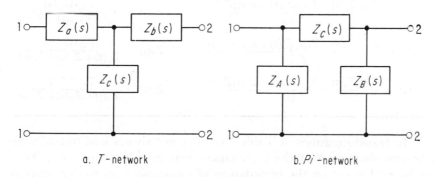

a. T-network   b. Pi-network

Fig. 10-4. T and Pi networks.

The relationships between the impedances of the T- and Pi-sections of Fig. 10-4 are easily derived by equating the driving-point impedance and admittance functions of each configuration. For instance, $z_{11}(s)$ for the network of Fig. 10-4a is equated to $z_{11}(s)$ for the network of Fig.

10-4b. Likewise, the functions $z_{22}(s)$, $y_{11}(s)$, and $y_{22}(s)$ are equated for each configuration. When this is done, the following set of functions results:

$$z_{11}(s) = Z_a(s) + Z_c(s) = \frac{[Z_C(s) + Z_B(s)]Z_A(s)}{Z_A(s) + Z_B(s) + Z_C(s)} \tag{10-4}$$

$$z_{22}(s) = Z_b(s) + Z_c(s) = \frac{[Z_C(s) + Z_A(s)]Z_B(s)}{Z_A(s) + Z_B(s) + Z_C(s)} \tag{10-5}$$

$$y_{11}(s) = \frac{Z_a(s)[Z_b(s) + Z_c(s)]}{Z_a(s) + Z_b(s) + Z_c(s)} = \frac{Z_A(s)Z_C(s)}{Z_A(s) + Z_C(s)} \tag{10-6}$$

$$y_{22}(s) = \frac{Z_b(s)[Z_a(s) + Z_c(s)]}{Z_a(s) + Z_b(s) + Z_c(s)} = \frac{Z_B(s)Z_C(s)}{Z_B(s) + Z_C(s)} \tag{10-7}$$

Equations (10-4) and (10-5) can be solved for $Z_a(s)$, $Z_b(s)$, and $Z_c(s)$ in terms of $Z_A(s)$, $Z_B(s)$, and $Z_C(s)$ by completing the multiplication and separating the parts. Equations (10-6) and (10-7) can be solved in much the same manner; however, all four equations are not needed to obtain the desired relationships. The results of this and a converse process give the transformations which are listed in Table 10-1 for the T and Pi networks of Fig. 10-4.

TABLE 10-1

T- and Pi-network transformations for Fig. 10-4

T-to-Pi transformations	Pi-to-T transformations
$Z_A(s) = \dfrac{Z_a(s)Z_b(s) + Z_b(s)Z_c(s) + Z_c(s)Z_a(s)}{Z_b(s)}$	$Z_a(s) = \dfrac{Z_A(s)Z_C(s)}{Z_A(s) + Z_B(s) + Z_C(s)}$
$Z_B(s) = \dfrac{Z_a(s)Z_b(s) + Z_b(s)Z_c(s) + Z_c(s)Z_a(s)}{Z_a(s)}$	$Z_b(s) = \dfrac{Z_B(s)Z_C(s)}{Z_A(s) + Z_B(s) + Z_C(s)}$
$Z_C(s) = \dfrac{Z_a(s)Z_b(s) + Z_b(s)Z_c(s) + Z_c(s)Z_a(s)}{Z_c(s)}$	$Z_c(s) = \dfrac{Z_A(s)Z_B(s)}{Z_A(s) + Z_B(s) + Z_C(s)}$

The transformations of Table 10-1 may not always lead to realizable networks since each of the impedances may be a function of s. Tests can be performed on the impedances of either network to demonstrate positive realness for any particular example. However, if it is assumed that a realizable Pi network is desired, the following sufficient conditions on $Z_a(s)$, $Z_b(s)$, and $Z_c(s)$ of the T network can be derived from further consideration of Table 10-1.

1. A realizable Pi-section will result if $Z_a(s)$, $Z_b(s)$, and $Z_c(s)$ are of the same form with the same poles and zeros.

2. A second possibility exists if two of the impedances, such as $Z_a(s)$ and $Z_b(s)$, are resistances. Then $Z_A(s)$, $Z_B(s)$, and $Z_C(s)$ will be realizable if the third impedance $Z_c(s)$ is realizable. This fact is evident when the numerator of the T-to-Pi transformation for $Z_C(s)$ in Table 10-1 is a constant.

3. A third condition leading to a realizable Pi-section occurs when one impedance, such as $Z_b(s)$, is inverse to a second, $Z_c(s)$ and the third impedance $Z_a(s)$ is inverse to the sum of the first two, $Z_b(s) + Z_c(s)$. In the case of a symmetrical T network, this condition can only be satisfied when all of the impedances are resistances.

A set of T-network impedances, which satisfy one of the above conditions, can be transformed by the relationships of Table 10-1 to yield the impedances of an equivalent realizable Pi network. The same conditions apply to the Pi-to-T transformations if the impedances are replaced by admittances. If a specified transfer function can be realized as either a T or Pi network, then by use of Table 10-1 it may be possible to convert the network to its alternate form. Sometimes this conversion can be accomplished with a reduction in the number of elements required for the realization or a desirable change in element values. However, the transformations will not always yield a realizable set of impedances. An example of this situation exists for the T network in which $Z_a(s) = Z_b(s) = 1/Cs$ and $Z_c(s) = R$. Using the transforms of Table 10-1 to convert to a Pi network, it is seen that $Z_C(s) = (2RCs + 1)/RC^2s^2$, which is not realizable as a driving-point impedance because of the double pole at $s = 0$. A table similar to Table 10-1 can be derived for the networks of Fig. 10-4 on an admittance basis.

10-3. Bartlett's Bisection Theorem

To establish the equivalence of more complicated ladder and lattice networks, it is instructive to study Bartlett's bisection theorem. A bisectable network is one which has physical symmetry about a plane passed through its center. From consideration of symmetrical networks, the following relationships are always true of a bisectable network:

$$z_{11}(s) = z_{22}(s) \quad \text{and} \quad z_{12}(s) = z_{21}(s)$$

or $$y_{11}(s) = y_{22}(s) \quad \text{and} \quad y_{12}(s) = y_{21}(s) \qquad (10\text{-}8)$$

Bartlett's theorem states that the impedances of a balanced lattice network, which is equivalent to a given symmetrical network, can be obtained by bisecting the symmetrical network and measuring its input impedance with the bisected terminals open and short-circuited. This theorem can be expressed analytically in terms of the lattice impedances $Z_A(s)$ and $Z_B(s)$ of Fig. 9-2 and the open-circuit driving-point and transfer impedances of any symmetrical two-port network. Let $Z_{OC(1/2)}$

and $Z_{SC(1/2)}$ represent the impedances seen looking into terminals 1-1 or 2-2 of a bisected symmetrical network with the bisected terminals open-circuited and short-circuited, respectively. In this case the following relationships apply:

$$Z_{OC(1/2)} = z_{11}(s) + z_{12}(s) = z_{22}(s) + z_{21}(s) = Z_B(s)$$

$$Z_{SC(1/2)} = z_{11}(s) - z_{12}(s) = z_{22}(s) - z_{21}(s) = Z_A(s) \quad (10\text{-}9)$$

Bartlett's theorem, as expressed by Eq. (10-9), provides a convenient method for obtaining a balanced lattice network equivalent to any given symmetrical two-port network, since it is generally easy to determine the open- and short-circuit impedances for half of a symmetrical network. Before investigating examples of Bartlett's theorem, it is instructive to consider the characteristics of parallel and cross-linked bisectable networks. In addition, the conditions leading to the formulation of Eq. (10-9) will be studied.

The T and Pi networks of Fig. 10-4 are examples of parallel-link networks, since there is no crossing over of impedances as in a lattice network. The bisection theorem as applied to networks having parallel links is most easily explained by use of a T network of the form shown in Fig. 10-4a. The branch impedances of this network are easily expressed in terms of the open-circuit driving-point and transfer impedances as follows:

$$Z_a(s) = z_{11}(s) - z_{12}(s)$$

$$Z_b(s) = z_{22}(s) - z_{12}(s)$$

$$Z_c(s) = z_{12}(s) = z_{21}(s) \quad (10\text{-}10)$$

The network of Fig. 10-4a can then be prepared for bisection by separating the impedance $Z_c(s)$ into two parallel impedances having

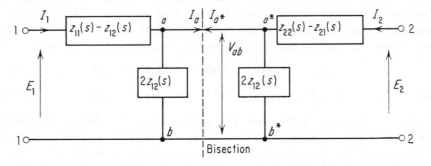

Fig. 10-5. Bisection of a T network.

values of $2Z_c(s)$. Substituting the relationships of Eq. (10-10), the T network is prepared for separation as shown in Fig. 10-5.

The relationship between the impedances $z_{11}(s)$, $z_{12}(s)$, and $z_{22}(s)$ and the impedances $Z_{OC(1/2)}$ and $Z_{SC(1/2)}$ for networks of the parallel-link type can be determined by considering the network of Fig. 10-5 under two conditions of applied voltage.

Case 1. Assume the network of Fig. 10-5 is symmetrical about the "bisection" line. In this case the following conditions are defined by the figure:

$$E_1 = E_2 = |E| \qquad z_{11}(s) = z_{22}(s) \qquad z_{12}(s) = z_{21}(s)$$

$$I_a = I_{a*} = 0 \quad \text{and} \quad I_1 = I_2 = |I| \tag{10-11}$$

The currents I_a and I_{a*} must be zero and I_1 equals I_2 since the voltages E_1 and E_2 applied to the symmetrical network are assumed to be equal in magnitude and polarity. Because the current flowing in lines a-$a*$ and b-$b*$ is zero, the network can be broken along the bisection line without disturbing the voltage or currents of either half. Consequently it is possible to define the "open-circuit impedance" for one-half of the network as

$$Z_{OC(1/2)} = \frac{E}{I} = [z_{11}(s) - z_{12}(s)] + 2z_{12}(s)$$

$$= z_{11}(s) + z_{12}(s) = z_{22}(s) + z_{21}(s) \tag{10-12}$$

This impedance is a driving-point function for one-half of the total network.

Case 2. Now assume the voltages E_1 and E_2 are equal in magnitude but opposite in polarity. This can be accomplished by reversing E_2 of Fig. 10-5 in which case the circuit conditions become

$$E_1 = -E_2 = |E| \qquad z_{11}(s) = z_{22}(s) \qquad z_{12}(s) = z_{21}(s)$$

$$I_a = -I_{a*} \quad \text{and} \quad I_1 = -I_2 = |I| \tag{10-13}$$

Under these conditions the voltage at point a will be the same as that at $a*$, and the same is true of points b and $b*$. Therefore, by Kirchhoff's potential law the voltages across the series impedances can be written as

$$I_1[z_{11}(s) - z_{12}(s)] = -I_2[z_{22}(s) - z_{12}(s)] = E \tag{10-14}$$

Substituting the conditions of Eq. (10-13) into (10-14), it is apparent that the voltage V_{ab} equals zero. Consequently, a shorting link can be placed between the parallel connecting links a-$a*$ and b-$b*$ without disturbing the network. If two shorting links are added, one from a to b and one from $a*$ to $b*$, the network can then be divided into two equivalent halves which have shorted outputs. The "short-circuit impedance" for one-half of the network can then be defined as

$$Z_{SC(1/2)} = \frac{E}{I} = z_{11}(s) - z_{12}(s) = z_{22}(s) - z_{21}(s) \tag{10-15}$$

The open and short-circuit impedances of Eqs. (10-12) and (10-15) are the impedances seen looking into the terminals of either half of a symmetrical network possessing parallel links after it has been bisected with the bisection links open and shorted, respectively. These relationships are general and can be applied independently of the number of parallel connecting links. Now that the relationships between $Z_{OC(1/2)}$ and $Z_{SC(1/2)}$ and the impedances $z_{11}(s)$, $z_{12}(s)$, and $z_{22}(s)$ for a symmetrical network having parallel links have been established, it is instructive to determine these relationships for networks having crossed links.

Crossed links are associated with lattice networks which can be drawn in a general form as illustrated in Fig. 10-6. It is assumed that this network is also symmetrical about the bisection line and that the voltages E_1 and E_2 are equal in magnitude. As in the above discussion, two cases must be studied; one in which E_1 and E_2 have polarities as shown in Fig. 10-6 and a second in which E_2 is of reversed polarity.

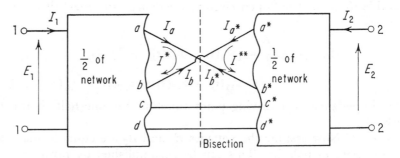

Fig. 10-6. Bisection of a network with crossed links.

Case 1. The parameters of Fig. 10-6 reflect the following conditions for a symmetrical network with crossed links:

$$E_1 = E_2 = |E| \qquad z_{11}(s) = z_{22}(s) \qquad z_{12}(s) = z_{21}(s)$$

$$I_a = -I_{b*} = I_{a*} = -I_b \qquad \text{and} \qquad I_1 = I_2 = |I| \quad (10\text{-}16)$$

Because of the symmetry, the currents I_a and I_b can be replaced by a single loop current I^*. Likewise, the currents I_{a*} and I_{b*} can be replaced by a loop current I^{**} where the magnitude of I^* and I^{**} are equal. Hence, the points a and b and the points a^* and b^* can be shorted together without affecting the network. Either half of the network can then be drawn in the form of Fig. 10-7a. Consideration of Fig. 10-7a reveals that the half-network is of the same form as Case 1 of the parallel-link configuration. Therefore, the open-circuit impedance of one-half of the network with crossed links is also given by Eq. (10-12) and is the same for networks with parallel or crossed links.

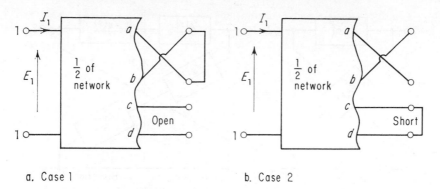

a. Case 1   b. Case 2

Fig. 10-7. Cases 1 and 2 for cross-linked networks.

Case 2. It is now useful to consider the case in which the voltages E_1 and E_2 of Fig. 10-6 are of opposite polarity. This can be accomplished by reversing the polarity of E_2 causing the following set of circuit conditions to exist:

$$E_1 = -E_2 = |E| \qquad z_{11}(s) = z_{22}(s) \qquad z_{12}(s) = z_{21}(s)$$

$$I_a = -I_{a*} \qquad I_b = -I_{b*} \qquad \text{and} \qquad I_1 = -I_2 = |I| \quad (10\text{-}17)$$

As a result of the change in polarity, the currents I_a and I_b equal a minus I_{a*} and I_{b*}. Consequently, there is no current flow in the crossed links; however, there will be current flowing in the parallel links. Therefore, in bisecting the network, the crossed links are left open, and the parallel links must be shorted as in Case 2 of the parallel link networks. This yields a half-network of the form shown in Fig. 10-7b, where the short-circuit impedance for one-half of the network is expressed by Eq. (10-15) and is the same for networks with parallel or crossed links.

Equations (10-12) and (10-15) represent partial proof of Eq. (10-9); however, to complete the proof it is still necessary to show that $Z_{OC(1/2)} = Z_B(s)$ and $Z_{SC(1/2)} = Z_A(s)$ for a symmetrical lattice such as Fig. 9-2. To accomplish this end, the lattice of Fig. 9-2 has been redrawn in Fig. 10-8 to show the required bisection line.

If the network of Fig. 10-8b is bisected, Fig. 10-9a shows one-half of the network under open-circuited conditions, and Fig. 10-9b shows the same half-network under short-circuited conditions. The open- and short-circuited impedances for the half-network become

$$Z_{OC(1/2)} = \frac{Z_B(s)}{2} + \frac{Z_B(s)}{2} = Z_B(s)$$

and

$$Z_{SC(1/2)} = \frac{Z_A(s)}{2} + \frac{Z_A(s)}{2} = Z_A(s) \qquad (10\text{-}18)$$

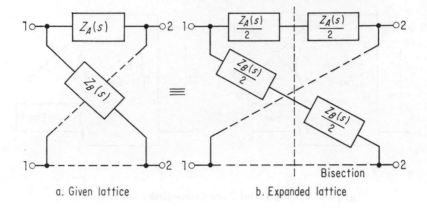

a. Given lattice   b. Expanded lattice

Fig. 10-8. Symmetrical lattice network.

Equating the relationships of Eq. (10-18) with those of Eqs. (10-12) and (10-15) gives the results expressed in Eq. (10-9), thereby completing the proof of Bartlett's bisection theorem.

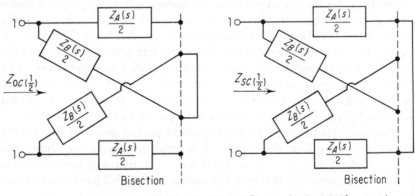

a. Open-circuited half-network   b. Short-circuited half-network.

Fig. 10-9. Bisected portions of Fig. 10-8b.

The application of Bartlett's bisection theorem can be demonstrated by considering the parallel-linked bridged-T network of Fig. 10-10a. If this network is bisected along its axis of symmetry, one-half of the network under open- and short-circuited conditions takes the form of Fig. 10-10b and 10-10c, respectively.

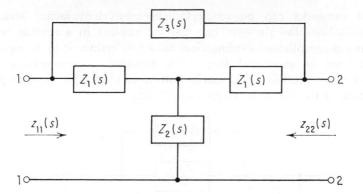

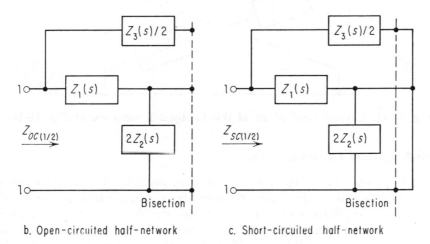

a. Symmetrical bridged–T network

b. Open–circuited half–network   c. Short–circuited half–network

Fig. 10-10. Bisection of a bridged-T network.

The open- and short-circuited impedances for the half-networks of Figs. 10-10b and 10-10c can be written as

$$Z_{OC(1/2)} = Z_1(s) + 2Z_2(s) \quad \text{and} \quad Z_{SC(1/2)} = \frac{Z_1(s)\left[\dfrac{Z_3(s)}{2}\right]}{Z_1(s) + \left[\dfrac{Z_3(s)}{2}\right]}$$

(10-19)

Substituting the impedances of Eq. (10-19) into Eq. (10-9) reveals that an equivalent symmetrical lattice network can be derived. This lattice, equivalent to the bridged-T network of Fig. 10-10a, is shown in Fig. 10-11. As a result, this example illustrates the manner in which parallel-linked networks can be converted to equivalent lattice structures. Bartlett's bisection theorem can also be applied in a reverse sense to simplify a complicated symmetrical lattice or reduce it to an equivalent unbalanced or grounded form. For instance, a symmetrical lattice similar in form to Fig. 10-11 can be converted to an equivalent bridged-T structure of the form shown in Fig. 10-10a.

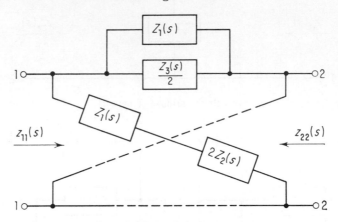

Fig. 10-11. Lattice equivalent of the bridged-T network of Fig. 10-10a.

10-4. Lattice Decomposition

As pointed out in the previous section, Bartlett's bisection theorem can be used in many cases to simplify a complicated symmetrical structure. Application of this theorem for the decomposition of lattice networks, particularly for reasons of converting to an unbalanced or grounded form, is well known. Therefore, the purpose of this section is to investigate some of the techniques which can be used to reduce the complexity of lattice structures, and each of these techniques can be verified by use of Eq. (10-9).

A. Series Removal of Elements. The lattice network of Fig. 10-12a is seen to have a series impedance $Z_C(s)$ in each branch. These impedances can be removed provided $Z_C(s)$ is inserted in series with each end of the lattice, as shown in Fig. 10-12b. The resulting network is electrically equivalent to that of Fig. 10-12a but contains fewer elements since two of the four $Z_C(s)$ impedances have been removed.

B. Parallel Removal of Elements. The lattice of Fig. 10-13a has an impedance $Z_C(s)$ in parallel with each branch. These impedances can be removed if $Z_C(s)$ is placed in parallel with each end of the lattice as

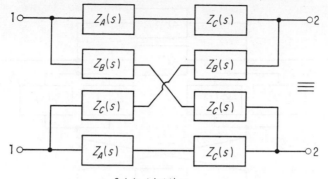

a. Original lattice.

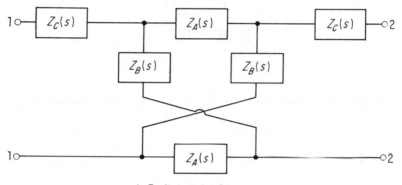

b. Equivalent lattice.

Fig. 10-12. Series removal of elements from a lattice.

shown in Fig. 10-13b. As in the previous case, the network of Fig. 10-13b is equivalent to that of Fig. 10-13a but has fewer elements. When the lattice portion of the equivalent network is symmetrical, as in Figs. 10-12b and 10-13b, it is often possible to apply Bartlett's bisection theorem to convert it to an unbalanced form such that the entire network will have a common ground.

C. Bridged-T Equivalent of Lattice. The network of Fig. 10-14a can be distorted to yield parallel branches as shown in Fig. 10-14b. This configuration is not unbalanced since there is no common ground; however, because of the symmetry of the network the two $Z_C(s)$ impedances will carry the same currents between the input and output terminals. Provided there are no circulating currents flowing in the

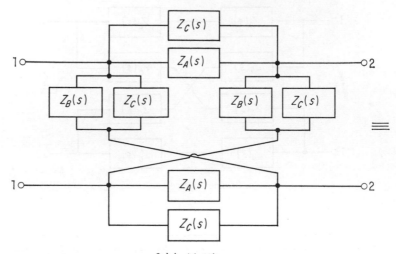

a. Original lattice.

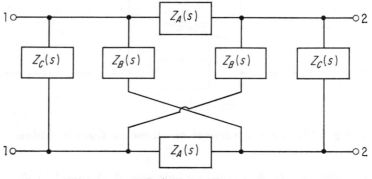

b. Equivalent lattice.

Fig. 10-13. Parallel removal of elements from a lattice.

parallel branches, the two $Z_C(s)$ impedances can be combined in the upper branch and the lattice formed by $Z_A(s)$ and $Z_B(s)$ can be replaced by an equivalent T network. In this manner the lattice of Fig. 10-14a becomes a bridged-T network as shown in Fig. 10-14c.

A useful example of the above transformation is the conversion of a constant-resistance lattice to an equivalent constant-resistance bridged-T network. In Chap. 9, Sec. 9-3, it was shown that for a lattice network to be a constant-resistance structure, the product of the impedances of the parallel and crossed branches must equal the square of the load resistance.

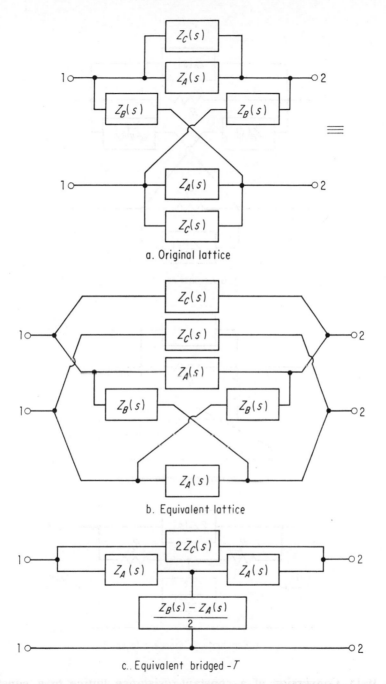

a. Original lattice

b. Equivalent lattice

c. Equivalent bridged -T

Fig. 10-14. Conversion of a lattice to an equivalent bridged-T network.

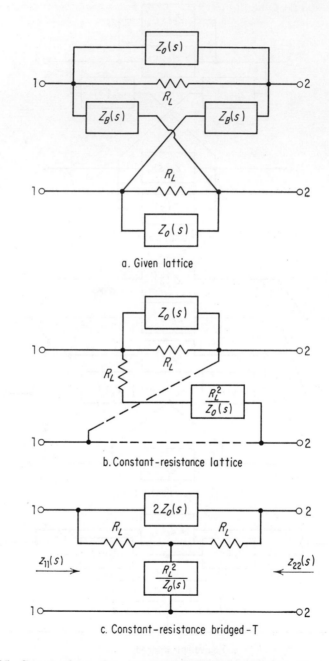

a. Given lattice

b. Constant-resistance lattice

c. Constant-resistance bridged-T

Fig. 10-15. Conversion of a constant-resistance lattice to a constant-resistance bridged-T network.

Assume the network of Fig. 10-15a is to be converted to an unbalanced constant-resistance configuration. The first step is to combine the impedances of the parallel branches to yield

$$Z_A(s) = \frac{R_L Z_o(s)}{R_L + Z_o(s)} \tag{10-20}$$

For a constant-resistance lattice, it is necessary that

$$Z_B(s)Z_A(s) = R_L{}^2 \quad \text{or} \quad Z_B(s) = \frac{R_L{}^2 Z_o(s) + R_L{}^3}{R_L Z_o(s)} = R_L + \frac{R_L{}^2}{Z_o(s)} \tag{10-21}$$

The constant-resistance lattice (minus its terminating load resistance) derived from the above considerations is shown in Fig. 10-15b. The conversion of Fig. 10-14 can be applied to the constant-resistance structure of Fig. 10-15b to provide the equivalent bridged-T configuration of Fig. 10-15c. The resulting bridged-T network, if terminated by a resistance of R_L, will have an input impedance of R_L no matter what value is chosen for $Z_o(s)$.

A second network form can be derived from the lattice of Fig. 10-15a by replacing the T-section of Fig. 10-14c by an equivalent Pi-section and combining the parallel branches. The Pi-network equivalent to Fig. 10-14a is shown in Fig. 10-16; however, it is not always possible to perform the conversions of Figs. 10-14 or 10-16 such that the resulting impedances are all physically realizable.

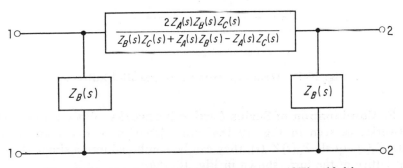

Fig. 10-16. Equivalent Pi-network form of Fig. 10-14a.

D. Decomposition into Parallel Lattices. Occasionally it is desirable to break up a lattice network, such as Fig. 10-17a, into parallel lattice structures as shown in Fig. 10-17b. This form of decomposition has no immediate advantage, unless it makes obvious some further change or permits the use of convenient element values.

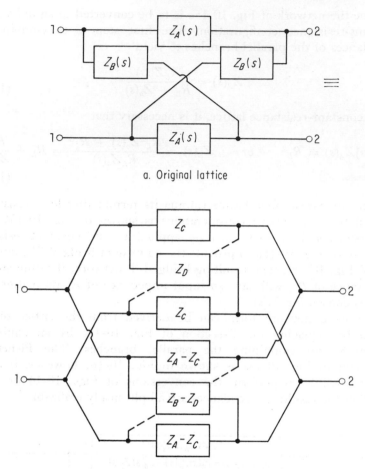

a. Original lattice

b. Equivalent parallel lattice

Fig. 10-17. Decomposition into parallel lattices.

E. Combination of Series Lattice Networks. When series lattice networks, as seen in Fig. 10-18a, are related in such a manner that $Z_A(s)Z_B(s)$ equals $Z_C(s)Z_D(s)$, they can be combined into a single equivalent lattice of the form shown in Fig. 10-18b.

The relationship $[Z_A(s)Z_B(s) = Z_C(s)Z_D(s)]$ implies that the cascade lattice structures of Fig. 10-18a possess the same "image impedance." Since the concept of image impedance has not been described, it is worthwhile to digress momentarily to investigate this topic. Image impedances have been defined according to their analogy with iterative or scattering parameters used in transmission line or distributed element network theory (See Chap. 7, Sec. 7-1). The derivation is most easily

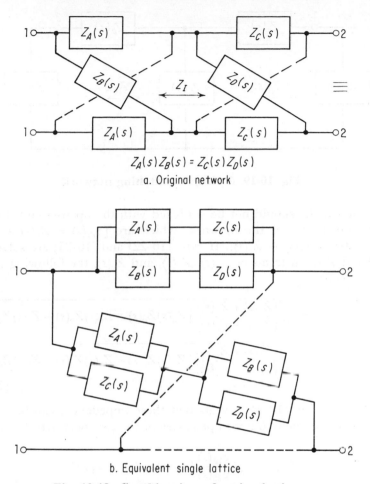

$$Z_A(s)Z_B(s) = Z_C(s)Z_D(s)$$

a. Original network

b. Equivalent single lattice

Fig. 10-18. Combination of series lattices.

accomplished by considering the T network of Fig. 10-19 which has source and load impedances of $Z_S(s)$ and $Z_L(s)$, respectively.

For optimum coupling between the source and the network, the driving-point impedance $Z_{I1}(s)$ seen looking into terminals 1-1 must equal the source impedance $Z_S(s)$. This can be written as

$$Z_S(s) = Z_{I1}(s) = Z_a(s) + \frac{Z_c(s)[Z_b(s) + Z_L(s)]}{Z_b(s) + Z_c(s) + Z_L(s)} \qquad (10\text{-}22)$$

Likewise, the driving-point impedance $Z_{I2}(s)$ seen looking into terminals 2-2 must equal the load impedance $Z_L(s)$.

$$Z_L = Z_{I2}(s) = Z_b(s) + \frac{Z_c(s)[Z_a(s) + Z_S(s)]}{Z_a(s) + Z_c(s) + Z_S(s)} \qquad (10\text{-}23)$$

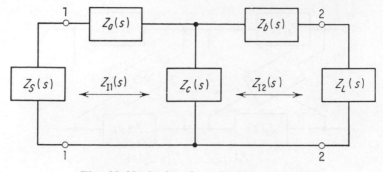

Fig. 10-19. A simple matching network

$Z_{I1}(s)$ and $Z_{I2}(s)$ should not be confused with the open-circuit driving-point impedances of the network, which are $[z_{11}(s) = Z_a(s) + Z_c(s)]$ and $[z_{22}(s) = Z_b(s) + Z_c(s)]$. If Eqs. (10-22) and (10-23) are solved for $Z_S(s)$ and $Z_L(s)$ in terms of $Z_a(s)$, $Z_b(s)$, and $Z_c(s)$, the following results are obtained:

$$Z_S(s) = Z_{I1}(s) = \sqrt{\frac{[Z_a(s) + Z_c(s)]}{[Z_b(s) + Z_c(s)]}\,[Z_a(s)Z_c(s) + Z_a(s)Z_b(s) + Z_b(s)Z_c(s)]}$$

$$Z_L(s) = Z_{I2}(s) = \sqrt{\frac{[Z_b(s) + Z_c(s)]}{[Z_a(s) + Z_c(s)]}\,[Z_a(s)Z_c(s) + Z_a(s)Z_b(s) + Z_b(s)Z_c(s)]}$$

$$(10\text{-}24)$$

Inspection of Eq. (10-24) reveals that these impedances can be written in terms of the open-circuit impedances of the two-port network as

$$Z_{I1}(s) = \sqrt{\frac{z_{11}(s)}{z_{22}(s)}\,[z_{11}(s)z_{22}(s) - z_{12}^2(s)]}$$

$$Z_{I2}(s) = \sqrt{\frac{z_{22}(s)}{z_{11}(s)}\,[z_{11}(s)z_{22}(s) - z_{12}^2(s)]}$$

$$(10\text{-}25)$$

These impedances are known as the image impedances of the input and output circuits of the network, and when expressed in the form of Eq. (10-25), they apply to any two-port network configuration.† Consequently, it is possible to define the image impedances of any two-port network as the impedances which terminate the network in such a manner that at both ends of the network the impedance seen looking in either direction will be the same.

---

† Because of the square root radical, Z_{I1} and Z_{I2} may be positive or negative; hence, the sign must be chosen to fit the particular situation. Further information concerning the use of image impedances is provided in M. B. Reed, *Electric Network Synthesis-Image Parameter Method* (Englewood Cliffs, N.J.: Prentice-Hall, Inc., 1955), Chaps. 2, 3, and 5.

Returning to the network of Fig. 10-18a, the open-circuit impedances of the lattice between terminals 1-1 and a-a are given by $z_{11}(s) = z_{22}(s) = [Z_B(s) + Z_A(s)]/2$ and $z_{12}(s) = [Z_B(s) - Z_A(s)]/2$. Similarly, the open-circuit impedances of the lattice between terminals a-a and 2-2 are given by $z_{11}^*(s) = z_{22}^*(s) = [Z_D(s) + Z_C(s)]/2$ and $z_{12}^*(s) = [Z_D(s) - Z_C(s)]/2$. For the image impedance $Z_I(s)$ seen looking in both directions from terminals a-a, to be the same, it is necessary from Eq. (10-25) that

$$Z_I(s) = \sqrt{\frac{z_{22}(s)}{z_{11}(s)} [z_{11}(s)z_{22}(s) - z_{12}^2(s)]}$$

$$= \sqrt{\frac{z_{11}^*(s)}{z_{22}^*(s)} [z_{11}^*(s)z_{22}^*(s) - z_{12}^{*2}(s)]}$$

$$= \sqrt{z_{11}^2(s) - z_{12}^2(s)} = \sqrt{z_{11}^{*2}(s) - z_{12}^{*2}(s)} \qquad (10\text{-}26)$$

Substituting the branch impedances of the lattice sections and squaring both sides yields

$$\frac{[Z_B(s) + Z_A(s)]^2}{(2)^2} - \frac{[Z_B(s) - Z_A(s)]^2}{(2)^2}$$

$$= \frac{[Z_D(s) + Z_C(s)]^2}{(2)^2} - \frac{[Z_D(s) - Z_C(s)]^2}{(2)^2}$$

or
$$Z_A(s)Z_B(s) = Z_C(s)Z_D(s) \qquad (10\text{-}27)$$

Consequently, if the impedances of Fig. 10-18a satisfy Eq. (10-27), the lattice sections possess the same image impedance. In this case the sections can be combined as shown in Fig. 10-18b, and Bartlett's bisection theorem can be used to verify the equivalence of the single-lattice configuration.

F. Reduction of a Lattice to an Unbalanced Form. Kirchhoff's voltage relationships for a symmetrical lattice such as Fig. 9-2 can be expressed in matrix form as follows:

$$\begin{bmatrix} E_1 \\ E_2 \end{bmatrix} = \begin{bmatrix} z_{11}(s) & z_{12}(s) \\ z_{21}(s) & z_{22}(s) \end{bmatrix} \begin{bmatrix} I_1 \\ I_2 \end{bmatrix} = \begin{bmatrix} \dfrac{Z_B(s) + Z_A(s)}{2} & \dfrac{Z_B(s) - Z_A(s)}{2} \\ \dfrac{Z_B(s) - Z_A(s)}{2} & \dfrac{Z_B(s) + Z_A(s)}{2} \end{bmatrix} \begin{bmatrix} I_1 \\ I_2 \end{bmatrix}$$

$$(10\text{-}28)$$

The matrix can then be broken into the sum of two matrices of the form

$$
\begin{bmatrix}
\dfrac{Z_B(s) + Z_A(s)}{2} & \dfrac{Z_B(s) - Z_A(s)}{2} \\[3mm]
\dfrac{Z_B(s) - Z_A(s)}{2} & \dfrac{Z_B(s) + Z_A(s)}{2}
\end{bmatrix}
$$

$$
= \begin{bmatrix}
\dfrac{Z_B(s)}{2} & \dfrac{Z_B(s)}{2} \\[3mm]
\dfrac{Z_B(s)}{2} & \dfrac{Z_B(s)}{2}
\end{bmatrix}
+ \begin{bmatrix}
\dfrac{Z_A(s)}{2} & \dfrac{-Z_A(s)}{2} \\[3mm]
\dfrac{-Z_A(s)}{2} & \dfrac{Z_A(s)}{2}
\end{bmatrix} \tag{10-29}
$$

The impedance matrices on the right-hand side of Eq. (10-29) represent two series networks as illustrated in Fig. 10-20a. These networks must eventually be connected by the dashed lines for the resulting network to be equivalent to the lattice of Fig. 9-2; however, terminals 1*-1* and 2*-2* cannot be connected without short-circuiting the impedance $Z_A(s)/2$. Fortunately the connection can be made if an ideal transformer is inserted in the network. Furthermore, the crossed links can be removed by using a turns ratio of -1. The resulting unbalanced equivalent network for the symmetrical lattice is shown in Fig. 10-20b.

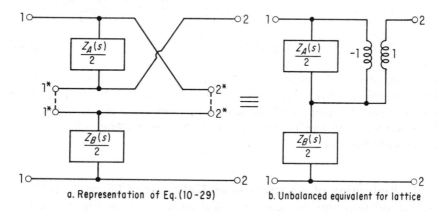

a. Representation of Eq. (10-29)   b. Unbalanced equivalent for lattice

Fig. 10-20. Decomposition of a lattice to an unbalanced form.

Using Kirchhoff's current relationships, a set of admittance matrices similar to those of Eqs. (10-28) and (10-29) can be derived. These functions lead to a second unbalanced-network configuration of the form shown in Fig. 10-21.

The unbalanced network of Fig. 10-20b possesses a common ground between the input and output terminals; however, this is not true of the

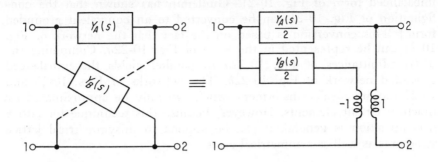

Fig. 10-21. Second unbalanced equivalent for a lattice.

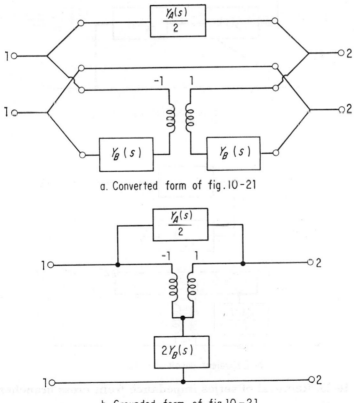

a. Converted form of fig. 10-21

b. Grounded form of fig 10-21

Fig. 10-22. Conversion of Fig. 10-21 to a grounded form.

unbalanced form of Fig. 10-21. Guillemin has shown that the configuration of Fig. 10-21 can be converted to an equivalent grounded form.† This conversion is based on the fact that the network of Fig. 10-21 can be represented in the form of Fig. 10-22a. Combining the $Y_B(s)$ admittances of Fig. 10-22a in parallel yields the unbalanced grounded network of Fig. 10-22b. The networks of Figs. 10-20 and 10-22 require ideal transformers which can only be approximated by practical circuit elements. However, because this technique for lattice decomposition is general, it can be applied to unsymmetrical lattice structures as well as symmetrical cases.

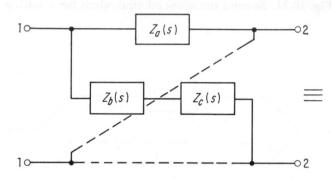

a. Original lattice

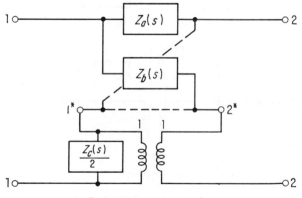

b. Equivalent unbalanced form.

Fig. 10-23. Removal of series impedance from cross branches.

† E. A. Guillemin, *Communications Networks*, Vol. 2 (New York: John Wiley & Sons, Inc., 1935), p. 161.

G. Removal of Series Impedance from the Cross Branches.

Weinberg has shown that it is possible to remove a series impedance from the cross branches of a lattice as shown in Fig. 10-23.† An ideal transformer is required to prevent circulating currents; however, it can be removed if the remaining lattice can be reduced to an unbalanced form having a common ground between terminals 1* and 2*. The network of Fig. 10-23b contains fewer elements than the original lattice, but because there is no common ground between input and output, this configuration can only be used as a grounded form for frequencies other than zero.

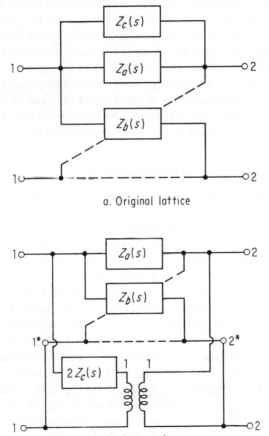

a. Original lattice

b. Equivalent form.

Fig. 10-24. Removal of shunt impedance from series branches.

† L. Weinberg, "A General RLC Synthesis Procedure," *Proc. IRE*, vol. 42, no. 2, February 1954, pp. 427–436.

H. Removal of Shunt Impedance from Parallel Branches. It is also possible to decompose a lattice by removing shunt impedances from the parallel branches. This impedance can be considered as a bridge across the remaining lattice as shown in Fig. 10-24. Again an ideal transformer is required, but it can be removed if the remaining lattice is transformed to an unbalanced form having a common ground between terminals 1* and 2*.

The process of reducing the complexity of a lattice network or converting it to an equivalent unbalanced form may require the application of several of the above techniques in addition to considerable ingenuity. In many cases it is not necessary to begin with a symmetrical lattice to remove elements provided the same impedances occur in the parallel and/or cross branches of the network. Care must be taken when using ideal transformers to insure that no circuit impedances are short-circuited and that proper polarities are observed. Caution should also be used in the removal of ideal transformers and in shorting their primaries and secondaries to form a common ground, since the paths of current flow may be altered. This possibility is most easily checked at zero frequency. Finally, additional equivalent network configurations may be suggested by impedance transformations of the type described in the following section.

10-5. Impedance-level Transformations

The problem of synthesizing a network such that its elements are readily realized in terms of commercially available components can be solved by techniques such as predistortion, equivalent networks, and impedance-level transformations. Fortunately, impedance transformations are also useful in developing equivalent-network configurations by replacing specific element values with combinations of elements which produce the same net result. Consequently, these transformations complement the various techniques described in the preceding sections for developing equivalent networks. In general, impedance-level transformations can be derived on either a loop or node basis and must take into account the positive real characteristics of the elements involved.

Consider the so-called "energy and loss functions" of a multiloop passive network as expressed in Chap. 2 by Eq. (2-6). The loop current variables $i_1, i_2, \ldots, i_p$ and their indefinite integrals or loop charges $q_1, q_2, \ldots, q_p$ may be subjected to a linear transformation such that

$$i_1 = \beta_{11} i_1^* + \beta_{12} i_2^* + \cdots + \beta_{1p} i_p^*$$

$$i_2 = \beta_{21} i_1^* + \beta_{22} i_2^* + \cdots + \beta_{2p} i_p^*$$

$$\cdot \quad \cdot \quad \cdot \quad \cdot \quad \cdot \quad \cdot \quad \cdot \quad \cdot \quad \cdot \quad \cdot$$

$$i_p = \beta_{p1} i_1^* + \beta_{p2} i_2^* + \cdots + \beta_{pp} i_p^* \tag{10-30}$$

The matrix $[\beta]$ of this transformation and its transposed or conjugate matrix $[\beta]^T$ can be written as

$$[\beta] = \begin{bmatrix} \beta_{11} & \beta_{12} & \cdots & \beta_{1p} \\ \beta_{21} & \beta_{22} & \cdots & \beta_{2p} \\ \cdot & \cdot & \cdot & \cdot \\ \beta_{p1} & \beta_{p2} & \cdots & \beta_{pp} \end{bmatrix} \quad \text{and} \quad [\beta]^T = \begin{bmatrix} \beta_{11} & \beta_{21} & \cdots & \beta_{p1} \\ \beta_{12} & \beta_{22} & \cdots & \beta_{p2} \\ \cdot & \cdot & \cdot & \cdot \\ \beta_{1p} & \beta_{2p} & \cdots & \beta_{pp} \end{bmatrix}$$

$$(10\text{-}31)$$

Using these matrices, the parameter matrices $[L]$, $[R]$, and $[S]$ of the multiloop network involved in the energy and loss functions of Eq. (2-6) can be operated on as follows:

$$[L^*] = [\beta]^T \times [L] \times [\beta]$$

$$[R^*] = [\beta]^T \times [R] \times [\beta]$$

$$[S^*] = [\beta]^T \times [S] \times [\beta] \qquad (10\text{-}32)$$

where $[L^*]$, $[R^*]$, and $[S^*]$ are transformed parameter matrices. These transformations will not alter the positive real characteristics of the energy and loss functions F, T, and V of Eq. (2-6) for real values of s, provided the transformation matrix of Eq. (10-31) is real and non-singular. Therefore, if the parameter matrices $[L]$, $[R]$, and $[S]$ represent a physically realizable network, the transformed parameter matrices $[L^*]$, $[R^*]$, and $[S^*]$ will also be physically realizable.†

When the given network has only a single pair of access terminals located in loop 1, it is desirable to choose the transformation matrix such that $(\beta_{11} = 1)$ and $(\beta_{1k} = 0)$ for $(k \neq 1)$. This choice insures that the current in loop 1, as a result of an applied voltage, will remain the same following the transformation. If the network has two sets of access terminals (located in loops 1 and p) and if it is desired that the driving-point and transfer impedances z_{11}, z_{1p}, and z_{pp} remain the same, it is necessary that the transformation matrix $[\beta]$ be chosen such that

$$\beta_{11} = 1 \qquad \beta_{1k} = 0 \quad \text{for} \quad k \neq 1$$

and $\qquad \beta_{pp} = 1 \qquad \beta_{pk} = 0 \quad \text{for} \quad k \neq p \qquad (10\text{-}33)$

Multiplying the terms of a row or column of the transformation matrix by a constant factor changes the currents in the loops for a given set of applied voltages. This result implies a change in the impedance levels or in other words an impedance level transformation.

---

† The matrix approach used in the above discussion was developed by E. A. Guillemin in his *The Mathematics of Circuit Analysis* (New York: John Wiley & Sons, Inc., 1949), pp. 135–137. The procedure has been further developed in his later book *Synthesis of Passive Networks* (New York: John Wiley & Sons, Inc., 1957), pp. 141–157.

As an example of an impedance transformation, consider the single resistor R_1 of Fig. 10-25a. This element has been redrawn in Fig. 10-25b as a two-loop network with an arbitrary choice of a resistor $R_2 = 4$ ohms in the second loop. The resistance matrix for this network can be written as

$$[R] = \begin{bmatrix} R_{11} & R_{12} \\ R_{21} & R_{22} \end{bmatrix} = \begin{bmatrix} 10 & 4 \\ 4 & 4 \end{bmatrix} \tag{10-34}$$

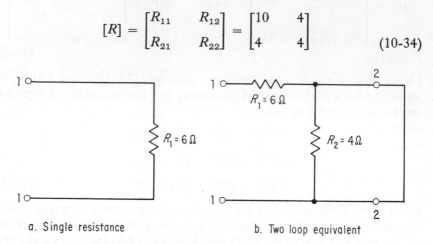

a. Single resistance   b. Two loop equivalent

Fig. 10-25. Example transformation of a single element.

By choosing an impedance transformation $[\beta]$ such that $(\beta_{11} = 1)$, it is possible to expand the number of loops and elements which will yield an equivalent driving-point resistance to that of Fig. 10-25. For example, if $[\beta]$ is chosen as

$$[\beta] = \begin{bmatrix} 1 & 0 \\ 0 & 2 \end{bmatrix} \quad \text{and} \quad [\beta]^T = \begin{bmatrix} \beta_{11} & 0 \\ 0 & \beta_{22} \end{bmatrix} = [\beta] \tag{10-35}$$

The transformed resistance matrix $[R^*]$ can be determined from Eqs. (10-32), (10-34), and (10-35) as

$$[R^*] = [\beta]^T \times [R] \times [\beta]$$

$$= \begin{bmatrix} 1 & 0 \\ 0 & 2 \end{bmatrix} \begin{bmatrix} 10 & 4 \\ 4 & 4 \end{bmatrix} \begin{bmatrix} 1 & 0 \\ 0 & 2 \end{bmatrix} = \begin{bmatrix} 10 & 8 \\ 8 & 16 \end{bmatrix} \tag{10-36}$$

This result can be obtained directly from Eq. (10-34) by multiplying the second row and column by the factor 2.

$$[R^*] = \begin{bmatrix} 10 & 4 \\ 4 & 4 \end{bmatrix} \xleftarrow{2} = \begin{bmatrix} 10 & 8 \\ 8 & 16 \end{bmatrix} \tag{10-37}$$

The network which realizes the transformed resistance matrices of Eqs. (10-36) or (10-37) is shown in Fig. 10-26.

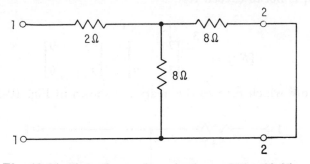

Fig. 10-26. Transformed equivalent of Fig. 10-25a.

The above example may seem trivial, since the reader can undoubtedly choose by intuition a number of resistance combinations equivalent to that of Fig. 10-25. However, this example demonstrates a procedure which can be used with R, L, and C elements when insight fails, or when it is desirable that the element values or the number of elements and loops be changed for practical reasons. The procedure can be repeated to form as many loops or elements as desired. It is possible not only to develop equivalent network configurations, but to transform the entire level of a particular impedance. For example, consider the resistance network of Fig. 10-27. The resistance matrix for this network can be written as

$$[R] = \begin{bmatrix} R_{11} & R_{12} \\ R_{21} & R_{22} \end{bmatrix} = \begin{bmatrix} 7 & 3 \\ 3 & 9 \end{bmatrix} \qquad (10\text{-}38)$$

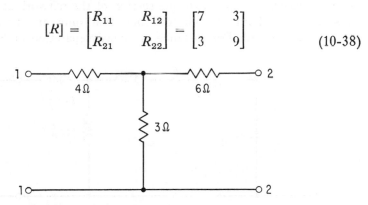

Fig. 10-27. Example resistance network.

Suppose it is desirable to increase the input-impedance level of this network to as high a value as possible without changing the output driving-point impedance. In this case $R_{12} = R_{21}$ can be no greater than R_{22} which equals 9 ohms. Since R_{12} must equal R_{21}, inspection of Eq.

(10-38) reveals that both the first row and first column of $[R]$ must be multiplied by the same factor. The largest possible factor is 3 if $R_{12} = R_{21}$ is not to exceed R_{22}.

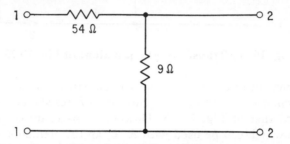

$$[R^*] = \overset{3}{\longrightarrow} \begin{bmatrix} \overset{\downarrow 3}{7} & 3 \\ 3 & 9 \end{bmatrix} = \begin{bmatrix} 63 & 9 \\ 9 & 9 \end{bmatrix} \qquad (10\text{-}39)$$

The network which realizes this matrix is shown in Fig. 10-28.

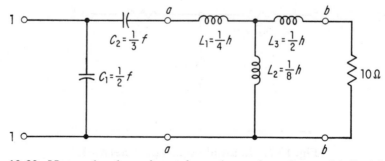

Fig. 10-28. Transformed version of Fig. 10-27 having same output and maximum input resistance.

As a final example of impedance-level transformations, consider the network of Fig. 10-29. Assume that it is desirable to multiply the input impedance of this network by 36. Fortunately, it is not necessary to transform the entire impedance level in one operation. In fact it is generally easier to work with one section of the network at a time, and these sections should be chosen such that only one type of circuit element is involved. For instance, a logical separation of Fig. 10-29 is

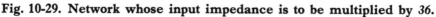

Fig. 10-29. Network whose input impedance is to be multiplied by 36.

given by the capacitance section between terminals 1-1 and a-a, the inductance section between terminals a-a and b-b, and finally, the terminating resistance of 10 ohms.

The elastance matrix that characterizes the capacitance section between terminals 1-1 and a-a of Fig. 10-29 can be written as

$$[S] = \begin{bmatrix} S_{11} & S_{12} \\ S_{21} & S_{22} \end{bmatrix} = \begin{bmatrix} \dfrac{1}{C_1} & \dfrac{1}{C_1} \\ \dfrac{1}{C_1} & \left(\dfrac{1}{C_1} + \dfrac{1}{C_2}\right) \end{bmatrix} = \begin{bmatrix} 2 & 2 \\ 2 & 5 \end{bmatrix} \tag{10-40}$$

If the input-impedance level is to be multiplied by 36, it is necessary to multiply S_{11} by 36; however, in order that the $S_{12} = S_{21}$, it is also necessary that the first row of $[S]$ be multiplied by the same factor as the first column. This can be accomplished as follows:

$$[S^*] = \xrightarrow{6} \begin{bmatrix} \overset{\displaystyle\downarrow 6}{S_{11}} & S_{12} \\ S_{21} & S_{22} \end{bmatrix} = \xrightarrow{6} \begin{bmatrix} \overset{\displaystyle\downarrow 6}{2} & 2 \\ 2 & 5 \end{bmatrix} = \begin{bmatrix} 72 & 12 \\ 12 & 5 \end{bmatrix} \tag{10-41}$$

From this equation it is seen that a negative elastance is developed in the second loop, since the transformed S_{22} term of 5 $(farads)^{-1}$ is less than the transfer elastance of 12 $(farads)^{-1}$. This problem can be removed by performing a second transformation as follows:

$$[S^{**}] = \begin{bmatrix} 72 & 12 \\ 12 & \underset{\underset{\frac{12}{5}}{\uparrow}}{5} \xleftarrow{\frac{12}{5}} \end{bmatrix} = \begin{bmatrix} 72 & \dfrac{144}{5} \\ \dfrac{144}{5} & \dfrac{144}{5} \end{bmatrix} = \begin{bmatrix} 72 & 28.8 \\ 28.8 & 28.8 \end{bmatrix}$$

$$\tag{10-42}$$

This elastance matrix is realizable as a capacitance section of the form shown in Fig. 10-30a.

Because the transformation of Eq. (10-42) increased the output elastance S_{22} of the input section by a multiplication factor of $144/25$, it is necessary to adjust the input impedance of the section between terminals a-a and b-b of Fig. 10-29 to compensate for this effect. The matrix which represents this inductance section can be written as follows:

$$[L] = \begin{bmatrix} L_{11} & L_{12} \\ L_{21} & L_{22} \end{bmatrix} = \begin{bmatrix} (L_1 + L_2) & L_2 \\ L_2 & (L_2 + L_3) \end{bmatrix} = \begin{bmatrix} \dfrac{3}{8} & \dfrac{1}{8} \\ \dfrac{1}{8} & \dfrac{5}{8} \end{bmatrix}$$

$$\tag{10-43}$$

Since S_{22} was multiplied by 144/25, it is necessary to multiply the input inductance L_{11} of Eq. (10-43), by the same factor in order to maintain the same impedance level in the second loop of the transformed network. This can be accomplished by multiplying both the first row and first column of Eq. (10-43) by 12/5.

$$[L^*] = \begin{array}{c} \frac{12}{5} \\ \longrightarrow \end{array} \overset{\displaystyle \frac{12}{5} \Big\downarrow}{\begin{bmatrix} \frac{3}{8} & \frac{1}{8} \\[2mm] \frac{1}{8} & \frac{5}{8} \end{bmatrix}} = \begin{bmatrix} \frac{54}{25} & \frac{3}{10} \\[2mm] \frac{3}{10} & \frac{5}{8} \end{bmatrix} \tag{10-44}$$

This matrix can be realized as the inductance network of Fig. 10-30b. Because the output impedance L_{22} did not change in the transformation of Eq. (10-44) it is not necessary to make further transformations.

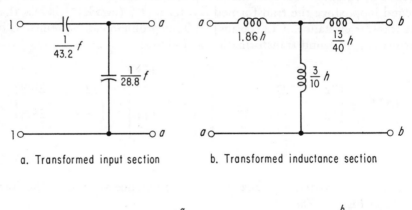

a. Transformed input section   b. Transformed inductance section

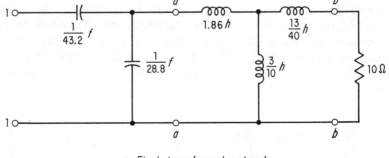

c. Final transformed network

Fig. 10-30. Transformed network with an input impedance 36 times that of Fig. 10-29.

Combining the transformed sections of Figs. 10-30a and 10-30b with the 10-ohm resistor of Fig. 10-29 gives the network of Fig. 10-30c which has an input impedance 36 times as high as that of Fig. 10-29.

To verify that the input impedance of Fig. 10-30c is 36 times that of Fig. 10-29, it is possible to solve both networks for their driving-point impedance. The driving-point impedance for the network of Fig. 10-29 is given by

$$Z_I = \frac{2(s^3 + 1.715s^2 + 8.58s + 13.72)}{s(s^3 + 1.72s^2 + 14.3s + 22.85)} \tag{10-45}$$

The driving-point impedance for the transformed network of Fig. 10-30c is

$$Z_I^* = \frac{(36)(2)(s^3 + 1.715s^2 + 8.58s + 13.72)}{s(s^3 + 1.72s^2 + 14.3s + 22.85)} \tag{10-46}$$

Consequently, $Z_I^* = 36Z_I$ and the network of Fig. 10-30c has an input impedance 36 times that of Fig. 10-29.

This concludes the discussion of impedance-level transformations. Care must be taken to insure that negative elements are not developed in the transformation process. However, if this happens the network may still be realizable by use of ideal transformers or by a different choice of the transformation matrix $[\beta]$. Finally, it should be pointed out that similar transformations can be developed on a node rather than a loop basis and can be applied to admittance as well as impedance functions.

References

In addition to the references listed in the footnotes, the following texts provide further information concerning equivalent networks:

1. E. A. Guillemin, *Communication Networks*, Vol. II (New York: John Wiley & Sons, Inc., 1935), Chaps. 6 and 10.
2. M. B. Reed, *Electric Network Synthesis: Image Parameter Method* (Englewood Cliffs, N.J.: Prentice-Hall, Inc., 1955), Chaps. 3, 5, and 11.
3. S. Seshu and N. Balabanian, *Linear Network Analysis* (New York: John Wiley & Sons, Inc., 1959), Secs. 8.3 through 8.6.
4. J. E. Storer, *Passive Network Synthesis* (New York: McGraw-Hill Book Co., Inc., 1957), Chaps. 16, 17, and 21.

Impedance transformations are considered in Chap. 5 of Ref. 1 and in Chap. 1 of the following reference:

5. J. L. Stewart, *Circuit Theory and Design* (New York: John Wiley & Sons, Inc., 1956).

Problems

10-1. Using the transformations of Table 10-1, convert a T network similar to Fig. 10-4a into an equivalent Pi network when $Z_a(s) = 2/s$, $Z_b(s) = 3/s$, and $Z_c(s) = 5$. Transform a Pi network similar to Fig. 10-4b into a T network when $Z_A(s) = (2s + 3)/s$, $Z_B(s) = (3s + 2)/s$, and $Z_C(s) = 5/s$. Synthesize the T network by series-parallel withdrawal of elements.

10-2. Using Bartlett's bisection theorem, determine the lattice equivalent for a symmetrical Pi network.

10-3. Using Bartlett's bisection theorem, determine the lattice equivalent for the twin-T network of Prob. 7-5, Fig. 7-42.

10-4. Remove as many elements as possible from the symmetrical lattice of Fig. 10-31. If possible, convert the resulting network to an unbalanced form possessing a common ground between the input and output circuits.

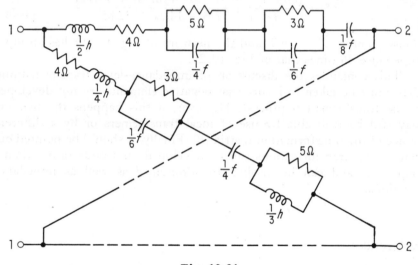

Fig. 10-31

10-5. Referring to the bridge network of Fig. 9-6, assume impedances of $Z_A(s) = s/5$, $Z_B(s) = 5/s$, and $R_L = 1$ ohm. Sketch the amplitude and phase-angle variation of E_2/E_1 for this network as a function of real frequency ($s = j\omega$). Repeat the procedure with $Z_A(s) = 5/s$, $Z_B(s) = s/5$, and $R_L = 1$ ohm. Make a pole-zero plot of E_2/E_1 for both cases and discuss the plot with regards to the amplitude and phase responses.

10-6. Using the network of Fig. 9-6 with $R_L(s) = 1$, $Z_A(s) = 8/(s + 2)$, and $Z_B(s) = 2(s + 2)/s$, plot the amplitude and phase response of E_2/E_1 for frequencies from $\omega = 0$ to $\omega = 10$. Reduce the lattice to an unbalanced form and discuss the results.

10-7. Determine the image impedances for the Pi-section of Fig. 10-4b when it is terminated by source and load impedances of $Z_S(s)$ and $Z_L(s)$, respectively. Check the result by using Eq. (10-24) for a T-section and the transformations of Table 10-1.

10-8. Demonstrate by equivalent one-port networks and impedance transformations that the Bott-Duffin network of Chap 5, Fig. 5-12, is equivalent to the example of Chap. 6, Fig. 6-7.

10-9. Increase the driving-point impedance of the network of Chap. 10, Fig. 10-29, by a factor of 49, using impedance level transformations. Maintain the load resistance at $R_L = 10$ ohms.

10-10. Prove that the impedance level of a network is multiplied by a factor δ if every resistance and inductance is multiplied by δ and every capacitance is divided by δ. Discuss the fact that the phase response of E_2/E_1 for a network is unchanged when the impedance level is scaled by a factor of δ. What can be said of the amplitude response of E_2/E_1 when the impedance is scaled by a factor of δ, assuming a constant input voltage?

Chapter 11

Consideration of Practical
Elements

In the synthesis procedures of preceding chapters it has been assumed that the elements required for a specific realization are pure or ideal components. Actually the resulting networks requiring ideal components can only be approximated in practice by commercially available elements. For example, an inductor has been represented as a purely reactive element with no distributed resistance due to the windings of the coil. Furthermore, no attempt has been made to compensate for distributed capacitance which exists between coil windings of commercial inductors. In many cases distributed effects such as these must be taken into account, particularly for high-frequency applications. Selection of a given commercial element for use in a network is generally a compromise between the element's electrical characteristics, mechanical configuration, space or volume requirements, economy, and accuracy or tolerance in the circuit operation. Therefore, the purpose of this chapter is to investigate more accurate or higher-order approximations of commercial components and means by which the synthesis procedures of preceding chapters can be altered to take these approximations into account.

11-1. Inductors

The manufacture of inductors with perfectly uniform characteristics from one element to the next is virtually impossible. It would involve a complex process of assembly procedures and selection of materials to insure proper magnetic and temperature stability and small physical size for the elements produced. Accordingly, economical considerations dictate that practical inductors have a low failure rate, a long life expectancy, and minimum distributed resistive and capacitance effects.

Thus far inductors have been symbolized by a coil which is an over-simplification of an actual element. In reality inductors are a complex combination of inductance, resistance, and capacitance which is more accurately approximated by the diagram of Fig. 11-1. This schematic shows the distributed parameters of the inductor L as equivalent lumped elements. For instance, R_s represents the distributed series resistances of the coil windings and core losses. These effects generally become greater as frequency increases. Distributed capacitance caused by the insulation between the windings and the core material is approximated by C_d. This capacitance will also vary since the dielectric constant of the insulation and the core is not constant with frequency; however, these effects can usually be neglected.

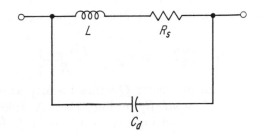

Fig. 11-1. Equivalent circuit of an inductor.

In most applications, R_s is small compared to the reactance; consequently it is convenient to express the apparent inductance L_a of the equivalent circuit of Fig. 11-1 as

$$L_a = \frac{L}{1 - \omega^2 C_d L} \tag{11-1}$$

Inductors to be used primarily at a single frequency or in resonant circuit applications are generally specified in terms of their apparent inductance. Tolerances on L_a in the order of ± 1 percent or one winding, whichever is larger, can be achieved in production. Since C_d affects the variation of L_a with frequency, the distributed capacitance becomes important in wide band or multiple frequency applications. A degree of control on C_d can be achieved by varying the method of winding the inductor. In decreasing order of capacitance, the design might use random continuous winding, progressive winding, or segmented winding. Wax, varnish, or plastic impregnation of an inductor increases C_d; however, the cost tends to increase as the distributed capacitance is decreased. When C_d must be specified, the accepted method is to set a maximum limit on C_d or tolerances on L_a at two different frequencies.

The quality of a reactive element such as an inductor is generally specified in terms of its Q factor. The fundamental definition of Q is the ratio of energy stored to energy dissipated per cycle or radian. For a resonant circuit, there are equivalent definitions based on the half-power bandwidth or rate of susceptance change at resonance.† However, for purposes of this discussion Q, which is a measure of the distributed losses in the element at a particular frequency, will be defined as the ratio of reactance to resistance.

$$Q = \frac{|\text{reactance}|}{|\text{resistance}|} = \frac{|Im[Z(j\omega)]|}{|Re[Z(j\omega)]|} \tag{11-2}$$

The impedance for the equivalent circuit of Fig. 11-1 is given by

$$Z(s) = \frac{Ls + R_s}{LC_d s^2 + R_s C_d s + 1} \tag{11-3}$$

Substituting Eq. (11-3) into Eq. (11-2) and evaluating at real frequencies yields

$$Q = \left| \frac{\omega L}{R_s} - R_s C_d \omega - \frac{L^2 C_d \omega^3}{R} \right| \tag{11-4}$$

When C_d is zero, the quality factor Q varies linearly with frequency as indicated by the line $Q = \omega L/R_s$ in Fig. 11-2. A finite value of C_d reduces the quality factor causing the variation of Q for a practical inductor to take the form of the curve labeled "practical element" in Fig. 11-2.

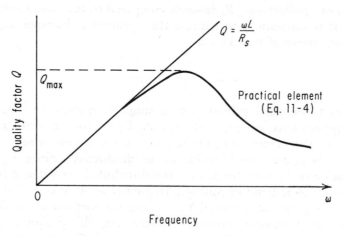

Fig. 11-2. Variation of Q as a function of frequency.

In the case of inductors, Q is usually specified in lieu of L_a and R_s, since most applications are concerned with the ratio of apparent inductive reactance to resistance. The accepted method for specifying Q is to

† For a detailed discussion of Q, see F. E. Terman, *Radio Engineering* (New York: McGraw-Hill Book Co., Inc., 1947), Chaps. 2 and 3.

set a limit on the minimum acceptable Q at the operating frequency or over a range of frequencies. Maximum values of Q in the order of 100 to 150 are reasonable limits to consider for network synthesis. Higher values of Q for commercial inductors are difficult to obtain. Unfortunately, the Q for a given design may vary as much as 20 percent from one inductor to the next at a particular frequency, depending on the construction procedures and materials used in the production process.

Finally, in applications where it is necessary to insure that L_a be reasonably constant over a wide range of frequencies or temperature, the design might require the use of temperature-stabilized core materials and a hermetically sealed enclosure. High voltage and current ratings lead to large inductors and increased costs. Although many of these factors enter into the selection of an inductor for a specific application, the most important single effect that must be taken into account in a synthesis procedure is the series resistance R_s. Fortunately, a technique known as predistortion can be used to place resistance in series with each inductor. This technique, described in Sec. 11-5, can be used in conjunction with most of the synthesis procedures of preceding chapters.

11-2. Capacitors

The design of practical capacitors is also based on the development of an element with a low failure rate, a long life expectancy, and minimum distributed resistive and inductive effects. Basically, capacitors consist simply of two conductors or plates separated by a dielectric

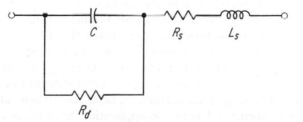

Fig. 11-3. Equivalent circuit of a capacitor.

material such as air, oil, mica, or plastic. This leads to the oversimplified schematic symbol used to represent capacitors in preceding chapters; however, a capacitor is a complex combination of resistance, inductance, and capacitance which is more accurately approximated by the diagram of Fig. 11-3. This schematic shows the distributed parameters of the capacitor C as equivalent lumped elements. For instance, R_s and L_s represent distributed series resistance and inductance of the capacitor's lead wires and plates. The resistance R_d represents the distributed resistance of the dielectric between the plates and insulation around the plates. Except in the case of electrolytic capacitors, the series resistance R_s is only a few ohms and can be neglected in most synthesis procedures.

The dielectric and insulation resistance R_d varies from a few thousand megohms to several million megohms, depending on the materials used. Therefore, because of its high value, it can be neglected in most synthesis problems. However, predistortion, as described in Sec. 11-5, can be used to place resistance in parallel with each capacitor, thereby removing the inaccuracy in the approximation caused by R_d. The inductive reactance caused by L_s becomes increasingly important as frequency increases, and at some frequency it will equal the capacitive reactance. When this occurs the capacitor will act as a resonant element. The same is true of inductors when the inductive and capacitive reactance for the equivalent circuit of Fig. 11-1 are equal.

Assume that the shunt resistance R_d is infinite. In this case the quality factor Q for the equivalent circuit of Fig. 11-3 can be written in terms of the definition of Eq. (11-2) as

$$Q = \left| \frac{\omega L_s}{R_s} - \frac{1}{\omega R_s C} \right| \tag{11-5}$$

This expression can be used for estimating the Q of a capacitor at any frequency once the distributed series resistance and inductance are known. Resonance occurs when $\omega = 1/\sqrt{L_s C}$; however, for small values of L_s and frequencies well below resonance, Q varies as $1/\omega R_s C$. The maximum Q of commercial capacitors is in the order of 10^4 for mica dielectrics: however, Q's as low as 15 to 20 are typical of electrolytic capacitors, and Q's near 100 can be obtained from ceramic or oil-impregnated paper capacitors.[†] In many cases the dissipation factor D, defined as the reciprocal of Q, is specified for capacitors since its variation is nearly a linear function of frequency (i.e., $D = 1/Q \approx \omega R_s C$).

The life expectancy of a capacitor is a direct function of the applied voltage and operating temperature. Therefore, when specifying a capacitor for a prescribed network application it is necessary to set a limit on the working voltage to be applied to the element. Empirical results indicate that the life expectancy is directly proportional to $T(E_A/E_W)^d$, where T is the time duration of an applied voltage, E_A; E_W is the rated or working voltage of the element; and d is a dimensionless exponent. The value of d is approximately 5 for paper or oil dielectrics and as high as 7 to 10 for mica and plastic film dielectrics. The heat generated within a capacitor is proportional to the voltage and frequency appearing across its terminals. This heat reduces the life

† E. I. Green, "The Story of Q," *American Scientist*, vol. 43, no. 4, October 1955, p. 590.

expectancy of the capacitor and its surrounding elements. In general the life expectancy of a capacitor is halved for every ten degrees centigrade increase in operating temperature. This effect is analogous to the chemical rule concerning the electrolytic action rate of solutions.

Neglecting the distributed resistances of Fig. 11-3, the apparent capacitance at any frequency is given by

$$C_a = \frac{C}{1 - \omega^2 L_s C} \tag{11-6}$$

This reduction in capacitance due to L_s must be taken into account when selecting an element for a specific application. The design and manufacture of capacitors can be controlled sufficiently well to insure the desired value of C to within one percent when necessary.

11-3. Resistors

Most commercial resistors closely approximate idealized elements except at extremely high frequencies. This is particularly true of deposited-film, ceramic, and molded-carbon type resistors; although, even wire-wound resistors can be made relatively free of distributed inductance and capacitance by special winding techniques. The equivalent circuit diagram for a practical resistor showing the distributed parameters as lumped elements is given in Fig. 11-4. There is generally

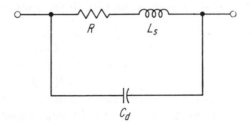

Fig. 11-4. Equivalent circuit of a resistor.

a small series distributed inductance L_s caused by the wires and terminals. This inductance is more apparent in wire-wound resistors unless special winding methods are used. A small distributed capacitance C_d developed between the terminal caps or connections is of secondary significance but can become important at high frequencies. Fortunately, L_s and C_d are usually small enough that they can be neglected in most synthesis applications. Therefore, aside from the value of the element, it is sufficient from an electrical standpoint to specify only the wattage and tolerance rating when selecting a resistor for a particular application. High wattage ratings (i.e., in the order of 50 watts or more) are more

difficult to obtain the higher the value of the resistor. Specified values
can generally be obtained within an accuracy of ± 1 percent. However,
elements with higher accuracy cost more since other factors such
as temperature, humidity, and manufacturing techniques become
important.

11-4. Transformers

Commercially available transformers generally possess a number of
distributed effects. Representing the distributed parameters as lumped
elements, the equivalent diagram which more accurately approximates
that of a practical transformer is shown in Fig. 11-5. In this figure C_p
and C_s represent distributed capacitances of the primary and secondary

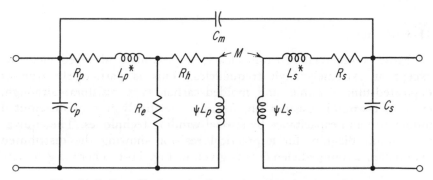

Fig. 11-5. Detailed equivalent circuit for a transformer.

circuits respectively. Likewise, R_p, R_s, L_p, and L_s represent distributed
resistances and inductances of the primary and secondary circuits. The
mutual inductance M is related to the primary and secondary inductances
by the coupling coefficient Ψ such that $M = \Psi\sqrt{L_pL_s}$. The resistances
R_e and R_h represent real power lost in the core of the transformer due
to eddy currents and hysteresis effects. Mutual capacitance between
windings of the primary and secondary is denoted by C_m, whereas
L_p^* and L_s^* represent leakage inductances of the primary and secondary
circuits and are related to L_p and L_s by the coupling coefficient [i.e.,
$L_p^* = (1 - \Psi)L_p$ and $L_s^* = (1 - \Psi)L_s$].

Manufacturers do not ordinarily list the coupling coefficient or many
of the distributed parameters shown in Fig. 11-5 when describing a
particular transformer. Instead, it is customary to specify the primary
to secondary turns ratio and the impedance levels of the primary and
secondary circuits over a prescribed range of frequencies. The resistances
R_p and R_s are sometimes specified; however, losses caused by these
resistances are generally small compared to those caused by L_p, L_s,
C_p, C_s, and C_m. Consequently, specification of the impedance levels is

usually adequate for most transformer applications. High coupling coefficients can be obtained, particularly in the case of power transformers, where Ψ is typically in the order of 0.9 to 0.98. An equivalent circuit, taking into account the primary-to-secondary turns ratio, is shown in Fig. 11-6. Second-order effects due to R_e, R_h, and C_m have been neglected in this figure, and the transformer has been replaced by its equivalent T-network configuration where secondary impedances are reflected by the square of the turns ratio.† The turns ratio loses significance in some applications. This is particularly true when dealing with low coupling coefficients as in the case of pulse transformers where $\Psi = 0.1$ can be excepted. In this case the voltage induced in the

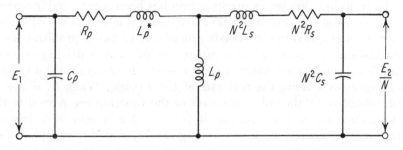

Fig. 11-6. Equivalent transformer circuit normalized to unity turns ratio.

secondary, as a result of a given primary voltage, may be much smaller than the turns ratio would predict because of voltage drops across the leakage impedances. Finally, it is customary to specify the maximum voltage and current ratings of the primary and secondary windings when selecting a transformer for a particular application.

It becomes apparent from the above discussion that a great number of parameters may be necessary to adequately specify a transformer for a particular application. To take all of these parameters into account during a synthesis procedure is out of the question; therefore it is wise to choose synthesis procedures that minimize or avoid the use of transformers whenever possible. Fortunately, in cases where transformers are required, predistortion can often be applied to add resistance in series with each inductor and in parallel with each capacitor. This resistance can be used to eliminate or reduce the effects caused by R_p, R_s, R_e, and R_h of a practical transformer. Finally, it was shown by example in Chap. 5, Sec. 5-3, that in some situations a considerable tolerance can be permitted in certain transformer parameters, such as Ψ, without

† More details concerning equivalent T and Pi circuits for a practical transformer are given in H. W. Lord, "An Equivalent Circuit for Transformers in Which Nonlinear Effects are Present," *AIEE Trans. Communications and Electronics*, no. 45, November 1959, pp. 580–586.

greatly changing the position of the desired poles and zeros. This fact suggests that it would be desirable to test a network for variations in its pole-zero positions caused by small changes in the required element values. Techniques designed to accomplish this end will be considered in Chap. 12. Consequently, when a transformer is being considered for a particular network application it is possible to test the sensitivity of pole-zero positions to distributed parameters not considered during the synthesis procedure.

11-5. Predistortion

The technique known as predistortion has been mentioned in several of the preceding sections as a means for associating resistance with each reactive element during a synthesis procedure. In brief, predistortion is accomplished by replacing the complex variable s in a driving-point or transfer function by a new variable ($\lambda = s + \delta$), where δ is a constant which can be measured along the real axis of the s-plane. When ($\lambda = s + \delta$) is substituted for s, the poles and zeros of the function are moved to the left by a distance δ. For example, if ($s = -s_0$) is a zero of a driving-point impedance $Z_1(s)$, as shown in Fig. 11-7a, and if s_0 is replaced by

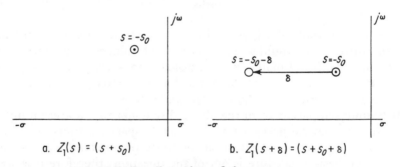

a. $Z_1(s) = (s + s_0)$ b. $Z_1(s + \delta) = (s + s_0 + \delta)$

Fig. 11-7. Predistortion of the zero, $s = -s_0$.

($\lambda_0 = s_0 + \delta$), then the zero is shifted to the left by a distance δ. This result is illustrated in Fig. 11-7b. Consequently, by moving all poles and zeros of an impedance or admittance function to the right by a distance δ before a synthesis procedure is started, it is possible to realize a resistance δ with each reactive element. This is accomplished by performing the reverse transformation following the synthesis procedure.

As an example of predistortion, consider the driving-point impedance

$$Z_1(s) = \frac{s + 1}{s^2 + 2s + 2} = \frac{s + 1}{(s + 1 + j1)(s + 1 - j1)} \qquad (11\text{-}7)$$

The poles and zero of this function are shown in Fig. 11-8. The first step in the procedure is to move all poles and zeros of the function to the right by ($\delta = 1$). Values of δ greater than unity will move these roots into the right half-plane, causing the resulting function to be unrealizable.

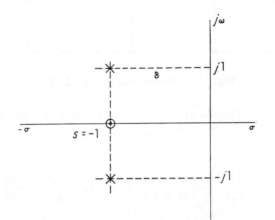

Fig. 11-8. Pole-zero plot for Eq. (11-7).

In order to move poles and zeros to the right, δ must be subtracted from s; hence substitution of the variable ($s = \lambda - \delta$) is appropriate. In this example ($\lambda - 1$) must be substituted for s in Eq. (11-7).

$$Z_1(s) = Z_1(\lambda - 1) = \frac{(\lambda - 1) + 1}{(\lambda - 1)^2 + 2(\lambda - 1) + 2} = \frac{\lambda}{\lambda^2 + 1} = \frac{1}{\lambda + \dfrac{1}{\lambda}}$$

$$(11\text{-}8)$$

This function in terms of λ can be synthesized by any of the procedures outlined in previous chapters after which it is possible to substitute $\lambda = s + 1$ back into the equation following the synthesis procedure. When this is done, the expansion of Eq. (11-8) in terms of s becomes

$$Z_1(\lambda - 1) = Z_1(s) = \frac{1}{s + 1 + \dfrac{1}{s + 1}} = \frac{1}{Cs + \dfrac{1}{R_1} + \dfrac{1}{Ls + R_2}}$$

$$(11\text{-}9)$$

Consequently, $Z_1(s)$ has been expanded such that a 1-ohm resistor is associated with each reactive term. The network which represents this expansion is shown in Fig. 11-9. Although this simple example can be solved by intuition such that a resistance is realized with each reactive element, it is seen that predistortion represents a systematic approach for achieving the same result.

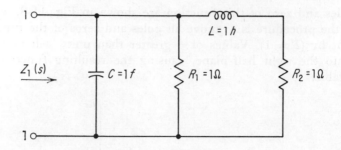

Fig. 11-9. Network for Eq. (11-7).

As a second example of predistortion, consider the driving-point impedance of Eq. (11-10). The pole-zero plot for this function is shown in Fig. 11-10.

$$Z_1(s) = \frac{s^3 + 11s^2 + 40s + 48}{s^3 + 12s^2 + 49s + 67} = \frac{(s + 3)(s + 4)(s + 4)}{(s + 3.33)(s + 4.35 \pm j1.18)}$$

$$(11\text{-}10)$$

The poles and zeros of Fig. 11-10 can be moved to the right by three units without moving any of them into the right half of the s-plane; however, for simplicity they will be predistorted only two units. This can be accomplished by replacing s in Eq. (11-10) by $(\lambda - 2)$.

$$Z_1(s)]_{s=\lambda-2} = Z_1(\lambda - 2) = \frac{\lambda^3 + 5\lambda^2 + 8\lambda + 4}{\lambda^3 + 6\lambda^2 + 13\lambda + 9} \qquad (11\text{-}11)$$

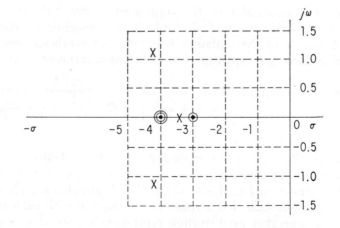

Fig. 11-10. Pole-zero plot for Eq. (11-10).

Equation (11-11) can be realized by several techniques, one of which is the procedure of series-parallel withdrawal. Applying this technique leads to the following expansion:

$$Z_1(\lambda - 2) = \cfrac{1}{Y_1(\lambda - 2)} = \cfrac{1}{1 + \cfrac{1}{\lambda + \cfrac{1}{\cfrac{\lambda}{3} + \cfrac{11}{9} + \cfrac{1}{27\lambda + 36}}}} \quad (11\text{-}12)$$

It is now possible to perform the reverse substitution $\lambda = s + 2$, in which case Eq. (11-12) becomes

$$Z_1(\lambda - 2)]_{\lambda = s+2} = Z_1(s) = \cfrac{1}{1 + \cfrac{1}{s + 2 + \cfrac{1}{\cfrac{s}{3} + \cfrac{17}{9} + \cfrac{1}{27s + 90}}}} \quad (11\text{-}13)$$

The network which represents Eq. (11-13) is shown in Fig. 11-11 and is seen to have a resistance associated with each reactive element.

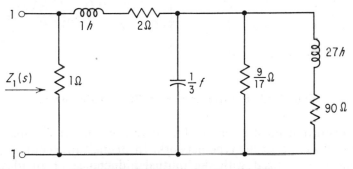

Fig. 11-11. Network for Eq. (11-10).

The criterion upon which predistortion is based is that all poles and zeros of a function must lie at least δ units to the left of the $j\omega$-axis. This implies that no predistortion can be practiced in the case of poles or zeros on the $j\omega$-axis, since these roots would be moved into the right half of the s-plane. For instance, it is impossible to predistort a pure LC network, since a pure reactance function contains no resistance. It is not even possible to predistort every RLC network function, but in some cases partial predistortion can be accomplished. In other words, it is sometimes possible to synthesize part of a specified function to remove $j\omega$-axis poles and/or zeros, at which point the remaining function can be predistorted before completing the synthesis procedure. If high-quality capacitors can be obtained, nonuniform predistortion can often be practiced such that a greater part of the resistance of a network is associated with the inductors and none with the capacitors.†

The application of predistortion to permit a higher degree of accuracy when constructing a network using practical inductors is straight-forward. Resistance, similar to R_s of Fig. 11-1, is placed in series with each inductor. However, in the case of capacitors it may be desirable to place a portion of the parallel resistance, obtained through use of pre-distortion, in series with the capacitor to approximate R_s of Fig. 11-3. This can be accomplished by applying the simple network transforma-tion of Fig. 11-12. Because the Q of a capacitor is generally very high, the capacitance is almost unchanged by this transformation. However, R_d must be very large in order to yield a value for R_s of only a few ohms, since the shunt and series resistors are related by Q^2.

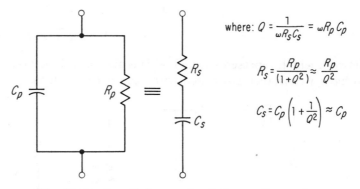

where: $Q = \dfrac{1}{\omega R_s C_s} = \omega R_p C_p$

$R_s = \dfrac{R_p}{(1+Q^2)} \approx \dfrac{R_p}{Q^2}$

$C_s = C_p\left(1+\dfrac{1}{Q^2}\right) \approx C_p$

Fig. 11-12. Parallel to series RC transformation.

Predistortion must be applied with care whenever a transformer is being used as in a Brune type network. In Brune's procedure a negative inductance is realized with the mutual inductance of an ideal trans-former. Because mutual inductance does not have a resistance associated with it, the advantage of predistortion is lost in this case. However, for the Brune network of Fig. 5-5, predistortion can be used on the elements L_2, C, and whichever of L_1 or L_3 is positive. This will add resistance to the primary or secondary of the transformer. Likewise, predistortion can be applied to the Bott-Duffin or Reza networks, but care must be used to insure that negative elements are not obtained. The best check against such a result is to make pole-zero plots of the remaining function

† Techniques for nonuniform predistortion have been suggested by P. R. Geffe, "A Note on Predistortion," *IRE Trans. Circuit Theory*, vol. CT-6, no. 4, December 1959, pp. 395–396, and "A Further Note on Predistortion," vol. CT-9, no. 3, September 1962, pp. 291–293. See also V. C. Tollefsrud, "A New Computational Method for Pre-distortion," *IRE Trans. Circuit Theory*, vol. CT-9, no. 1, March 1962, pp. 92–93.

at intervals in the synthesis procedure. It should be clear, however, that predistortion is of limited usefulness when approximating the distributed resistances of a practical transformer.

11-6. Summary of Practical Element Considerations

A number of considerations pertaining to the use of commercially available elements and equivalent circuits representing higher order approximations for practical inductors, capacitors, resistors, and transformers have been described in this chapter. First-, second-, and third-order approximations for practical inductors, capacitors, and resistors are summarized in Fig. 11-13. The order of the approximation to be used in a specific synthesis application is dictated by the degree of accuracy desired for the network response.

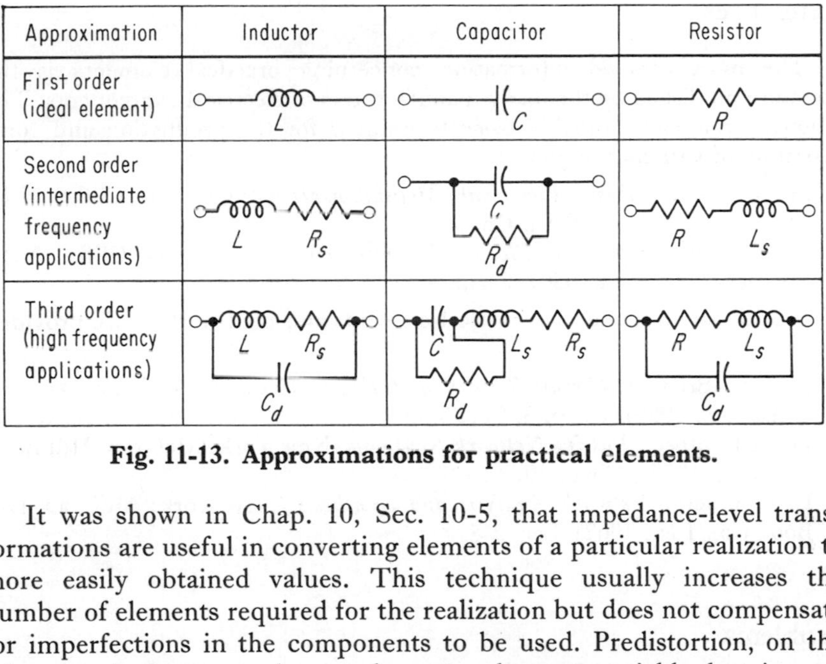

Approximation	Inductor	Capacitor	Resistor
First order (ideal element)	L	C	R
Second order (intermediate frequency applications)	L R_s	C R_d	R L_s
Third order (high frequency applications)	L R_s C_d	C L_s R_s R_d	R L_s C_d

Fig. 11-13. Approximations for practical elements.

It was shown in Chap. 10, Sec. 10-5, that impedance-level transformations are useful in converting elements of a particular realization to more easily obtained values. This technique usually increases the number of elements required for the realization but does not compensate for imperfections in the components to be used. Predistortion, on the other hand, does not change element values appreciably but insures partial or complete compensation for most distributed resistance effects illustrated in Fig. 11-13. Fortunately, it is seldom necessary to apply second- or third-order approximations for resistors, since most commercial resistors do not possess appreciable distributed reactance.

Most synthesis problems lead to a number of equivalent-network configurations. This fact provides the designer with an additional degree of freedom when selecting practical elements to achieve the realization of a specific driving-point or transfer characteristic. One configuration may require more easily obtained component values; fewer elements possessing secondary distributed effects; and/or smaller volume, weight, or cost than other electrically equivalent networks. Transformers must not be ruled out completely, since they can often be used to achieve a considerable saving in the number of elements. The above factors must be evaluated during the network design and appropriate trade-offs made to select an optimum configuration in one sense or another. The choice of an optimum configuration should also take into account such factors as reliability or life of the components and variations in the network response due to changes or tolerances of the available elements. Network response and pole-zero variations caused by changes in element values will be considered in Chap. 12.

References

The most detailed information concerning practical elements is the literature published by the many manufacturers of electrical components. The following references provide basic techniques for the production and compensation of various components:

1. M. B. Stout, *Basic Electrical Measurements* (Englewood Cliffs, N.J.: Prentice-Hall, Inc., 1950), Chap. 13.
2. C. R. Vail, *Circuits in Electrical Engineering* (Englewood Cliffs, N.J.: Prentice-Hall, Inc., 1950), Chap. 4.

Additional discussion of practical elements and predistortion are provided in:

3. John L. Stewart, *Circuit Theory and Design* (New York: John Wiley & Sons, Inc., 1956), Chap. 3, Sec. 3.5.
4. James E. Storer, *Passive Network Synthesis* (New York: McGraw-Hill Book Co., Inc., 1957), Chap. 10.
5. L. Weinberg, *Network Analysis and Synthesis* (New York: McGraw-Hill Book Co., Inc., 1962), Sec. 2-5.

Problems

11-1. Sketch the variation of Q [defined by Eq. (11-12)] as a function of frequency for the equivalent circuits of commercially available inductors, capacitors, and resistors presented in Figs. 11-1, 11-3, and 11-4. Discuss the effects of the various distributed impedances on the variation of Q in each case.

11-2. Which of the various RC and RL driving-point function canonic forms are most easily realized in terms of practical elements? Discuss the merits of each form.

11-3. Sketch the magnitude of the impedance for a series combination of R, L, and C as a function of ω. Replace these simple elements by their third-order approximations of Table 11-1 and sketch the new response. Discuss the results.

11-4. Determine the voltage transfer ratio for the equivalent transformer network of Fig. 11-5. Discuss the effects of the various parameters of this network and sketch the magnitude variation of E_2/E_1 as a function of ω.

11-5. Synthesize the following driving-point impedance by predistorting the poles and zeros by five units:

$$Z_1(s) = \frac{s^2 + 16s + 68}{s^2 + 14s + 48}$$

11-6. Discuss the possibility of predistorting transfer functions such that zeros are moved into the right half-plane. What conditions must be imposed on the poles or associated driving-point functions?

11-7. Synthesize the following driving-point impedance by predistorting the poles and zeros by two units:

$$Z_1(s) = \frac{s^3 + 16s^2 + 85s + 148}{s^4 + 20s^3 + 150s^2 + 500s + 609}$$

11-8. Synthesize the impedance of Prob. 11-7 such that a maximum amount of resistance is realized with each reactive element.

Chapter 12

Network Response and Sensitivity

Considerations

Response is a general term used to denote the manner in which a circuit reacts to the application of a specific voltage or current to its input. There are a number of different response characteristics which can be used to describe a particular network; however, it is customary to consider two principal types, the so-called "steady-state" or "frequency" response and the "transient" response. The frequency response implies the manner in which the network reacts to the application of real frequencies following the decay of all transient effects. The transient response describes the manner in which the network reacts to the application of a voltage or current prior to achieving steady-state conditions. In other words, the frequency response expresses the characteristics of a network as a function of frequency, whereas the transient response describes characteristics of a network as a function of time. This distinction leads to the terminology "frequency domain" and "time domain" often used in the specification of a desired network response, discussion pertaining to approximation problems, and employment of Laplace transformations. The purpose of this chapter is to investigate methods for describing and computing the frequency and transient response of networks. Consideration is also given to practical aspects pertaining to variations in pole-zero positions caused by changes in element values and the resulting effects these have on network response. Finally, sensitivity functions and their use in predicting the effects of pole-zero variations will be described for situations in which one or more elements vary in a random manner.

12-1. Frequency Response

When the driving-point or transfer function of a network is known in terms of the complex frequency variable s, the frequency response is

358

easily determined by letting $s = j\omega$. The resulting function will generally yield a complex number which can be represented by an amplitude A and an associated phase angle ϕ at any particular frequency. If A and ϕ are plotted as a function of ω, the resulting curves are known as the "amplitude response" and "phase response" respectively. The amplitude and phase response indicate the manner in which the network reacts to the application of sinusoidal voltages or currents of any frequency in the spectrum. Together they completely define the steady-state or frequency response of the network. The amplitude response is of primary importance in most applications; however, the characteristics of a network are not completely defined unless both amplitude and phase are specified for all real frequencies. Generally, a network designer is only interested in the response over a finite range of frequencies. In this case several different networks may satisfy the desired response characteristics.

It is possible to determine the amplitude response (within a multiplying factor) and the phase response graphically from a pole-zero plot of the function. In this case the frequency response can be determined by moving a test point ω_t from the origin upwards along the $j\omega$-axis. The amplitude response as a function of ω is obtained from the length of vectors from each of the poles and zeros to the test point. The phase response is obtained from the angles formed by these vectors with respect to the horizontal. Moving a test point along the $j\omega$-axis is the same as substituting $s = j\omega$ in the function under consideration; however, in making a pole-zero plot constant multiplying factors of a function are neglected. Therefore the amplitude response determined graphically will only be within a multiplying factor of the actual amplitude response. Because multiplying factors do not affect the phase angle, the phase response determined graphically will be identical to that determined by substituting $s = j\omega$ in the function under consideration.

The following example of the graphical method for determining amplitude and phase responses will help to clarify the above discussion. Consider the simple pole-zero plot of Fig. 12-1a in which the test point ω_t is moved along the $j\omega$-axis to obtain the response curves of Fig. 12-1b. The amplitude response at the test point is given by the product of the vector lengths from the zeros divided by the product of the vector lengths from the poles. For this example, A is given by ($A = c/ab$) at any value of ω_t. The phase response is the sum of the phase angles from the zeros minus the sum of the phase angles from the poles at any value of ω_t. The total phase angle ϕ can be expressed as

$$\phi = \sum_{k=1}^{n} \phi_{z_k} - \sum_{k=1}^{m} \phi_{p_k} \qquad (12\text{-}1)$$

The phase angle at ω_t for this example is

$$\phi = \phi_{z_1} - (\phi_{p_1} + \phi_{p_2}) \qquad (12\text{-}2)$$

The resulting phase and amplitude responses obtained as the test point is moved along the $j\omega$-axis of Fig. 12-1a is shown in Fig. 12-1b. From the symmetrical nature of the pole-zero plot, it is seen that if the test point were moved downward along the $j\omega$-axis from the origin, the symmetrical image of the amplitude and skew-symmetric image of the phase response would be obtained for negative frequencies. This negative frequency response has no physical significance but is simply a result of the pole-zero approach using the s-plane.

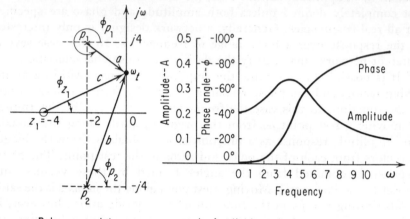

a. Pole-zero plot   b. Amplitude and phase response

Fig. 12-1. Graphical determination of frequency response.

Assume the amplitude and phase responses of Fig. 12-1b represent the voltage transfer ratio of a two-port network. In this case the transfer function can be written as follows:

$$\frac{E_2}{E_1} = \frac{K(s + 4)}{(s + 2 - j4)(s + 2 + j4)} = \frac{K(s + 4)}{s^2 + 4s + 20} \qquad (12\text{-}3)$$

A constant K is inserted to adjust the amplitude response. This can be accomplished by comparing the amplitude response to the magnitude of the transfer function at any real frequency. The value of K is most easily obtained at $(s = j\omega = 0)$; however, for this example $(K = 1)$ will be used. Generally, K will be specified with the transfer function and will not bear a one-to-one relationship with that obtained by the graphical approach. In many cases it is unnecessary to calculate the value of K, since the relative amplitude response is of primary importance.

A convenient method for expressing amplitude response in terms of relative amplitudes is afforded by decibel notation. A bel is defined as the logarithm of a power ratio P_2/P_1 at a particular frequency; a decibel, denoted by db, is one-tenth of a bel.

$$db = 10 \log_{10} \frac{P_2}{P_1}$$ (12-4)

If P_1 is considered to be the input power to a network and P_2 is the output power, then the decibels of power gain or attenuation at any frequency can be found by Eq. (12-4). If the input and output powers of the network are measured across the same resistance values, then according to the definition of power

$$db = 10 \log_{10} \frac{P_2}{P_1} = 10 \log_{10} \frac{E_2{}^2}{E_1{}^2} = 20 \log_{10} \frac{E_2}{E_1}$$ (12-5)

The input and output power of a network are seldom considered, and rarely is the resistance of the input and output circuits equal. Consequently, for practical reasons, it is convenient to simply define the decibel as

$$db \equiv 20 \log_{10} \frac{E_2}{E_1} \quad \text{or} \quad db \equiv 20 \log_{10} \frac{I_2}{I_1}$$ (12-6)

It must be understood that the power relationship of Eq. (12-5) only holds when E_2 and E_1 or I_2 and I_1 are measured across the same resistance values.

The relative amplitude response in terms of decibels can be determined at any frequency for the example of Fig. 12-1 by applying Eq. (12-6). The peak response in Fig. 12-1b occurs at a frequency of 4 radians/sec, so this value will be used as the reference. In other words, the ratio of E_2 to E_1 will be assumed to be unity at $\omega = 4$, then in terms of decibels $A = 20 \log_{10} (1) = 0$. Scaling the amplitude response of Fig. 12-1b such that its value at $\omega = 4$ is unity and expressing the results in terms of decibels yields the response curve of Fig. 12-2. The frequency at which the amplitude response peaks is known as the resonant frequency. More complicated networks may possess several peaks or resonant frequencies.

The range of frequencies between the points on the amplitude response at which the amplitude is down 3 db from its maximum value is known as the bandwidth. Because of symmetry of most resonant peaks, it is convenient to denote the resonant frequency as ω_c, since it falls near the center of the bandwidth. This is particularly true for networks having complex poles located a large distance from the origin but close to the $j\omega$-axis. The bandwidth specification is an indication of the filtering action of a network as illustrated in Fig. 12-3a. The frequencies at which the response is down 3 db from its maximum value represent

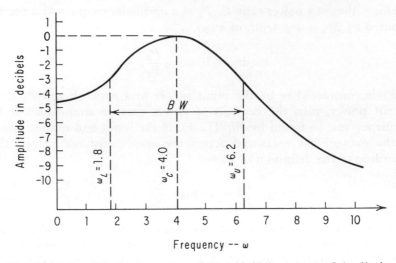

Fig. 12-2. Amplitude response of Fig. 12-1b in terms of decibels.

points at which the power ratio of Eq. (12-5) is $1/2$ or the voltage or current ratios of Eq. (12-6) are $1/\sqrt{2}$ of their maximum values. Consequently, ω_L and ω_U of Figs. 12-2 and 12-3a are known respectively as the lower and upper, "3 db," "half power," or "cutoff" frequencies. The bandwidth can be expressed in terms of these frequencies as $BW = \omega_U - \omega_L$.

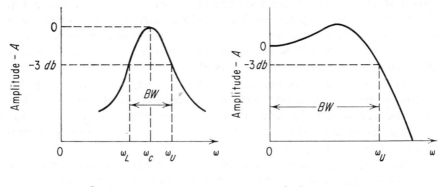

a. Bandpass response   b. Low-pass response

Fig. 12-3. Typical bandpass and low-pass amplitude responses.

When a network has a finite response at $\omega = 0$, as in Figs. 12-2 and 12-3b, specification of the bandwidth may not be sufficient to adequately describe the amplitude characteristics. Under these conditions the bandwidth is usually understood to include the range of frequencies between $\omega = 0$ and the frequency at which the amplitude response has fallen off 3 db from its value at $\omega = 0$. However, it is also necessary to state that the response is of a low-pass type. If the response has a peak at some frequency within the bandwidth region, the characteristics of the peak, such as its amplitude and resonant frequency, should be given. Consider the network of Fig. 12-2, for example. In this case the amplitude response is not symmetrical about ω_c because the poles of the transfer function, Eq. (12-3), are located near the origin and not very close to the $j\omega$-axis. Furthermore, the zero at $s = -4$ distorts the shape of the response for low values of ω. As a result, the response may be described as having a bandwidth of $BW = \omega_U - \omega_L = 6.2 - 1.8 = 4.4$ radians/sec and a center frequency of $\omega_c = 4$ radians/sec. However, the response of Fig. 12-2 might be more accurately described as being of a low-pass type with a bandwidth of 8.7 radians/sec and a peak having an amplitude of 4.6 db at $\omega = 4$ radians/sec. This description agrees with the definition suggested by Fig. 12-3b.

In many cases it is desirable that a network have a "flat" amplitude response over a prescribed range of frequencies. A flat response implies that the amplitude of all signals transmitted within the passband will be unchanged; however, it is customary to specify tolerances on any variations that may take place. For example, it might be stated that the amplitude response does not vary more than two decibels for frequencies between 20 and 20,000 cycles/sec. The same statement can be made by specifying that the amplitude is flat within two decibels over the same frequency range. In some applications the cutoff characteristics of a network are also important. Cutoff can be considered as a measure of the rate at which the amplitude response changes for frequencies outside the bandwidth region, beginning at the cutoff frequencies. Usually the cutoff is specified in terms of decibels per octave or decibels per decade of frequency.

The primary advantage of the s-plane when designing a network to give a prescribed response is that the effect of each pole and zero of the transfer function is made clear. When accuracy is not required and only a general idea of the response is desired, it is usually possible to neglect the effect of a pole and zero lying close to each other. For low values of frequency the poles and zeros near the origin have the greatest effect on the response, those lying 5 to 10 times as far from the origin can generally be neglected. Resonant peaks of the amplitude response do not ordinarily coincide exactly with the frequency corresponding to the vertical coordinates of the poles of the pole-zero plot. However, as the poles approach the $j\omega$-axis the accuracy of this approximation increases. When a pole falls on the $j\omega$-axis the amplitude response becomes infinite at the frequency of the coordinate of the pole. Approximations of the type described above are often useful in determining whether or not a function whose pole-zero plot is being considered is giving the desired amplitude, phase, or transient response. However, because the amplitude and phase response are both derived from the same pole-zero plot, it is impossible to obtain functions or networks having arbitrary combinations of amplitude and phase response for all values of ω.†

The purpose of this section has been to acquaint the reader with some of the techniques and terminology employed in specifying and determining the frequency response of a network when using complex frequency notation. It should be clear that variations in either the amplitude or phase response caused by changes in pole-zero positions can readily be predicted or determined graphically from the s-plane. Combinations of poles and zeros that lead to a desired amplitude and/or phase response are the subject of the approximation procedures of Chap. 14. However, variations in response caused by changes in element values and pole-zero positions are considered in the following sections.

12-2. Displacement of Zeros Due to Incremental Variations in Elements

To estimate changes in network response caused by variations in element values, it is first necessary to compute the expected changes in pole-zero positions. If the network impedance or admittance functions are rational, variations in any parameter will generally affect both the pole and zero positions. For instance, the impedance of a network can be expressed in terms of s and any parameter x as $Z(x,s) = KP(x,s)/Q(x,s)$. Computation of new pole-zero positions caused by changes in x may be difficult, and in higher-order functions it might require numerical techniques. Fortunately the displacement of zeros can be computed using a procedure suggested by Papoulis.‡ Applying the procedure to both the impedance and admittance functions of a network, it is possible to determine the expected variations in pole and zero positions caused by changes in individual elements.

Consider an impedance function $Z(s)$ with zeros at $s_1, s_2, \ldots, s_n$. If an incremental impedance $\delta z(s)$ is added to $Z(s)$, the zeros will be moved to new positions, $s_1^*, s_2^*, \ldots, s_n^*$. In this case it is possible to write

$$Z(s)]_{s=s_k} = 0 \quad \text{and} \quad Z(s) + \delta z(s)]_{s=s_k^*} = 0 \qquad (12\text{-}7)$$

When a particular set of elements are remotely located within a network and are varied by $\delta z(s)$, the conditions of Eq. (12-7) hold, provided $Z(s)$ is the impedance seen looking into the terminals of $\delta z(s)$. However,

† H. W. Bode, *Network Analysis and Feedback Amplifier Design* (New York: D. Van Nostrand Co., Inc., 1945), Chap. XIV.

‡ A. Papoulis, "Displacement of the Zeros of the Impedance Z(p) Due to Incremental Variations in the Network Elements," *Proc. IRE*, vol. 43, no. 1, January 1955, pp. 79–82.

because the zeros of an impedance or admittance function are also roots of the network's characteristic determinant, the variation in their locations can be established by considering the impedance or admittance seen from any point.

Assume that the particular zero in question s_k is of multiplicity m. In this case the value of $(s - s_k)^m/Z(s)$, when computed at $s = s_k$, must be finite and nonzero. This statement is based on the fact that for driving-point functions, zeros of $Z(s)$ are the poles of $1/Z(s)$, and the coefficient of the $(s - s_k)^{-m}$ term in the partial-fraction expansion of $1/Z(s)$ must be finite and nonzero.† Therefore, it follows that

$$\frac{(s - s_k)^m}{Z(s)}\bigg]_{s = s_k} = A_k \neq 0 \tag{12-8}$$

Evaluating Eq. (12-7) at $(s = s_k^*)$, multiplying by $(s_k^* - s_k)^m$, transposing the results, then taking the mth root of both sides yields

$$(s_k^* - s_k) = \sqrt[m]{\frac{-\delta z(s_k^*)(s_k^* - s_k)^m}{Z(s_k^*)}} \tag{12-9}$$

The expression under the radical represents the following function $F(s)$ evaluated at $(s = s_k^*)$.

$$F(s) = \frac{-\delta z(s)(s - s_k)^m}{Z(s)} \tag{12-10}$$

Provided s_k is not a zero of $\delta z(s)$, it is possible to evaluate $F(s)$ at $s = s_k$. This can be interpreted in terms of Eq. (12-8) as

$$F(s)]_{s = s_k} = -\delta z(s_k)A_k \neq 0 \tag{12-11}$$

Consequently, if the displacement of the zero is small $F(s_k)$ can be used to approximate $F(s_k^*)$, and Eq. (12-9) becomes

$$(s_k^* - s_k) \approx \sqrt[m]{-\delta z(s_k)A_k} \tag{12-12}$$

This approximate expression can be used to evaluate small displacements in the position of the zero s_k in terms of an added impedance $\delta z(s)$ and the coefficient A_k of the $(s - s_k)^{-m}$ term of the partial-fraction expansion of $1/Z(s)$.

It can be concluded from Eq. (12-12) that for small variations in network elements, each zero of multiplicity m will generate m simple zeros which lie at equal intervals around the circumference of a circle. The center of the circle is at s_k, and the radius is given by the modulus of Eq. (12-12). For incremental changes in resistance, inductance, or capacitance, the displacement in the position of zeros is given by

$$(s_k^* - s_k) \approx \sqrt[m]{-\delta R A_k} \qquad \sqrt[m]{-\delta L s_k A_k} \qquad \text{or} \qquad \sqrt[m]{\frac{\delta C A_k}{C^2 s_k}} \tag{12-13}$$

† See Chap. 1, Sec. 1-7, for coefficients of higher-order poles.

The minus sign under the radical disappears in the case of changes in capacitance, since the difference in capacitance is given by

$$\frac{1}{(C + \delta C)s} - \frac{1}{Cs} \approx \frac{-\delta C}{C^2 s} \qquad (12\text{-}14)$$

Equation (12-13) reveals that for a second-order real zero and a negative value of A_k, a small reduction in resistance δR anywhere in the network causes s_k to split into conjugate complex zeros with a real part closely approximated by s_k and an imaginary part of $\sqrt{\delta R A_k}$. An increase in resistance causes the zeros to separate along the real axis with each zero moving $\sqrt{\delta R A_k}$ in opposite directions from s_k. For a reactance network in which $s_k = j\omega_k$ and A_k is a real number greater than zero, a small increase in resistance displaces the zeros to the left, parallel to the real axis, but a decrease in resistance is impossible except in the case of transfer functions, since the zeros move into the right half-plane. Changes in reactive elements of δL or δC will cause a zero at $j\omega_k$ to move along the $j\omega$-axis by $\omega_k \delta L A_k$ or $\delta C A_k / \omega_k C^2$, respectively. Finally, the approximations of Eq. (12-13) can be improved by repeating the procedure in an iterative manner. For example, if the new zero established by Eq. (12-13) is presumed to be given by

$$s_k^* = s_k + \sqrt[m]{F(s_k)} \qquad (12\text{-}15)$$

a second more accurate position at s_k^{**} can be computed from

$$s_k^{**} = s_k + \sqrt[m]{F(s_k^*)} \qquad (12\text{-}16)$$

This approach can be continued with each result acting as a measure of the accuracy of the preceding approximation. When two successive approximations give identical results, an exact solution has been achieved.

To establish variations in the positions of zeros caused by changes in mutual inductance, it is necessary to investigate in more detail certain aspects pertaining to transfer functions. Assume that the open-circuit impedances of a transformer coupled two-port network are given by $z_{11}(s) = Z_a(s)$, $z_{22}(s) = Z_b(s)$, and $z_{12}(s) = Ms$ where M is the mutual coupling between the input and output circuits. Zeros of the impedance determinant $[z_{11}(s)z_{22}(s) - z_{12}(s)^2]$ form the poles of the short-circuit admittance functions; hence they are restricted to the left half-plane. Furthermore, because these functions are rational functions, the conditions of Eq. (12-8) can be applied. Therefore, if Ms is the zero of the transfer impedance and M is changed by δM, the new zero s_k^* must satisfy

$$\{z_{11}(s)z_{22}(s) - [z_{12}(s) + \delta z_{12}(s)]^2\}_{s = s_k^*}$$

$$= Z_a(s_k^*)Z_b(s_k^*) - (M + \delta M)^2(s_k^*) \quad (12\text{-}17)$$

Proceeding with the analysis as in Eqs. (12-7) through (12-12) and neglecting the $(\delta M)^2$ term yields

$$s_k^* - s_k \approx \sqrt[m]{2\delta z_{12}(s_k)A_k} = \sqrt[m]{2\delta M s_k A_k}$$

where

$$A_k = \frac{(s - s_k)^m z_{12}(s)}{[z_{11}(s)z_{22}(s) - z_{12}^2(s)]}\Bigg|_{s=s_k} = \frac{(s - s_k)^m Ms}{[Z_a(s)Z_b(s) - M^2 s^2]}\Bigg|_{s=s_k} \neq 0$$

(12-18)

When the input and output circuits are only loosely coupled (i.e., $M \rightarrow 0$) and s_k is a zero of multiplicity m of $Z_a(s)$ but not a zero $Z_b(s)$, it follows that

$$s_k^* - s_k \approx \sqrt[m]{\frac{(s_k \delta M)^2}{Z_b(s_k)} A_{ak}} \quad \text{where} \quad A_{ak} = \frac{(s - s_k)^m}{Z_a(s)}\Bigg|_{s=s_k} \neq 0$$

(12-19)

Likewise, if s_k is an mth order zero of $Z_a(s)$ and a pth order zero of $Z_b(s)$ and M is small, the above approach gives

$$s_k^* - s_k \approx \sqrt[m+p]{(s_k \delta M)^2 A_{ak} A_{bk}}$$

(12-20)

where A_{ak} and A_{bk} are the coefficients of the $(s - s_k)^{-m}$ and $(s - s_k)^{-p}$ terms in the partial-fraction expansions of $1/Z_a(s)$ and $1/Z_b(s)$.

As a simple example of the above results, consider a series combination of resistance R and inductance L. In this case the impedance is given by $Z(s) = R + Ls$ and has a simple zero at $s_1 = -R/L$. Expanding $1/Z(s)$ in the form of Eq. (12-8) yields

$$\frac{1}{Z(s)} = \frac{1}{L\left(s + \dfrac{R}{L}\right)} \quad \text{so} \quad A_1 = \frac{1}{L}$$

(12-21)

If a small resistance δR is added in series with R and L, Eq. (12-13) can be used to predict the displacement of the zero s_1.

$$s_1^* - s_1 \approx \sqrt[1]{-\delta R A_k} = \frac{-\delta R}{L} \quad \text{or} \quad s_1^* = s_1 - \frac{\delta R}{L} = \frac{-(R + \delta R)}{L}$$

(12-22)

Clearly the zero formed by the series combination of $(R + \delta R)$ and L is at $s_1^* = -(R + \delta R)/L$; hence, the result of Eq. (12-22) is exact. However, consider the addition of a small inductance δL in series with R and L. In this case Eq. (12-13) yields

$$s_1^* - s_1 \approx \sqrt[1]{-\delta L s_1 A_k} = \frac{-\delta L s_1}{L} \quad \text{or} \quad s_1^* \approx -\frac{R}{L}\left[1 - \frac{\delta L}{L}\right]$$

(12-23)

Actually the zero produced by the series combination of R, L, and δL is at $s_1^* = -R/(L + \delta L)$. Therefore, Eq. (12-23) is approximate and holds only for small values of δL. More accurate results can be obtained by repeating the process.

$$s_1^{**} = s_1 + \sqrt[1]{F(s_1^*)} = s_1 - \frac{\delta L s_1^*}{L} = s_1 - \frac{\delta L s_1}{L} + \frac{(\delta L)^2 s_1}{L^2}$$

or

$$s_1^{**} = -\frac{R}{L}\left[1 - \frac{\delta L}{L} + \frac{(\delta L)^2}{L^2}\right] \tag{12-24}$$

The quantity in the brackets represents the first three terms in the series expansion of $1/(L + \delta L)$.

As a second example, consider the case of two loosely coupled circuits consisting of series L and C elements. The driving-point impedances of these circuits are given by

$$Z_a(s) = L_a s + \frac{1}{C_a s} \quad \text{and} \quad Z_b(s) = L_b s + \frac{1}{C_b s} \tag{12-25}$$

The zeros of $Z_a(s)$ and $Z_b(s)$ are at

$$s_{a1,a2} = \pm\frac{j}{\sqrt{L_a C_a}} = \pm j\omega_a \quad \text{and} \quad s_{b1,b2} = \pm\frac{j}{\sqrt{L_b C_b}} = \pm j\omega_b$$

$$\tag{12-26}$$

If the two circuits are coupled by a transformer with mutual inductance δM and primary and secondary inductances of L_a and L_b respectively, the coupling coefficient of the transformer can be written as $\Psi = \delta M/\sqrt{L_a L_b}$. The problem is to estimate the effect of changes in Ψ on the frequencies ω_a and ω_b. This can be accomplished by use of Eq. (12-19); however, it is first necessary to evaluate A_{ak} and $1/Z_b(s_k)$. Therefore, considering the zero s_{a1}, it follows that

$$\frac{1}{Z_a(s)} = \frac{1}{L_a s + \dfrac{1}{C_a s}} = \frac{1}{2L_a}\left[\frac{1}{s + s_{a1}} + \frac{1}{s + s_{a2}}\right] \quad \text{or} \quad A_{a1} = \frac{1}{2L_a}$$

and

$$\frac{1}{Z_b(s_{a1})} = \frac{s}{L_b\left(s^2 + \dfrac{1}{L_b C_b}\right)}\bigg|_{s=s_{a1}} = \frac{j\omega_a}{L_b(\omega_b^2 - \omega_a^2)} \tag{12-27}$$

Substituting $\Psi = \delta M/\sqrt{L_a L_b}$ and the results of Eq. (12-27) into Eq. (12-19) and evaluating at the zero, s_{a1} yields

$$s_{a1}^* - s_{a1} \approx \sqrt[1]{\frac{(s_{a1}\delta M)^2}{Z_b(s_{a1})}} A_{a1} = \frac{j\omega_a(\omega_a \Psi)^2}{2(\omega_a^2 - \omega_b^2)} \tag{12-28}$$

Consequently, the $j\omega$-axis zeros of the coupled networks are shifted as a function of Ψ to new values, ω_a^* and ω_b^*, accordingly.

$$\omega_a^* \approx \omega_a\left[1 + \frac{\Psi'^2}{2\left(1 - \frac{\omega_b^2}{\omega_a^2}\right)}\right] \quad \text{and} \quad \omega_b^* \approx \omega_b\left[1 + \frac{\Psi'^2}{2\left(1 - \frac{\omega_a^2}{\omega_b^2}\right)}\right]$$

(12-29)

The limiting case of these results can be computed from Eq. (12-20) when ω_a equals ω_b in which case $s_{a1}^* - s_{a1} \approx j\omega_a\Psi/2$ or $\omega_a^* \approx \omega_a(1 \pm \Psi/2)$.

12-3. Sensitivity Functions

Although the displacement of the poles and zeros of driving-point and transfer functions due to variations in an element has been considered, a question remains concerning the effects of these displacements on network response. One approach for solving this problem is to plot the displaced poles and zeros on the s-plane, then determine the new response by the techniques of Sec. 12-1. This may involve considerable work, but in many cases the work can be reduced by testing the function or its various poles and zeros to determine their sensitivity to changes in a particular parameter. Cases in which the function is not sensitive to changes in the parameter may reduce the required computation. Furthermore, attention can be focused directly on the most sensitive poles and/or zeros when estimating changes in the response. Consequently this section is devoted to a discussion of various sensitivity functions and their applications.

Pole-zero or root sensitivity was first suggested by Bode[†] and was later redefined by Truxal[‡] as the per unit change in root position in the s-plane due to a unit change in the parameter in question. In other words, if s_k is the root of a polynomial dependent on a parameter x, the root sensitivity $S_x^{s_k}$ is given by

$$S_x^{s_k} = \frac{\frac{\Delta s_k}{s_k}}{\frac{\delta x}{x}}$$

(12-30)

For differential increments, this expression can be written as

$$S_x^{s_k} = \frac{\frac{ds_k}{s_k}}{\frac{dx}{x}} = \frac{x}{s_k}\frac{ds_k}{dx} = \frac{d(\log s_k)}{d(\log x)}$$

(12-31)

† H. W. Bode, *Network Analysis and Feedback Amplifier Design* (New York: D. Van Nostrand Co., Inc., 1945), pp. 52–64.

‡ J. G. Truxal, *Automatic Feedback Control System Synthesis* (New York: McGraw-Hill Book Co., Inc., 1955), pp. 120–127.

This relationship is commonly referred to as the pole-zero or root-sensitivity function; however, a second form based on the change in root position per unit change in a specific parameter is sometimes used. The second form can be expressed analytically as

$$S_x^{*s_k} = \frac{ds_k}{\frac{dx}{x}}$$

(12-32)

Either Eq. (12-31) or Eq. (12-32) can be used as a measure of the sensitivity of a specific pole or zero; however, the designer is usually interested in the broader aspects pertaining to the rate of change of the entire driving-point or transfer functions to variations of an element. A more general expression that can be used as a measure of the driving-point or transfer sensitivity can be defined in the form of Eq. (12-31) as

$$S_x^{H(s)} = \frac{\frac{dH(s)}{H(s)}}{\frac{dx}{x}}$$

(12-33)

where $H(s)$ represents the driving-point or transfer function in question. In general, $H(s)$ can be written as

$$H(s) = \frac{K \sum\limits_{i=1}^{m} (s + z_i)}{\sum\limits_{k=1}^{n} (s + p_k)}$$

(12-34)

If the gain factor K, zeros z_i, and poles p_k are all functions of a parameter x, the total logarithmic derivative of Eq. (12-33) becomes

$$\frac{dH(s)}{H(s)} = dx \left[\frac{\frac{\partial K}{\partial x}}{K} + \sum_{i=1}^{m} \frac{\frac{\partial z_i}{\partial x}}{(s + z_i)} + \sum_{k=1}^{n} \frac{-\frac{\partial p_k}{\partial x}}{(s + p_k)} \right]$$

(12-35)

Dividing Eq. (12-35) by dx/x yields

$$S_x^{H(s)} = \frac{\frac{dH(s)}{H(s)}}{\frac{dx}{x}} = \frac{\frac{\partial K}{\partial x}}{\frac{K}{x}} + \sum_{i=1}^{m} \frac{\frac{\partial z_i}{\partial x}}{(s + z_i)} + \sum_{k=1}^{n} \frac{\frac{\partial(-p_k)}{\partial x}}{(s + p_k)}$$

(12-36)

This relationship expresses the sensitivity of $H(s)$ as a partial-fraction expansion where all of the critical frequencies z_i and p_k become poles. The residues of these poles are recognized to be of the same form as the second definition for pole-zero sensitivity given by Eq. (12-32).

The sensitivity function $S_x^{H(s)}$ will usually be a complicated function of s; consequently it may be difficult to predict the percentage change in the amplitude or phase response at real frequencies due to a given change in x. For example, consider the driving-point impedance of Eq. (5-35), used in the presentation of Brune's procedure. This impedance is expressed in Eq. (5-50) with the transformer coupling coefficient Ψ as a variable. This function is rewritten below for reference, and the variation in the position of its zeros due to changes in Ψ is presented in Table 5-1.

$$Z(s) = \frac{2(1 - \Psi'^2)s^3 + 5s^2 + (7 - 4\Psi')s + 4}{s^2 + 2s + 2} = \frac{P(s)}{Q(s)} \quad (12\text{-}37)$$

Differentiating Eq. (12-37) with respect to Ψ yields

$$\frac{dZ(s)}{d\Psi} = \frac{-4s(\Psi's^2 + 1)}{s^2 + 2s + 2} = \frac{M(s)}{Q(s)} \quad (12\text{-}38)$$

The sensitivity function can now be written from Eqs. (12-37) and (12-38) as

$$S_\Psi^{Z(s)} = \frac{\dfrac{dZ(s)}{Z(s)}}{\dfrac{d\Psi}{\Psi}} = \frac{\Psi}{Z(s)}\left[\frac{dZ(s)}{d\Psi}\right] = \frac{\Psi Q(s)}{P(s)}\left[\frac{M(s)}{Q(s)}\right]$$

$$= \frac{\Psi M(s)}{P(s)} = \frac{-\Psi'4s(\Psi's^2 + 1)}{2(1 - \Psi'^2)s^3 + 5s^2 + (7 - 4\Psi')s + 4} \quad (12\text{-}39)$$

The sensitivity is zero when $(s = 0)$, $(s = j/\sqrt{\Psi'})$, and the trivial case in which $(\Psi' = 0)$. Poles of the sensitivity function are identical to the zeros presented as a function of Ψ in Table 5-1. A sensitivity of zero or infinity merely indicates that the function of s has zero or infinite slope with respect to the variable in question. Unfortunately this cannot generally be interpreted directly in terms of changes in the response at real frequencies. Perhaps, by evaluating $S_\Psi^{Z(s)}$ at real frequencies, it may be possible to predict changes in the amplitude and phase responses of $Z(s)$ for variations in Ψ. Hence, it follows that

$$S_\Psi^{Z(j\omega)} = \frac{-j\Psi'4\omega(-\Psi'\omega^2 + 1)}{(-5\omega^2 + 4) + j\omega[(7 - 4\Psi') - 2(1 - \Psi'^2)\omega^2]} \quad (12\text{-}40)$$

The magnitude of this expression is plotted as a function of ω for $(\Psi' = 0.7)$ and $(\Psi' = 1.0)$ in Fig. 12-4. Likewise, the magnitude of the impedance of Eq. (12-37) is shown as a function of ω for $(\Psi' = 0)$, $(\Psi' = 0.7)$, and $(\Psi' = 1)$ in Fig. 12-5. This figure reveals that the amplitude is nearly insensitive to variations in Ψ at frequencies below $(\omega = 0.2)$ and between $(\omega = 1.5)$ and $(\omega = 2.5)$. The response becomes more dependent on Ψ at frequencies above ($\omega = 2.5$) and between ($\omega = 0.2$) and ($\omega = 1.5$).

The sensitivity curves of Fig. 12-4 tend to predict the gross variations in the response of Fig. 12-5. For instance, the sensitivity approaches zero below ($\omega = 0.2$) and becomes large for frequencies above ($\omega = 2.5$). Furthermore, a minimum sensitivity exists between these frequencies,

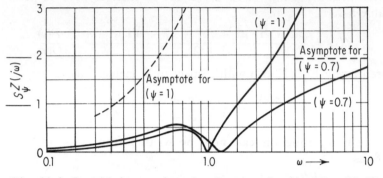

Fig. 12-4. Sensitivity as given by the magnitude of Eq. (12-40).

but it occurs near ($\omega = 1$) rather than between ($\omega = 1.5$) and ($\omega = 2.5$) which would be consistent with the amplitude response. Finally, as Ψ decreases in Fig. 12-4, the sensitivity at most frequencies decreases. In Fig. 12-5 the response varies at a greater rate for smaller values of Ψ. These observations tend to contradict each other; however, the phase response of the sensitivity function and driving-point impedance have not been included in the consideration. Perhaps the combined magnitude and phase of the sensitivity function might supply sufficient information to predict variations in the combined amplitude and phase response of the driving-point or transfer function at real frequencies. However, for practical reasons it can be concluded that the sensitivity functions, when expressed in terms of real frequency, cannot be relied upon for predicting changes in the amplitude and phase response of driving-point or transfer functions.

Before investigating sensitivity functions which are dependent on more than one parameter, it is of interest to consider the pole-zero or root sensitivity of Eq. (12-37). Only the zeros of this function are dependent on Ψ, and the sensitivity of these zeros can be computed directly from Table 5-1 using the definition of root sensitivity given by Eq. (12-30). The sensitivity of the real zero of Eq. (12-37) or Table 5-1 has been computed and is shown as a function of Ψ in Fig. 12-6. It is noted in Fig. 12-6 that the real zero is particularly sensitive at large values of Ψ. Since the real zero approaches infinity for larger values of Ψ

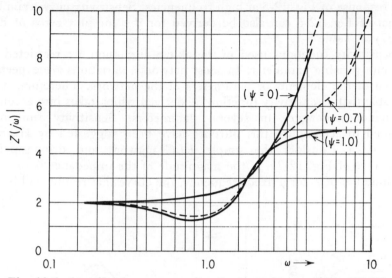

Fig. 12-5. Amplitude response for the impedance of Eq. (12-37).

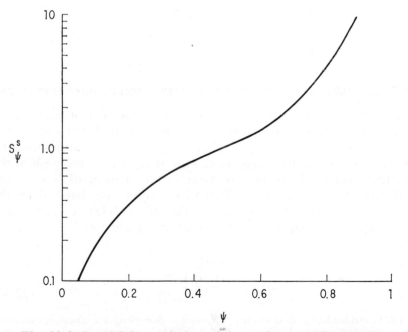

Fig. 12-6. Sensitivity variation of the real zero of Eq. (12-37).

(See Table 5-1), this accounts for the increased sensitivity in the amplitude response of Fig. 12-5 at high frequencies. Sensitivity curves similar to that of Fig. 12-6 can also be derived for the complex zeros of Eq. (12-37) or Table 5-1.

Sensitivity functions used in the above discussion are restricted to only one variable parameter. In most networks, variations are expected in each of the elements or parameters of the network. Therefore, it is desirable that a sensitivity function be derived which takes into account simultaneous changes in several parameters. Sensitivity functions designed to accomplish this purpose have been suggested by Hakimi and Cruz.† Consider the simple *RLC* network and driving-point impedance of Fig. 12-7*a*. If the magnitude of the impedance is plotted as a function of *L* for a fixed frequency, the curve that results will be of

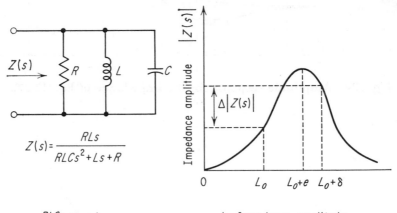

$$Z(s) = \frac{RLs}{RLCs^2 + Ls + R}$$

a. *RLC* network   b. Impedance amplitude

Fig. 12-7. Parallel *RLC* network and impedance amplitude characteristic.

the form shown in Fig. 12-7*b*. Assume the nominal value of the inductor is L_o in which case a variation in the element of δ will change the impedance by $\Delta|Z(s)|$. Suppose that δ represents the manufacturer's tolerance on a particular component, then if L_o is near the peak of the impedance amplitude curve, variations in the element of $(e < \delta)$ can cause large hidden changes in $Z(s)$ that may not be detected by the sensitivity functions of Eqs. (12-30) through (12-33). Consequently, Hakimi and Cruz suggest that the sensitivity function of Eq. (12-33) be redefined as

$$S_x^{H(s)} = \frac{\dfrac{\Delta H(s)}{H(s)}}{\delta} \Bigg]_{\substack{\max \\ 0 \le |e| \le \delta}} \tag{12-41}$$

† S. L. Hakimi and J. B. Cruz, Jr., "Measures of Sensitivity for Linear Systems with Large Multiple Parameter Variations," *IRE WESCON Convention Record*, vol. 4, part 2, 1960, pp. 109–115.

where δ is the tolerance and e is the per unit variation of x. When there are n variable parameters, the sensitivity function becomes

$$S_{x_1, x_2, \ldots, x_n}^{H(s)} = \left. \frac{\dfrac{\Delta H(s)}{H(s)}}{\delta_1, \delta_2, \ldots, \delta_n} \right]_{\substack{\max \\ 0 \leq |e_i| \leq \delta}} \qquad (i = 1, 2, \ldots, n)$$

$$(12\text{-}42)$$

For a given $H(s)$ and frequency, the only part of Eq. (12-42) that changes as the e_i's vary is $\Delta H(s)$. Determination of the maximum $\Delta H(s)$ may be a difficult problem requiring variational techniques. One approach for solving this problem is to determine $H(s)_{\max}$ and $H(s)_{\min}$ from which $[\Delta H(s)_{\max} = H(s)_{\max} - H(s)_{\min}]$ for all possible values of e_i.

For some applications it may be desirable to handle the parameter or element tolerances as statistical quantities. In this case the designer may be satisfied if $\Delta|H(s)|$ is within a prescribed region with a given confidence. A statistical measure of sensitivity that can be used in these situations is given by

$$S \equiv \frac{\dfrac{\sqrt{[\Delta|H(s)|]^2}}{H(s)_{\text{nom}}}}{\sigma_1, \sigma_2, \ldots, \sigma_n}$$

$$(12\text{-}43)$$

where $\sqrt{[\Delta|H(s)|]^2}$ is the root-mean-square value of $\Delta|H(s)|$ and $\sigma_1, \sigma_2, \ldots, \sigma_n$ are the standard deviations of the variables $e_1, e_2, \ldots, e_n$, respectively. As the e_i's vary, $H(s)$ fluctuates, making it necessary to compute a nominal value $H(s)_{\text{nom}}$ and the root-mean-square of the deviation $\Delta|H(s)|$. Furthermore, several possibilities exist in the application of Eq. (12-43). For instance, a uniform distribution of the e_i's between the limits $-\delta_i$ and $+\delta_i$ or a normal distribution with a standard deviation equal to δ_i might be selected. Finally, the excessive computation associated with most statistical problems suggests that the sensitivity function of Eq. (12-43) should probably be evaluated on a digital computer.

The sensitivity functions defined in this section have been considered from an analysis viewpoint. The more interesting and difficult problem of how to use these functions in the synthesis of a network, such that the effect of variations in element values on the network function or response is minimized in some sense, has not yet been solved. However, sensitivity functions can be used to establish the most critical elements and their acceptable tolerances for a given network configuration. This information is also useful when comparing equivalent-network configurations to determine which is most easily realized with commercially available elements.

12-4. Bounds on the Frequency Response of a Network

When a network function $H(s)$ is dependent on several parameters, it is sometimes useful to compute the maximum and minimum bounds on $H(j\omega)$ due to simultaneous changes in the variables. Hakimi and Cruz have also proposed a technique for solving this problem.† This technique is most easily explained by reconsidering the network and driving-point impedance of Fig. 12-7a. Assume that each of the elements R, L, and C is variable within tolerances δ_R, δ_L, and δ_C, such that

$$
\begin{aligned}
R &= R_o(1 + e_R) \\
L &= L_o(1 + e_L) \\
C &= C_o(1 + e_C)
\end{aligned}
\quad \text{where} \quad
\begin{cases}
-\delta_R \le e_R \le \delta_R \\
-\delta_L \le e_L \le \delta_L \\
-\delta_C \le e_C \le \delta_C
\end{cases}
\tag{12-44}
$$

Expressing the driving-point impedance of Fig. 12-7a in terms of Eq. (12-44) yields

$$
\begin{aligned}
Z(s, e_R, e_L, e_C) &= \frac{R_o(1+e_R)L_o(1+e_L)s}{R_o(1+e_R)L_o(1+e_L)C_o(1+e_C)s^2 + L_o(1+e_L)s + R_o(1+e_R)} \\[2mm]
&= \frac{R_oL_os + (e_R + e_L + e_Re_L)R_oL_os}{(R_oL_oC_os^2 + L_os + R_o) + (e_R + e_L + e_C + e_Re_L + e_Re_C \\ + e_Le_C + e_Re_Le_C)R_oL_oC_os^2 + e_LL_os + e_RR_o}
\end{aligned}
\tag{12-45}
$$

Generally, the network function will take the following form when expressed in terms of the variable parameters:

$$
\begin{aligned}
H(s, e_1, e_2, \ldots, e_n) &= \frac{P(s, e_1, e_2, \ldots, e_n)}{Q(s, e_1, e_2, \ldots, e_n)} \\[2mm]
&= \frac{P_o(s) + \sum e_iP_i(s) + \sum_{i \ne j} e_ie_jP_{ij}(s) + \cdots}{Q_o(s) + \sum e_iQ_i(s) + \sum_{i \ne j} e_ie_jQ_{ij}(s) + \cdots}
\end{aligned}
\tag{12-46}
$$

The numerator and denominator are multilinear functions of the e_i's and the $P(s)$'s and $Q(s)$'s are polynomials as in the example of Eq. (12-45).

Given a function such as Eq. (12-46), the problem is to establish at each real frequency the maximum and minimum values of amplitude and phase. These values must be determined subject to the constraint $|e_i| \le \delta_i$ for all i. To solve this problem it is necessary to compute the maximum and minimum values of the amplitude and phase for the numerator of $H(j\omega)$ separately and then repeat the procedure for the

† *Ibid.*, pp. 110–111.

denominator. This computation can be accomplished using a theorem derived by Myers, which states that for a polynomial of the form

$$P(j\omega, e_1, e_2, \ldots, e_n) = P_o(j\omega) + \sum e_i P_i(j\omega) + \sum_{i \neq j} e_i e_j P_{ij}(j\omega)$$

$$+ \sum_{i \neq j \neq k} e_i e_j e_k P_{ijk}(j\omega) + \cdots + (e_1 e_2 \ldots e_n) P_{1,2,\ldots,n}(j\omega) \quad (12\text{-}47)$$

where the e_i's are real numbers and a frequency ω_o is specified. The value of $P(j\omega_o, e_1, e_2, \ldots, e_n)$ falls in or on the polygon enclosing the extreme values of the e's.[†] In this discussion the extreme values of e_i are $\pm \delta_i$; hence, if there are n e_i's, there will be 2^n extreme values that form the polygon.

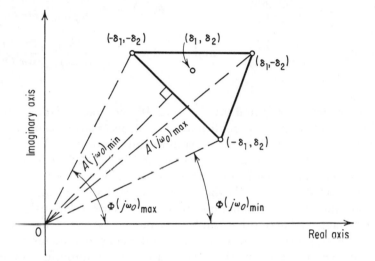

Fig. 12-8. Typical plot of a multilinear function of two variables on the complex $A(j\omega_o)$ plane.

To illustrate the above concept, consider a polynomial $A(j\omega, e_1, e_2)$, which is dependent on only two variables. In this case it is necessary at specific frequencies to plot $A(j\omega_o, e_1, e_2)$ for four sets of extreme values, $e_1 = -\delta_1$, $e_2 = -\delta_2$; $e_1 = -\delta_1$, $e_2 = \delta_2$; $e_1 = \delta_1$, $e_2 = -\delta_2$, and $e_1 = \delta_1$, $e_2 = \delta_2$. The complex value of $A(j\omega_o, e_1, e_2)$ for each of these four combinations can be plotted as shown in Fig. 12-8. The polygon enclosing the four points of Fig. 12-8 is a triangle, and according to Myers' theorem the maximum and minimum values of $A(j\omega_o, e_1, e_2)$ lie inside or on it. The minimum value is represented by the shortest vector from the origin to a point on the triangle and has a magnitude of

† B. R. Myers, "Two Theorems in Multiweighted Sums and Their Application in the Stability Analysis of Active Linear Systems," *Technical Note No. 10*, Circuit Theory Group, University of Illinois, February 1959.

$A(j\omega_o)_{min}$. Likewise, the maximum value is represented by the longest vector from the origin to a point on the triangle and has a magnitude of $A(j\omega_o)_{max}$. The maximum and minimum phase angles are denoted by $\phi(j\omega_o)_{max}$ and $\phi(j\omega_o)_{min}$ respectively and do not necessarily result from the same combination of e_i's as the maximum and minimum amplitudes.

Once the maximum and minimum values of the amplitude and phase have been determined over the frequency range of interest for both the numerator and denominator of the function in question, it is possible to combine the results to obtain bounds on the network's amplitude and phase responses due to simultaneous variations in all of the boundaries from the following

$$|H(j\omega)|_{max} = \frac{|P(j\omega)_{max}|}{|Q(j\omega)_{min}|} \qquad \phi(j\omega)_{max} = \frac{\phi(j\omega)_{max} \text{ for } P(j\omega)}{\phi(j\omega)_{min} \text{ for } Q(j\omega)}$$

$$|H(j\omega)|_{min} = \frac{|P(j\omega)_{min}|}{|Q(j\omega)_{max}|} \quad \text{and} \quad \phi(j\omega)_{min} = \frac{\phi(j\omega)_{min} \text{ for } P(j\omega)}{\phi(j\omega)_{max} \text{ for } Q(j\omega)}$$

$$(12\text{-}48)$$

The boundaries computed by Eq. (12-48) are pessimistic, since the maximum and minimum amplitudes do not necessarily result from the same combination of e_i's as the maximum and minimum values of phase. This point is clear from the illustration of Fig. 12-8. Furthermore, the combinations of e_i's that form the numerators of Eq. (12-48) at a specific frequency are not necessarily the same as those that form the denominators, nor do these combinations maintain a fixed relationship as frequency changes. Therefore it can be concluded that the actual amplitude and phase response resulting from simultaneous parameter variations lies somewhere between the maximum and minimum boundaries computed from Eq. (12-48).

As an example of this procedure, assume the nominal element values of Fig. 12-7a are $R_o = 10$ ohms, $L_o = 2$ henries, and $C_o = 1/2$ farad. These parameters, when used in Eq. (12-45), lead to the nominal amplitude and phase responses shown in Fig. 12-9. Furthermore, assume that these parameters have tolerances of ± 5 percent or $\delta_R = 0.5$ ohm, $\delta_L = 0.1$ henry, and $\delta_C = 0.025$ farad. Since there are three parameters, there are 2^3 or 8 combinations of extreme values which can be listed as follows:

1. $\delta_R, \delta_L, \delta_C$ 5. $-\delta_R, \delta_L, \delta_C$

2. $\delta_R, \delta_L, -\delta_C$ 6. $-\delta_R, \delta_L, -\delta_C$

3. $\delta_R, -\delta_L, \delta_C$ 7. $-\delta_R, -\delta_L, \delta_C$

4. $\delta_R, -\delta_L, -\delta_C$ 8. $-\delta_R, -\delta_L, -\delta_C$

Substituting each combination listed above into Eq. (12-45) for the respective e's yields 8 values of amplitude and phase for the numerator and a similar set for the denominator at any frequency. By selecting frequencies within the range of interest, the 8 values for the numerator were plotted as illustrated in Fig. 12-8, and the maximum and minimum

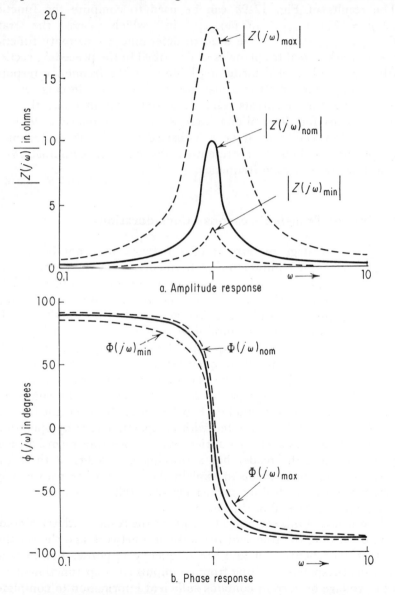

a. Amplitude response

b. Phase response

Fig. 12-9. Amplitude and phase responses for Fig. 12-7a where $R = 10 \pm 0.5$ ohms, $L = 2 \pm 0.1$ henries, and $C = 0.5 \pm 0.025$ farad.

amplitude and phase were obtained from these plots. The same procedure was repeated at each frequency for the 8 values representing the denominator of Eq. (12-45). The results of this procedure were then combined according to Eq. (12-48) to give the maximum and minimum boundaries for the amplitude and phase of Fig. 12-9.

The results of Fig. 12-9a can be used to compute the function $\Delta|Z(j\omega)| = |Z(j\omega)_{\max}| - |Z(j\omega)_{\min}|$, in which case the ratio $\Delta|Z(j\omega)_{\max}|/|Z(j\omega)_{\mathrm{non}}|$ can be used to determine a sensitivity function for the network at real frequencies as described in the preceding section. Clearly, the problem of determining bounds on the frequency response of more complicated networks may involve considerable computation. When the network elements vary in a statistical manner, the only practical means for determining bounds on the response is to use a computer. However, it must be emphasized that the above technique yields pessimistic bounds representing the extreme combinations of element tolerances at each frequency.

12-5. Time or Transient-response Considerations

The input voltage or current of a network may not be a single frequency or simple combination of frequencies. On the contrary, it is often a sharp impulse, a step change in level, or some other form which is most easily described as a function of time. An impulse or step change, for example, can be considered to be composed of an infinite number of frequencies with various amplitudes and phase relationships. The output of a network, as a consequence of such an input, may also be a complicated combination of frequencies most easily described as a function of time, and known as the time or transient response. To compute the transient response by considering each of the component frequencies individually would be a hopeless task. However, the transient response can usually be computed with comparative ease by operational transform procedures such as Fourier and Laplace transforms. Because it is assumed that the reader has a working knowledge of these procedures, no attempt is made to explain the details of transform techniques. Several texts dealing exclusively with this subject are listed in the references at the end of the chapter.

The purpose of this section is to acquaint the reader with terminology used in describing the transient response of a network and the relationships that exist between it and the frequency response. For instance, the transient response resulting from an impulse or step-function change in input voltage or current contains sufficient information to completely define the characteristics of a network and its impedance or admittance functions. This fact follows since an impulse or step input, effectively composed of an infinite number of real frequencies, excites all of the natural frequencies of the network. In fact the transient response contains precisely the same amount of information concerning the characteristics of a network as the combined amplitude and phase response. This fact will be demonstrated in the following discussion.

Consider the two-port network of Fig. 12-10 where $H(s)$ represents the voltage transfer ratio. The input and output voltages can be expressed as functions of time as $i(t)$ and $o(t)$, respectively. Using the direct Laplace transformation, defined by Eq. (12-49), the input and output voltages can (if they are transformable) be converted to functions of s.

$$F(s) \equiv \lim_{\substack{a \to 0 \\ T \to \infty}} \left[\int_a^T f(t)e^{-st}\, dt \right] = \int_0^\infty f(t)e^{-st}\, dt \qquad (12\text{-}49)$$

In other words, the input and output voltages can be expressed in an alternate form as $I(s)$ and $O(s)$. Using this notation, the input and output functions can be related through the network transfer ratio as follows:

$$O(s) = I(s)H(s) \qquad \text{or} \qquad \frac{O(s)}{I(s)} = H(s) \qquad (12\text{-}50)$$

Consequently, if $i(t)$ can be Laplace transformed by Eq. (12-49) to yield $I(s)$ and if the transfer ratio of the network $H(s)$ is known, $O(s)$ can be computed directly, using Eq. (12-50). Then $O(s)$ can be converted to a function of time $o(t)$ by applying the inverse Laplace transformation defined by Eq. (12-51).†

$$f(t) \equiv \frac{1}{2\pi j} \int_{c-j\infty}^{c+j\infty} F(s)e^{ts}\, ds \qquad \text{where} \begin{cases} 0 \leq t \\ \sigma_a < \sigma = c \end{cases} \qquad (12\text{-}51)$$

The combinations $f(t) \leftrightarrow F(s)$, $i(t) \leftrightarrow I(s)$, and $o(t) \leftrightarrow O(s)$ are known as Laplace transform pairs. A short list of useful transform pairs is given in Table 12-1.

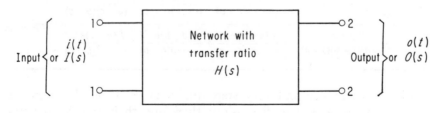

Fig. 12-10. Typical two-port network.

† For $f(t)$ to be Laplace transformable by Eqs. (12-49) and (12-51), it is necessary that $F(s)$ converges absolutely for $\sigma_a < \sigma$ to an analytic function in the half-plane $\sigma_a < \sigma$. For more information concerning this constraint see M. F. Gardner and J. L. Barnes, *Transients in Linear Systems*, Vol. 1 (New York: John Wiley & Sons, Inc., 1942), Chap. III, pp. 93–107.

The techniques described above can be used for determining the response of networks when either voltages or currents are applied provided $H(s)$ represents the proper transfer ratio. Similarly, combinations of input current and output voltage or vice versa can be handled with proper transfer ratios. In the case of one-port networks, Laplace transformations can be employed to compute the voltage response when a current source is used with the driving-point impedance or the current response when a voltage source is used with the admittance function.

TABLE 12-1
Laplace Transform Pairs

No.	F(s)	f(t) where $0 \leqq t$	
1	1	$u_1(t) \equiv \lim_{a \to 0} \dfrac{u(t) - u(t-a)}{a}$	unit impulse at $t = 0$
2	$\dfrac{1}{s}$	$u(t) = 1$ unit step at $t = 0$	
3	$\dfrac{K}{(s+a)^n}$	$\dfrac{K}{(n-1)!} t^{n-1} e^{-at}$	where n is a positive integer
4	$\dfrac{K}{(s+a)(s+b)}$	$\dfrac{K}{(b-a)} [e^{-at} - e^{-bt}]$	
5	$\dfrac{K\omega}{s^2 + \omega^2}$	$K \sin \omega t$	
6	$\dfrac{Ks}{s^2 + \omega^2}$	$K \cos \omega t$	
7	$\dfrac{K(s+c)}{(s+a)(s+b)}$	$\dfrac{K}{(b-a)} [(c-a)e^{-at} - (c-b)e^{-bt}]$	
8	$\dfrac{K}{(s+a)(s+b)(s+c)}$	$\dfrac{Ke^{-at}}{(b-a)(c-a)} + \dfrac{Ke^{-bt}}{(a-b)(c-b)} + \dfrac{Ke^{-ct}}{(a-c)(b-c)}$	
9	$\dfrac{K(s+d)}{(s+a)(s+b)(s+c)}$	$\dfrac{K(d-a)e^{-at}}{(b-a)(c-a)} + \dfrac{K(d-b)e^{-bt}}{(a-b)(c-b)} + \dfrac{K(d-c)e^{-ct}}{(a-c)(b-c)}$	

The unit impulse and unit step functions of Table 12-1 are of immediate interest to this discussion; therefore, their transform pairs will be derived. The unit impulse is defined as a pulse of width a and amplitude $1/a$ starting at time $t = 0$ and taken in the limit as a approaches zero. This definition leads to the expression

$$u_1(t) = \lim_{a \to 0} \frac{1}{a} [u(t) - u(t - a)] \tag{12-52}$$

where $u(t)$ is a unit step at $t = 0$ and $u(t - a)$ is a second unit step at $t = a$. The transform pair for a unit step function is easily obtained from Eq. (12-49) by letting $f(t)$ equal unity and is listed as the second transform of Table 12-1. Applying this transformation to Eq. (12-52) gives

$$U_1(s) = \frac{1}{a}\left[\frac{1}{s} - \frac{e^{-as}}{s}\right] = \frac{1}{as}[1 - e^{-as}] \tag{12-53}$$

Expanding the expression in a Maclaurin series about $a = 0$ yields

$$U_1(s) = 1 - \frac{as}{2!} + \frac{a^2s^2}{3!} - \frac{a^3s^3}{4!} + \cdots \tag{12-54}$$

As a approaches zero, $U_1(s)$ approaches unity, thereby verifying the first transform pair of Table 12-1. Consequently, when the input function $i(t)$ of a network is a unit impulse, its transform $I(s)$ is unity, and it follows from Eq. (12-50) that $O(s) = H(s)$. Therefore, the transient response $o(t)$ given by the inverse transform of $O(s)$ contains the same information as the transfer ratio $H(s)$. Similarly, when a unit current impulse is applied to a one-port network, the transient response of the voltage carries the same information as the driving-point impedance. If the input is a unit step function, such that $I(s) = 1/s$, it follows from Eq. (12-50) that $O(s) = H(s)/s$. Because division by s in the frequency domain is equivalent to integration in the time domain, differentiation of the transient response due to a unit step input yields the same information as $H(s)$. These facts make the transient response, due to unit impulse and unit step functions, particularly useful in the analysis and synthesis of networks.

Before leaving the subject of transformations, it is useful to consider Fourier integrals. Assume that $f(t)$ is a periodic function of time with a period T defined in the interval $-T/2 \le t \le T/2$. Then if $f(t)$ is specified as a series of n finite frequency components, it can be expressed in Fourier series form as

$$f(t) = \sum_{n=-\infty}^{\infty} a_n e^{j\omega nt}$$

where

$$a_n = \frac{1}{T}\int_{-T/2}^{T/2} f(t)e^{-j\omega nt}\, dt \quad\text{and}\quad T = \frac{2\pi}{\omega} \tag{12-55}$$

The summation and integral terms of this expression are essentially inverse relations; therefore, as T approaches infinity, $f(t)$ becomes

$$f(t) = \frac{1}{2\pi}\int_{-\infty}^{\infty} e^{j\omega t}\, d\omega \int_{-\infty}^{\infty} f(t)e^{-j\omega t}\, dt \tag{12-56}$$

It is convenient to denote the second integral as

$$F(j\omega) = \int_{-\infty}^{\infty} f(t)e^{-j\omega t}\, dt \qquad (12\text{-}57)$$

This expression is known as the Fourier transform and is equivalent to the direct Laplace transform when s of Eq. (12-49) is replaced by $j\omega$ and the limits of time are extended from minus infinity to plus infinity. Combining Eqs. (12-56) and (12-57) yields the inverse Fourier transform given by

$$f(t) = \frac{1}{2\pi} \int_{-\infty}^{\infty} F(j\omega)e^{j\omega t}\, d\omega \qquad (12\text{-}58)$$

Consequently, the Fourier transform pair of Eqs. (12-57) and (12-58) relates any periodic function of time to its real frequency spectrum.†

When the input to a network is a unit impulse, it follows from the Fourier transform of Eq. (12-57) that $I(j\omega)$ is unity. Hence, the output response, $O(j\omega)$ is identical to the network function $H(j\omega)$. In this case if the network's transient response $o(t)$ is known, it is possible from Eq. (12-57) to write

$$H(j\omega) = \int_{-\infty}^{\infty} o(t)e^{-j\omega t}\, dt \qquad (12\text{-}59)$$

By the inverse transform of Eq. (12-58), $o(t)$ becomes

$$o(t) = \frac{1}{2\pi} \int_{-\infty}^{\infty} H(j\omega)e^{j\omega t}\, d\omega$$

$$= \frac{1}{2\pi} \int_{-\infty}^{\infty} \{Re[H(j\omega)] \cos \omega t - Im[H(j\omega] \sin \omega t\}\, d\omega$$

$$+ \frac{j}{2\pi} \int_{-\infty}^{\infty} \{Re[H(j\omega)] \sin \omega t + Im[H(j\omega)] \cos \omega t\}\, d\omega \qquad (12\text{-}60)$$

where $Re[H(j\omega)]$ and $Im[H(j\omega)]$ represent the real and imaginary parts of the network function, respectively. The imaginary component of this expansion must be zero; otherwise, $o(t)$ is a nonphysical time function. If $o(t)$ is zero for negative time, the odd and even components of the first integral must be equal and opposite for $t < 0$, and hence they are equal for $t > 0$. Therefore it follows from Eq. (12-59) that

$$Re[H(j\omega)] = \int_{0}^{\infty} o(t) \cos \omega t\, dt$$

and

$$Im[H(j\omega)] = - \int_{0}^{\infty} o(t) \sin \omega t\, dt \qquad (12\text{-}61)$$

† The factor $1/2\pi$ of Eq. (12-56) is sometimes associated with Eq. (12-57) rather than Eq. (12-58). A detailed derivation of the above results can be found in E. A. Guillemin, *The Mathematics of Circuit Analysis* (New York: John Wiley & Sons, Inc., 1949), Chap. VII.

It is necessary that the real part of driving-point functions be greater than or equal to zero for all frequencies. This constraint imposes bounds on the impulse transient responses which are investigated in the next section, using the relationships of Eq. (12-61). Inverse relationships between the transient response $H(j\omega)$, $Re[H(j\omega)]$, and $Im[H(j\omega)]$ can be derived from the transformation of Eq. (12-58). Furthermore, similar sets of relationships can be derived for networks with unit step or various other input functions.

As in the case of the frequency response, there are a number of terms which may be used to describe the transient response of a network. For example, consider the typical step function response of Fig. 12-11. In this example it is assumed that a unit step function is applied to the input of the network at time t_0 and the response is described in the following terms:

1. Time delay, T_D, is a measure of the time between the application of the input until the appearance of a significant response. There is no standard definition or quantitative value for defining a significant response, although the time required for the response to reach half of its final value is often used as a criterion.

2. Rise time, T_R, is in effect a measure of the slope of the leading edge of the response. Here again there is no accepted standard; however, in Fig. 12-11, rise time is defined as the time required for the response to go from 10 to 90 percent of its final value. In some cases it is more useful to define rise time as the reciprocal of the slope of the response at the instant the response is half-way to its final value. Rise time in the time domain is similar to bandwidth in the frequency domain, since both tend to define the range of frequencies that will pass through the network unchanged.

3. Overshoot defines the relative resonance of the network, and the allowable amount of overshoot depends on the intended use of the network. In some instances nearly 100 percent overshoot may be desired, whereas other applications may require no overshoot. A compromise is often made on the allowable overshoot to maintain a short rise time.

4. Settling time, T_S is generally defined as the time required for oscillations in the response to decay below some prescribed percentage of the final value. Hence T_S is a measure of how quickly the response approaches its final value. Again no standard criterion applies, but T_S is often measured to the point at which the response has settled to within 5 percent of its final value.

5. The term "damping" might also be used to describe the rate at which the response approaches its final value, although damping is usually defined quantitatively in terms of the so-called damping factor. A complete definition is not warranted; however, it is generally stated in terms of the relative position of the principal poles of the network function in the frequency domain.† To simply state that a response damps out in 10 secs implies that it reaches its final value in 10 secs with no appreciable error.

† For more information concerning the damping factor, the reader is directed to J. G. Truxal, *Automatic Feedback Control System Synthesis* (New York: McGraw-Hill Book Co., Inc., 1955), pp. 37–43.

These terms are often used in modified forms to describe the transient response of networks due to unit impulse and various other input functions. In some cases further definition is required to convey the precise meaning of a term.

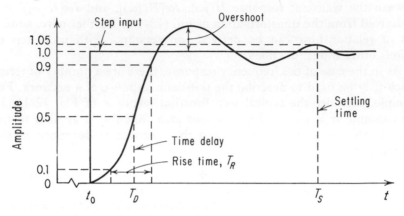

Fig. 12-11. Typical network response to a unit step function input.

12-6. Bounds on the Transient Response of Various types of Networks

In the preceding section it was mentioned that the unit impulse and step responses of various networks are bounded due to restrictions on the real and imaginary parts of the network functions and the nature of the direct and inverse Fourier transforms. Several theorems pertaining to these bounds have been derived by Zemanian.† The more complicated problem of determining the general effect of pole-zero locations on the transient response of a network has been studied by Mulligan.‡ The purpose of this section is to investigate some of the techniques and theorems that have been derived for predicting bounds on the unit impulse and step response of networks possessing certain known characteristics in the frequency domain.

Consider the case of a unit impulse or step of current applied to the terminals of a one-port network at $t = 0$. To compute bounds on the resulting voltage transient, it is necessary to restrict the driving-point impedance $Z(s) = KP(s)/Q(s)$ such that there are no poles on the

---

† A. H. Zemanian, "Bounds Existing on the Time and Frequency Response of Various Types of Networks," *Proc. IRE*, vol. 42, no. 5, May 1954, pp. 835–839; also "Further Bounds Existing on the Transient Response of Various Types of Networks," vol. 43, no. 3, March 1955, pp. 322–326; and "Improvements in Some Bounds on Transient Responses," vol. 46, no. 12, December 1958, pp. 1958–1959.

‡ J. H. Mulligan, Jr., "The Effect of Pole and Zero Locations on the Transient Response of Linear Dynamic Systems," *Proc. IRE*, vol. 37, no. 5, May 1949, pp. 516–529.

$j\omega$-axis and the degree of $Q(s)$ is equal to or greater than that of $P(s)$. These restrictions insure convergence of integrals which arise in the discussion. Within these constraints, it is possible to expand $Z(s)$ into two infinite series, one about the origin and the other as s approaches infinity.

$$Z(s) = R + \frac{1}{Cs} + \frac{K_2}{s^2} + \frac{K_3}{s^3} + \cdots \qquad |s| \geq a \qquad (12\text{-}62)$$

$$Z(s) = r + Ls + k_2 s^2 + k_3 s^3 + \cdots \qquad |s| \leq b \qquad (12\text{-}63)$$

Because these expansions are only used in the vicinity of ($s = 0$) and ($s = \infty$), an additional restriction has been imposed such that a is a number greater than unity and also greater than the distance from the origin to the furthest pole of $Z(s)$. Likewise, b is a number less than unity and also less than the distance from the origin to the nearest pole of $Z(s)$. Finally, it is convenient to denote the voltage transient response, due to a unit impulse and satisfying the constraints mentioned above, as $U_1(t)$. The unit step response will be denoted by $S_1(t)$. With these conditions in mind, the theorems derived by Zemanian can be stated as follows:

Theorem 1. When $Z(s)$ is such that R of Eq. (12-62) is zero and $Re[Z(j\omega)] \geq 0$ for all ω then $U_1(t) \leq (1/C)$ for all t. This fact is easily proved using the following inverse Fourier transform relating $U_1(t)$ to the $Re[Z(j\omega)]$.

$$U_1(t) = \frac{2}{\pi} \int_0^\infty Re[Z(j\omega)] \cos \omega t \, d\omega \qquad (12\text{-}64)$$

Since $Re[Z(j\omega)]$ is never negative, it can be concluded that

$$[U_1(t)] = \left[\frac{2}{\pi} \int_0^\infty Re[Z(j\omega)] \cos \omega t \, d\omega \right] \leq \frac{2}{\pi} \int_0^\infty Re[Z(j\omega)] \, d\omega \qquad (12\text{-}65)$$

Because $Z(s)$ has no right half-plane or $j\omega$-axis poles, integrating $Z(s)$ around the right half-plane yields a value for the right side of Eq. (12-65) of $1/C$. Therefore it follows that $U_1(t) \leq (1/C)$, where C represents the shunting capacitance between the input terminals of the network at ($\omega = \infty$). As a consequence of this result it can be concluded by integration that the slope of the unit step response $S_1(t)$ of a network satisfying the above conditions cannot be greater than $1/C$. If the final value of $S_1(t)$ is r, the rise time from zero to r cannot be less than rC, nor can the rise time from $0.1r$ to $0.9r$ be less than $0.8rC$.

Theorem 2. When $Z(s)$ is such that $(R = 0)$ and the real part of the function decreases monotonically to zero as ω increases from zero to infinity (i.e., $\{dRe[Z(j\omega)]/d\omega\} \leqq 0$ for $0 \leqq \omega$), it will have an impulse response bounded by

$$|U_1(t)| \leqq \frac{1}{C} \left[\frac{\sin \dfrac{\pi t}{2rC}}{\dfrac{\pi t}{2rC}} \right] \qquad \text{for} \qquad 0 \leqq t \leqq rC \tag{12-66}$$

and $\qquad |U_1(t)| \leqq \dfrac{2r}{\pi t} \qquad \text{for} \qquad rC \leqq t \leqq \infty$ $\tag{12-67}$

Proof of this theorem is based on expanding Eq. (12-64) as follows:

$$U_1(t) = \frac{2}{\pi} \int_0^{\pi/2t} Re[Z(j\omega)] \cos \omega t \, d\omega + \frac{2}{\pi} \int_{\pi/2t}^{\infty} Re[Z(j\omega)] \cos \omega t \, d\omega$$
$$= A(t) + B(t) \tag{12-68}$$

It can be shown that the second term $B(t)$ is always negative; consequently, $U_1(t) \leqq A(t)$. This can be accomplished by integrating $B(t)$ by parts and making use of the fact that $\sin \omega t \leqq 1$. To evaluate upper bounds on $A(t)$, it is useful to consider the function $(\sin \omega t/\omega t)$. This function is positive and monotonically decreasing within the interval $0 \leqq \omega \leqq (\pi/t)$. The positive rectangular pulse defined by Eq. (12-69) represents an upper bound on this function and hence leads to a larger value for $A(t)$.

$$\left. \begin{array}{lll} Re^*[Z(j\omega)] = r & \text{for} & |\omega| \leqq \omega_c \\ Re^*[Z(j\omega)] = R & \text{for} & \omega_c \leqq |\omega| \end{array} \right\} R < r \tag{12-69}$$

and

Consequently, when $(\pi/2t) \geqq \omega_c$ such that $t \leqq rC$, $A(t)$ of Eq. (12-68) and the upper bounds on $U_1(t)$ are given by Eq. (12-66). Likewise, for $(\pi/2t) \leqq \omega_c$ such that $t \geqq rC$, $A(t)$ and the upper bounds on $U_1(t)$ are given by Eq. (12-67). Lower bounds on $U_1(t)$ can be determined in the same manner by using the fact that $\sin \omega t \geqq -1$. Therefore, the impulse response is bounded from above and below by the conditions of Eqs. (12-66) and (12-67). The region of the time domain within which this response is constrained by these conditions is shown in Fig. 12-12 as a cross-hatched area.

Theorem 3. Provided $Z(s)$ is such that $R = 1/C = 0$ and $Im[Z(j\omega)] \leqq 0$ for $0 \leqq \omega$, the impulse response will be bounded such that $|U_1(t)| \leqq K_2 t$. This fact is based on the relationship between the $Im[Z(j\omega)]$ and the impulse response given by

$$U_1(t) = \frac{-2}{\pi} \int_0^{\infty} Im[Z(j\omega)] \sin \omega t \, d\omega \tag{12-70}$$

because

$$Im[Z(j\omega)] \leqq 0 \qquad \text{and} \qquad |\sin \omega t| \leqq \omega t$$

it follows that

$$|U_1(t)| \leqq \frac{-2t}{\pi} \int_0^\infty \omega Im[Z(j\omega)] \, d\omega \qquad (12\text{-}71)$$

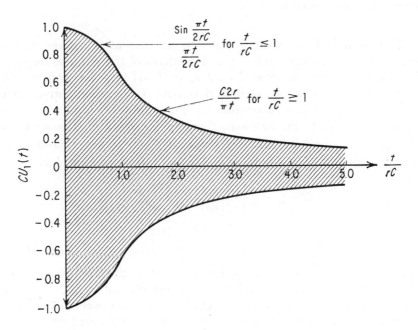

Fig. 12-12. Permissible region for the impulse response of Theorem 2.

Integrating $sZ(s)$ around the right half of the s-plane and avoiding the simple zero at the origin, it is possible to show that

$$\frac{2}{\pi} \int_0^\infty \omega Im[Z(j\omega)] \, d\omega = -K_2 \qquad (12\text{-}72)$$

Hence, from Eqs. (12-71) and (12-72), it follows that $|U_1(t)| \leqq K_2 t$. Using this bound on $U_1(t)$, it is possible to conclude by integration that $S_1(t)$ of a network satisfying the same conditions will be bounded by $(K_2/2)t^2$.

Theorem 4. Conversely, if $U_1(t)$ is such that $\int_0^\infty U_1(t) \, dt = r$ and $U_1(t) \geqq 0$ for all t, then $|Z(j\omega)| \leqq r$, $|Re[Z(j\omega)]| \leqq r$, and $|Im[Z(j\omega)]| \leqq r$ for all ω. The condition $\int_0^\infty U_1(t) \, dt = r$ is equivalent to stating that $R = 0$, since for $R \neq 0$ the impulse response has a singularity at $t = 0$ and the integral does not exist. This fact is based on the Fourier transforms of Eqs. (12-59) and (12-61) and is accomplished in the same manner as the proof of Theorem 1. As a consequence of Theorem 4, it can be concluded that if $|Z(j\omega)|$ or $|Re[Z(j\omega)]|$ at any frequency is greater than its value at $\omega = 0$, then $U_1(t)$ must be negative for some value of t. Therefore, the unit step response of the network cannot increase monotonically.

Theorem 5. In a manner converse to that of Theorem 2, it is possible to derive rules applying to derivatives of the impulse response. For instance, when the first derivative of $U_1(t)$ is never positive, two bounds exist. When the second derivative is never negative, three bounds on $|Z(j\omega)|$ can be established. Extending this argument to the general case leads to the following theorem. Provided $U_1(t)$ is such that $\int_0^\infty U_1(t)\, dt = r$ and the mth derivative of $U_1(t)$ is never positive (or never negative), then the bounds on $|Z(j\omega)|$ can be expressed as

$$|Z(j\omega)| \leqq \left| \sum_{k=0}^{n-1} \frac{1}{(j\omega)^{k+1}} \left[\frac{d^k U_1(t)}{dt^k} \right]_{t=0} \right|$$
$$+ \left| \frac{2}{(j\omega)^{n+1}} \left[\frac{d^n U_1(t)}{dt^n} \right]_{t=0} \right| \tag{12-73}$$

where $n = 1, 2, \ldots, m$. This theorem is based on the transformations of Eqs. (12-59) and (12-61) which are repeatedly integrated by parts; however, proof is too lengthy to include in this discussion. The initial and final values used in this integration process are based on the facts that $U_1(t)$ approaches zero as t becomes infinite and derivatives of $U_1(t)$ at $t = 0$ are the limiting values that these derivatives approach as t goes to zero from the positive direction. From this theorem when $(m = 1)$, it can be shown that any impulse response which approaches zero as t goes to infinity and is concave upward with a finite, nonzero initial value will have a Fourier transform with a real part that is never negative. This can be useful from the standpoint of realizability when synthesizing a network from transient-response information.

Theorem 6. When $Z(s)$ is such that $Im[Z(j\omega)] \leqq 0$ for $\omega \leqq 0$, the unit step response $S_1(t)$ is bounded such that

$$R \leqq S_1(t) < 2r - R \tag{12-74}$$

This relationship is based on the following Fourier transform.

$$S_1(t) = \frac{2}{\pi} \int_0^\infty \frac{Im[Z(j\omega)]}{\omega} \cos \omega t \, d\omega + r \tag{12-75}$$

Because $|\cos \omega t| \leq 1$, integrating $Z(s)/s$ around the right half of the s-plane, avoiding the pole at the origin, yields:

$$\left| \int_0^\infty \frac{Im[Z(j\omega)]}{\omega} \cos \omega t \, d\omega \right| \leq \int_0^\infty \frac{|Im[Z(j\omega)]|}{\omega} \, d\omega = \frac{\pi}{2}(r - R)$$

$$(12\text{-}76)$$

Finally, because this integral is a positive quantity, it follows that $r \geq R$ and hence the conditions of Eq. (12-74) result. From Eq. (12-74) it can be concluded that no RC one-port network can have a percentage overshoot (or undershoot) in its voltage response, due to a unit current step input, that exceeds 100 percent. The same conclusion applies to an RL one-port network on an admittance basis. If $Z(s)$ of an RC network approaches R as ω goes to infinity, the overshoot (or undershoot) expressed in percent must be less than $100(r - R)/r$.

Theorem 7. Any network whose driving-point impedance has $Re[Z(j\omega)]$ which decreases monotonically as ω increases from zero to infinity (i.e., $\{dRe[Z(j\omega)]/d\omega\} \leq 0$ for $\omega \geq 0$) will have a unit step response with an overshoot of less than 18 percent when $R = 0$ and a rise time, from the application of the step until the response crosses the final value, of greater than $1.22(r - R)C$. In general the bounds on $S_1(t)$ of a network satisfying these restrictions can be expressed analytically as

$$R \leq S_1(t) \leq R + \frac{2}{\pi}(r - R)Si\left[\frac{\pi t}{2(r - R)C} \right]$$

$$\text{for} \qquad 0 \leq t \leq 2(r - R)C$$

$$R \leq S_1(t) \leq R + \frac{2}{\pi}(r - R)Si(\pi) < R + 1.18(r - R)$$

$$\text{for} \qquad 2(r - R)C \leq t < \infty$$

NOTE: $Si(x) = \int_0^x (\sin u/u) \, du \ldots$ first sine integral $\qquad (12\text{-}77)$

Proof of Eq. (12-77) is based on the Fourier transform relating $S_1(t)$ to the $Re[Z(j\omega)]$ which can be written and expanded as follows:

$$S_1(t) = \frac{2}{\pi} \int_0^\infty Re[Z(j\omega)] \frac{\sin \omega t}{\omega} \, d\omega$$

$$= \frac{2t}{\pi} \int_0^{\pi/t} Re[Z(j\omega)] \frac{\sin \omega t}{\omega t} \, d\omega + \frac{2t}{\pi} \int_{\pi/t}^\infty Re[Z(j\omega)] \frac{\sin \omega t}{\omega t} \, d\omega$$

$$= D(t) + E(t) \qquad\qquad (12\text{-}78)$$

The second term can be integrated by part to give

$$E(t) = R - \frac{2}{\pi} Si(\pi) Re[Z(j\omega)]_{\omega=\pi/t} + \frac{2}{\pi} \int_{\pi/t}^{\infty} \left\{ \frac{-dRe[Z(j\omega)]}{d\omega} \right\} Si(\omega t)\, d\omega$$

(12-79)

Because $\{dRe[Z(j\omega)]/d\omega\} \leq 0$ and $Si(\omega t) \leq Si(\pi)$, Eq. (12-79) yields

$$E(t) \leq R\left[1 - \frac{2}{\pi} Si(\pi) \right]$$

(12-80)

This represents part of the solution; however, it is still necessary to establish bounds on the first term $D(t)$ of Eq. (12-78).

To evaluate $D(t)$ it is useful to reconsider the function $(\sin \omega t/\omega t)$ and the rectangular pulse defined by Eq. (12-69). Integrating $[Z(s) - R]$ around the right half-plane (as in Theorem 1) leads to

$$\frac{2}{\pi} \int_{0}^{\infty} \{Re[Z(j\omega)] - R\}\, d\omega = \frac{1}{C}$$

(12-81)

Applying this to the $Re^*[Z(j\omega)]$ of Eq. (12-69) and solving for ω_c yields

$$\omega_c = \frac{\pi}{2(r - R)C}$$

(12-82)

Consequently, when $(\pi/t) \geq \omega_c$ such that $t \leq 2(r - R)C$, $D(t)$ becomes

$$D(t) \leq \frac{2t}{\pi} \int_{0}^{\omega_c} r \frac{\sin \omega t}{\omega t}\, d\omega + \frac{2t}{\pi} \int_{\omega_c}^{\pi/t} R \frac{\sin \omega t}{\omega t}\, d\omega$$

$$\leq \frac{2}{\pi} (r - R) Si(\omega_c t) + \frac{2}{\pi} R Si(\pi)$$

(12-83)

When $(\pi/t) \leq \omega_c$ such that $t \geq 2(r - R)C$, $D(t)$ reduces to

$$D(t) \leq \frac{2r}{\pi} Si(\pi)$$

(12-84)

Combining Eqs. (12-80), (12-83), and (12-84), where $S_1(t) = D(t) + E(t)$ as in Eq. (12-78), leads to the bounds on the unit step response given by Eq. (12-77). The region of the time domain within which this response can lie has been computed from Eq. (12-77) for $R = 0$ and is shown as a cross-hatched area in Fig. 12-13.

Zemanian has also derived a lower bound on the settling time of a network's response due to unit impulse and step inputs. This bound is based on an extension of Theorem 1, but because of its complexity, the derivation will not be included in this discussion. Therefore, it is convenient to define the settling time T_S as the least time between application of a step or impulse until the step response remains within $r(1 - \delta)$

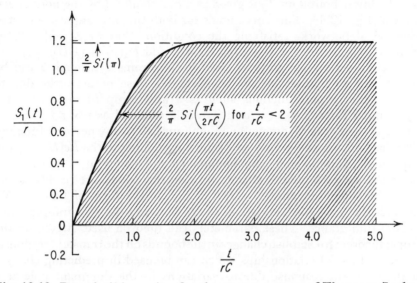

Fig. 12-13. Permissible region for the step response of Theorem 7 when $R = 0$.

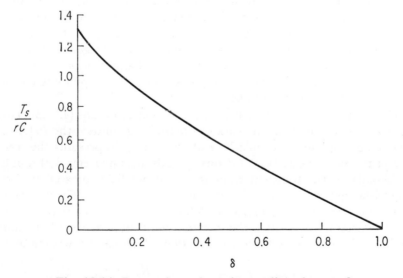

Fig. 12-14. Lower bound on the settling time to δ.

of its final value r or the impulse response remains within $\delta(1/C)$ of its initial value $1/C$ where δ is a positive number less than unity. In this case the lower bound on T_S is given as a function of δ by the normalized curve of Fig. 12-14. This curve holds for both the unit impulse and step response of networks satisfying the conditions that $Re[Z(j\omega)] \geq 0$ for all ω, $|U_1(t)| \leq (\delta/C) < (1/C)$ for $T_S = t$, and $U_1(0) = (1/C)$.

Techniques similar to those used in Theorems 1 through 7 can be used to derive bounds on the transient response of networks due to various other input functions such as a unit ramp (defined as 0 for $t \leq 0$ and t for $t \geq 0$) or a unit parabola (defined as 0 for $t \leq 0$ and t^2 for $t \geq 0$). These theorems can also be applied to any network function $H(s)$ that satisfies the proper constraints pertaining to the $Re[H(j\omega)]$ and $Im[H(j\omega)]$. Variations in the bounds on the transient response of a particular network, due to changes in element values, are readily determined by expanding the network function in the form of Eqs. (12-62) and (12-63) to establish variations in R, C, r, and the remaining parameters of importance. These parameters can then be used directly in the proper theorem to establish changes in the bounds on the transient response.

Several useful relationships which can be used in predicting changes in the transient response due to variations in the dominant pole-zero positions of a network have resulted from the above analysis and the work of J. H. Mulligan, Jr. For example, complex zeros at large values of ω or complex poles close to the origin tend to reduce the overshoot, whereas complex poles at large values of ω or zeros near the origin tend to increase the overshoot. Real poles or zeros to the left of dominant complex poles of a network tend to decrease or increase the overshoot respectively. The transient response becomes more sensitive to these real roots the closer they are to the dominant poles. In general the overshoot and settling time are affected more by changes in pole-zero positions in the vicinity of the dominant poles than by corresponding changes in remote regions of the s-plane.

One additional point worth mention is that R of Eq. (12-62) represents the resistance of the network or the limiting value of the $Re[Z(j\omega)]$ at extreme frequencies. Similarly, r of Eq. (12-63) represents the resistance of the network at $\omega = 0$. Consequently in Theorems 1 through 7 the bounds on the transient response are generally expressed in terms of a resistance and a capacitance such as rC, or $(r - R)C$. The resistance-capacitance product in each case is defined as the characteristic network "time constant." Consider the driving-point impedance of a simple parallel resistance-capacitance combination which can be written as

$$Z(s) = \frac{1}{C_o s + \dfrac{1}{R_o}} = \frac{R_o}{R_o C_o s + 1}$$

$$(12\text{-}85)$$

Both $Z(s)$ and R_o must have dimensions of ohms. Unity is obviously dimensionless; hence, R_oC_os must also be dimensionless. However, s has the dimensions of frequency, clearly when $s = j\omega = j2\pi f$. Therefore, R_oC_o must have the dimensions of reciprocal frequency or time. Consequently R_oC_o is known as the time constant of the RC combination, and a dimensional analysis reveals that the product of ohms and farads has units of time in seconds. Hence, the characteristic network time constant, defined above as the product of rC, RC, or $(r - R)C$, becomes more meaningful. A similar argument using a series resistance-inductance network indicates that L_o/R_o also has dimensions of time. As a result, the bounds on the transient response might also be derived and defined in terms of the time constants L/r, L/R, or $L/(r - R)$, where L is the equivalent series inductance of the network given by Eq. (12-63) at low frequencies.

12-7. Relationship between Frequency and Time-domain Errors

Sections 12-4 and 12-6 have been devoted to establishing bounds on the frequency and transient response of a network when its characteristics are known in the frequency domain. Emphasis has been placed on the variation of these bounds due to changes in element values or pole-zero locations. For the sake of completeness, it is desirable that deviations or errors generated in the frequency response, due to element or pole-zero changes, be transformed for direct interpretation in terms of variations in the transient response. This problem has been investigated by Gumowski using several different error criterions.†

Of the various possible methods for describing an error in the frequency domain, consideration of the magnitude of the error at each frequency is probably the easiest to handle mathematically. For instance, assume that $H(j\omega)$ represents the transfer or driving-point function of a network having a unit impulse response denoted by $U_1(t)$. Similarly, let $H^*(j\omega)$ represent the same function following a change in one or more of the network elements or pole-zero locations. The unit impulse response related to $H^*(j\omega)$ will be defined as $U_1^*(t)$, and from the inverse Fourier transform of Eq. (12-58), it follows that

$$U_1(t) = \frac{1}{2\pi} \int_{-\infty}^{\infty} e^{j\omega t} H(j\omega)\, d\omega \quad \text{and} \quad U_1^*(s) = \frac{1}{2\pi} \int_{-\infty}^{\infty} e^{j\omega t} H^*(j\omega)\, d\omega$$

$$(12\text{-}86)$$

† I. Gumowski, "Some Relations Between Frequency and Time-Domain Errors in Network Synthesis Problems," *IRE Trans. Circuit Theory*, vol. CT-5, no. 1, March 1958, pp. 66–69.

The error in the frequency domain can be written as $[E(j\omega) = H(j\omega) - H^*(j\omega)]$ in which case the error in the time domain $e(t)$ becomes†

$$e(t) = U_1(t) - U_1^*(t) = \frac{1}{2\pi} \int_{-\infty}^{\infty} e^{j\omega t}[H(j\omega) - H^*(j\omega)]\, d\omega$$

$$= \frac{1}{2\pi} \int_{-\infty}^{\infty} e^{j\omega t} E(j\omega)\, d\omega \tag{12-87}$$

If the magnitude of the error is of primary concern, Eq. (12-87) can be rewritten as

$$|e(t)| = \frac{1}{2\pi} \left| \int_{-\infty}^{\infty} e^{j\omega t} E(j\omega)\, d\omega \right| \leq \frac{1}{2\pi} \int_{-\infty}^{\infty} |E(j\omega)|\, d\omega \tag{12-88}$$

Consequently the error in the unit impulse response is less than or equal to $1/2\pi$ times the area under the error function $|E(j\omega)|$ in the frequency domain. It should be pointed out that $|E(j\omega)| = |H(j\omega) - H^*(j\omega)|$ is not the same as the difference between the amplitude responses of $H(j\omega)$ and $H^*(j\omega)$. This fact becomes clear from Fig. 12-15, which illustrates the relationship between these vectors at a specific

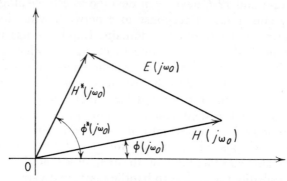

Fig. 12-15. Typical relationship between $H(j\omega)$, $H^*(j\omega)$, and $E(j\omega)$ at ω_o.

frequency ω_o. However, practical use can be made of $H(j\omega)$ and $H^*(j\omega)$, since it can be shown that $|E(j\omega)| \geq |H(j\omega)| - |H^*(j\omega)|$. Figure 12-15 also reveals that the difference in the phase angle $\phi(j\omega_o)$ and $\phi^*(j\omega_o)$ is not necessarily equal to the argument of $E(j\omega_o)$; hence the argument of $E(j\omega)$ does not generally equal $\phi(j\omega) - \phi^*(j\omega)$.

Application of Eq. (12-88) appears straightforward, but unfortunately, $|E(j\omega)|$ may not be absolutely integrable within the limits

---

† In general, if the input function is denoted by $i(t)$ with a Fourier transform, $I(j\omega)$, the error in the time domain will be of the form

$$e(t) = \frac{1}{2\pi} \int_{-\infty}^{\infty} e^{j\omega t} E(j\omega) I(j\omega)\, d\omega$$

But when $i(t)$ is a unit impulse, $I(j\omega)$ becomes unity and $e(t)$ reduces to the form of Eq. (12-87).

$-\infty < \omega < +\infty$ since the area under $|E(j\omega)|$ may be infinite. In this event, it is possible to obtain an upper bound on the time-domain error $e(t)$ by replacing $E(j\omega)$ with a function $E^*(j\omega)$ that is integrable and whose modulus encloses an equal or larger area than $E(j\omega)$. One convenient choice is an ideal filter characterized by a constant value within an interval $|\omega_1| < |\omega| < |\omega_2|$ and zero everywhere else. The approximation of $E(j\omega)$ can be made as accurate as desired by using a series of these filters for $E^*(j\omega)$ where each ideal filter has a rectangular area that is easily integrated. A least upper bound on $e(t)$ is obtained by considering both the magnitude and argument of $E(j\omega)$ in Eq. (12-87). In many cases $E(j\omega)$ can be determined directly from $H(j\omega)$ and $H^*(j\omega)$; however, when this is not possible, bounds on $e(t)$ determined from $|E(j\omega)|$ or $|E^*(j\omega)|$ are usually conservative. If $E(j\omega)$ is specified in the form of variations in the amplitude and phase response or as tabulated data, approximation or numerical techniques can be employed to establish a suitable expression for $|E^*(j\omega)|$. Finally, a number of different error criterions can be used for defining $E(j\omega)$. For instance, it may be desirable to minimize the error defined by $E(j\omega) = \int_{-\infty}^{\infty} |H(j\omega) - H^*(j\omega)|^\beta \, d\omega$ where β is a real constant or $E(j\omega) = \left| \int_{-\infty}^{\infty} [H(j\omega) - H^*(j\omega)]^\beta G(\omega) \, d\omega \right|$ where $G(\omega)$ is a chosen convergent function. The approach used in the above discussion can still be employed provided the desired error function can be approximated with sufficient accuracy by an expression $E^*(j\omega)$ which can then be applied as shown in Eq. (12-88).

References

Because most of the topics of this chapter have not yet appeared in textbook form, the reader is directed to the references listed in the footnotes. However, transform procedures of the types introduced in Sec. 12-5 are presented in detail in the following books:

1. J. A. Aseltine, *Transform Method in Linear System Analysis* (New York: McGraw Hill Book Co., Inc., 1958), Chaps. 1 through 8 and Chap. 13.
2. S. Fich, *Transient Analysis in Electrical Engineering* (Englewood Cliffs, N.J.: Prentice-Hall, Inc., 1951), Chaps. 6, 7, and 10.
3. M. F. Gardner and J. L. Barnes, *Transients in Linear Systems* (New York: John Wiley & Sons, Inc., 1942), Chaps. 3 through 9 and Appendices A and B.
4. L. A. Pipes, *Applied Mathematics for Engineers and Physicists* (New York: McGraw-Hill Book Co., Inc., 1958), Chaps. 3 and 21.

Frequency and time-domain response characteristics can be found in almost all network analysis and synthesis texts. The following references are representative of the work being done in the field of sensitivity functions:

5. R. Y. Huang, "The Sensitivity of the Poles of Linear, Closed-Loop Systems," *AIEE Trans., Applications and Industry*, September 1958, pp. 182–186, and discussion on pp. 186–187.
6. F. F. Kuo, "A Sensitivity Theorem," *IRE Trans. Circuit Theory*, vol. CT-6, no. 1, March 1959, p. 131.
7. W. A. Lynch, "A Formulation of the Sensitivity Function," *IRE Trans. Circuit Theory*, vol. CT-4, no. 3, September 1957, p. 289.
8. J. J. Mikulski, "The Correlation Between Classical and Pole-Zero Sensitivity," *Doctorial Thesis*, University of Illinois, Urbana, Illinois, 1959.
9. D. T. McRuer and R. L. Stapleford, "Sensitivity and Modal Response for Single-Loop and Multiloop Systems," Air Force Systems Command, Wright-Patterson AFB, Ohio, Report No. ASD-TDR-62-812, January 1963.

Additional papers dealing with variations in network response are:

10. J. D. Graham, "An Approximation of Transient Response from Frequency Response Data," *Proc. IRE*, vol. 47, no. 4, April 1959, p. 591.
11. L. A. Zadah, "The Determination of the Impulsive Response of Variable Networks," *J. Appl. Phys.*, vol. 21, July 1950, pp. 642–645.
12. A. H. Zemanian, "Bounds on the Fourier Transforms of Monotonic Functions," *Duke Mathematical Journal*, vol. 24, December 1957, pp. 499–504.

Problems

12-1. Plot the poles and zeros of the following function and determine the amplitude and phase response by graphically measuring the angles and distances from the poles and zeros to a test point which is moved from the origin to $j\omega = j15$. Convert the amplitude values to decibels referenced to the peak response.

$$\frac{E_2}{E_1} = \frac{s(s + 6)}{(s + 2)(s^2 + 2s + 26)}$$

12-2. Repeat the requirements of Prob. 12-1 for the following transfer ratio, taking into account the multiplying factor:

$$\frac{E_2}{E_1} = \frac{400}{(s^2 + 2s + 101)^2}$$

12-3. Sketch the amplitude and phase response for the following function by plotting its poles and zeros and determining the nature of the response directly from the s-plane:

$$\frac{E_2}{E_1} = \frac{(s^2 + 8s + 41)}{(s + 12)(s^2 + 4s + 104)(s^2 + 6s + 2509)}$$

12-4. Consider a series RLC network so designed that the zeros of its impedance function both lie at the same point on the negative real axis. Determine to a first-order approximation the variation in position of the zeros if the resistance is changed by δr. Show that when R is decreased by δr the network will be resonant at approximately $\omega_o = \sqrt{\delta r R / 2L^2}$.

12-5. Consider a parallel LC combination with an admittance function having zeros at $s_1 = \pm jw_o/\sqrt{LC}$. Show by a second-order approximation that if a small conductance ($\delta y = 1/\delta R$) is added in parallel with L and C, the zeros move to $s_1^{**} \approx 1/2\delta RC \pm j[w_o - 1/8w_o(\delta R)^2 C^2]$. How does this approximation compare with the exact location of the new zeros? Discuss the effects of adding δC or δL in parallel with L and C.

12-6. Determine the driving-point impedance for the Brune network of Chap. 5, Fig. 5-9, in terms of the mutual inductance of the transformer M. Using this function, determine an approximate expression for the variation in the position of its zeros due to changes in M of δM. Check the results by using Eqs. (5-32) and (5-48) and the data of Table 5-1.

12-7. Sketch the sensitivity function [as defined by Eq. (12-33)] for the zeros of the following driving-point impedance with respect to the resistance R_1 when both zeros lie at the same point on the negative real axis. Realize the impedance by series-parallel withdrawal and sketch its amplitude response for values of $R_1 = R$, $5R$, and $10R$. Discuss implications of the sensitivity function as it applies to the amplitude response.

$$Z(s) = \frac{R_1 LCs^2 + (R_1 R_2 C + L)s + R_1 + R_2}{LCs^2 + R_2 Cs + 1}$$

12-8. Sketch the sensitivity functions [as defined by Eq. (12-33)] for the poles of the impedance of Prob. 12-7 as a function of R_2 for cases in which $R_2 = 2\sqrt{L/C}$, $R_2 < 2\sqrt{L/C}$, and $R_2 > 2\sqrt{L/C}$.

12-9. Compute the amplitude response for the impedance of Prob. 12-7 when $R_1 = 1$ ohm, $R_2 = 2$ ohms, $L = 1/2$ henry, and $C = 1/10$ farad for frequencies from $w = 0$ to $w = 20$. Determine the maximum and minimum bounds on the amplitude response over this range of frequencies when each of the elements is permitted to vary by 5 percent. Use the procedures of Sec. 12-4.

12-10. Using Table 12-1, compute the unit impulse and step responses for a network possessing the voltage transfer ratio of Prob. 12-1 for values of time between $t = 0$ and $t = 5$ sec.

12-11. Using Table 12-1 and the impedance function of Prob. 12-7 compute the transient current response when a 1-volt step is applied (use the element values listed in Prob. 12-9). The period of interest is between $t = 0$ and $t = 4$ sec. Repeat the above calculations for variations in the capacitance of ± 10 percent.

12-12. Determine bounds on the current response when a unit impulse and unit step voltage are applied to networks possessing the following driving-point impedances:

(a) $Z(s) = \dfrac{(9s^2 + 9)}{(6s^3 + 2s)}$

(b) $Z(s) = \dfrac{(s^2 + 4s + 16)}{(s^2 + s + 4)}$

(c) $Z(s) = \dfrac{5(6s^2 + s + 3)}{3(2s^2 + 2s + 1)}$

12-13. Determine bounds on the unit impulse response of a network possessing the voltage transfer ratio of Prob. 12-1. Compute the variation in these bounds when the coefficients of each term in the transfer ratio is increased by 5 percent.

12-14. The curves of Fig. 12-9 represent the variations in the amplitude and phase response of the driving-point impedance of Fig. 12-7a ($R_o = 10$ ohms, $L_o = 2$ henrys, and $C_o = 1/2$ farad) where each of the elements are permitted to change by 5 percent. Using the procedures of Sec. 12-7, compute the errors that are likely to result in the impulse response based on the upper and lower bounds of the frequency response. (Judgment is necessary to complete this problem, since several approximations may be required.)

Chapter 13

Frequency Transformations

In many cases it is possible to extend existing network designs or synthesis procedures beyond their original scope by applying frequency transformations. These transformations are generally used for purposes of scaling, inversion, and translation of frequency-response characteristics of a network. For example, rather than attempt to realize a bandpass network directly by a complicated procedure, it is often easier to realize a low-pass structure which can be transformed to a bandpass configuration. However, frequency transformations can also be used to change the characteristics of the transient response or add resistance to a network. A prime example of the latter application is the technique of predistortion in Chap. 11, Sec. 11-5. Furthermore, frequency transformations enable the designer to accomplish the bulk of the numerical work with convenient numbers, thereby minimizing the chance of errors. In this respect they provide simplification similar to that of impedance-level transformations described in Chap. 10, Sec. 10-5. Several of the more useful frequency transformations are described in this chapter with examples to illustrate frequency scaling, inversion, and translation. The preliminary discussion is based on a graphical interpretation of frequency transformations suggested by Stewart.[†] This approach emphasizes the general characteristics of the transformations and places in evidence several facts that are easily overlooked when considering the mathematical aspects of the transformations.

13-1. Graphical Interpretation of Frequency Transformations

Consider the possibility of replacing the complex frequency variable s of a driving-point or transfer function by a new frequency variable s^*, where $s = F(s^*)$. In this case if the function is denoted by $H(s)$ and s is replaced by $F(s^*)$, then $H[F(s^*)]$ will be positive real provided both

[†] J. L. Stewart, "Graphical Interpretations for Frequency Transformations," *IRE WESCON Convention Record* (1958), Part 2, Circuit Theory, pp. 42–45.

$H(s)$ and $F(s^*)$ are positive real functions. Furthermore, if $H(s)$ has poles and zeros which can be written in factored form as $(s + \beta_i)$, subsequent transformation to $H[F(s^*)]$ will yield poles and zeros which can be written in factored form as $[F(s^*) + \beta_i]$. Therefore, poles and zeros of a transformed function $H[F(s^*)]$ can be determined directly from those of $H(s)$.

In Chap. 12, Sec. 12-1, it was shown that the frequency response for a function $H(s)$ can be evaluated by plotting its poles and zeros on the s-plane and measuring the vector lengths and phase angles from the various roots to the points on the $j\omega$-axis at which the evaluation is desired. In other words, for every value of $s = j\omega$ there exists a unique complex value for $H(s)$. Similarly, for every $s = j\omega$ there exists a unique value for $s = F(s^*) = F(j\omega^*)$ which can be plotted on or to the right of the $j\omega$-axis provided $F(s^*)$ is a positive real function. Consequently it is possible to superimpose on the pole-zero plot of $H(s)$ the locus of $F(j\omega^*)$ which constitutes a transformed $j\omega$-axis. Therefore the frequency response of the transformed function $H[F(s^*)]$ can be evaluated by the vector lengths and phase angles from the poles and zeros of $H(s)$ to the corresponding points on the $F(j\omega^*)$ locus. This geometry is illustrated in Fig. 13-1 where numerical values denote corresponding real frequencies.

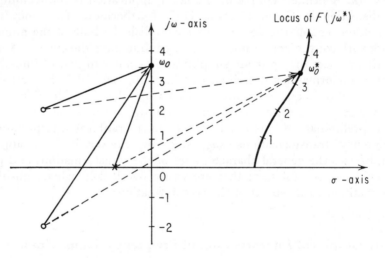

Fig. 13-1. Illustration of transformed frequency interpretation.

When $F(s^*)$ is a reactance function, the locus of $F(j\omega^*)$ is constrained to the $j\omega$-axis. The simplest example of this type is $s = F(s^*) = Ks^*$ where K is real and positive. Using this transformation, the $j\omega$-axis is modified linearly to provide frequency scaling. Similarly, $F(s^*) = K/s^*$ can be used to scale and invert the frequency response. In this case as

ω increases along the positive $j\omega$-axis towards $+j\infty$, $F(j\omega^*)$ must return from $-j\infty$ towards the origin. Therefore, $F(j\omega^*)$ must go from $+j\infty$ to $-j\infty$ by way of an infinite semicircle in the right half-plane. Consequently, transformations of this type permit repeated mapping of the original driving-point or transfer function making it possible to convert a low-pass network to a high-pass configuration as will be demonstrated later. Double mapping can be accomplished with the transformations, $F(s^*) = K_1 s^* + K_2/s^*$ and $F(s^*) = 1/(K_1 s^* + K_2/s^*)$, which are useful for scaling and translation of the frequency response. These transformations are useful for converting a low-pass to a band-pass network and a low-pass to a band-rejection configuration respectively. More complicated reactance transformations can be derived to produce multiple-pass and rejection bands; however, the bands cannot be placed arbitrarily close together and their amplitude-response characteristics will generally have the same shapes. Pass or rejection bands possessing different amplitude response characteristics can only be realized from original network functions having two or more pass or rejection bands with different amplitude response characteristics.

When a frequency transformation possesses a positive finite real part, resistance is added to the network. For example, the case in which $F(s^*) = K_1 + K_2 s^*$ represents the predistortion transformation described in Chap. 11, Sec. 11-5, combined with frequency scaling. Substituting $F(s^*) = K_1 + K_2 s^*$ for s in a network causes each inductor L to be replaced by an inductor $K_2 L$ and series resistor of K_1 ohms. Each capacitor C is replaced by $K_2 C$ and a parallel resistor of K_1 mhos. The s-plane representation of $F(j\omega^*)$ for this transformation is shown in Fig. 13-2a. The transformation $F(s^*) = K_1 s^*/(s^* + K_2)$ converts an inductor L to a parallel RL combination and a capacitor C to a series RC combination. The s-plane representation for this transformation is shown in Fig. 13-2b.

Any $F(s^*)$ that has the characteristics of an RL driving-point impedance (or RC admittance) will convert inductors of an original network to RL combinations and capacitors to RC combinations. In this case the locus of $F(j\omega^*)$ will always lie in the first quadrant of the s-plane or on its boundaries. Similarly, if $F(s^*)$ has the characteristics of an RC driving-point impedance (or RL admittance), it will convert inductors of the original network to RC combinations and capacitors to RL combinations. This form of transformation is restricted such that the locus of $F(j\omega^*)$ will always lie in the fourth quadrant of the s-plane or on its boundaries. The resulting networks in either case can always be realized as Foster or Cauer canonic forms.

Consider the possibility of superimposing contours of constant magnitude of $H(j\omega)$ on the pole-zero plot of the original function $H(s)$. If the locus of $F(j\omega^*)$ lies along one of these contours over a prescribed range of frequencies, the transformed function $H[F(s^*)]$ will have nearly a constant amplitude response in the same frequency interval. Likewise, contours of constant phase for $H(j\omega)$ can be superimposed on the pole-zero plot of $H(s)$. In this case the transformed function will have a relatively constant phase response provided the locus of $F(j\omega^*)$ lies

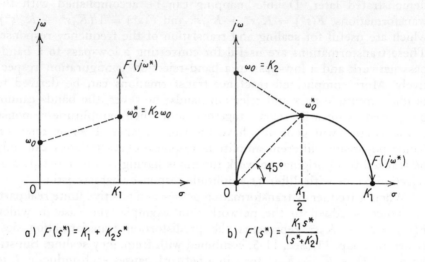

Fig. 13-2. Example transformations with finite real parts.

along one of the contours over the range of frequencies of interest. If $H(s)$ represents an RC network and if $F(s^*)$ is an RL driving-point impedance (or RC admittance), $H[F(s^*)]$ will yield an RC network. Therefore, when $H(s)$ possesses an equal number of finite poles and zeros, it is possible to obtain a realizable function $H[F(s^*)]$ that possesses relatively constant amplitude and phase over a finite range of frequencies.

A number of other interesting and useful results can be obtained by applying frequency transformations to well-known network functions. For instance, the simplest all-pass lattice network possesses a transfer function with a single pole on the negative real axis and a zero at its mirror image on the positive real axis. All possible lossless all-pass lattice networks can be derived from this simple case by using frequency transformations with reactance characteristics. Furthermore, all possible all-pass lattice networks with losses can be obtained by applying a react-ance transformation followed by a dissipation transformation, thereby adding resistance by shifting the poles and zeros of the original function to the right. The remainder of this chapter is devoted to further consideration of some of the more useful frequency transformations.

13-2. Frequency Scaling of Networks

A network which has been synthesized to have a specified frequency response with certain critical frequencies (e.g., resonance or half-power points) can be transformed to one having the same frequency responses with new critical frequencies by applying the linear transformation $s = F(s^*) = Ks^*$. For instance, a low-pass network with a cutoff frequency ω_{co} and a given amplitude at some frequency ω_x can be converted to a low-pass network with a new cutoff frequency at ω_{co}^* and the same amplitude at $\omega_x^* = \omega_x(\omega_{co}^*/\omega_{co})$. To demonstrate this, the low-pass network of Fig. 13-3a will be scaled to yield the network of Fig. 13-3b.

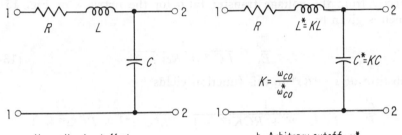

a. Normalized cutoff at ω_{co} b. Arbitrary cutoff, ω_{co}^*

Fig. 13-3. Typical low-pass filter network transformation.

This example has been selected since Fig. 13-3a can also be used to illustrate frequency inversion and translation in the following sections. However, these techniques, involving linear transformations, are general and can be applied to any network independent of its response characteristics.

The cutoff frequency of a low-pass network has been defined as the frequency at which the amplitude response has fallen 3 db from its value at $\omega = 0$. If the network of Fig. 13-3a is designed to have a cutoff frequency of ω_{co}, then to obtain a cutoff frequency at some new arbitrary frequency, ω_{co}^* it is possible to apply the linear transformation $s = F(s^*) = Ks^*$, which can be written in terms of real frequency as $\omega = K\omega^*$ or $\omega_{co}^* = K\omega_{co}^*$. Referring to Figs. 13-3a and 13-3b, the inductive and capacitive reactances of each network can be written in terms of their cutoff frequencies as

$$\left.\begin{aligned} X_L &= j\omega_{co}L \\ X_C &= \frac{1}{j\omega_{co}C} \end{aligned}\right\} \begin{aligned} \text{cutoff} \\ \text{at } \omega_{co} \end{aligned} \quad \text{and} \quad \left.\begin{aligned} X_{L*} &= j\omega_{co}^*L^* \\ X_{C*} &= \frac{1}{j\omega_{co}^*C^*} \end{aligned}\right\} \begin{aligned} \text{cutoff} \\ \text{at } \omega_{co}^* \end{aligned}$$

$$(13\text{-}1)$$

Equating the two inductive and two capacitive reactances yields

$$X_L = X_{L*} = j\omega_{co}L = j\omega_{co}^*L^* \qquad \text{or} \qquad L^* = \frac{\omega_{co}}{\omega_{co}^*} L = KL$$

and

$$X_C = X_{C*} = \frac{1}{j\omega_{co}C} = \frac{1}{j\omega_{co}^*C^*} \qquad \text{or} \qquad C^* = \frac{\omega_{co}}{\omega_{co}^*} C = KC$$

$$(13\text{-}2)$$

Therefore, based on the network of Fig. 13-3a with a cutoff frequency of ω_{co}, the network having a cutoff of an arbitrary frequency ω_{co}^* takes the form of Fig. 13-3b where $K = \omega_{co}/\omega_{co}^*$. Identical results can be obtained directly from the voltage transfer ratio for the network of Fig. 13-3a which is given by

$$\frac{E_2}{E_1} = \frac{1}{LCs^2 + Rcs + 1}$$

$$(13\text{-}3)$$

Substituting $s = Ks^*$ in this function yields

$$\frac{E_2}{E_1} = \frac{1}{LCK^2s^{*2} + RCKs^* + 1} = \frac{1}{L^*C^*s^{*2} + RC^*s^* + 1}$$

where $\qquad L^* = KL \quad C^* = KC \quad$ and $\quad K = \dfrac{s}{s^*} = \dfrac{\omega}{\omega^*} = \dfrac{\omega_{co}}{\omega_{co}^*} \quad (13\text{-}4)$

Because Eq. (13-4) is of the same form as Eq. (13-3), it leads to the network of Fig. 13-3b which has the same response characteristics but at the new frequency, $s^* = j\omega^*$.

From the above example, it is seen that once a network has been designed with a critical frequency ω_x the frequency can be shifted or scaled to an arbitrary frequency ω_x^* by simply multiplying the inductor and capacitor values of the original network by K. Resistance is not a function of frequency; hence, the transformation $s = Ks^*$ does not change the resistors of a network. Furthermore, because the transformation is linear, it can be used to make corrective adjustments in networks that do not meet their design characteristics. However, one restriction must be observed. If two frequencies ω_1 and ω_2 are shifted by K to new points ω_1^* and ω_2^* the spacing will be equal to K times the spacing between ω_1 and ω_2. Consequently, the frequency spectrum is expanded or contracted by the transformation.

When the frequency response of a network has been scaled by K, the transient response is divided by K. For instance, assume that a voltage source of frequency ω_1 is applied to a given network and results in a frequency response of amplitude β and a transient response that decays to an arbitrary level in t_1 seconds. Then if the network is scaled such that the frequency response is multiplied by K, a new voltage source of frequency $K\omega_1$ will yield a frequency response of amplitude β and a transient response which decays to the same level in t_1/K sec. In fact, all time constants of the network are divided by K, and all natural or resonant frequencies are multiplied by K independently of the source. However, the overall impedance level of the network is not affected by frequency scaling, since the frequency response curves of the scaled network possess the same maxima as the original network except that each value occurs at K times the original frequency.

As an example of frequency scaling, assume the element values for the network of Fig. 13-3a are given by $R = 4$ ohms, $C = 1/6$ farad, and $L = 2$ henrys. Substituting this information into Eq. (13-3) gives the voltage transfer ratio, which can be written in terms of real frequencies as

$$\frac{E_2}{E_1} = \left.\frac{1}{\dfrac{s^2}{3} + \dfrac{2s}{3} + 1}\right]_{s=j\omega} = \frac{1}{\dfrac{-\omega^2}{3} + 1 + \dfrac{j2\omega}{3}} \tag{13-5}$$

When $\omega = 0$, the amplitude response of the network is unity or zero decibels. The cutoff frequency occurs when $|E_2/E_1|$ is down 3 db from its value at $\omega = 0$ (i.e., $|E_2/E_1|$ at cutoff is -3 db or $1/\sqrt{2}$). Therefore, equating the magnitude of the denominator of Eq. (13-5) with $\sqrt{2}$ gives

$$\left[\frac{-\omega^2}{3} + 1 + j\frac{2\omega}{3}\right] = \sqrt{2} \quad \text{or} \quad \left(\frac{-\omega^2}{3} + 1\right)^2 + \left(\frac{2\omega}{3}\right)^2 = 2 \tag{13-6}$$

The only positive real value of ω that satisfies this equation is $\omega = 2.04$; hence, this frequency represents ω_{co} for the example low-pass network.

Now assume that it is desirable to transform the network such that its response characteristics will remain the same except that the cutoff frequency will be moved to $\omega_{co}^* = 1000$ radians/sec. The resistance of the network will remain $R = 4$ ohms. However, the inductance ($L = 2$ henrys) and capacitance ($C = 1/6$ farad) of the original network must be scaled according to Eq. (13-2). This can be accomplished as follows:

$$L^* = \frac{\omega_{co}}{\omega_{co}^*} L = \frac{2.04}{1000}(2) = 4.08 \times 10^{-3} \text{ henry}$$

and

$$C^* = \frac{\omega_{co}}{\omega_{co}^*} C = \frac{2.04}{1000}\left(\frac{1}{6}\right) = 0.34 \times 10^{-3} \text{ farad} \tag{13-7}$$

Using these impedances, the transfer ratio of the network having a cutoff frequency of $\omega_{co}^* = 1000$ can be written as

$$\frac{E_2}{E_1} = \frac{1}{L^*C^*s^{*2} + RC^*s^* + 1} = \frac{1}{1.39 \times 10^{-6}s^{*2} + 1.36 \times 10^{-3}s^* + 1} \tag{13-8}$$

This transfer ratio will have the same form of frequency response as Eq. (13-5) except that its cutoff frequency will be at $\omega_{co}^* = 1000$ rather than $\omega_{co} = 2.04$ radians/sec. The resulting network is given by Fig. 13-3b, where $R = 4$ ohms, $L^* = 4.08 \times 10^{-3}$ henry, and $C^* = 0.34 \times 10^{-3}$ farad.

13-3. Frequency Inversion of Networks

The second transformation of interest is that of frequency inversion. In brief, frequency inversion is accomplished by performing the substitution $s = K/s^*$, which causes every inductor of the original network to be replaced by a capacitor and every capacitor by an inductor. Resistance values of the network remain unchanged and there is no scaling of the response when K is unity. In terms of real frequency, the inverse transformation can be written as

$$ s = j\omega = \frac{K}{s^*} = \frac{K}{j\omega^*} \quad \text{or} \quad \omega = \frac{-K}{\omega^*} \tag{13-9} $$

Consequently, the amplitude response of the new network will be identical to that of the original network except that each original frequency ω_x will be replaced by $\omega_x^* = K/\omega_x$ and the phase response will be the negative of the phase response of the original network. To clarify these statements, it is useful to reconsider the low-pass network of Fig. 13-3a. Substituting Eq. (13-9) in the inductive and capacitive reactances yields

$$ X_L = Ls \Big]_{s=\frac{K}{s^*}} = \frac{1}{C^* s^*} \quad \text{where} \quad C^* = \frac{1}{KL} $$

and

$$ X_C = \frac{1}{Cs} \Big]_{s=\frac{K}{s^*}} = L^* s^* \quad \text{where} \quad L^* = \frac{1}{KC} \tag{13-10} $$

Because the resistance is unchanged by the inverse transformation of Eq. (13-9), the low-pass network of Fig. 13-3a is converted to the high-pass configuration of Fig. 13-4. Therefore if the cutoff frequency of a low-pass network is ω_{co}, and a high-pass network having a cutoff frequency of ω_{co}^* is desired, then each capacitor C of the low-pass network must be replaced by an inductor $L^* = 1/KC$ and each inductor L must be replaced by a capacitor $C^* = 1/KL$, where $K = \omega_{co}\omega_{co}^*$.

As an example of the low-pass to high-pass frequency transformation, assume that the low-pass network represented by Eq. (13-5) and Fig. 13-3a is to be converted to a high-pass configuration having a cutoff frequency $\omega_{co}^* = 1000$ radians/sec. The elements of the low-pass network are $R = 4$ ohms, $L = 2$ henrys, and $C = 1/6$ farad, and its cutoff frequency is $\omega_{co} = 2.04$ radians/sec. Using this information in the transformations of Fig. 13-4 gives the following reactive element values:

$$C^* = \frac{1}{\omega_{co}\omega_{co}^* L} = \frac{1}{(2.04)(1000)(2)} = 0.245 \times 10^{-3} \text{ farad}$$

$$L^* = \frac{1}{\omega_{co}\omega_{co}^* C} = \frac{1}{(2.04)(1000)\left(\frac{1}{6}\right)} = 2.94 \times 10^{-3} \text{ henry}$$

(13-11)

These values, when used with a resistance of 4 ohms in the network of Fig. 13-4, will yield a high-pass network having a cutoff frequency of $\omega_{co}^* = 1000$ radians/sec.

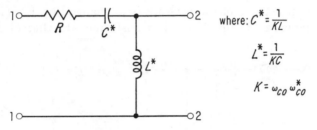

where: $C^* = \frac{1}{KL}$

$L^* = \frac{1}{KC}$

$K = \omega_{co}\,\omega_{co}^*$

Fig. 13-4. High-pass transformation based on the low-pass network of Fig. 13-3a.

It should be emphasized that the transformation of Eq. (13-9) is general and can be used to invert the response of any network. For instance, a bandpass network is easily converted to a band-rejection configuration by replacing each inductor of L henrys by a capacitor of $(1/L)$ farads and each capacitor of C farads by an inductor of $(1/C)$ henrys. In this case the frequency variable ω is replaced by $1/\omega$.

13-4. Frequency Translation of Networks

Frequency translation is accomplished by replacing s with a new variable s^* of the form $s = K_1 s^* + K_2/s^*$. This transformation can be written in terms of real frequencies as

$$s = j\omega = K_1 s^* + \frac{K_2}{s^*} = jK_1\omega^* + \frac{K_2}{j\omega^*} \qquad \text{or} \qquad \omega = K_1\omega^* - \frac{K_2}{\omega^*}$$

(13-12)

This transformation is equivalent to placing a capacitor in series with each inductor and an inductor in parallel with each capacitor of the original network.

As an example of frequency translation, reconsider the low-pass network of Fig. 13-3a. The inductive reactance of this network can be written in terms of the new frequency variable of Eq. (13-12) as

$$X_L = Ls\Big]_{s=K_1 s^* + \frac{K_2}{s^*}} = L^* s^* + \frac{1}{C^* s^*} \qquad \text{where} \qquad \begin{aligned} L^* &= K_1 L \\ C^* &= \frac{1}{K_2 L} \end{aligned}$$

(13-13)

Similarly, the capacitive reactance becomes

$$X_C = \frac{1}{Cs}\Big]_{s=K_1 s^* + \frac{K_2}{s^*}} = \frac{1}{C^{**} s^* + \frac{1}{L^{**} s^*}} \qquad \text{where} \qquad \begin{aligned} C^{**} &= K_1 C \\ L^{**} &= \frac{1}{K_2 C} \end{aligned}$$

(13-14)

Because the resistance of the network is unchanged by Eq. (13-12), the low-pass network of Fig. 13-3a is transformed to that of Fig. 13-5,

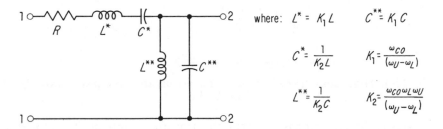

where: $L^* = K_1 L \qquad C^{**} = K_1 C$

$C^* = \frac{1}{K_2 L} \qquad K_1 = \frac{\omega_{CO}}{(\omega_U - \omega_L)}$

$L^{**} = \frac{1}{K_2 C} \qquad K_2 = \frac{\omega_{CO} \omega_L \omega_U}{(\omega_U - \omega_L)}$

Fig. 13-5. Band-pass transformation based on the low-pass network of Fig. 13-3a.

which is recognized as a bandpass configuration. To insure a physically realizable network, K_1 and K_2 must be positive real numbers; however, their values can be selected to establish the desired upper and lower cutoff frequencies of the bandpass response.

The response curve of $|E_2/E_1|$ for the low-pass network of Fig. 13-3a will take the form of Fig. 13-6a when it is plotted for both positive and negative values of ω. In this case the cutoff frequency is denoted by ω_{co}. Likewise, the response curve for the bandpass network of Fig. 13-5 for both positive and negative frequencies takes the form of Fig. 13-6b, where ω_U and ω_L are the upper and lower cutoff frequencies and ω_c is the center frequency of the bandpass. It is desired that K_1 and K_2 of Eq. (13-12) be evaluated such that the frequencies of Fig. 13-6a between $-\omega_{co}$ and ω_{co} will be located between ω_L and ω_U of Fig. 13-6b. This can be accomplished by writing the transformation of Eq. (13-12) as follows:

$$-\omega_{co} = K_1 \omega_L - \frac{K_2}{\omega_L} \qquad \text{and} \qquad \omega_{co} = K_1 \omega_U - \frac{K_2}{\omega_U} \qquad (13\text{-}15)$$

Solving these expressions for K_1 and K_2 in terms of ω_{co}, ω_L, and ω_U gives

$$K_1 = \frac{\omega_{co}}{\omega_U - \omega_L} \quad \text{and} \quad K_2 = \frac{\omega_{co}\omega_L\omega_U}{\omega_U - \omega_L} \qquad (13\text{-}16)$$

The bandwidth of the network is given by $BW = (\omega_U - \omega_L)$. Because the reactances of Eqs. (13-13) and (13-14) do not have geometric symmetry about a given frequency ω^* the bandpass response will not be geometrically symmetric about ω_c. The arithmetic center frequency can be written as $\omega_c = (\omega_U + \omega_L)/2$; however, the antisymmetric center frequency is based on $\omega_L/\omega_c = \omega_c/\omega_U$ or $\omega_c^2 = \omega_L\omega_U$. If only a

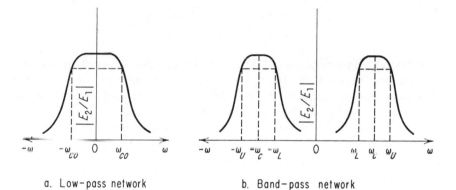

a. Low-pass network   b. Band-pass network

Fig. 13-6. Response of networks for positive and negative values of ω.

narrow band of frequencies around ω_c is considered, the antisymmetric case approaches the arithmetic case. Under these conditions, $\omega_c^2 = \omega_L\omega_U$ and $BW = \omega_U - \omega_L$ can be substituted into Eq. (13-16) to give

$$K_1 = \frac{\omega_{co}}{BW} \quad \text{and} \quad K_2 = \frac{\omega_{co}\omega_c^2}{BW} \qquad (13\text{-}17)$$

Since ω_U, ω_L, and ω_{co} are positive real numbers and ω_U is always larger than ω_L, it follows that K_1 and K_2 must also be positive real numbers.

To review the low-pass to bandpass transformation, the cutoff frequency of the low-pass network ω_{co} and the element values as in Fig. 13-3a, R, L, and C are known. Likewise, the upper and lower cutoff frequencies ω_U and ω_L of the desired bandpass network are known. Therefore, using Eq. (13-16) or (13-17), the values of K_1 and K_2 can be determined. Using the values of K_1, K_2, L, and C, the values of L^*, C^*, L^{**}, and C^{**} of the bandpass network of Fig. 13-5 can be determined from Eqs. (13-13) and (13-14). The resistance of the network remains unchanged by the transformation. Finally, the transformation can be generalized by substituting K_1 and K_2 of Eq. (13-17) into Eq. (13-12).

$$\omega = K_1\omega^* - \frac{K_2}{\omega^*} = \frac{\omega^*\omega_{co}}{BW} - \frac{\omega_{co}\omega_c{}^2}{\omega^*(BW)} = \frac{\omega_{co}\omega_c}{BW}\left[\frac{\omega^*}{\omega_c} - \frac{\omega_c}{\omega^*}\right]$$

$$(13\text{-}18)$$

This expression relates any frequency ω of a low-pass network to any frequency ω^* of the bandpass configuration. The converse can be determined by solving Eq. (13-18) for ω^*.

$$\omega^* = \frac{\omega(BW)}{2\omega_{co}} \pm \sqrt{\left[\frac{(BW)\omega}{2\omega_{co}}\right]^2 + \omega_c{}^2} \qquad (13\text{-}19)$$

The relationships of Eqs. (13-18) and (13-19) can be used to convert any low-pass network to a bandpass structure by replacing each inductor of the low-pass network by a series LC combination and each capacitor of the low-pass network by a parallel LC combination.

As an example of frequency translation, assume that the network of Fig. 13-3a represents the transfer ratio of Eq. (13-5). The element values of the low-pass network have been given as $R = 4$ ohms, $L = 2$ henrys, and $C = 1/6$ farad, and the resulting cutoff frequency is $\omega_{co} = 2.04$ radians/sec. Furthermore, assume that it is desirable to convert the low-pass network to a bandpass structure having a center frequency of $\omega_c = 1000$ and a bandwidth of $BW = 200$ radians/sec. The upper and lower cutoff frequencies are then $\omega_U = 1100$ and $\omega_L = 900$ radians/sec. With this information, the values of K_1 and K_2 can be determined from Eq. (13-17) as follows:

$$K_1 = \frac{\omega_{co}}{BW} = \frac{2.04}{200} = 1.02 \times 10^{-2}$$

$$K_2 = \frac{\omega_{co}\omega_c{}^2}{BW} = \frac{(2.04)(1000)^2}{200} = 1.02 \times 10^4 \qquad (13\text{-}20)$$

Using K_1, K_2, and L, the values of L^* and C^* for the bandpass network can be determined from Eq. (13-13) or Fig. 13-5 as

$$L^* = K_1L = [1.02 \times 10^{-2}](2) = 20.4 \times 10^{-3} \text{ henry}$$

$$C^* = \frac{1}{K_2L} = \frac{1}{[1.02 \times 10^4](2)} = 49.0 \times 10^{-6} \text{ farad} \qquad (13\text{-}21)$$

Likewise, K_1, K_2, and C can be used in Eq. (13-14) or Fig. 13-5 to determine L^{**} and C^{**}.

$$C^{**} = K_1 C = [1.02 \times 10^{-2}]\left(\frac{1}{6}\right) = 1.70 \times 10^{-3} \text{ farad}$$

$$L^{**} = \frac{1}{K_2 C} = \frac{1}{[1.02 \times 10^4]}\left(\frac{1}{6}\right) = 0.588 \times 10^{-3} \text{ henry} \tag{13-22}$$

The resistance $R = 4$ ohms does not change; hence, the element values determined in Eqs. (13-21) and (13-22), when combined with the 4-ohm resistor in the form of Fig. 13-5, will yield a bandpass network having a center frequency of $\omega_c = 1000$ and a bandwidth of $BW = 200$ radians/sec.

Also in the category of frequency translation is the low-pass to band-rejection transformation which can be accomplished by replacing s by a new variable such that

$$s = F(s^*) = \frac{1}{K_1 s^* + \dfrac{K_2}{s^*}} \tag{13-23}$$

Expressed in terms of real frequency, this transformation becomes

$$\omega = \frac{-1}{K_1 \omega^* - \dfrac{K_2}{\omega^*}} \tag{13-24}$$

As in the previous case, K_1 and K_2 must be properly chosen to insure a physically realizable band-rejection network.

To accomplish the low-pass to band-rejection transformation, it is useful to substitute Eq. (13-23) in the relationships for the inductive and capacitive reactances of the network of Fig. 13-3a. In the case of the inductive reactance, it follows that

$$X_L = Ls\bigg]_{F(s^*)} = \frac{1}{C^* s^* + \dfrac{1}{L^* s^*}}$$

where $\qquad C^* = \dfrac{K_1}{L} \qquad$ and $\qquad L^* = \dfrac{L}{K_2} \tag{13-25}$

Similarly, the capacitive reactance yields

$$X_C = \frac{1}{Cs}\bigg]_{F(s^*)} = L^{**} s^* + \frac{1}{C^{**} s^*}$$

where $\qquad L^{**} = \dfrac{K_1}{C} \qquad$ and $\qquad C^{**} = \dfrac{C}{K_2} \tag{13-26}$

Consequently the transformation of Eq. (13-23) causes the inductor of the low-pass network to be replaced by a parallel $L*C*$ combination and the capacitor is replaced by a series $L**C**$ combination to yield the band-rejection configuration shown in Fig. 13-7. In general, the transformation of Eq. (13-23) replaces each inductor of an original network by a parallel LC combination and each capacitor by a series LC combination. The resistance of the network remains unchanged.

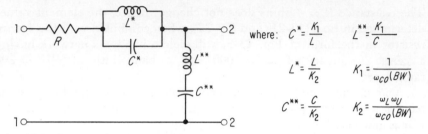

where: $C* = \dfrac{K_1}{L}$ $L** = \dfrac{K_1}{C}$

$L* = \dfrac{L}{K_2}$ $K_1 = \dfrac{1}{\omega_{co}(BW)}$

$C** = \dfrac{C}{K_2}$ $K_2 = \dfrac{\omega_L \omega_U}{\omega_{co}(BW)}$

Fig. 13-7. Band-rejection transformation based on the low-pass network of Fig. 13-3a.

Consideration of Eqs. (13-25) and (13-26) reveals that K_1 and K_2 must be real and positive to insure that $L*$, $C*$, $L**$, and $C**$ will be physically realizable. The values of K_1 and K_2 can be determined by requiring the cutoff frequency ω_{co} of the low-pass network to correspond to ω_L of the band-rejection network and $-\omega_{co}$ to ω_U according to Eq. (13-24).

$$\omega_{co} = \frac{-1}{K_1 \omega_L - \dfrac{K_2}{\omega_L}} \quad \text{and} \quad -\omega_{co} = \frac{-1}{K_1 \omega_U - \dfrac{K_2}{\omega_U}} \quad (13\text{-}27)$$

Solving these relationships for K_1 and K_2 yields

$$K_1 = \frac{1}{\omega_{co}(\omega_U - \omega_L)} = \frac{1}{\omega_{co}(BW)}$$

$$K_2 = \frac{\omega_L \omega_U}{\omega_{co}(\omega_U - \omega_L)} = \frac{\omega_c^2}{\omega_{co}(BW)} \quad (13\text{-}28)$$

where the bandwidth and antisymmetric center frequency are given by $BW = \omega_U - \omega_L$ and $\omega_c^2 = \omega_L \omega_U$. Combining Eqs. (13-24) and (13-28) results in a general frequency transformation for the low-pass to band-rejection network conversion given by

$$\omega = \frac{1}{\dfrac{\omega_c}{\omega_{co}(BW)}\left(\dfrac{\omega*}{\omega_c} - \dfrac{\omega_c}{\omega*}\right)}$$

or

$$\omega* = \frac{-\omega_{co}(BW)}{2\omega} \pm \sqrt{\left[\frac{\omega_{co}(BW)}{2\omega}\right]^2 + \omega_c^2} \quad (13\text{-}29)$$

The element values for the band-rejection network of Fig. 13-7 can be computed from the element values of the low-pass configuration of Fig. 13-3a and the relationships of Eqs. (13-25) and (13-26). The values of K_1 and K_2 can be determined from Eq. (13-28) once the choice of bandwidth and center frequency or ω_L and ω_U have been made.

This concludes the discussion of frequency translations. It should be pointed out, however, that frequency scaling associated with each of the transformations of this chapter tends to change the relationship between the reactance and resistance of a network. Consequently, Q of the various branches of the network, defined as the ratio of reactance to resistance, must be taken into account during the frequency-transformation process to insure a realizable network in terms of commercially available elements. In this respect frequency transformations are directly related to impedance-level transformations and predistortion. Finally, it is possible by these transformations to convert network specifications, which are generally prescribed at high frequencies, to a low-frequency range. The network can then be synthesized in terms of its low-frequency characteristics, after which it can be transformed back to the frequency range of interest.

References

Almost all recent texts dealing with the subjects of network analysis and synthesis have sections devoted to frequency transformations. A few notable examples are listed below.

1. E. A. Guillemin, *Communication Networks*, Vol. II (New York: John Wiley & Sons, Inc., 1935), pp. 392–422.
2. E. S. Kuh and D. O. Pederson, *Principles of Circuit Synthesis* (New York: McGraw-Hill Book Co., Inc., 1959), Chap. 8.
3. M. B. Reed, *Electric Network Synthesis: Image Parameter Method* (Englewood Cliffs, N.J.: Prentice-Hall, Inc., 1955), Chap. 5.
4. S. Seshu and N. Balabanian, *Linear Network Analysis* (New York: John Wiley & Sons, Inc., 1959), Sec. 11-6.
5. J. E. Storer, *Passive Network Synthesis* (New York: McGraw-Hill Book Co., Inc., 1957), Chap. 14.

Additional material concerning frequency transformations can be found in the following articles:

6. E. Brenner and S. R. Parker, "Seven Rules for Scaling Impedance Level and Frequency," *Electronic Design*, September 1959, pp. 28–31.
7. M. Dishal, "Design of Dissipative Band-Pass Filters Producing Desired Exact Amplitude-Frequency Characteristics," *Proc. IRE*, vol. 37, no. 9, September 1949, pp. 1050–1069.
8. R. C. Rowlands, "Frequency Transformation and Resistance Compensation," *IRE Trans. Circuit Theory*, vol. CT-7, no. 2, June 1960, pp. 179–180.

Problems

13-1. Sketch the locus of $F(j\omega^*)$ for the following frequency transformations. Discuss the effect each has on a network's frequency response and its elements.

$$(a) \quad F(s^*) = \frac{K_1}{K_2 s^* + 1} \qquad (b) \quad F(s^*) = K_1 + K_2 s^* + \frac{1}{K_3 s^*}$$

$$(c) \quad F(s^*) = \frac{K_1(s^* + K_2)}{s^{*2} + K_2 s^* + K_3}$$

$$(d) \quad F(s^*) = \frac{(4s^{*3} + 5s^{*2} + 16s^* + 16)}{(s^{*3} + 4s^{*2} + 3s^* + 8)}$$

13-2. Develop a frequency transformation $F(s^*)$ that will invert the amplitude response of networks while simultaneously predistorting the network by 3 units and moving all critical frequencies to twice their original values. Sketch the locus of $F(j\omega^*)$ and check the result by transforming the impedance $Z(s) = (s + 1)$.

13-3. A low-pass network similar to Fig. 13-3a is given with element values of $R = 100$ ohms, $L = 10 \times 10^{-3}$ henry, and $C = 1 \times 10^{-6}$ farad. Using these values, determine the voltage transfer ratio and cutoff frequency ω_{co} such that a low-pass network having a new cutoff frequency of $\omega_{co}^* = 1000$ radians/sec can be obtained. Determine the element values for the new network.

13-4. Using the element values given in Prob. 13-3 for the low-pass network, transform the network to a high-pass form having a new cutoff frequency of $f_{co}^* = 1000$ cps.

13-5. Transform a low-pass network having $R = 500$ ohms, $L = 1/2$ henry, and $C = 100 \times 10^{-6}$ farad into a band-pass configuration having a center frequency of $f_c = 100,000$ cps and a bandwidth of 1000 cps.

13-6. Using the element values listed in Prob. 13-5, realize a band-rejection network having a center frequency of $f_c = 100,000$ cps and a bandwidth of 1000 cps.

Chapter 14

Approximation in the
Frequency Domain

Thus far a number of powerful synthesis procedures have been described for realizing various arrangements of network elements to provide a desired response once the characterizing functions have been formulated. However, in practical synthesis problems the desired response characteristics are seldom given in terms of a rational driving-point or transfer function. Instead, the desired response may be prescribed in either the frequency or time domains as an analytical expression, empirically derived graphs, or tabulations of data. More often the frequency response is simply defined in terms of its passbands, resonant frequencies, bandwidths, or cutoff characteristics, whereas the transient response may be defined in terms of its time delay, overshoot, or settling time. The use of such terms to define a desired network response leaves a great deal unspecified. In these cases, and in those in which the form of the specified response is not directly amenable to realization, approximation procedures must be used to formulate realizable functions.

Once the desired response characteristics for a network have been specified, two important steps must be taken in performing the necessary approximation. The first step is the selection of an approximating function which can later be used directly in a realization procedure. Polynomials and rational functions in terms of the complex frequency variable s or real frequency variable ω are ideally suited when making approximations in the frequency domain. However, combinations of trigonometric and/or exponential functions, power series, differential and integral equations, and even difference equations may be useful approximating functions in the time domain provided they can be properly transformed into rational functions for purposes of realization. The choice of the approximating function for a given problem may be dependent on several factors; however, when the choice has been made, a second important step must be taken. This is the selection of an error

417

criterion which can be used to measure how accurately the approximating function matches the specified response characteristics. A number of different error criteria might satisfy the requirements of a particular problem; again, the selection of a specific criterion may be dependent on several factors.

From the above discussion, it is seen that solution of the approximation problem can be a complicated task involving choices between approximating functions and error criteria. Approximate data and methods may be used and often there is no unique or "best" solution. Fortunately there is a vast reservoir of knowledge available, both in mathematical literature and the field of network synthesis, pertaining to various approximation techniques. Some of the more useful and well-known frequency-domain procedures will be considered in this chapter following a brief discussion of error criteria. Chapter 15 is devoted to procedures that can be used for approximating specified response characteristics in the time domain.

14-1. Selection of Error Criteria

When a selected function is being used to approximate a prescribed response characteristic, an error criterion is required to measure the accuracy or quality of the approximation. Error is a relative term and may only be expressed quantitatively when considered with respect to an exact or desired frame of reference. Error, therefore, can be defined as the difference between what is actually obtained and what is considered exact or desirable. In a more limited sense, the error can be expressed analytically as

$$E(x) = f^*(x) - f(x) \qquad (14\text{-}1)$$

where $E(x)$ is the error function of x, $f^*(x)$ is the approximating function, and $f(x)$ is the desired or exact function. The quality of a given approximation becomes increasingly better as $f^*(x)$ approaches $f(x)$ or as E approaches zero for each value of x.

Three different types of error functions $E(x)$ result from typical approximation procedures. These forms are illustrated in Fig. 14-1 for a range of interest between x_a and x_b. In Fig. 14-1a the error tends to oscillate in an apparent random or haphazard manner. This result is typical of cases in which the desired function is not well behaved or the approximation procedure is based on an error criterion that does not smooth the result appreciably. The error function of Fig. 14-1b is said to be point-coincident in that $f^*(x)$ becomes an exact representation for $f(x)$ at one point x_p within the range of interest. Error functions of this form are obtained when a smoothly varying response is approximated

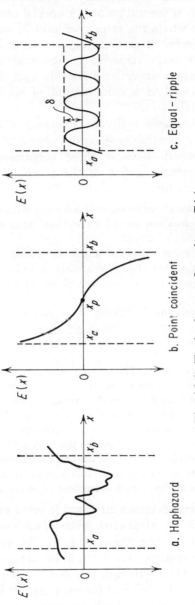

Fig. 14-1. Typical error functions, $E(x)$.

by a function with similarly well-behaved characteristics. The error in this case generally increases as the limits of the region are approached; however, the approximating function may become point-coincident with the prescribed function at several points. A special case of this situation is shown in Fig. 14-1c where the error oscillates in such a manner that the magnitude of the error at each maxima and minima has the same value δ. This type of error response is obtained when the desired function is either constant or varies smoothly and the approximating function can be expressed as a combination of sinusoids, hyperbolic functions, or polynomials.

The above discussion explains the characteristics of some typical error functions; however, the constraints generally placed on an error function have not been mentioned. Because these constraints determine the quality of an approximation, a few of the more useful error criteria deserve further consideration.

1. **Maximum E.** In some instances, it is sufficient to restrict the magnitude of the error such that it does not exceed a specified value within the region of interest.

2. **Average E.** The error criterion might be based on minimizing the integrated or average value of error throughout the range of interest. Unfortunately, the average value may approach zero even though the maximum errors are quite large.

3. **Average magnitude of E.** Minimization of the integrated or average magnitude of the error may be useful but is not always convenient, particularly when the error is expressed as a function which cannot be easily handled mathematically.

4. **Average of squared error.** The average value of the error squared is both meaningful and easily handled mathematically. However, a more popular criterion is the minimization of the square root of the average value of the error squared, generally known as the root-mean-square or rms error. Minimization of the average value of the error squared is termed a least-mean-square criterion and is often considered optimum in that it minimizes the effects of random errors. It is felt by some that nature employs something akin to a least-mean-square criterion; however, for purposes of fitting $f^*(x)$ to $f(x)$, it is possible to minimize the average value of the error raised to any even-ordered power as an error criterion.

This list by no means exhausts all possible error criteria but is considered to be representative. Most error criteria, such as those mentioned above, do not account for the distribution of the error along x. For example, the root-mean-squared error might be the same for each of the error functions of Fig. 14-1, although the distribution of the error as a function of x is considerably different for each case. It is seldom possible to find a criterion which controls both the magnitude and distribution of errors in an optimum manner, but both considerations must be taken into account if an adequate representation of the quality of an approximation is to be obtained.

It becomes clear that several basic considerations must be taken into account in the selection of an error criterion. For example, it must be capable of giving a quantitative measure for the magnitude of the error. It should also restrict the distribution of the error in an acceptable manner. Furthermore, it should be relatively easy to apply and meaningful when expressed in terms of the physics of the problem. The criterion and procedure selected must take into account the degree of accuracy necessary and the amount of labor and/or time required to yield a solution. This implies a knowledge of available computing facilities and an estimation of the complexity of the problem in question.

14-2. Approximation by Semi-infinite Slopes

The first approximation technique to be considered is based on reduction of the error magnitude between a prescribed amplitude and/or phase response and an approximating function having poles and zeros restricted to the real axis of the s-plane. This procedure was developed by H. W. Bode and is accomplished by approximating the desired response plotted on a logarithmic frequency axis by a series of semi-infinite straight-line segments.† Presentation of an amplitude response as a logarithmic function of frequency is particularly useful for two reasons. The first is that the amplitude response of physically realizable networks approaches straight-line asymptotes at both high and low frequencies. Secondly, amplitudes are readily expressed in decibels making it possible to combine the responses of cascaded networks by addition or factor them by subtraction.

Consider the RC network of Fig. 14-2a. The voltage transfer ratio of this network can be written as

$$\frac{E_2}{E_1} = \frac{\frac{1}{Cs}}{R + \frac{1}{Cs}} = \frac{1}{RCs + 1} = \frac{1}{Ts + 1} \tag{14-2}$$

where $T = RC$ is the characteristic time constant. The pole of Eq. (14-2) lies on the negative real axis at $s = -1/T$ as shown in Fig. 14-2b. The frequency response for this network can be obtained from Eq. (14-2) by letting $s = j\omega$, and the amplitude response in particular can be determined from

$$\left|\frac{E_2}{E_1}\right| = \frac{1}{|j\omega T + 1|} \tag{14-3}$$

† H. W. Bode, *Network Analysis and Feedback Amplifier Design* (New York: D. Van Nostrand Co., Inc., 1945), Chap. 15.

This relationship can be expressed in terms of decibels, according to Eq. (12-6), as follows:

$$db = 20 \log \left| \frac{E_2}{E_1} \right| = 20 \log \frac{1}{|j\omega T + 1|} = -20 \log |j\omega T + 1|$$

$$(14\text{-}4)$$

The resulting actual response curve, when plotted logarithmically as a function of ω takes the form shown in Fig. 14-2c.

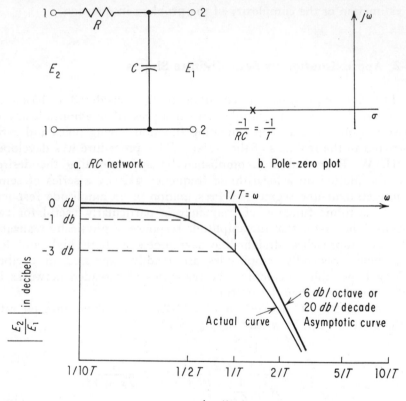

a. RC network   b. Pole-zero plot

c. Amplitude response

Fig. 14-2. RC network, pole-zero plot, and related amplitude response.

The amplitude response of Fig. 14-2c is seen to approach the following two asymptotes at extreme frequencies:

$$\left| \frac{E_2}{E_1} \right| \to -20 \log 1 = 0 \qquad \text{when} \qquad \omega \ll \frac{1}{T}$$

and

$$\left| \frac{E_2}{E_1} \right| \to -20 \log \omega T \qquad \text{when} \qquad \omega \gg \frac{1}{T} \qquad (14\text{-}5)$$

The maximum deviation between the actual curve and these asymptotes occurs when $\omega = 1/T$, and the error at this point is 3.01 db. This point $\omega = 1/T$ is known as the break frequency and is the frequency at which the asymptotes intersect. For $\omega < 1/T$ the asymptote has a slope of zero, and for $\omega > 1/T$ the slope of the asymptote is -6 db per octave or -20 db per decade of frequency.† These results apply to a function having only a simple pole, in which case the break frequency is directly related to the position of the pole on the real axis as shown in Fig. 14-2b. Similar results are obtained for a function possessing a single real axis zero except that the high-frequency asymptote has a slope of $+6$ db per octave or $+20$ db per decade of frequency. Furthermore, a network represented by a function composed of many real axis poles and/or zeros may have an amplitude response characterized by several break frequencies. Complex poles and zeros also produce break frequencies and can be useful when approximating a given amplitude response; however, they will be considered later in the chapter.

In general, the voltage transfer ratio for a two-port network possessing only real axis poles and zeros can be written as

$$\frac{E_2}{E_1} = \frac{a_n s^n + a_{n-1} s^{n-1} + \cdots + a_1 s + a_0}{b_m s^m + b_{m-1} s^{m-1} + \cdots + b_1 s + b_0}$$

$$= K \frac{(T_n s + 1)(T_{n-1} s + 1)(T_{n-2} s + 1) \cdots}{(T_m s + 1)(T_{m-1} s + 1)(T_{m-2} s + 1) \cdots} \qquad (14\text{-}6)$$

Each pole and zero of the factored form can be considered to represent a simple RC or RL network with its own time constant T and break frequency $\omega = 1/T$. These subnetworks are combined in cascade to yield the total voltage transfer ratio. Each pole causes the amplitude response to approach an asymptote of -6 db per octave at high frequencies, whereas each zero yields a high-frequency asymptote of $+6$ db per octave. Consequently as ω approaches infinity the amplitude response for the entire transfer ratio of Eq. (14-6) approaches a slope of $6(n - m)$ db per octave. Likewise, each zero adds 90° phase shift and each pole subtracts 90° as ω approaches infinity; hence the phase response at high frequencies approaches $90(n - m)°$.

In brief, Bode's procedure of semi-infinite slopes is accomplished by approximating the desired amplitude response by a series of straight-line segments having slopes of $\pm 6N$ db per octave, where N is a real positive number. The intersecting points of these line segments represent break frequencies, thereby establishing the T's of the approximating function. The phase response and amplitude errors are corrected in a second phase of the procedure by multiplying the first approximation by a series of carefully chosen poles and zeros. Details of the procedure and problems

† The term *octave* denotes a twofold change in frequency, whereas a *decade* represents a factor-of-ten change in frequency.

encountered in its application are most easily illustrated by an example. Therefore, assume that the amplitude and phase responses of Fig. 14-3 are to be approximated for frequencies between $\omega = 1$ and $\omega = 100$ radians/sec.

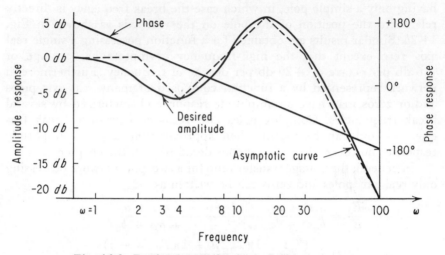

Fig. 14-3. Desired amplitude and phase response.

A first approximation for the amplitude response of Fig. 14-3 is given by the dashed straight-line segments. These line segments have been chosen on the basis of the following logic. A first-order pole at $\omega = 2 = 1/T_1$ is used to produce the first break frequency with a -6 db per octave slope, and a second-order zero at $\omega = 4 = 1/T_2$ cancels the -6 db octave slope and produces a $+6$ db per octave slope. A second-order pole at $\omega = 16 = 1/T_3$ cancels the $+6$ db per octave slope and produces a -6 db per octave slope, and a first-order pole at $\omega = 32 = 1/T_4$ increases the slope to -12 db per octave. Assuming the desired response of Fig. 14-3 is that of a voltage transfer ratio, the first approximation becomes

$$\frac{E_2}{E_1} = K \frac{(T_2 s + 1)^2}{(T_1 s + 1)(T_3 s + 1)^2(T_4 s + 1)}$$

where $T_1 = 1/2$, $T_2 = 1/4$, $T_3 = 1/16$, and $T_4 = 1/32$ (14-7)

The progress of the procedure can be determined by substituting $s = j\omega$ into this expression and evaluating the amplitude response for frequencies between $\omega = 1$ and $\omega = 100$ radians/sec. The amplitude of

Eq. (14-7) can be expressed in terms of decibels at any frequency as follows:

$$db = 20 \log \left|\frac{E_2}{E_1}\right| = 20 \log K - 20 \log \left|\frac{j\omega}{2} + 1\right| + 40 \log \left|\frac{j\omega}{4} + 1\right|$$

$$- 40 \log \left|\frac{j\omega}{16} + 1\right| - 20 \log \left|\frac{j\omega}{32} + 1\right| \qquad (14\text{-}8)$$

The value of K can be chosen as ($K = 1.07$) in order that the response of Eq. (14-7) equals zero db at $\omega = 1$ radian/sec. The resulting amplitude response can then be computed from Eq. (14-8) and is shown as the first approximation curve of Fig. 14-4.

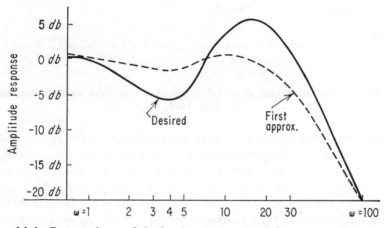

Fig. 14-4. Comparison of desired response and first approximation.

From Fig. 14-4 it is seen that the first approximation is fairly good in that it follows the general shape of the desired response. However, an error of approximately 5 db exists at $\omega = 4$ and $\omega = 16$. These errors are due to the accumulation of the deviations between the actual response and the straight-line approximations. Errors of this type become increasingly bothersome when the straight-line approximations cover only one or two octaves and have slopes exceeding ± 6 db per octave. It is often possible to reduce or remove the errors by carefully adjusting the pole-zero locations. A sophisticated technique for accomplishing a correction has been suggested by J. G. Linvill.† The procedures of Chap. 12, Secs. 12-1 through 12-4, may also be useful in this respect. However, a straightforward correction can be achieved by applying the procedure of semi-infinite slopes to the error function. For example, the

---

† A detailed presentation of Linvill's procedure for testing the effects of small changes in pole-zero positions is provided in J. G. Truxal, *Automatic Feedback Control System Synthesis* (New York: McGraw-Hill Book Co., Inc., 1955), pp. 360–375.

error between the desired amplitude response and first approximation of Fig. 14-4 can be plotted as a function of frequency, as shown in Fig. 14-5. This error curve can be approximated by straight-line segments as seen in the figure to give an approximate error function which can be used to correct the first approximation of Eq. (14-7).

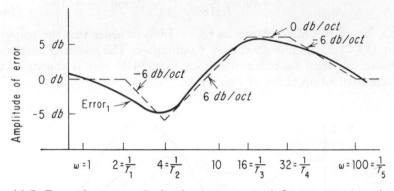

Fig. 14-5. Error between desired response and first approximation of Fig. 14-4.

The same break frequencies have been selected for the approximation of the error curve to keep the number of break frequencies to a minimum. The first occurs at $\omega = 2 = 1/T_1$ where the curve breaks downward with a slope of -6 db per octave requiring a pole at $1/T_1$. At $\omega = 4 = 1/T_2$ the response is increasing at a rate of 6 db per octave, requiring a second-order zero at $1/T_2$ to overcome the -6 db-per-octave slope. At $\omega = 16 = 1/T_3$ a pole is needed to cancel the 6 db-per-octave slope, and at $\omega = 32 = 1/T_4$ an additional pole is required to yield a -6 db-per-octave slope. To cancel this effect, a final zero has been added at $\omega = 100 = 1/T_5$. The resulting error function can then be written as

$$\text{Error}_1 = \frac{(T_2 s + 1)^2 (T_5 s + 1)}{(T_1 s + 1)(T_3 s + 1)(T_4 s + 1)}$$

where
$$T_5 = 1/100 \tag{14-9}$$

The first amplitude-response approximation can be corrected by multiplying Eq. (14-7) by this error function to yield a second approximation of the form

$$\frac{E_2}{E_1} = \left[K \frac{(T_2 s + 1)^2}{(T_1 s + 1)(T_3 s + 1)^2 (T_4 s + 1)} \right] \left[\frac{(T_2 s + 1)^2 (T_5 s + 1)}{(T_1 s + 1)(T_3 s + 1)(T_4 s + 1)} \right]$$

$$= K \frac{(T_2 s + 1)^4 (T_5 s + 1)}{(T_1 s + 1)^2 (T_3 s + 1)^3 (T_4 s + 1)^2} \tag{14-10}$$

By substituting $s = j\omega$ and using the time constants of Eqs. (14-7) and (14-9), the amplitude response of this approximation can be compared with that of the desired response. The value of K must be adjusted to ($K = 1.14$) such that the amplitude will be zero db at $\omega = 1$. However, since the maximum error of Eq. (14-10) is less than 3 db at any point within the frequency range of interest, it will be assumed that the amplitude approximation is sufficiently accurate, and attention will be turned to the phase response.

The first step in adjusting the phase response is to plot the phase associated with the final approximation of the amplitude response. Hence the phase response of Eq. (14-10) has been determined and is compared with the desired response in Fig. 14-6. In this figure the phase is by no means linear in the region from $\omega = 1$ to $\omega = 10$: however, it approaches $-180°$ for $\omega > 10$, since the order of the denominator of Eq. (14-10) is two higher than that of the numerator.

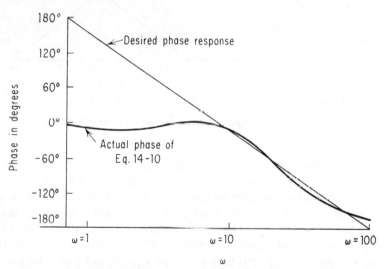

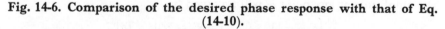

Fig. 14-6. Comparison of the desired phase response with that of Eq. (14-10).

To adjust the phase response, it is often possible to use a pole-zero combination that does not appreciably affect the amplitude response in the frequency range of interest. For example, if a pole and zero are close together, as shown in Fig. 14-7a, the amplitude of the vectors to a point ω is given by

$$A = \frac{|s + \sigma_2|}{|s + \sigma_1|}\Bigg]_{s=j\omega} = \frac{|\sigma_2 + j\omega|}{|\sigma_1 + j\omega|} = \left|\frac{b}{a}\right| \qquad (14\text{-}11)$$

If the distance between the pole and zero is small, the magnitude of A will approach unity. This condition will hold for all values of ω between

ω_L and ω_U provided σ_1 and σ_2 are more than 4 to 10 times ω_U. However, the phase at ω in Fig. 14-7a is given by $\phi = \phi_2 - \phi_1$; therefore, depending on the placement of the pole and zero, the effect on the phase response can be made greater than that on the amplitude response. Consequently, pole-zero combinations of this type are useful for making phase corrections, particularly near the high-frequency end of the response. At low frequencies a large number of these pole-zero combinations may be required.

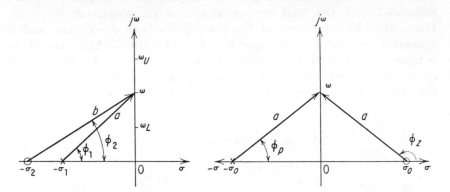

a. Left half-plane combination.   b. Right and left half-plane combination.

Fig. 14-7. Phase adjustment pole-zero combinations.

A second procedure for adjusting the phase response without affecting the amplitude response is based on the use of a left half-plane pole and right half-plane zero as shown in Fig. 14-7b. The zero is only realizable as part of a nonminimum phase-transfer function; consequently, this procedure for phase correction cannot be used when an approximation is intended to represent a driving-point function. Because the pole at $-\sigma_o$ and zero at σ_o are equidistant from the $j\omega$-axis, the amplitude at any point ω will be given by

$$A = \frac{|s - \sigma_o|}{|s + \sigma_o|}\bigg]_{s=j\omega} = \frac{|-\sigma_o + j\omega|}{|\sigma_o + j\omega|} = \left|\frac{a}{a}\right| = 1 \qquad (14\text{-}12)$$

Therefore, the pole-zero combination of Fig. 14-7b does not affect the amplitude response, although the phase response at ω is given by $\phi = \phi_z - \phi_p$. For small values of ω, ϕ will approach $180°$; whereas, ϕ goes to zero as ω approaches infinity.

Returning to the approximation of Eq. (14-10) and Fig. 14-6, it is seen that a maximum phase error of about $180°$ exists for frequencies near $\omega = 1$. Furthermore, the phase response is almost correct for $\omega > 10$; therefore, if a pole-zero combination similar to Fig. 14-7b can be used to adjust the phase from $\omega = 1$ to $\omega = 10$, it should not appreciably affect the results for $\omega > 10$. The pole-zero combination of Eq. (14-13) very nearly satisfies these conditions; hence it will be used to complete the approximation.

$$\frac{(T_1 s - 1)}{(T_1 s + 1)}\bigg]_{s=j\omega} = \frac{\left(\dfrac{j\omega}{2} - 1\right)}{\left(\dfrac{j\omega}{2} + 1\right)} \tag{14-13}$$

The final approximation for this example is obtained by combining Eqs. (14-10) and (14-13) as follows:

$$\frac{E_2}{E_1} = \underbrace{\left[K \frac{(T_2 s + 1)^4 (T_5 s + 1)}{(T_1 s + 1)^2 (T_3 s + 1)^3 (T_4 s + 1)}\right]}_{\text{Amplitude}} \underbrace{\left[\frac{(T_1 s - 1)}{(T_1 s + 1)}\right]}_{\substack{\text{Phase} \\ \text{correction}}}$$

$$= \frac{(1.14)\left(\dfrac{s}{2} - 1\right)\left(\dfrac{s}{4} + 1\right)^4\left(\dfrac{s}{100} + 1\right)}{\left(\dfrac{s}{2} + 1\right)^3\left(\dfrac{s}{16} + 1\right)^3\left(\dfrac{s}{32} + 1\right)} = \frac{23.3(s - 2)(s + 4)^4(s + 100)}{(s + 2)^3(s + 16)^3(s + 32)}$$

$$\tag{14-14}$$

since $K = 1.14$, $T_1 = 1/2$, $T_2 = 1/4$, $T_3 = 1/16$, $T_4 = 1/32$, and $T_5 = 1/100$. The amplitude and phase responses of this function are shown in Fig. 14-8 for the frequency range of interest $\omega = 1$ to $\omega = 100$. It will be assumed that this approximation is sufficiently accurate for purposes of demonstration; although, a higher degree of accuracy can be achieved by repeating the procedure.

The above example illustrates that it is possible to approximate amplitude and phase characteristics that are specified independently of each other over a given range of frequencies. This task becomes increasingly more difficult the larger the frequency range, and in the limit it is generally impossible to completely satisfy independently specified amplitude and phase characteristics over an infinite range of frequencies. Fortunately, the procedure always leads to a realizable driving-point or transfer function (within a multiplying factor), since all poles and zeros are restricted to the real axis. However, it is often easier to approximate a desired response if other portions of the s-plane are utilized. For example, the use of complex conjugate poles and zeros might yield an approximation for the desired response, requiring a lower-order function. This in turn might lead to a realization requiring fewer network elements.

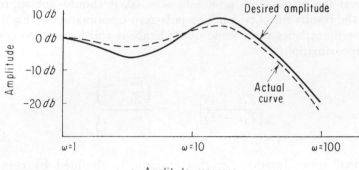

a. Amplitude response

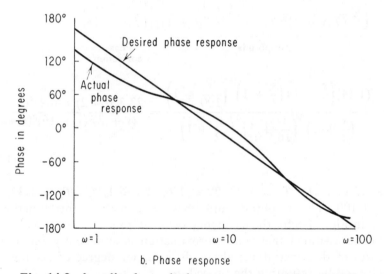

b. Phase response

Fig. 14-8. Amplitude and phase response of Eq. (14-14).

14-3. Butterworth's Maximally Flat Amplitude Approximation

A classical problem in the field of network theory involves the characteristics of an ideal filter. The amplitude and phase response curves which define an ideal low-pass filter are shown in Fig. 14-9. This response is particularly useful in network synthesis, control system analysis, and noise-spectrum studies because of its ability to pass all signals up to the cutoff frequency ω_{co} with no change in amplitude while completely blocking all higher frequencies. Unfortunately, the ideal filter cannot be realized exactly in terms of physical elements; therefore it becomes necessary to approximate the response. It will be seen that the approximation is most easily achieved using combinations of complex conjugate roots. Furthermore, the resulting approximation can be frequency transformed to yield idealized bandpass or band-rejection functions.

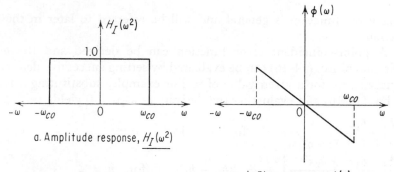

a. Amplitude response, $H_I(\omega^2)$

b. Phase response, $\phi(\omega)$

Fig. 14-9. Ideal low-pass filter.

The ideal filter of Fig. 14-9 has been approximated by several techniques involving different error criteria. Typical examples are Butterworth's "maximally flat" and Chebyshev's "equal ripple" approximations of the amplitude response and Thomson's "maximally flat delay" approximation designed to consider the phase characteristics.† Some of these procedures are described in this and later sections beginning with Butterworth's maximally flat amplitude approximation. The function chosen to approximate the amplitude response is a ratio of even-ordered polynomials in ω having a squared magnitude that approaches unity in the passband. This function takes the following form when all zeros are assumed to be at infinity:

$$H_n(\omega^2) = \frac{1}{Q_n(\omega^2)} = \frac{1}{1 + b_1\omega^2 + b_2\omega^4 + \cdots + b_n\omega^{2n}} \quad (14\text{-}15)$$

where n is the order of the approximation and the b coefficients must be determined according to an acceptable error criterion. The lead coefficient of the denominator b_0 is chosen as unity such that $H_n(\omega^2)$ will coincide with the desired response at $\omega = 0$. Using the ideal filter of Fig. 14-9a and the approximating function of Eq. (14-15), it is possible

† Due to transliteration differences, Chebyshev's name is also found in the literature as Tchebyscheff, thereby accounting for the symbol $T_n(\omega)$ used to denote Chebyshev polynomials.

to define an error function $[E(\omega^2) = H_l(\omega^2) - H_n(\omega^2)]$ such that the error within the passband is given by

$$E(\omega^2) = 1 - \frac{1}{Q_n(\omega^2)} = \frac{Q_n(\omega^2) - 1}{Q_n(\omega^2)} = \frac{b_1\omega^2 + b_2\omega^4 + \cdots + b_n\omega^{2n}}{1 + b_1\omega^2 + b_2\omega^4 + \cdots + b_n\omega^{2n}}$$

$$(14\text{-}16)$$

This error function is general and will be referred to later in the discussion.

A point-coincident error function can be derived and the b coefficients of Eq. (14-16) can be evaluated by setting successive derivatives equal to zero for a given value of n. For example, substituting x for ω^2 in Eq. (14-16) and evaluating the derivatives at $x = 0$ yields

$$\frac{d}{dx}\left[\frac{b_1 x}{1 + b_1 x}\right]_{x=0} = b_1 \qquad \text{for} \quad n = 1$$

$$\frac{d^2}{dx^2}\left[\frac{b_1 x + b_2 x^2}{1 + b_1 x + b_2 x^2}\right]_{x=0} = 2(b_2 - b_1^2) \qquad \text{for} \quad n = 2$$

$$\frac{d^3}{dx^3}\left[\frac{b_1 x + b_2 x^2 + b_3 x^3}{1 + b_1 x + b_2 x^2 + b_3 x^3}\right]_{x=0} = 6(b_3 - 2b_1 b_2 - b_1^3) \qquad \text{for} \quad n = 3$$

$$\cdot \quad \cdot \quad \cdot \quad \cdot \quad \cdot \quad \cdot \quad \cdot \quad \cdot \quad \cdot \quad \cdot$$

$$(14\text{-}17)$$

If the first derivative is to vanish, b_1 must be zero. Likewise, for the second derivative to vanish, b_2 must also be zero, and the same is true of b_3 if the third derivative is set equal to zero. Hence it becomes apparent that all but the b_n coefficient can be set equal to zero. In this case Eq. (14-15) reduces to the following form and has a maximum possible number of zero derivatives at $\omega = 0$:

$$H_n(\omega^2) = \frac{1}{1 + b_n\omega^{2n}}$$

$$(14\text{-}18)$$

The amplitude response associated with this function is said to be maximally flat.

Normally the passband of Fig. 14-9a is defined between $\omega = 0$ and $\omega = 1$, since it can easily be scaled to any desired width by frequency transformations. For the amplitude response of Eq. (14-18) to go through the half-power point at $\omega_{co} = 1$, it is necessary that $b_n = 1$. In this case the approximation can be written as

$$H_n(\omega^2) = \frac{1}{1 + \omega^{2n}} \qquad \text{such that} \qquad H_n(1) = \frac{1}{2}$$

$$(14\text{-}19)$$

Substituting $-s^2$ for ω^2 or $(s = j\omega)$ yields

$$H_n(-s^2) = H_n(s)H_n(-s) = \left[\frac{1}{Q_n(s)}\right]\left[\frac{1}{Q_n(-s)}\right] = \frac{1}{1 + (-1)^n s^{2n}}$$

$$(14\text{-}20)$$

The poles of this function occur at $(s^{2n} = \pm 1)$ where the plus sign is used for odd values of n and the minus for even values. These poles fall on a unit circle centered at the origin of the s-plane with equal angular spacing between poles. The only portion of $H_n(-s^2)$ that is physically realizable is $H_n(s)$ having poles that lie in the left half of the s-plane. These poles are represented in Eq. (14-20) by $Q_n(s)$ and are tabulated for reference in Table 14-1 for low values of n. Quadratic factors of Table 14-1 are written as $(s + a \pm jb)$ such that their real and imaginary components are evident. These factors are easily combined in the form $(s^2 + 2as + a^2 + b^2)$ and multiplied together to yield the so-called Butterworth polynomials.†

Butterworth's approximation for the amplitude response of Fig. 14-9a is achieved by writing $|H_n(s)| = 1/|Q_n(s)|$ in terms of real frequencies. When this is done, the Butterworth polynomials of Table 14-1 reduce such that

$$|H_n(j\omega)| = \frac{1}{|Q_n(j\omega)|} = \frac{1}{\sqrt{1 + \omega^{2n}}} \qquad (14\text{-}21)$$

This approximation is illustrated in Fig. 14-10a for $n = 1$, 2, and 3. Because the zeros of the approximating function, Eq. (14-15), are all at $\omega = \infty$, the amplitude response always approaches zero at extreme frequencies. The phase response associated with the Butterworth approximation can be obtained from the argument of $H_n(j\omega) = 1/Q_n(j\omega)$. The resulting phase response approaches $-90n°$ for high values of frequency and is shown for $n = 1$, 2, and 3 in Fig. 14-10b. Finally, it is possible to Laplace transform $H_n(s) = 1/Q_n(s)$ to obtain the unit impulse or step response of the approximation in the time domain.

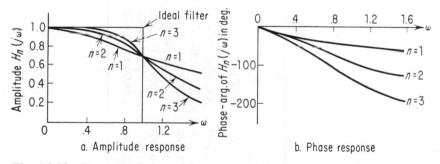

a. Amplitude response   b. Phase response

Fig. 14-10. Characteristics of Butterworth approximation for $n = 1$, 2, and 3.

† This approximation was originally developed by S. Butterworth in his paper: "On the Theory of Filter Amplifiers," *Wireless Engineer*, vol. 7, October 1930, pp. 536–541.

TABLE 14-I

Factors of Butterworth Polynomials

n	$Q_n(s)$
1	$(s + 1)$
2	$(s + 0.7071 \pm j0.7071)$
3	$(s + 1)(s + 0.5000 \pm j0.8660)$
4	$(s + 0.3927 \pm j0.9239)(s + 0.9239 \pm j0.3927)$
5	$(s + 1)(s + 0.3090 \pm j0.9511)(s + 0.8090 \pm j0.5878)$
6	$(s + 0.2588 \pm j0.9659)(s + 0.7071 \pm j0.7071)(s + 0.9659 \pm j0.2588)$
7	$(s + 1)(s + 0.2225 \pm j0.9749)(s + 0.6235 \pm j0.7818)(s + 0.9010 \pm j0.4339)$
8	$(s + 0.1951 \pm j0.9808)(s + 0.5556 \pm j0.8315)(s + 0.8315 \pm j0.5556)(s + 0.9808 \pm j0.1951)$
9	$(s + 1)(s + 0.1736 \pm j0.9848)(s + 0.5000 \pm j0.8660)(s + 0.7660 \pm j0.6428)(s + 0.9397 \pm j0.3420)$
10	$(s + 0.1564 \pm j0.9877)(s + 0.4540 \pm j0.8910)(s + 0.7071 \pm j0.7071)(s + 0.8910 \pm j0.4540)(s + 0.9877 \pm j0.1564)$

The poles of $H_n(s)$ [i.e., zeros of $Q_n(s)$ given by Table 14-1] lie on a unit circle centered at the origin and lead to the maximally flat response illustrated in Fig. 14-10a. However, by frequency transformations, these poles can be shifted to yield a bandpass response centered at a given frequency some distance from the origin. In this case the pole arrangement and resulting amplitude and phase responses take the form illustrated in Fig. 14-11. The same results can be obtained by the following

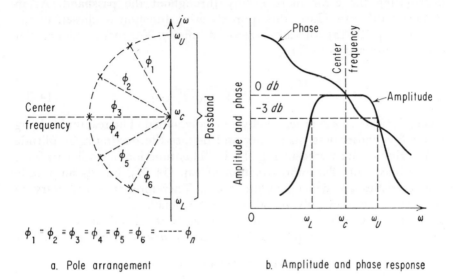

a. Pole arrangement
b. Amplitude and phase response

Fig. 14-11. Butterworth approximation for bandpass filters.

logic. If a group of complex conjugate poles are chosen to yield a flat bandpass response about a specified center frequency, several observations become clear as the poles are moved on the s-plane. For instance, as they move away from the $j\omega$-axis, the amplitude over the entire range of real frequencies decreases. The closer the poles are grouped together the narrower the bandwidth of the resulting response. Consequently, to obtain a given bandwidth the poles must be spread out as they are moved closer to the $j\omega$-axis. To keep the amplitude from falling off at the ends of the passband, the poles nearest the ends must be placed closer to the $j\omega$-axis than those near the center of the passband. This effect tends to flatten the response as the distance from each pole to the center frequency approaches the same value. Hence maximum flatness is obtained when the poles are spaced at equal angular intervals around a circle as shown in Fig. 14-11a. Because of the conjugate groupings of poles, however, the phase response associated with this configuration may not be a linear function of frequency in the passband.

14-4. Equal-ripple Amplitude Approximations

A second form of amplitude approximation is obtained if the poles of the approximating function are located on the periphery of an ellipse rather than a circle. This form was probably introduced by Cauer and makes use of a series of polynomials formulated by the Russian mathematician, P. L. Chebyshev.[†] The primary advantage of Chebyshev approximations is that they minimize the largest peak errors, thereby distributing the error more evenly throughout the passband. As in Butterworth's procedure, the approximating function is chosen in the form of Eq. (14-15) with all its zeros at infinity. For real frequencies, it can be expressed as follows:

$$H_n(j\omega) = \frac{1}{\sqrt{1 + \delta^2 T_n^2(\omega)}} \tag{14-22}$$

where $T_n(\omega)$ is an nth order Chebyshev polynomial. The real multiplying factor δ is chosen less than unity and defines the maximum amplitude of the ripples illustrated in Fig. 14-1c. This function is similar in form to the maximally flat approximation of Eq. (14-21), but its amplitude characteristics are dependent on $T_n(\omega)$. Therefore, it is necessary to consider Chebyshev polynomials in greater detail.

Chebyshev polynomials represent linearly independent solutions of the differential equation $[(1 - \omega^2)y'' - \omega y' + n^2 y = 0]$ and are given by

$$y = T_n(\omega) = \cos(n \arccos \omega)$$

and $$y = U_n(\omega) = \sin(n \arccos \omega) \tag{14-23}$$

These functions can be expressed in several alternate forms. For example, $T_n(\omega)$ can be written as

$$T_n(\omega) = \cos n\phi = Re[e^{jn\phi}] = Re[\cos \phi + j \sin \phi]^n$$

where $$\phi = \arccos \omega \tag{14-24}$$

Substituting ω for $\cos \phi$ and $\sqrt{1 - \omega^2}$ for $\sin \phi$ and applying the binomial expansion yields

$$T_n(\omega) = Re[\omega + j\sqrt{1 - \omega^2}]^n = \omega^n - \frac{n(n - 1)}{2!} \omega^{n-2}(1 - \omega^2)$$

$$+ \frac{n(n - 1)(n - 2)(n - 3)}{4!} \omega^{n-4}(1 - \omega^2)^2 - \cdots \tag{14-25}$$

[†] The development history of equal-ripple approximations is presented in a comprehensive survey on the subject by Stanley Winkler in "The Approximation Problem of Network Synthesis," *IRE Trans. Circuit Theory*, vol. CT-1, no. 3, September 1954, pp. 5–20.

Likewise, $U_n(\omega)$ can be expressed as the $Im[\omega + j\sqrt{1 - \omega^2}]^n$ and expanded in the same manner. When this is done, the lower-order Chebyshev polynomials listed in Table 14-2 are readily determined. Additional polynomials for higher values of n can be obtained by use of the recurrence formulas:

$$T_{n+1}(\omega) = 2\omega T_n(\omega) - T_{n-1}(\omega)$$

and
$$U_{n+1}(\omega) = 2\omega U_n(\omega) - U_{n-1}(\omega) \qquad (14\text{-}26)$$

Consideration of Table 14-2 reveals that the amplitudes of these functions oscillate between -1 and 1 in the frequency range $-1 \leq \omega \leq 1$. Unfortunately, $U_n(\omega)$ always vanishes at $\omega = 1$ because of the $\sqrt{1 - \omega^2}$ term; however, $T_n(\omega)$ is well-behaved and is shown for $n = 2$, 3, and 4 in Fig. 14-12a. Furthermore, the magnitude of $T_n(\omega)$ approaches infinity as the nth power of ω, thereby driving $H_n(j\omega)$ of Eq. (14-22) to zero at extreme frequencies. Consequently, the polynomials $T_n(\omega)$ are ideally suited for achieving an equal-ripple approximation for the ideal filter of Fig. 14-9a when used in Eq. (14-22).

TABLE 14-2

Chebyshev Polynomials

n	$T_n(\omega)$	$\dfrac{U_n(\omega)}{\sqrt{1 - \omega^2}}$
0	1	0
1	ω	1
2	$2\omega^2 - 1$	2ω
3	$4\omega^3 - 3\omega$	$4\omega^2 - 1$
4	$8\omega^4 - 8\omega^2 + 1$	$8\omega^3 - 4\omega$
5	$16\omega^5 - 20\omega^3 + 5\omega$	$16\omega^4 - 12\omega^2 + 1$
6	$32\omega^6 - 48\omega^4 + 18\omega^2 - 1$	$32\omega^5 - 32\omega^3 + 6\omega$
7	$64\omega^7 - 112\omega^5 + 56\omega^3 - 7\omega$	$64\omega^6 - 80\omega^4 + 24\omega^2 - 1$
8	$128\omega^8 - 256\omega^6 + 160\omega^4 - 32\omega + 1$	$128\omega^7 - 192\omega^5 + 80\omega^3 - 8\omega$

When the $T_n(\omega)$ polynomials are squared, multiplied by a factor ($\delta^2 \leq 1$), and substituted into Eq. (14-22), the resulting amplitude response takes the form shown in Fig. 14-12b. The minimum value of the response in the passband becomes $1/\sqrt{1 + \delta^2}$ and occurs whenever $|T_n(\omega)|$ is unity. Inspection of Table 14-2 reveals that this situation exists at $\omega = 0$ for all even-ordered polynomials; however, the odd-ordered functions begin at $|T_n(0)| = 0$ or $|H_n(j\omega)| = 1$. For small values of δ, the distance between maxima and minima of the ripples becomes $[1 - 1/\sqrt{1 + \delta^2} \approx \delta^2/2]$. Actually, when the square of Eq. (14-22) is considered, the peak ripple magnitude becomes $\delta^2/(1 + \delta^2)$, and the ripples are centered at $(2 + \delta^2)/2(1 + \delta^2)$. At high frequencies, the response approaches $1/\delta T_n(\omega)$; therefore, in a given problem, the

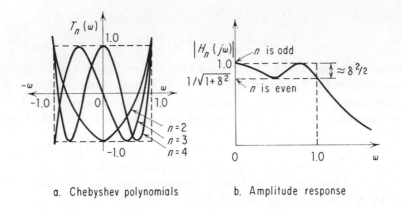

a. Chebyshev polynomials   b. Amplitude response

Fig. 14-12. Chebyshev polynomials and typical amplitude response.

permissible amount of ripple establishes δ, and the order of the polynomial is chosen to yield the desired reduction in amplitude outside the passband.

It is now useful to determine the pole locations which lead to the approximating function of Eq. (14-22). This can be accomplished by setting $[1 + \delta^2 T_n^2(\omega)]$ equal to zero or, in other words, $T_n(\omega) = \pm j/\delta$. Assume that ϕ of Eq. (14-24) is a complex quantity denoted by $\phi = u + jv$, in which case $T_n(\omega) = T_n(s/j)$ can be expanded as follows:

$$T_n(s/j) = \cos n(u + jv) = \cos nu \cosh nv - j \sin nu \sinh nv = \pm 1/\delta$$
$$(14-27)$$

Equating the real and imaginary parts yields

$$\cos nu \cosh nv = 0$$

and $$\sin nu \sinh nv = \pm 1/\delta \qquad (14-28)$$

Since $\cosh nv$ is never zero, $\cos nu$ must be zero. This condition is satisfied at $u = (2k + 1)\pi/2n$ for $k = 0, 1, 2, \ldots, 2n - 1$. The value of $\sin nu$ is ± 1 at these points; hence, it follows that

$$\sinh nv = \frac{1}{\delta} \quad \text{or} \quad v = \frac{1}{n} \sinh^{-1} \frac{1}{\delta} \qquad (14-29)$$

Applying the identities $\sinh^2 x = \cosh^2 x - 1$ and $e^x = \cosh x + \sinh x$, it is possible to write

$$\cosh nv = \sqrt{\frac{1}{\delta^2} + 1} \quad \text{and} \quad e^v = \left[\sqrt{\frac{1}{\delta^2} + 1} + \frac{1}{\delta} \right]^{1/n} \quad (14\text{-}30)$$

The resulting s-plane roots of $T_n(s/j)$ become

$$s_k = \sinh v \sin \frac{(2k + 1)\pi}{2n} + j \cosh v \cos \frac{(2k + 1)\pi}{2n}$$

where

$$k = 0, 1, 2, \ldots, 2n - 1 \quad (14\text{-}31)$$

Substituting Eq. (14-29) and keeping only the left half-plane poles gives

$$s_k = \sigma_k + j\omega_k \quad \text{where} \quad \begin{cases} \sigma_k = \sinh \left(\frac{1}{n} \sinh^{-1} \frac{1}{\delta} \right) \sin \frac{(2k + 1)\pi}{2n} \\ \\ \omega_k = \cosh \left(\frac{1}{n} \sinh^{-1} \frac{1}{\delta} \right) \cos \frac{(2k + 1)\pi}{2n} \end{cases}$$

for

$$k = 0, 1, 2, \ldots, n - 1 \quad (14\text{-}32)$$

Because δ and n are chosen for any particular problem, v can be established from Eq. (14-29), or σ_k and ω_k for each pole can be determined from Eq. (14-32). Squaring the real and imaginary parts and adding them together yields

$$\frac{\sigma_k^2}{\sinh^2 \left(\frac{1}{n} \sinh^{-1} \frac{1}{\delta} \right)} + \frac{\omega_k^2}{\cosh^2 \left(\frac{1}{n} \sinh^{-1} \frac{1}{\delta} \right)} = 1 \quad (14\text{-}33)$$

This function represents an ellipse having a semi-major axis $\cosh v$ along the $j\omega$-axis and semi-minor axis $\sinh v$ along the negative σ-axis of the s-plane. The foci of the ellipse occurs at $\omega = \pm 1$.

The characteristics of a Chebyshev filter are easily compared to those of a Butterworth approximation. Specifically, the real part of a Chebyshev pole is the $\sinh v$ times the real part of the corresponding Butterworth pole, and the imaginary part of a Chebyshev pole is $\cosh v$ times that of the Butterworth pole. Furthermore, for small δ the frequency $\omega = 1$ of the Butterworth case corresponds to the frequency $\omega^* = \cosh v$ of the Chebyshev case. This fact follows since the ellipse of Eq. (14-33) crosses the $j\omega$-axis at ω^* in which case

$$T_n(\omega^*) = \cosh n \cosh^{-1} \cosh v = \cosh nv \quad (14\text{-}34)$$

But this result is provided in terms of δ by Eq. (14-30); therefore, at ω^* the polynomials become

$$T_n(\omega^*) = \sqrt{\frac{1}{\delta^2} + 1} \quad (14\text{-}35)$$

The magnitude of $H_n(j\omega)$ at this frequency is

$$H_n(j\omega^*) = \frac{1}{\sqrt{1 + \delta^2 T_n^2(\omega^*)}} = \frac{1}{\sqrt{2 + \delta^2}} \qquad (14\text{-}36)$$

Consequently for small values of δ the amplitude response of $H_n(j\omega)$ approaches $1/\sqrt{2}$ at $\omega^* = \cosh v$. This frequency corresponds to the cutoff frequency of the Butterworth filter. Finally, to facilitate the use of Chebyshev approximations, it is useful to relate the percentage ripple to the factor δ in a more practical manner. Typically, the allowable ripple is specified in terms of decibels; therefore, considering the square of the amplitude response of Fig. 14-12b, the peak to peak ripple can be written as $[1 - 1/(1 + \delta^2) = \delta^2/(1 + \delta^2)]$. Comparing this amount of ripple to a desired response of unity, taking the square root, and expressing the result in terms of decibels give

$$\text{db} = 20 \log \frac{\delta}{\sqrt{1 + \delta^2}} \qquad (14\text{-}37)$$

This function is plotted for $0 \leq \delta \leq 1$ in Fig. 14-13.

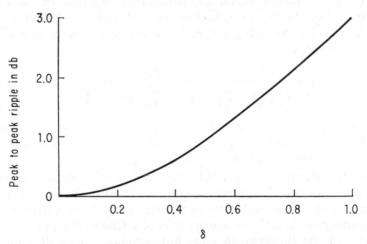

Fig. 14-13. Chebyshev ripple expressed in decibels.

As in the Butterworth case, illustrated in Fig. 14-11, the poles of a Chebyshev low-pass filter approximation can be frequency transformed to yield a bandpass approximation. The resulting pole arrangement and response characteristics are illustrated in Fig. 14-14. If the poles of Fig. 14-14a are distributed on an ellipse such that their projections on the $j\omega$-axis are equally spaced $\Delta\omega$ units apart, the resulting phase response, shown in Fig. 14-14b, will be nearly linear throughout the passband. In the next section it will be seen that approximations possessing these characteristics have interesting properties in terms of their time-domain or transient response. A compromise must generally be made between the linearity of the phase response and the amplitude of the ripples of the amplitude response.

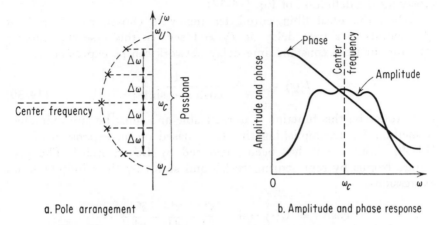

a. Pole arrangement   b. Amplitude and phase response

Fig. 14-14. Chebyshev approximation for bandpass filters.

14-5. Maximally Flat Delay Approximations

Two forms of amplitude-response approximation have been described for the ideal filter shown in Fig. 14-9. It is now useful to consider the linear-phase response of Fig. 14-9b and its approximation. Once again the approximating function will be chosen with all its zeros at infinity; however, attention will first be focused on the negative derivative of the phase known as the "delay" or "group delay" function. This function can be written as

$$T_D = \frac{-d\phi(\omega)}{d\omega}$$

(14-38)

where $\phi(\omega)$ is the angle of $H(j\omega)$. The definition of Eq. (14-38) is based on the assumption that an ideal time delay is a constant T_D. For instance, if $e_1(t)$ having a Laplace transform $E_1(s)$ is applied to a network, it is desired that the output be a function of the form $e_2(t) = e_1(t - T_D)$. In this case it follows from a fundamental theorem of Laplace transformations that $\mathscr{L}[e_1(t - T_D)] = e^{-sT_D}\mathscr{L}[e_1(t)]$ or $E_2(s) = e^{-sT_D}E_1(s)$. This result is easily verified by use of the Laplace transformation of Eq. (12-49). Hence, if the network is to have a constant time delay of T_D sec, its transfer ratio must be of the form $E_2/E_1 = e^{-sT_D}$. Therefore, a constant time-delay transfer ratio can be written in terms of real frequencies as $H(j\omega) = e^{-j\omega T_D} = e^{j\phi(\omega)}$ where the magnitude of the function is $|H(j\omega)| = 1$ and the phase is $\phi(\omega) = \text{Arg } H(j\omega) = -\omega T_D$. These are the characteristics of the ideal filter of Fig. 14-9 and, furthermore, T_D is given by the negative of the phase response slope, thereby satisfying the definition of Eq. (14-38).

When the ideal filter cutoff frequency is chosen as $\omega_{co} = 1$, it corresponds to a time delay of $T_D = 1$ sec. In this case the transfer ratio for the ideal constant time-delay network can be expressed as

$$H(s) = e^{-s} = \frac{1}{\cosh s + \sinh s} \qquad (14\text{-}39)$$

Unfortunately, this function is unrealizable and must be approximated. A method for accomplishing this task, based on an expansion of Eq. (14-39) about $s = 0$, has been suggested by Leo Storch.† The procedure begins by representing $\cosh s$ and $\sinh s$ by their infinite series expressions:

$$\cosh s = M(s) = 1 + \frac{s^2}{2!} + \frac{s^4}{4!} + \frac{s^6}{6!} + \cdots$$

$$\sinh s = N(s) = s + \frac{s^3}{3!} + \frac{s^5}{5!} + \frac{s^7}{7!} + \cdots \qquad (14\text{-}40)$$

Dividing both numerator and denominator of Eq. (14-39) by $\sinh s$ yields

$$H(s) = \frac{1}{\sinh s \, (\coth s + 1)} \qquad (14\text{-}41)$$

where $\coth s$ can be considered as an infinite continued-fraction expansion of $M(s)/N(s)$.

$$\coth s = \frac{M(s)}{N(s)} = \frac{1}{s} + \cfrac{1}{\cfrac{3}{s} + \cfrac{1}{\cfrac{5}{s} + \cfrac{1}{\cfrac{7}{s} + \cdots}}} \qquad (14\text{-}42)$$

An nth order approximation for this expansion is obtained by truncating Eq. (14-42) at its $(2n - 1)/s$ term. For instance, when $n = 4$, the expansion is truncated at its $7/s$ term giving

$$\frac{M(s)}{N(s)} \approx \frac{s^4 + 45s^2 + 105}{10s^3 + 105s} \qquad (14\text{-}43)$$

† L. Storch, "Synthesis of Constant-Time Delay Ladder Networks Using Bessel Polynomials," *Proc. IRE*, vol. 42, no. 11, November 1954, pp. 1666–1675.

The same approach can be used to approximate $M(s)/N(s)$ for all other values of n. Furthermore, this approach always leads to a reactance function having simple poles and zeros which alternate along the $j\omega$-axis.

According to Eqs. (14-39) and (14-40), the denominator of $H(s)$ can be written as $M(s) + N(s)$. However, $M(s) + N(s)$ can be approximated by an nth order polynomial $B_n(s)$ determined in the manner outlined by Eqs. (14-42) and (14-43) [i.e., when $n = 4$, $B_4(s) = s^4 + 10s^3 + 45s^2 + 105s + 105$]. Consequently the desired approximation of Eq. (14-39) can be written in the form

$$H_n(s) = \frac{b_0}{B_n(s)} = \frac{b_0}{b_0 + b_1 s + \cdots + b_n s^n} \qquad (14\text{-}44)$$

where $B_n(s) \approx M(s) + N(s)$. The factor b_0 is included in the numerator to adjust the amplitude response to unity for small values of s. By truncating the expansion of Eq. (14-42) at different values of n, a set of $B_n(s)$ polynomials is obtained. These polynomials are presented in factored form for low values of n in Table 14-3, and their roots always lie in the left half-plane. Quadratic factors are written as $(s + a \pm jb)$ such that their real and imaginary components are evident, but they are easily combined in the form $(s^2 + 2as + a^2 + b^2)$. Higher-order polynomials can be obtained by use of the recursion formula

$$B_n(s) = (2n - 1)B_{n-1}(s) + s^2 B_{n-2}(s) \qquad (14\text{-}45)$$

Further consideration of Table 14-3 reveals that these polynomials can be expressed in an alternate form as

$$B_n(s) = \sum_{k=0}^{n} \frac{(2n - k)!\, s^k}{2^{n-k}(n - k)!\, k!} \qquad \text{for} \qquad k = 0, 1, 2, \ldots, n \quad (14\text{-}46)$$

This relationship is useful for determining the exact coefficient of any particular power of s or for writing the function in expanded form. These functions are often classified as Bessel polynomials, although Bessel polynomials are generally expressed as $B_n^*(p) = b_0^* + b_1^* p + \cdots + b_n^* p^n$ where $p = 1/s$ and $b_k^* = (n + k)!/2^k(n - k)!\, k!$ for $k = 0, 1, 2, \ldots, n$. The relationship that exists between these forms is given by $B_n(s) = s^n B_n^*(p) = s^n B_n^*(1/s)$ and explains the $B_n(s)$ notation used in the above discussion.

At this point it is useful to consider the accuracy of the approximation and the resulting errors. Because Eq. (14-44) is based on an expansion of Eq. (14-39) about the origin, the desired response characteristics are closely approximated near $\omega = 0$. However, for an nth order approximation, the accuracy decreases the higher the frequency. Consequently, the error curves for the amplitude and time-delay (or negative slope of the

TABLE 14-3
Factors of $B_n(s)$ for Constant Time-delay Approximations

n	b_0	$B_n(s)$
0	1	1
1	1	$(s + 1)$
2	3	$(s + 1.5000 \pm j0.8660)$
3	15	$(s + 2.3222)(s + 1.8389 \pm j1.7544)$
4	105	$(s + 2.8962 \pm j0.8672)(s + 2.1038 \pm j2.6574)$
5	945	$(s + 3.6467)(s + 3.3520 \pm j1.7427)(s + 2.3247 \pm j3.5710)$
6	10,395	$(s + 4.2484 \pm j0.8675)(s + 3.7357 \pm j2.6263)(s + 2.5159 \pm j4.4927)$
7	135,135	$(s + 4.9718)(s + 4.7583 \pm j1.7393)(s + 4.0701 \pm j3.5172)(s + 2.6857 \pm j5.4207)$
8	2,027,025	$(s + 5.5879 \pm j0.8676)(s + 2.8390 \pm j6.3539)(s + 4.3683 \pm j4.414)(s + 5.2048 \pm j2.6162)$

phase) functions take the form shown in Fig. 14-15 for a particular value of n. The magnitude of the time-delay and amplitude-response errors can be computed using Bessel polynomials and Bessel functions of half-integral order.† This derivation is lengthy and will not be developed here; however, a few significant results are worth mention. For example, the phase response of Eq. (14-44) can be written as

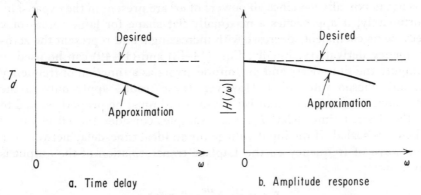

a. Time delay   b. Amplitude response

Fig. 14-15. Typical deviations between ideal and maximally flat delay approximations.

$\phi(\omega) = -\omega + \phi_e(\omega)$, where $-\omega$ represents the ideal phase associated with Eq. (14-39) and $\phi_e(\omega)$ is the error due to the approximation. Using the definition of time delay provided by Eq. (14-38), it follows that

$$T_D = -\frac{d\phi}{d\omega} = 1 - \frac{d\phi_o(\omega)}{d\omega} \tag{14-47}$$

The error term of this approximation can be expressed in the form of a power series as

$$\frac{d\phi_e(\omega)}{d\omega} = \frac{1}{b_0^2}\left[\omega^{2n} - \frac{\omega^{2n+2}}{(2n-1)} + \frac{2(n-1)\omega^{2n+4}}{(2n-1)^2(2n-3)} - \cdots\right] \tag{14-48}$$

Since this monotonic function of frequency begins with the nth power of ω^2, the first $(n-1)$ derivatives with respect to ω^2 are zero. This result occurs because the truncation of Eq. (14-42) provides an $(n-1)$st order or maximally flat delay approximation for Eq. (14-39).

The error in the amplitude response due to the approximation is most easily obtained by considering the squared magnitude of Eq. (14-44) evaluated at real frequencies. Comparison of the resulting power-series

† A detailed derivation of these error functions is provided in N. Balabanian, *Network Synthesis* (Englewood Cliffs, N.J.: Prentice-Hall, Inc., 1958), Sec. 9-3 and also in L. Weinberg, *Network Analysis and Synthesis* (New York: McGraw-Hill Book Co., Inc., 1962), Sec. 11-4.

expansion with the time delay error of Eq. (14-48) reveals the interesting fact that

$$|H_n(j\omega)|^2 = \frac{b_0^2}{\omega^{2n}}\left[\frac{d\phi_e(\omega)}{d\omega}\right] = 1 - \frac{\omega^2}{(2n-1)} + \frac{2(n-1)\omega^4}{(2n-1)^2(2n-3)} - \cdots$$

$$(14\text{-}49)$$

This relationship is also a monotonic function of frequency; however, it is not maximally flat since all powers of ω^2 are present in the expansion. Fortunately, it approaches a maximally flat shape for large values of n because its coefficients decrease with increasing n and represent the zero-frequency derivatives. Finally, Eqs. (14-48) and (14-49) can be used to compute the time-delay and magnitude errors as a function of frequency for any chosen value of n. However, these results apply only to the normalized approximation of Eq. (14-39) and must be properly scaled to fit the desired time delay T_D. For example, consider the effect on ωt when ω is scaled. If the input voltage for an ideal time-delay network is a sine wave of frequency ω, the Laplace transformation of the output is given by

$$E_2(s) = \frac{\omega}{s^2 + \omega^2} e^{-T_D s} \tag{14-50}$$

Scaling the frequency and time delay such that $\omega^* = \omega/\beta$ and $T_D^* = \beta T_D$ causes the response to be converted to

$$E_2^*(s) = \frac{1}{\beta} \frac{\dfrac{\omega}{\beta}}{\left[s^2 + \left(\dfrac{\omega}{\beta}\right)^2\right]} e^{-\beta T_D s} \tag{14-51}$$

The inverse transformation of this function is given by

$$e_2^*(s) = \frac{1}{\beta} \sin \omega^*(t - T_D^*) \tag{14-52}$$

Hence, it is seen that to scale the time delay, the time-frequency product $\omega T_D = \omega^* T_D^*$ must remain constant. As a result, the order of the approximation necessary to satisfy the desired time-delay character-istics should be chosen before attempting frequency scaling.

14-6. Additional Frequency-domain Approximation Techniques

Several approximation techniques employing error magnitudes, point coincident, and equal-ripple error criteria have been described in the preceding sections. There are many other procedures that can be used to approximate a specified frequency response; consequently this section is devoted to a brief investigation of certain possibilities. Some of these techniques have only limited usefulness and others experience difficulties in their mathematical development; however, the limitations should become evident as the discussion progresses.

The first technique to be considered is based on applying a least-mean-square error criterion to approximate the amplitude response of the ideal filter of Fig. 14-9a. For convenience, the approximating function is again chosen in the form of Eq. (14-15) such that the response converges to zero at high frequencies. The error function for the ideal filter can be expressed in the form of Eq. (14-16) as

$$E(\omega^2) = 1 - \frac{1}{Q_n(\omega^2)} \qquad \text{for} \qquad 0 \leqq \omega \leqq \omega_{co}$$

and

$$E(\omega^2) = \frac{1}{Q_n(\omega^2)} \qquad \text{for} \qquad \omega_{co} \leqq \omega \leqq \infty$$

where
$$Q_n(\omega^2) = 1 + b_1\omega^2 + b_2\omega^4 + \cdots + b_n\omega^{2n} \tag{14-53}$$

In general, a least-square approximation can be performed by squaring the error functions of Eq. (14-53), integrating from $\omega = 0$ to $\omega = \infty$, and choosing the b coefficients to minimize the results. Hence, it is possible to write

$$I_{Ln} = \int_0^{\omega_{co}} \left[1 - \frac{1}{Q_n(\omega^2)}\right]^2 d\omega + \int_{\omega_{co}}^{\infty} \left[\frac{1}{Q_n(\omega^2)}\right]^2 d\omega \tag{14-54}$$

where I_{Ln} denotes the integrated error. The first integral possesses a finite value within the passband for any chosen n and corresponding set of b coefficients; however, a closed-form solution for the second integral exists only for very low values of n, and numerical integration techniques break down when considering an infinite limit. Consequently, the mathematics of this approach become extremely complicated and the usefulness of the procedure for solving this problem is in doubt.

Ignoring these problems for the moment, it is worthwhile to consider a special case in which the approximation is forced to go through the half-power point at $\omega_{co} = 1$. Under these conditions, it follows from Eq. (14-15) that

$$H_n(1) = \frac{1}{1 + b_1\omega^2 + b_2\omega^4 + \cdots + b_n\omega^{2n}}\bigg]_{\omega_{co}=1} = \frac{1}{2}$$

or
$$b_1 + b_2 + \cdots + b_n = 1 \tag{14-55}$$

Hence, $b_1 = 1$ for $n = 1$, thereby giving the same result as the first order maximally flat amplitude and time delay approximations. The least square error within the passband for this case is given by

$$I_{L1}^* = \int_0^{\omega_{co}=1} \frac{\omega^4 \, d\omega}{(1 + \omega^2)^2} = \left[\omega + \frac{\omega}{2(1 + \omega^2)} - \frac{3}{2}\tan^{-1}\omega\right]_0^1 = 0.07190 \tag{14-56}$$

Some interesting results are obtained by comparing a least-square approximation within the passband to the maximally flat Butterworth approximation. The integral of the squared error within the passband for the Butterworth case is given by $I_{Bn}^* = \int_0^1 \omega^{4n} \, d\omega/(1 + \omega^{2n})^2$. This expression has been evaluated numerically for low values of n and the results are shown as the solid curve of Fig. 14-16a. The least-square approximation is obtained by determining the b coefficients that minimize $I_{Ln}^* = \int_0^1 [1 - 1/Q_n(\omega^2)]^2 \, d\omega$. The minimum values of I_{Ln}^* are shown as a dashed curve in Fig. 14-16a and the corresponding polynomials are tabulated in Table 14-4 as $Q_{Ln}(\omega^2)$. Substituting $-s^2$ for ω^2 in $Q_{Ln}(\omega^2)$ and retaining only the left half-plane roots yields the $Q_{Ln}(s)$ factors presented in Table 14-4. The accuracy of the coefficients for these functions decreases as n increases.

TABLE 14-4

Least-square Polynomials: $Q_{Ln}(\omega^2)$ and $Q_{Ln}(s)$.

n	$Q_{Ln}(\omega^2)$
1	$1 + \omega^2$
2	$1 - 0.700\omega^2 + 1.700\omega^4$
3	$1 + 0\omega^2 - 1.50\omega^4 + 2.40\omega^6$
4	$1 - 0.28\omega^2 + 0.58\omega^4 - 2.79\omega^6 + 3.49\omega^8$
5	$1 - 0.22\omega^2 - 0.5\omega^4 + 1.2\omega^6 - 4.1\omega^8 + 4.63\omega^{10}$

n	$Q_{Ln}(s)$
1	$(1)(s + 1)$
2	$(1.3038)(s^2 + 1.05658s + 0.76700)$
3	$(1.581)(s + 0.763)(s^2 + 0.684 + 0.829)$
4	$(1.87)(s^2 + 1.38s + 0.62)(s^2 + 0.51s + 0.86)$
5	$(2.15)(s + 0.76)(s^2 + 0.44s + 0.86)(s^2 + 1.22s + 0.71)$

The amplitude response characteristics of the resulting approximation can be determined from $|H_{Ln}(j\omega)| = 1/|Q_{Ln}(j\omega)|$ by substituting $s = j\omega$ into $Q_{Ln}(s)$ of Table 14-4. Response curves for this approximation are shown for $n = 2, 3,$ and 4 in Fig. 14-16b and are seen to be similar to the Chebyshev equal-ripple approximations except that they peak only once in the passband. Furthermore, the $Q_{Ln}(s)$ factors of Table 14-4 tend to lie very near or on an ellipse having a semi-major axis of $\omega = 0.95$ and semi-minor axis of $\sigma = -0.76$. Therefore, logic suggests that a least-square approximation in the passband can almost be achieved by a somewhat less complicated Chebyshev approximation, and the resulting integral of the squared error will lie between the two curves of Fig. 14-16a but closer to the dashed line. The phase response for the least-square approximation is given by the argument of $H_{Ln}(j\omega)$ and is nearly the same as that shown in Fig. 14-10b for the Butterworth or maximally flat approximation. This is due to the fact that the poles of

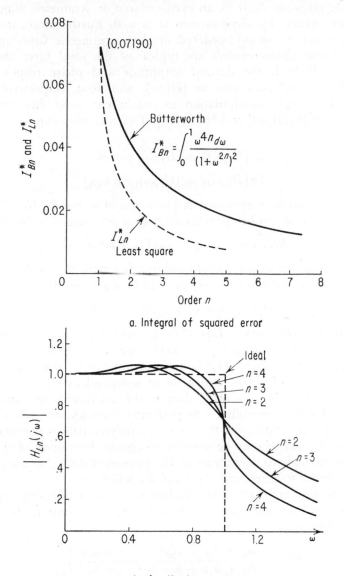

a. Integral of squared error

b. Amplitude response

Fig. 14-16. Least square approximation and corresponding integral of the squared error for $0 \leq \omega \leq 1$.

each approximation tend to have nearly the same projections on the $j\omega$-axis and lie on or within a unit circle about the origin of the s-plane.

A second technique deserving further study is based on performing a power-series expansion of the desired function about $s = 0$. From previous discussions (e.g., Chap. 12, Sec. 12-1), it is clear that the amplitude response must be an even-ordered or symmetric function of frequency; hence, its slope is zero at $\omega = 0$. Furthermore, the phase response must be an odd-ordered or skew-symmetric function about $\omega = 0$. These characteristics are typical of the ideal filter shown in Fig. 14-9. If both the desired amplitude and phase responses are specified at low frequencies as $|H(j\omega)|$ and $\phi(\omega)$, respectively, it is possible by simple manipulation to obtain curves or functions that represent the $Re[H(j\omega)]$ and $Im[H(j\omega)]$. This operation can be expressed as

$$Re[H(j\omega)] = |H(j\omega)| \cos \phi(\omega)$$

and
$$Im[H(j\omega)] = |H(j\omega)| \sin \phi(\omega) \tag{14-57}$$

Because $\cos \phi(\omega)$ is an even-ordered function of ω, the $Re[H(j\omega)]$ is also even-ordered and can be approximated by a polynomial of the form

$$Re[H(j\omega)] \approx c_0 + c_2\omega^2 + c_4\omega^4 + \cdots \tag{14-58}$$

Likewise, since $\sin \phi(\omega)$ is an odd-ordered function, the $Im[H(j\omega)]$ must be odd-ordered and can be approximated by a polynomial of the form

$$Im[H(j\omega)] \approx d_1\omega + d_3\omega^3 + d_5\omega^5 + \cdots \tag{14-59}$$

The c and d coefficients of Eqs. (14-58) and (14-59) can be determined from the converted data of Eq. (14-57) by several methods. For example, the polynomials of Eqs. (14-58) and (14-59) can be truncated after a selected number of terms, and a set of independent equations can be written to relate the converted data to the coefficients at various frequencies. Another possibility is to perform a least-square approximation for the converted data using the truncated polynomials as approximating functions. Finally, it may be possible to equate derivatives of the truncated polynomials to derivatives of the converted data at some point or points in order to determine the c and d coefficients.

The desired approximation, leading to the specified amplitude and phase-response characteristics, can be written as a rational fraction of the following form:

$$H(s) = \frac{a_0 + a_1s + a_2s^2 + \cdots + a_ns^n}{b_0 + b_1s + b_2s^2 + \cdots + b_ms^m}\bigg]_{m \geq n} \tag{14-60}$$

Expanding this function in a power series about $s = 0$ yields

$$H(s) = A_0 + B_1s + A_2s^2 + B_3s^3 + \cdots$$

where

$$A_0 = a_0/b_0$$
$$B_1 = (a_1 b_0 - a_0 b_1)/b_0{}^2$$
$$A_2 = (a_2 b_0{}^2 - a_0 b_0 b_2 - a_1 b_0 b_1 + a_0 b_1{}^2)/b_0{}^3$$
$$B_3 = (a_3 b_0{}^3 - a_0 b_0{}^2 b_3 - a_1 b_0{}^2 b_2 + 2 a_0 b_0 b_1 b_2 - a_2 b_1 b_0{}^2$$
$$+ a_1 b_0 b_1{}^2 - a_0 b_1{}^3)/b_0{}^4$$

$$\cdots \cdots \cdots \cdots \cdots \quad (14\text{-}61)$$

This expansion can be expressed in terms of real frequencies as

$$H(j\omega) = A_0 + j\omega B_1 + A_2 \omega^2 - j\omega^3 B_3 + \cdots$$

where

$$Re[H(j\omega)] = A_0 - A_2 \omega^2 + \cdots$$

and

$$Im[H(j\omega)] = B_1 \omega - B_3 \omega^3 + \cdots \qquad (14\text{-}62)$$

Equating the coefficients of like powers of ω in Eqs. (14-58), (14-59), and (14-62) and arbitrarily selecting b_0 as unity gives

From the $Re[H(j\omega)]$

$$A_0 = a_0 = c_0$$
$$A_2 = (a_2 - a_0 b_2 - b_1 a_1 + a_0 b_1{}^2) = -c_2$$

$$\cdots \cdots \cdots \cdots \cdots \cdots$$

From the $Im[H(j\omega)]$

$$B_1 = (a_1 - a_0 b_1) = d_1$$
$$B_3 - (a_3 - a_0 b_3 - a_1 b_2 + 2 a_0 b_1 b_2 - a_2 b_1 + a_1 b_1{}^2 - a_0 b_1{}^3) = d_3$$

$$\cdots \cdots \cdots \cdots \cdots \cdots \quad (14\text{-}63)$$

In these equations the c and d coefficients are assumed to be known from the approximations of Eqs. (14-58) and (14-59). The desired a and b coefficients must be determined, and unfortunately they occur in sets of cross products. Since there are an excess of independent equations, it is often possible to achieve a satisfactory solution by simply choosing values for certain coefficients. For instance, using A_0 it is seen that $a_0 = c_0$; therefore, B_1 can be reduced to $(a_1 - c_0 b_1) = d_1$. In this case either a_1 or b_1 can be chosen as a positive number such that the other will also be positive. When this is done, the technique can be repeated on A_2 to establish values for a_2 and b_2. In turn B_3 can be used to establish values for a_3 and b_3 and so forth until a satisfactory approximation is achieved over the desired range of frequencies.

As an example of the above technique, consider the amplitude and phase data $|H(j\omega)|$ and $\phi(\omega)$ specified in Table 14-5. The real and imaginary parts of $H(j\omega)$ can be determined by applying the relationships of Eq. (14-57). At this point it is possible to approximate the $Re[H(j\omega)]$ and the $Im[H(j\omega)]$ by polynomials of the form of Eqs. (14-58) and (14-59). Arbitrarily selecting the three values of the $Re[H(j\omega)]$ marked by asterisks, it is possible to write independent equations in terms of ω and the c_0, c_2, and c_4 coefficients of Eq. (14-58). Likewise, using the three values of the $Im[H(j\omega)]$ marked by asterisks, three more independent equations can be written in terms of ω and the d_1, d_3, and d_5 coefficients of Eq. (14-59). Solving the resulting sets of equations yields the following approximations:

$$Re[H^*(j\omega)] = c_0 + c_2\omega^2 + c_4\omega^4 = 0.6297 - 0.0301\omega^2 + 0.00039\omega^4$$

$$Im[H^*(j\omega)] = d_1\omega + d_3\omega^3 + d_5\omega^5 = -0.1734\omega + 0.0050\omega^3 - 0.00004\omega^5$$

$$(14-64)$$

It is noted that these approximations are independent and not necessarily based on fitting the $Re[H(j\omega)]$ and $Im[H(j\omega)]$ at the same frequencies. However, the points should be spread over the frequency range of interest. Furthermore, a check can be made on the progress of the procedure by evaluating the results of Eq. (14-64) and comparing them with the converted data of Table 14-5.

TABLE 14-5

Data for Example Approximation

ω	$H(j\omega)$	$\phi(\omega)$, degrees	$Re[H(j\omega)]$	$Im[H(j\omega)]$
0	0.667	0	0.667	0
1	0.632	−18.4	0.600*	−0.169
2	0.555	−33.7	0.461	−0.308*
3	0.471	−45.0	0.333	−0.395
4	0.400	−53.2	0.249*	−0.417
5	0.343	−59.1	0.177	−0.294*
6	0.299	−63.5	0.134	−0.290
7	0.263	−66.7	0.104*	−0.245
8	0.237	−69.5	0.083	−0.222*

* Values used in the approximation.

The c and d coefficients of Eq. (14-64) can be used to establish the a and b coefficients of the power series expansion of Eq. (14-60) according to Eq. (14-63) where $b_0 = 1$. For instance, it follows from A_0 that $a_0 = c_0 = 0.6297$. Substituting this result in B_1 yields ($a_1 - 0.6297b_1 = d_1 = -0.1734$). Let $b_1 = 1$, in which case the positive value $a_1 = 0.4563$ is obtained. Substituting these parameters in A_2 gives ($a_2 - 0.6297b_2 - 0.4563 + 0.6297 = -c_2 = 0.0301$); hence, it is possible to select $a_2 = 0$

in which case $b_2 = 0.2276$. Substituting these results in B_3 of Eq. (14-63) yields $[a_3 - 0.6297b_3 - (0.4563)(0.2276) + 2(0.6297)(0.2276) + 0.4563 - 0.6297 = -d_3 = -0.0050]$. In this case a_3 can also be chosen as zero and $b_3 = 0.0226$ is still positive. The procedure can be continued using c_4 and d_5 to establish higher a and b coefficients; however, it is not considered necessary for this problem since c_4 and d_5 are small and only influence the results at higher frequencies. Therefore, combining the above coefficients in the form of Eq. (14-60) completes the approximation:

$$H^*(s) = \frac{0.6297 + 0.4563s}{1 + s + 0.2276s^2 + 0.0226s^3} \qquad (14\text{-}65)$$

This function represents one possible approximation for the data of Table 14-5 and can be evaluated in terms of real frequencies to determine its accuracy. The solid curves of Fig. 14-17 show the amplitude- and phase-response characteristics specified in Table 14-5. This data was derived from the function $H(s) = 2/(s + 3)$. The dashed curves of Fig. 14-17 indicate the response of the approximation given by Eq. (14-65).

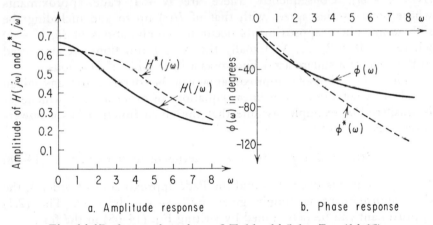

a. Amplitude response   b. Phase response

Fig. 14-17. Approximation of Table 14-5 by Eq. (14-65).

The approximation of Eq. (14-65) is not particularly accurate, as is evident from Fig. 14-17; however, it serves to illustrate the technique. More accurate results can generally be obtained by extending the approximation to higher-order terms or by judicious selection of the a and b coefficients. Usually the procedure involves several different approximations making it difficult to predict errors. Furthermore, there is no guarantee that the result will be a realizable function. Although it is possible to approximate independently specified amplitude and phase characteristics over a finite range of frequencies, the procedure becomes complicated when a high degree of accuracy is required over an extended frequency range. In the limit, it is impossible to accomplish an approximation over an infinite frequency spectrum.

The above procedure may be recognized as a form of Padé approximation. Specifically, a Padé approximation is achieved when a rational function, defined by polynomials of degrees m and n, is expanded in a power series and matched term by term with the expansion of a desired function up to and including the $(m + n)$th term. Therefore, if the desired function has a power-series expansion of the form

$$H(s) = \sum_{k=0}^{\infty} A_k s^k \tag{14-66}$$

The so-called Padé approximant $H^*(s)$ for $H(s)$ is provided by

$$H^*(s) = \frac{P_n(s)}{Q_m(s)} = \sum_{k=0}^{m+n} A_k s^k + \sum_{m+n+1}^{\infty} B_k s^k \tag{14-67}$$

Padé approximants of this type are unique and said to be of order $(N = n + m)$. Consequently, there are $N + 1$ Padé approximants whose power series agrees with that of $H(s)$ up to and including the s^Nth term. These approximants occur for combinations of $(k, N - k)$ where $k = 0, 1, 2, \ldots, N$. Usually the $N + 1$ functions are presented in the form of a square array known as a Padé table of functions.

The table of Padé approximants can be derived for any given problem by solving a set of linear equations of order m or n, whichever is smaller. For example, assume that the given function has a power-series expansion of the form

$$H(s) = 2 + s - 3s^2 + s^3 + \text{terms of higher orders} \tag{14-68}$$

In this case if it is desired to find the Padé approximants of order 3, the $(3,0)$ approximant is simply given by $2 + s - 3s^2 + s^3$. The $(2,1)$ approximant can be determined by writing Eq. (14-68) in the form

$$H^*(s) = \frac{(2 + s - 3s^2 + s^3)(1 + \beta s)}{1 + \beta s} + 0 \text{ (higher-order terms)}$$

$$= \frac{2 + (1 + 2\beta)s + (-3 + \beta)s^2 + (1 - 3\beta)s^3}{1 + \beta s} + 0(s^4) \tag{14-69}$$

By letting $\beta = 1/3$, the s^3 term vanishes, and the resulting approximant $H^*(s)_{2,1}$ is obtained.

$$H^*(s)_{2,1} = \frac{6 + 5s - 8s^2}{3 + s} \tag{14-70}$$

Similarly, to find the (1,2) approximant, Eq. (14-68) can be written as

$$H^*(s) = \frac{(2 + s - 3s^2 + s^3)(1 + \beta_1 s + \beta_2 s^2)}{1 + \beta_1 s + \beta_2 s^2} + 0 \text{ (higher-order terms)}$$

$$= \frac{2 + (1 + 2\beta_1)s + (-3 + \beta_1 + 2\beta_2)s^2 + (1 - 3\beta_1 + \beta_2)s^3}{1 + \beta_1 s + \beta_2 s^2}$$

$$+ 0(s^4) + 0(s^5) \qquad (14\text{-}71)$$

Solving for β_1 and β_2 such that the s^2 and s^3 terms of the numerator vanish gives $\beta_1 = 5/7$ and $\beta_2 = 8/7$. Therefore, the (1,2) approximant becomes

$$H^*(s)_{1,2} = \frac{14 + 17s}{7 + 5s + 8s^2} \qquad (14\text{-}72)$$

A simple check reveals that Eqs. (14-70) and (14-72) both possess power-series expansions having the first four terms identical to those of Eq. (14-68). Hence they represent rational approximants for the given expansion. The additional approximants required to complete a Padé table can be computed in the same manner; however, there is no guarantee that the results will be realizable functions. For instance, Eq. (14-70) possesses right half-plane zeros although the poles and zeros of Eq. (14-72) all lie in the left half-plane.

In conclusion, Padé approximants are useful for cases in which the network requirements can be expressed in the form of a power series in s. In these cases a table of rational approximants can be constructed, and in many instances a suitable choice of a realizable function can be made. This technique can also be used to establish additional rational-fraction representations for the approximation procedure described by Eqs. (14-57) through (14-63). Unfortunately, there is no simple method for determining which approximant best satisfies the requirements of a given problem. Finally, it should be emphasized that the procedures of this chapter do not exhaust all possible frequency-domain approximation techniques. For example, potential analogue procedures, which are often useful and referenced in much of the literature, have not been covered since they require considerable space and advanced mathematics for proper presentation.† Other useful approximations employing elliptic functions have been derived to represent the ideal filter such that ripples occur in the stopband as well as the passband. These approximations generally require functions possessing both poles and zeros. Some

† An excellent presentation of potential analogue techniques is provided in D. F. Tuttle, *Network Synthesis, Vol. I* (New York: John Wiley & Sons, Inc., 1958), Chap. 14. See also J. E. Storer, *Passive Network Synthesis* (New York: McGraw-Hill Book Co., Inc., 1957), Chaps. 29 and 30.

of these techniques can be applied in conjunction with time-domain approximation procedures to convert transformed functions to rational-fraction forms.

References

A great deal has been published concerning various approximation techniques, and one of the most thorough surveys of this literature is provided in Stanley Winkler, "The Approximation Problem of Network Synthesis," *IRE Trans. Circuit Theory*, vol. CT-1, no. 3, September 1954, pp. 5–20. The procedure of semi-infinite slopes is presented in several texts on control system theory such as J. G. Truxal, *Automatic Feedback Control System Synthesis* (New York: McGraw-Hill Book Co., Inc., 1955), Chap. 6. An earlier and more detailed discussion of this technique is contained in R. F. Baum, "A Contribution to the Approximate Problem," *Proc. IRE*, vol. 36, no. 7, July 1948, pp. 863–860. See also the following texts:

1. M. E. Van Valkenburg, *Modern Network Synthesis* (New York: John Wiley & Sons, Inc., 1960), Chap. 9.
2. L. Weinberg, *Network Analysis and Synthesis* (New York: McGraw-Hill Book Co., Inc., 1962), Sec. 11-11.

Maximally flat amplitude and delay and equal-ripple approximations are outlined in Chap. 13 of Ref. 1 and Chap. 11 of Ref. 2. These procedures are also presented in the following:

3. N. Balabanian, *Network Synthesis* (Englewood Cliffs, N.J.: Prentice-Hall, Inc., 1958), Chap. 9.
4. E. A. Guillemin, *Synthesis of Passive Networks* (New York: John Wiley & Sons, Inc., 1957), Chap. 14.

Padé approximants are described in J. E. Storer, *Passive Network Synthesis* (New York: McGraw-Hill Book Co., Inc., 1957), Chap. 28.

Problems

14-1. Is a 6 db/octave slope identical to a 20 db/decade slope? Discuss the relationship between these values and which is a more accurate representation for practical networks.

14-2. Plot the data of Table 14-6 on semi-logarithmic paper and draw a smooth curve through the points. Approximate the amplitude response using semi-infinite slopes of $\pm 6N$ db per octave and reduce the error magnitude to less than 1 db between $\omega = 1$ and $\omega = 1000$.

TABLE 14-6	
ω	$\lvert H(j\omega)\rvert$, db
1	0
5	$+1.0$
10	$+3.8$
20	$+6.0$
50	$+5.0$
100	$+1.0$
200	-3.0
350	-4.0
600	-2.7
1000	-1.0
2000	-0.5

TABLE 14-7	
ω	$\phi(\omega)$, degrees
1	$2°$
2	$10°$
5	$28°$
10	$34°$
20	$14°$
40	$-30°$
60	$-46°$
100	$-59°$
200	$-68°$
500	$-74°$
1000	$-78°$

14-3. Repeat the requirements of Prob. 14-2 by approximating the phase response of Table 14-7 such that the error magnitude is less than $10°$ at any frequency between $\omega = 1$ and $\omega = 1000$. Sketch the resulting amplitude response.

14-4. Perform a maximally flat amplitude approximation using 5 sets of complex conjugate poles to provide a bandpass filter between the cutoff frequencies of $\omega_L = 100$ and $\omega_U = 600$. Write the transfer function in terms of the poles and a constant K. Determine K such that the response will be zero db at $\omega_C = 350$. For this value of K, plot the amplitude and phase response for frequencies from $\omega = 50$ to $\omega = 1000$.

14-5. Show that the Chebyshev polynomials of Eqs. (14-24) and (14-25) can be expressed in an alternate form for $\omega > 1$ as

$$T_n(\omega) = \frac{(\omega \pm \sqrt{\omega^2 - 1})^n + (\omega \pm \sqrt{\omega^2 - 1})^{-n}}{2}$$

14-6. Apply the trigonometric identity, $\cos^2 n\phi = (\cos 2n\phi + 1)/2$, to Eq. (14-24) to show that $T_n^2(\omega) = [T_{2n}(\omega) + 1]/2$.

14-7. Plot the response characteristics of $U_n(\omega)$ of Table 14-2 between $\omega = -1$ and $\omega = 1$ for $n = 3, 4$, and 5. Discuss the results and their usefulness in approximation.

14-8. A Chebyshev low-pass response function is to have a peak-to-peak ripple of 0.5 db and 6 poles. Determine the cutoff or -3 db frequency. Sketch the amplitude response from $\omega = 0$ to $\omega = 2$. What is the minimum value of n to have a cutoff frequency of $\omega = 1.05$ and a ripple of not more than 0.25 db?

14-9. Determine the percentage delay error as a function of ωT_D for $n = 2, 4$, and 6, using the power series of Eq. (14-48). Do the same for the amplitude error using Eq. (14-49). Plot the results for values of ωT_D between 0 and 4.

14-10. Determine the transfer function for a network having a time delay of 2 millisec. The delay error is to be less than 5 percent at a frequency of $\omega = 1000$ radians/sec. The amplitude loss at this frequency should be less than 3 db.

14-11. Compute the values of b_1 and b_2 that minimize the least square error approximation for the ideal filter of Fig. 14-9a when $n = 2$ and $0 \leq \omega \leq \infty$. Apply the condition of Eq. (14-55) to simplify the error functions of Eqs. (14-53) and (14-54). Plot the amplitude response of the approximation for $0 \leq \omega \leq 2$ and discuss the results. (Numerical techniques may be required.)

14-12. Using the data of Table 14-5 not marked by asterisks, perform an approximation of $H(j\omega)$ and $\phi(\omega)$. Carry the approximation to the c_4 and d_5 terms of Eqs. (14-58) and (14-59) and the $A_4 s^4$ term of Eq. (14-61). Check the results by plotting the amplitude and phase characteristics of the resulting approximation.

14-13. Complete and construct a table of Padé approximants of order 3 for the power series of Eq. (14-68). The combinations (3,0), (2,1), and (1,2) are presented in the text. Discuss the results that are realizable as driving-point and transfer functions.

14-14. Repeat the requirements of Prob. 14-13 for all approximants of order 4 that satisfy the power series $H(s) = 3 - s + 2s^2 + s^3 - s^4 +$ terms of higher order.

14-15. Using the approximations of Eq. (14-64), write the power-series expansion of $H^*(s)$ in the form of Eq. (14-61) up to and including the $B_5 s^5$ terms. Determine the 5th order Padé approximant (2,3) that satisfies this expansion and plot its amplitude and phase response for $0 \leq \omega \leq 8$. Compare the results with the desired response shown in Fig. 14-17.

Chapter 15

Approximation in the Time Domain

The transient response of a network in the time domain contains precisely the same amount of information concerning the network characteristics as the combined amplitude and phase responses contain in the frequency domain. This fact is apparent from the discussion of Chap. 12, Sec. 12-5, and implies that specification of the transient response completely defines the frequency response and its associated driving-point or transfer function. Therefore, approximation of a desired transient response establishes the approximation of the frequency-domain characteristics. Because Laplace and Fourier transformations make it possible to convert given functions of time to equivalent functions of frequency, it is possible to apply the procedures of Chap. 14 to the approximation of transient-response characteristics. However, when the response is specified in the time domain, it is usually desirable to perform the approximation in the time domain. In this case the accuracy of the approximation is immediately evident, although the results must still be transformed to the frequency domain for the realization of a network. Consequently the problem is to find a function $h^*(t)$ which approximates the specified or known function of time $h(t)$ in such a manner that its transform $H^*(s)$ will be a realizable rational function of s. Fortunately, the error criteria described in Chap. 14, Sec. 14-1, can be applied to the problem, and a variety of time functions can be used for the approximation.

Inspection of the Laplace transformations of Table 12-1 or Eqs. (12-49) and (12-51) reveals that rational functions of s are assured if the transient response can be expressed as an exponential series of the form

$$h(t) = \left[\sum_{q=0}^{n} b_q t^q \right]\left[\sum_{k=0}^{m} K_k e^{s_k t} \right] \qquad \text{for} \qquad t > 0$$

and
$$h(t) = 0 \qquad \text{for} \qquad t < 0 \qquad\qquad (15\text{-}1)$$

where the b_q terms are real numbers, but each K_k and s_k may be either real or complex. Since $h(t)$ must be a real function, complex terms of Eq. (15-1) occur in conjugate pairs. In general this expression may represent combinations of simple exponential terms of the form Ke^{-at}, damped sinusoids of the form $Ke^{-at} \sin \omega t$ or $Ke^{-at} \cos \omega t$, simple sine functions $\sin \omega t$ or $\cos \omega t$, and polynomials of the form $b_0 + b_1 t + b_2 t^2 + \cdots + b_n t^n$. If the approximation function is chosen in the form of Eq. (15-1), or either part enclosed by brackets, the resulting approximation will yield a rational function of s but not necessarily a realizable function. However, a realizable result is obtained provided $\sum_{k=0}^{m} K_k e^{s_k t}$ is used as the approximating function and each s_k has a negative or zero real part. Consequently, this chapter is devoted to a presentation of techniques which can be used in the approximation of specified transient-response characteristics by functions of the form described above.

15-1. Approximation Using Time Moments

A straightforward approximation technique has been suggested by W. H. Huggins and later by F. BaHli based on replacing e^{-st} of the direct Laplace transformation by its power-series expansion and integrating the result term by term.† In this case the transformation of Eq. (12-49) can be expressed as a function of the form

$$H^*(s) = \int_0^\infty h(t) \left[1 - st + \frac{(st)^2}{2!} - \frac{(st)^3}{3!} + \cdots \right] dt$$

$$= A_0 - A_1 s + A_2 s^2 - A_3 s^3 + \cdots$$

where
$$A_n = \frac{1}{n!} \int_0^\infty t^n h(t) \, dt \tag{15-2}$$

In this relationship A_0 is the area under the given function $h(t)$ and is known as the zeroth moment of the transient response. If $h(t)$ is normalized such that $A_0 = 1$, then A_1 represents the "center of gravity" and $2A_2$ is the "moment of inertia" of the response about the line $t = 0$. This similarity to functions encountered in mechanics accounts for the terminology "time moments" used in the description of this technique.

The procedure is easily expressed in terms of Eq. (15-2) as a series of steps. First, the specified data, curve, or function of time must be examined to determine whether it can be conveniently integrated for $0 \leq t \leq \infty$, and if it cannot, it must be truncated at some finite value of t. Using the results of this step, the A_n coefficients of Eq. (15-2) are

† W. H. Huggins, "Network Approximation in the Time Domain," Air Force Cambridge Research Laboratories, Massachusetts, Report No. E5048A, October 1949, and F. BaHli, "A General Method for Time Domain Synthesis," *IRE Trans. Circuit Theory*, vol. CT-1, no. 3, September 1954, pp. 21–28.

determined by integration and lead directly to the power-series approximation for $H^*(s)$. Padé approximants, as described in Chap. 14, Sec. 14-6, can then be applied to establish acceptable rational functions possessing the same power-series representation as $H^*(s)$. Higher-order moments are particularly sensitive to the values of $h(t)$ for large t; consequently, the procedure generally yields a good approximation to the prescribed duration of the response, although its shape may not be accurate.

As an example of this procedure, consider the idealized transient response represented by the solid curve of Fig. 15-1. This response can be expressed analytically as

$$h(t) = h_1(t) + h_2(t) + h_3(t)$$

where
$$h_1(t) = 6t \qquad \text{for} \quad 0 \le t \le 0.2$$

$$h_2(t) = -1.5t + 1.5 \quad \text{for} \quad 0.2 \le t \le 1$$

$$h_3(t) = 0 \qquad \text{for} \quad 1 \le t < \infty \qquad (15\text{-}3)$$

Integrating $h(t)$ to obtain the A_n coefficients according to Eq. (15-2) yields

$$A_0 = \int_0^{0.2} 6t\, dt + 1.5 \int_{0.2}^1 (-t + 1)\, dt = 0.6000$$

$$A_1 = \int_0^{0.2} 6t^2\, dt + 1.5 \int_{0.2}^1 (-t^2 + t)\, dt = 0.2400$$

$$A_2 = \frac{1}{2} \int_0^{0.2} 6t^3\, dt + \frac{1.5}{2} \int_{0.2}^1 (-t^3 + t^2)\, dt = 0.0620$$

$$A_3 = \frac{1}{6} \int_0^{0.2} 6t^4\, dt + \frac{1.5}{6} \int_{0.2}^1 (-t^4 + t^3)\, dt = 0.0125$$

$$\cdots \cdots \cdots \cdots \cdots \qquad (15\text{-}4)$$

Using these values, the approximation $H^*(s)$ can be written in the form of Eq. (15-2) as

$$H^*(s) = 0.6000 - 0.2400s + 0.0620s^2 - 0.0125s^3 + \cdots \qquad (15\text{-}5)$$

At this point it is possible to compute various Padé approximants that satisfy the power series. For instance, using only the first three terms of the series, it is possible to determine the $H^*(s)_{0.2}$ approximant from

$$H^*(s) = \frac{(0.600 - 0.240s + 0.062s^2)(1 + \beta_1 s + \beta_2 s^2)}{1 + \beta_1 s + \beta_2 s^2}$$

$$+ 0 \text{ (higher-order terms)} \qquad (15\text{-}6)$$

Solving for β_1 and β_2 such that the s and s^2 terms vanish gives ($\beta_1 = 0.400$) and ($\beta_2 = 0.0567$); therefore, $H^*(s)_{0.2}$ becomes

$$H^*(s)_{0.2} = \frac{0.600}{1 + 0.400s + 0.0567s^2} = \frac{10.59}{(s + 3.53)^2 + (2.28)^2} \quad (15\text{-}7)$$

As a check of the procedure, the inverse Laplace transformation of this function is given by Eq. (15-8) and is plotted on Fig. 15-1 as a dashed curve for comparison purposes:

$$h^*(t)_{0.2} = 4.64e^{-3.53t} \sin 2.28t \quad (15\text{-}8)$$

A more accurate approximation is readily achieved by considering the first four terms of Eq. (15-5), in which case the $H^*(s)_{1.2}$ approximant can be determined from

$$H^*(s) = \frac{(0.6000 - 0.2400s + 0.0620s^2 - 0.0125s^3)(1 + \beta_1 s + \beta_2 s^2)}{1 + \beta_1 s + \beta_2 s^2}$$

$$+ \ 0 \ (\text{higher-order terms}) \quad (15\text{-}9)$$

Solving for β_1 and β_2 such that the s^2 and s^3 terms vanish gives ($\beta_1 = 0.362$) and ($\beta_2 = 0.0414$); therefore, $H^*(s)_{1.2}$ and $h^*(t)_{1.2}$ become

$$H^*(s)_{1.2} = \frac{0.600 - 0.0230s}{1 + 0.362s + 0.0414s^2} = \frac{14.50 - 0.556s}{(s + 4.37)^2 + (2.25)^2}$$

and $$h^*(t)_{1.2} = -7.56e^{-4.37t} \sin (2.25t + 175.8°) \quad (15\text{-}10)$$

This approximation possesses a right half-plane zero and has considerable error near $t = 0$; however, for $t > 0.02$ sec, it satisfies the prescribed response of Eq. (15-3) more accurately than does Eq. (15-8). Other combinations of Padé approximants can be derived to match the power series of Eq. (15-5) and may lead to more desirable approximations than those shown in Fig. 15-1.

The approximation near $t = 0$ can be improved by proper selection of the Padé approximants. This can be accomplished by applying the initial value theorem which states that if a function $h(t)$ and its first derivative are Laplace transformable and if $h(t)$ has a transform $H(s)$ such that the $\lim sH(s)$ exists as s approaches infinity, then[†]

$$\lim_{s \to \infty} sH(s) = \lim_{t \to 0} h(t) \quad (15\text{-}11)$$

Since the desired $H^*(s)$ is a ratio of polynomials, it can be written for large values of s as $H^*(s) \approx a_n s^n / b_m s^m$. Therefore, according to Eq. (15-11), the initial value of $h(t)$ can be used to establish $sH^*(s) = a_n s^{n+1} / b_m s^m = h(0)$. Consequently, m and n and the ratio a_n / b_m can be

---

[†] This theorem is proved in M. F. Gardner and J. L. Barnes, *Transients in Linear Systems*, Vol. I (New York: John Wiley & Sons, Inc., 1942), pp. 267–270.

chosen to provide a good fit near $t = 0$. The final value theorem states that if $h(t)$ and its first derivative are Laplace transformable and if $h(t)$ has a transform $H(s)$ such that $sH(s)$ is analytic on the $j\omega$-axis and in the right half-plane, then†

$$\lim_{s \to 0} sH(s) = \lim_{t \to \infty} h(t) \tag{15-12}$$

Fortunately, $H^*(s)$, when written in the form of Eq. (15-2), satisfies the final value theorem; therefore, as s approaches zero, the terms involving

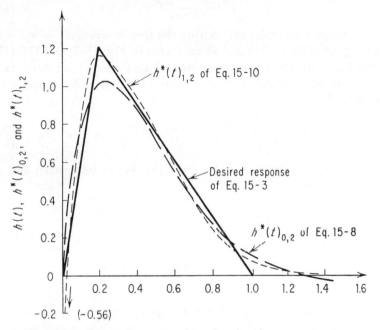

Fig. 15-1. Example approximation by time moments.

higher powers of s become insignificant and the behavior of $h(t)$ for large t is closely approximated by the procedure.

The expansion of Eq. (15-2) may also be interpreted as a differential operator which expresses the response $o(t)$ of a filter network caused by an input signal $i(t)$.

$$o(t) = \left[A_0 - A_1 \frac{d}{dt} + A_2 \frac{d^2}{dt^2} - A_3 \frac{d^3}{dt^3} + \cdots \right] i(t) \tag{15-13}$$

In this case the distortion of $i(t)$ as it passes through the filter can be written in terms of the various time derivatives, and if the coefficients are given by $A_n = D_n/n!$, the right-hand side of Eq. (15-13) represents a Taylor-series expansion of $i(t - D)$. Thus, the A_n moment coefficients

† *Ibid.*, pp. 265–267.

tend to give a response having the same shape as $i(t)$ but delayed in time by D sec. Equation (15-13) converges and can be used for estimating the distortion of a signal passing through the network provided changes in $i(t)$ are sufficiently slow and smooth. Finally, the results of Eq. (15-2) can also be derived by considering the time response in discrete increments. For instance, the Laplace integral can be expressed even for discontinuous functions of time as

$$H(s) = \sum_{n=1}^{\infty} a_n e^{-\tau_n s} \tag{15-14}$$

where a_n is the area under $h(t)$ during the time interval $\Delta\tau = \tau_n - \tau_{n-1}$. This element is illustrated as a shaded area in Fig. 15-2, and Eq. (15-14) is known as Dirichlet's time sequence, since the $e^{-\tau_n s}$ are delay factors. For each value of n the term $e^{-\tau_n s}$ can be replaced by a power-series expansion of the form

$$e^{-\tau_q s} = 1 - \frac{\tau_q s}{1!} + \frac{(\tau_q s)^2}{2!} - \frac{(\tau_q s)^3}{3!} + \cdots \tag{15-15}$$

In this case an approximation for Eq. (15-14) can be written and truncated at its rth term as follows:

$$H^*(s) = \sum_{q=1}^{r} a_q e^{-\tau_q s}$$

$$= a_1\left[1 - \tau_1 s + \frac{(\tau_1 s)^2}{2!} - \frac{(\tau_1 s)^3}{3!} + \cdots\right]$$

$$+ a_2\left[1 - \tau_2 s + \frac{(\tau_2 s)^2}{2!} - \frac{(\tau_2 s)^3}{3!} + \cdots\right]$$

$$\cdot \ \cdot \ \cdot \ \cdot \ \cdot \ \cdot \ \cdot \ \cdot \ \cdot \ \cdot$$

$$+ a_r\left[1 - \tau_r s + \frac{(\tau_r s)^2}{2!} - \frac{(\tau_r s)^3}{3!} + \cdots\right]$$

or

$$H^*(s) = \sum_{q=1}^{r} a_q - s\sum_{q=1}^{r} a_q \tau_q + \frac{s^2}{2!}\sum_{q=1}^{r} a_q \tau_q{}^2 - \frac{s^3}{3!}\sum_{q=1}^{r} a_q \tau_q{}^3 + \cdots$$

$$= A_0 - A_1 s + A_2 s^2 - A_3 s^3 + \cdots$$

where

$$A_n = \frac{1}{n!}\sum_{q=1}^{r} a_q \tau_q{}^n \tag{15-16}$$

This relationship, for a function of time expressed as discrete samples, is seen to be of the same form as Eq. (15-2).

It can be concluded from the above discussion that time moments offer several advantages when approximating a given function of time. For example, the moments are easily calculated from the specified data even if it is presented in graphical form. The accuracy of the approximation can be improved by determining higher-order coefficients for the power-series representation without reevaluating lower-order terms.

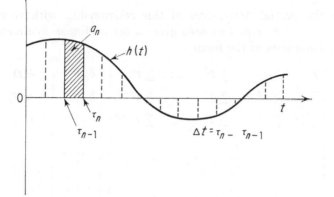

Fig. 15-2. Function of time expressed as discrete moments.

Furthermore, the moment coefficients bear a simple relationship through Padé approximants to desired rational functions of s. These coefficients are also the coefficients of a differential equation that satisfies the given function of time. However, the error in the approximation cannot be predicted in advance, and moments exist only for a certain class of functions which are sufficiently bounded in magnitude and time. Generally, functions that are single-valued for $0 \leq t \leq \infty$, approach zero as t becomes infinite, are zero for negative t, and are piecewise continuous or have only finite discontinuities, satisfy the necessary conditions for approximation by time moments.

15-2. Baker's Procedure for Reduction of Error Magnitudes

A second procedure for approximating a function of time is achieved by simply fitting the desired function by a polynomial of the form $h^*(t) = b_0 + b_1 t + b_2 t^2 + \cdots + b_n t^n$. The b coefficients can be determined such that the polynomial is point coincident with the desired response at n points by writing a set of n independent simultaneous equations in terms of the b's and time. This technique was illustrated in Chap. 14, Sec. 14-6, as a means for fitting the polynomials $Re[H^*(j\omega)]$ and $Im[H^*(j\omega)]$ to the example data of Table 14-5. A second method for determining the coefficients is to apply a least-square error criterion. In this case assume the desired response at time t_i is given by $h(t_i)$. The approximating polynomial can be written as $h^*(t_i)$ and the error becomes $E(t_i) = h(t_i) - h^*(t_i)$. Substituting the polynomial for $h^*(t_i)$, squaring the resulting error function, and summing over all the desired data points (i.e., from the first to the rth sample) yields

$$\sum_{i=1}^{r} E^2(t_i) = \sum_{i=1}^{r} [h(t_i) - b_0 - b_1 t_i - b_2 t_i^2 - \cdots - b_n t_i^n]^2 \tag{15-17}$$

Setting the partial derivatives of this relationship with respect to b_0, b_1, b_2, ..., and b_n equal to zero gives a set of linear symmetric simultaneous equations of the form

$$
\begin{vmatrix}
r & \sum t & \sum t^2 & \cdots & \sum t^n \\
\sum t & \sum t^2 & \sum t^3 & \cdots & \sum t^{n+1} \\
\sum t^2 & \sum t^3 & \sum t^4 & \cdots & \sum t^{n+2} \\
 & & \cdot & & \\
 & & \cdot & & \\
\sum t^n & \sum t^{n+1} & \sum t^{n+2} & \cdots & \sum t^{2n}
\end{vmatrix}
\begin{vmatrix}
b_0 \\ b_1 \\ b_2 \\ \cdot \\ \cdot \\ b_n
\end{vmatrix}
=
\begin{vmatrix}
\sum h(t) \\ \sum t h(t) \\ \sum t^2 h(t) \\ \cdot \\ \cdot \\ \sum t^n h(t)
\end{vmatrix}
\tag{15-18}
$$

Because the error function is squared, the odd powers of time, when summed over the desired data, become zero. By solving this set of equations for the b coefficients, the polynomial approximation is completed. This technique will be applied as part of the procedure described in Sec. 15-4.

The resulting polynomial determined by either of the above approaches must be Laplace-transformed to establish the rational approximation $H^*(s)$. However, transforming the nth order polynomial $h^*(t)$ term by term yields

$$H^*(s) = \frac{b_0}{s} + \frac{b_1}{s^2} + \frac{2! b_2}{s^3} + \cdots + \frac{n! b_n}{s^{n+1}} \tag{15-19}$$

Multiplying out the result provides a rational function having $(n + 1)$ poles at the origin which is not desirable from a realization standpoint. Consequently, even though the polynomial leads to a straightforward solution, it does not provide a realizable function in terms of s, except for the trivial case when $n = 0$. As a result, Walter Baker has proposed an approximation technique based on the product of a finite polynomial and a single exponential term.† This represents a special case of Eq.

---

† W. L. Baker, "A New Approach to the Approximation Problem," *IRE Convention Record*, Part 2—Circuit Theory, 1955, pp. 35–40.

(15-1) and tends to remove the objection concerning the poles of $H^*(s)$ when only a polynomial is used. Furthermore, the exponential term aids in approximating functions that change rapidly with time, since it can be made to converge on the desired results in a shorter time interval than a polynomial of reasonably low order. The remainder of this section, therefore, is devoted to consideration of Baker's procedure.

A least-square approximation reflects the general trend of a prescribed response without reproducing local fluctuations; hence it tends to average abrupt changes that occur. This is not always desirable. To insure that large errors do not result at any point along the time axis, it is possible to minimize the magnitude of the error at each point in the interval $0 \leq t < \infty$. Hence, the error can be expressed in logarithmic form as

$$E(t) = \log |h(t)| - \log |h^*(t)| = \log \left| \frac{h(t)}{h^*(t)} \right| \leq |\delta| \quad (15\text{-}20)$$

where $h(t)$ is the desired response function, $h^*(t)$ is the approximating function, and δ is an arbitrarily small real number. Clearly, $E(t)$ is zero for values of t at which $h(t)$ and $h^*(t)$ coincide. Positive values of $E(t)$ indicate that $h^*(t)$ is less than $h(t)$; whereas, a negative sign implies that $h^*(t)$ is larger. This error function is useful in that the percentage error is immediately available at any point in time by taking the antilog of $E(t)$. Before discussing the application of $E(t)$, it is worthwhile to consider the approximating function in more detail.

An nth order polynomial in t can be factored into n roots, some of which may be real and different, some which may be real and repeated, and others that may be complex and occur in conjugate pairs. Therefore a prescribed function of time having finite duration and amplitude can be approximated by a function of the form

$$h^*(t) = K[(t - t_0)(t - t_1)(t - t_2) \cdots (t - t_n)]e^{-t} \quad (15\text{-}21)$$

where $t_0, t_1, t_2, \ldots, t_n$ represent real or complex roots of a polynomial in t. The positive real roots of Eq. (15-21) are points at which the function crosses the real-time axis; however, complex conjugate roots do not introduce zeros on the real-time axis. In other words, t can be considered as a complex variable as illustrated in Fig. 15-3 where each root is represented by a vector from the point in question to any variable point t^*. The value of $h^*(t)$ can be obtained by computing the product of the individual vector lengths as t^* is moved from $t = 0$ along the positive real axis towards $t = \infty$. This is identical to the graphical technique described for computing the amplitude response as a function of frequency in Chap. 12, Sec. 12-1.

Based on the above discussion, the problem is to determine the polynomial roots for Eq. (15-21) such that the error function of Eq. (15-20) approaches zero within specified limits set by δ. Baker's procedure for accomplishing this task begins with the selection of a set of real roots for $h^*(t)$ determined by the points at which the ordinate values of $h(t)$ cross the t-axis. The product of these roots and e^{-t} gives a first approximation from which an error function is obtained using Eq. (15-20). Conjugate complex roots are then introduced into the original

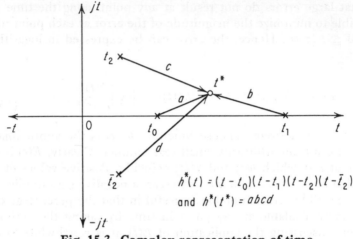

Fig. 15-3. Complex representation of time.

approximating function and the procedure is repeated to reduce the error. Each pair of complex roots adds a quadratic factor to $h^*(t)$ increasing the order of the polynomial by 2. Constant factors may be chosen during various steps of the procedure to reduce the average value of the error function to zero. These factors, when combined, yield the multiplying constant K for the approximating function of Eq. (15-21).

The above explanation implies that once the real roots are chosen, the remainder of the approximation is achieved by trial and error. However, this is not the case since the complex roots can be selected by inspection of the error function. A study of the complex time plane reveals that the real part of a complex conjugate root is closely approximated by the point on the real-time axis at which the minimum-error function occurs. The imaginary part of the complex roots must be chosen to produce the change in slope of the error function necessary to satisfy the specified tolerance on $E(t)$. This is harder to evaluate and follows from the fact that the distance from the real axis (i.e., the imaginary part of a complex root) is related to the rate of variation of the real-time function at points close to the complex roots. These aspects of the procedure become apparent when an example is studied; therefore, consider the arbitrarily specified data $h(t)$ provided in Table 15-1. This data has been plotted and is shown as the solid curve of Fig. 15-4.

Suppose that it is desirable to approximate $h(t)$ of Table 15-1 or Fig. 15-4 such that the magnitude of the error does not exceed 50 percent at any point between $t = 0$ and $t = 5$ sec. This implies that δ of the

TABLE 15-1

Specimen Calculations for Baker's Procedure

1	2	3	4	5	6	7	8
t	$h(t)$	$h_1^*(t)$	$E_1(t)$	$c_1(t)$	$h_2^*(t)$	$h_3^*(t)$	$E_3(t)$
0	0	0	0	1.50	0	0	0
0.5	2.70	3.033	−0.050	1.25	3.794	4.055	−0.176
1.0	4.00	2.576	0.192	1.50	3.864	4.130	−0.014
1.5	3.60	1.506	0.378	2.25	3.390	3.623	−0.002
2.0	2.60	0.677	0.584	3.50	2.370	2.533	0.012
2.5	1.30	0.205	0.802	5.25	1.076	1.150	0.053
3.0	0	0	0	7.50	0	0	0
3.5	−0.90	−0.053	1.230	10.25	−0.543	−0.581	0.190
4.0	−0.75	−0.037	1.307	13.50	−0.500	−0.534	0.148
4.5	0	0	0	16.25	0	0	0
5.0	0.25	0.034	0.866	21.50	0.731	0.781	−0.494
5.5	0.10	0.056	0.252	26.25	1.470	1.570	−1.196
6.0	0.05	0.067	−0.126	31.50	2.110	2.225	−1.654

error function, Eq. (15-20), must be less than 0.176 everywhere within the specified time interval. Inspection of the data reveals that $h(t)$ crosses the real-time axis at $t = 0$, $t = 3$, and $t = 4.5$; therefore, the first approximation by Baker's procedure can be written in the form of Eq. (15-21) as

$$h_1^*(t) = t(t - 3)(t - 4.5)e^{-t} \qquad (15\text{-}22)$$

This first approximation is readily evaluated and is presented in Table 15-1 for reference. It is also shown in Fig. 15-4 as a dashed curve. The first error function can be written as $E_1(t) = \log |h(t)/h_1^*(t)|$ and can be computed directly from the second and third columns of Table 15-1. This error function is plotted in Fig. 15-5 as a solid curve and reveals two interesting facts. The average value of $E_1(t)$ is near 0.5, and hence, the first approximation can be improved by multiplying $h_1^*(t)$ by a factor, antilog $0.5 = 3.16$. The multiplication will not be done at this point, since a second approximation is necessary to reduce the error below $|\delta| = 0.176$. The second useful fact concerning $E_1(t)$ is that it has a minimum value within the interval $0 < t < 5$ at about $t = 0.5$

and nearly a constant slope out to $t = 4$, ignoring the zero at $t = 3$. Therefore the approximation can be improved by use of a quadratic factor possessing complex roots.

The selection of the quadratic factor for the second approximation is more difficult. Its form can be written as $(t - a + jb)(t - a - jb) = (t^2 - 2at + a^2 + b^2)$ where the real part of each root is chosen to coincide with the point on the real-time axis at which the minimum error

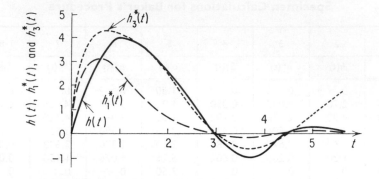

Fig. 15-4. Example functions of time from Table 15-1.

function occurs. In this example $E_1(t)$ is minimum at $t = 0.5$; hence, $a = 0.5$ and the quadratic factor becomes $t^2 - t + 0.25 + b^2$. The value of b must be chosen to satisfy the slope of the error function. Fortunately, various values of b can quickly be checked, since b^2 appears only as an additive constant in the quadratic form. For instance, consider the quadratic correction factor $c_1(t) = t^2 - t + 1.5$. This factor is evaluated in Col. 5 of Table 15-1 and is seen to have a minimum value at $t = 0.5$. To test a second correction factor such as $c_2(t) = t^2 - t + 4$, it is only necessary to add 2.5 to each value of $c_1(t)$. The second approximation is completed by multiplying Cols. 3 and 5 of Table 15-1 together to yield $h_2^*(t) = c_1(t)h_1^*(t)$ which is presented in Col. 6. This is a reasonably accurate approximation of $h(t)$ for $0 < t < 5$; however, it can be improved by selecting an appropriate multiplying factor of 1.068. The resulting approximation can be written as

$$h_3^*(t) = 1.068t(t - 3)(t - 4.5)(t^2 - t + 1.5)e^{-t}$$

$$= 21.63te^{-t} - 26.43t^2e^{-t} + 24.03t^3e^{-t} - 9.078t^4e^{-t} + 1.068t^5e^{-t}$$

$$(15\text{-}23)$$

This function has been evaluated in Table 15-1 and is shown as a dotted curve in Fig. 15-4. The resulting error function $E_3(t) = \log|h(t)/h_3^*(t)|$ is also evaluated in Table 15-1 and shown as a dotted curve in Fig. 15-5.

The error function $E_3(t)$ given in Table 15-1 and shown in Fig. 15-5 is seen to very nearly satisfy the desired condition that it remain less than $|\delta| = 0.176$ within the interval $0 < t < 5$. It only slightly exceeds this bound at $t = 3.5$ and above $t = 4.8$; consequently, it will be assumed that $h_3^*(t)$ given by Eq. (15-23) adequately approximates the specified data. It is noted that the error becomes large for $t > 6$; however, the function is certain to converge for large values of t because of the e^{-t} term. The efficiency of the approximation is often improved by selecting

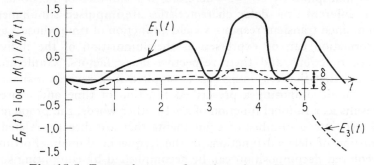

Fig. 15-5. Example error functions from Table 15-1.

in the beginning an exponential term $e^{-\beta t}$ where β is chosen to remove the average value of $\log |h(t)/e^{-\beta t}|$. This process is not always easy but is generally more optimum than simply using e^{-t} as indicated in Eq. (15-21). The inverse Laplace transformation of Eq. (15-23) is given as follows and is seen to represent a rational function possessing six poles at $s = -1$.

$$H_3^*(s) = \frac{21.63s^4 + 33.66s^3 + 115.38s^2 - 1.57s + 23.24}{(s + 1)^6} \qquad (15\text{-}24)$$

The minus sign in the numerator indicates the presence of a right half-plane zero, and if $e^{-\beta t}$ had been used in the approximating function, the six poles would have occurred at $s = -\beta$.

Baker's procedure becomes somewhat cumbersome as the complexity of the given function increases and as the error tolerance δ is made smaller. Furthermore, even though the error can be reduced over a specified time interval, there is no control of the error for larger values of t except to force the function to zero as t approaches infinity. The degree of the polynomial becomes large if there are many fluctuations or a large time interval is covered. This problem can be avoided by increasing the allowed error tolerance, permitting the use of rational polynomials in t, or breaking up the prescribed function into the summation of two or more simple functions each of which can be approximated separately. Finally, the error criterion may not always be satisfactory; however, it is easy to apply, involves less work than conventional least-square techniques, and provides a direct estimate of the accuracy at any point in the procedure.

15-3. Guillemin's Impulse Method of Approximation

In Chap. 14, Sec. 14-5, it was shown that the transient response of a network is delayed in time by T_D seconds if its characterizing function $H(s)$ is multiplied by e^{-sT_D}. Therefore, if a number of networks each having different time-delay characteristics are impulsed simultaneously the combined transient responses yield a function of time whose Laplace transformation can be expressed as the summation of the individual network functions and their respective delay factors. Guillemin has suggested that this reasoning can be applied in a reverse manner as a means for decomposing a prescribed function of time and expressing the results as a rational function of s.† In other words, the problem is to break $h(t)$ into a number of components that are directly related to a summation of delayed functions in the frequency domain. Fortunately the required decomposition can be accomplished by computing successive derivatives of $h(t)$; consequently an approximation can be achieved by fitting a series of simplified functions to $h(t)$ and then taking their successive derivatives.

The differentiation theorem of Laplace transform theory states that if $f(t)$ and $F(s)$ comprise a transformation pair, then

$$\mathscr{L}[f'(t)] = sF(s) - f(0^+) \tag{15-25}$$

where $\mathscr{L}[f'(t)]$ is the Laplace transformation for the derivative of $f(t)$, and $f(0^+)$ is the value of $f(t)$ as t approaches zero from the positive side. When $f(t)$ is an impulse having zero width, $f(0^+)$ vanishes. Therefore, if $h(t)$ is approximated by $h^*(t)$ and if $h^*(t)$ is differentiated q times until only a series of impulses remains, the impulses represent an approximation of the qth derivative of $h(t)$. Furthermore, $H(s)$ and the qth derivative of $h(t)$ are directly related as indicated by repeated application of Eq. (15-25). Hence, the impulses can be used to determine an approximation for $H(s)$.

Equation (15-25) reflects the fact that differentiation with respect to time corresponds to multiplication of $H(s)$ by s [$h(0^+)$ does not apply since impulses are used]; therefore, if $h^q(t)$ represents the qth derivative of $h(t)$, the direct Laplace transformation can be written as

$$H(s) = \frac{1}{s^q} \int_0^\infty h^q(t)e^{-st}\, dt \tag{15-26}$$

† E. A. Guillemin, "Computational Techniques which Simplify the Correlation between Steady-State and Transient Responses of Filters and Other Networks," *Proc. National Electronics Conference*, vol. 9, February 1954, pp. 513–532.

However, $h^q(t)$ is approximated by $h^{*q}(t)$ which is represented by a series of n impulses occurring at times $t_1, t_2, \ldots, t_n$. This approximation can be expressed as

$$h^{*q}(t) = \sum_{i=1}^{n} a_i u(t - t_i) \tag{15-27}$$

where a_i is the magnitude of the impulse $u(t - t_i)$. Substituting the approximation of Eq. (15-27) into Eq. (15-26) yields an approximation for $H(s)$ of the form

$$H^*(s) = \sum_{i=1}^{n} \frac{a_i e^{-st_i}}{s^q} \tag{15-28}$$

It is seen that this approximation possesses q poles at the origin where q is the number of differentiations necessary to obtain the impulses. However, this problem can be solved by expanding the individual e^{-st_i} terms of $H^*(s)$ in power series, combining like powers of s, then dividing the result by s^q to yield a series representation that can be truncated and converted to a rational fraction by Padé approximants.

If a set of data $h(t)$ is prescribed as a function of time, it is possible to approximate it over various intervals by straight-line segments. A single differentiation will then yield the necessary impulses; however, if $h(t)$ is complicated, a large number of straight-line segments may be required to give a satisfactory approximation. The given data can also be approximated by a series of parabolas of the form $(at^2 + bt + c)$ where a, b, and c are chosen such that the parabolas are point coincident with $h(t)$ at various points in selected intervals of time. In this case double differentiation of the parabolas yields the desired impulses. The problem of determining the parabolas is avoided and better accuracy can often be achieved if $h(t)$ is differentiated before performing the approximation. This technique is outlined in the example that follows.

Consider the arbitrarily specified function $h(t)$ shown in Fig. 15-6. A straight-line approximation for this function would require many segments to achieve a high degree of accuracy. However, $h(t)$ can be approximated by the following set of parabolas.

$$\begin{aligned}
p_1(t) &= -7t^2 + 9.5t & \text{for} \quad 0 \leq t \leq 1 \\
p_2(t) &= 5t^2 - 13.5t + 11 & \text{for} \quad 1 \leq t \leq 2 \\
p_3(t) &= -3t^2 + 17t - 18 & \text{for} \quad 2 \leq t \leq 4 \\
p_4(t) &= 1.8t^2 - 19.7t + 52 & \text{for} \quad 4 \leq t \leq 6
\end{aligned} \tag{15-29}$$

This approximation is shown as a dashed curve in Fig. 15-6, and upon differentiation, it leads to a straight-line approximation for $h'(t)$ given by

$$\begin{aligned}
p_1'(t) &= -14t + 9.5 & p_2'(t) &= 10t - 13.5 \\
p_3'(t) &= -6t + 17 & \text{and} \quad p_4'(t) &= 3.6t - 19.7
\end{aligned} \tag{15-30}$$

These derivatives are shown in Fig. 15-7 as dashed straight lines. The actual derivative of $h(t)$, as obtained numerically, is shown as a solid curve in Fig. 15-7; hence, comparison reveals that the approximation of Eq. (15-29) is comparatively accurate. A more accurate result is obtained with less labor by determining $h'(t)$ directly from $h(t)$ and then approximating it by a series of straight-line segments.

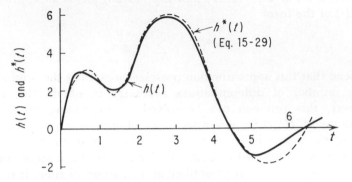

Fig. 15-6. Example data for Guillemin's procedure and parabolas of (Eq. 15-29).

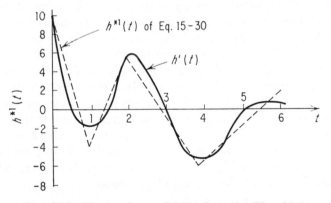

Fig. 15-7. Derivatives of $h(t)$ given by Fig. 15-6.

The second derivatives of Eq. (15-29) yield a set of amplitudes that approximate the actual second derivative of $h(t)$. These amplitudes are illustrated in Fig. 15-8a and lead to the series of impulses or third derivatives shown in Fig. 15-8b. In these figures it has been assumed that $h(t)$ returns and remains at zero for $t > 8$; consequently, the summation of the positive and negative amplitudes equal zero. Once the sequence of impulses has been obtained, the approximation can be completed in the form of Eq. (15-28). Using the impulses from the third derivative shown in Fig. 15-8b yields

$$H^*(s) = \frac{1}{s^3}(-14 + 24e^{-s} - 16e^{-1.9s} + 9.6e^{-4s} - 3.6e^{-8s})$$

$$(15\text{-}31)$$

As it stands, this approximation is of little value; therefore it must be expanded such that Padé approximants can be applied. This can be accomplished by expanding the exponential terms in their power series:

$$e^{-as} = 1 - as + \frac{(as)^2}{2!} - \frac{(as)^3}{3!} + \frac{(as)^4}{4!} - \cdots$$

$$(15\text{-}32)$$

Applying this expansion to Eq. (15-31) gives

$$H^*(s) = \frac{1}{s^3}(-3.2s - 55.2s^2 + 219.6s^3 + \cdots$$

$$(15\text{-}33)$$

This function can be truncated after a selected number of terms and represents an approximation to the Laplace transformation of the desired $h(t)$.

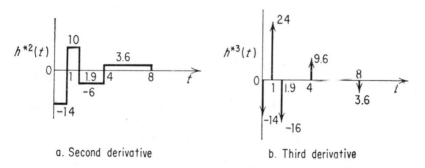

a. Second derivative   b. Third derivative

Fig. 15-8. Second and third derivative approximations.

Guillemin's procedure permits approximation of a time function by curves of higher order than can ordinarily be achieved by inspection. Furthermore, the procedure can be applied in reverse to convert a frequency-domain approximation to an equivalent transient response. In this case it is necessary to substitute $s = j\omega$ and evaluate the inverse Fourier integral of $H^*(j\omega)$. However, both techniques rely on reduction of the error by a process of selective judgments and resulting errors are generally difficult to evaluate.

15-4. Least-square Approximation Using Difference Equations

In some cases the specified function or data contains random errors or noise that should not be included in the approximation. A least-square error criterion is ideally suited for minimizing these effects; however, it is still desirable that the result be expressed in the form of a rational function of s. Both of these objectives can be achieved by a more complicated but highly accurate procedure based on using a difference equation as the approximating function.† Before discussing details of the analysis, it is useful to consider the step-by-step approach used in the procedure.

1. A specified function or set of data denoted by $h(t)$ is given, and its Laplace transformation $H(s)$ will not, in general, be a rational fraction. Hence, the first step in the procedure is to convert the given data or function to a tabulated series of amplitudes which are equally spaced in time Δt units apart as illustrated in Fig. 15-9. In the case of continuous functions no loss of information results from this step, since Δt can be taken as small as required.

2. The tabulated data can be approximated by an mth order homogeneous difference equation of the form

$$h_t - Ah_{(t-\Delta t)} - Bh_{(t-2\Delta t)} - \cdots - Mh_{(t-m\Delta t)} = 0 \tag{15-34}$$

The coefficients of this equation are determined by a least-square technique using the tabulated data of Step 1. The order of the difference equation establishes the number of poles for the approximate function $H^*(s)$.

3. Using the difference equation coefficients established in Step 2, it is possible to compute the positions of the poles of $H^*(s)$.

4. The zeros of $H^*(s)$ are then computed from the original data and its derivatives at time $(t = 0)$ by successive application of the initial value theorem. This is straightforward; however, similar results can be achieved by inverse transforming the general form of $H^*(s)$ and determining the remaining coefficients from $h(t)$.

Completion of Step 4 yields the desired rational approximation $H^*(s)$; however, the underlying principles are probably not apparent. Therefore, consider a function possessing a single pole:

$$H(s) = \frac{K}{(s + a)} \tag{15-35}$$

The inverse Laplace transformation of this function is

$$h(t) = Ke^{-at} \tag{15-36}$$

This function can be fit exactly by a first-order difference equation provided the coefficient A of the difference equation meets certain

---

† This procedure was developed in W. C. Yengst, "Approximation to a Specified Time Response," *IRE Trans. Circuit Theory*, vol. CT-9, no. 2, June 1962, and "Comments on Approximation to a Specified Time Response," *IEEE Trans. Circuit Theory*, vol. CT-10, no. 1, March 1963.

restrictions. To determine the necessary restrictions, the first-order difference equation is written from Eq. (15-34) at times t_i and $t_{(i-1)}$ as

$$h_i - Ah_{(i-1)} = 0 \qquad (15\text{-}37)$$

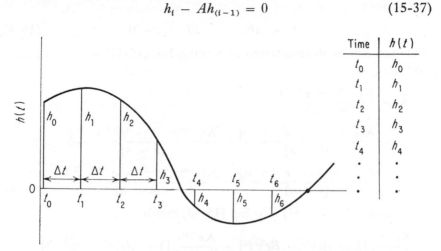

Time	$h(t)$
t_0	h_0
t_1	h_1
t_2	h_2
t_3	h_3
t_4	h_4
$\vdots$	$\vdots$
$\vdots$	$\vdots$

Fig. 15-9. Tabulation of specified data or function of time.

Similarly, Eq. (15-36) can be written at times t_i and $t_{(i-1)}$ as

$$h_i = Ke^{-at_i} \qquad \text{and} \qquad h_{(i-1)} = Ke^{-at_{(i-1)}} = Ke^{-a(t_i - \Delta t)} \qquad (15\text{-}38)$$

Substituting Eq. (15-38) into Eq. (15-37) gives

$$Ke^{-at_i} - AKe^{-a(t_i - \Delta t)} = 0 \qquad \text{or} \qquad Ke^{-at_i}(1 - Ae^{a\,\Delta t}) = 0 \qquad (15\text{-}39)$$

Assuming that K is nonzero, the only way Eq. (15-39) can be zero for all values of t_i is for the expression in the parentheses to be zero. Consequently, it follows that $A = e^{-a\,\Delta t}$, thereby revealing that A must be a real positive number greater than zero. Furthermore, if a first-order difference equation is used to approximate a set of data such that A is greater than zero, then using the known value of Δt, it is possible to compute a. The value of a determines the poles of $H(s)$ and also establishes the form of $h(t)$ that approximates the original data. The initial value theorem or a least-square technique can then be used to compute K.

It is now useful to consider a second-order function of the following form where a and b may be either real or complex conjugate numbers.

$$H(s) = \frac{K}{(s+a)(s+b)} \qquad (15\text{-}40)$$

The inverse Laplace transformation of this function is

$$h(t) = \frac{K(e^{-at} - e^{-bt})}{(b-a)} \qquad (15\text{-}41)$$

This function can be fitted exactly by a second-order difference equation of the following form provided the coefficients A and B meet certain restrictions.

$$h_i - Ah_{(i-1)} - Bh_{(i-2)} = 0 \qquad (15\text{-}42)$$

This fact can be demonstrated by writing Eq. (15-41) at times t_i, $t_{(i-1)}$, and $t_{(i-2)}$ as

$$h_i = \frac{K(e^{-at_i} - e^{-bt_i})}{(b-a)}$$

$$h_{(i-1)} = \frac{K[e^{-at_{(i-1)}} - e^{-bt_{(i-1)}}]}{(b-a)} = \frac{K[e^{-a(t_i - \Delta t)} - e^{-b(t_i - \Delta t)}]}{(b-a)}$$

$$h_{(i-2)} = \frac{K[e^{-at_{(i-2)}} - e^{-bt_{(i-2)}}]}{(b-a)} = \frac{K[e^{-a(t_i - 2\Delta t)} - e^{-b(t_i - 2\Delta t)}]}{(b-a)} \qquad (15\text{-}43)$$

Substituting Eq. (15-43) into Eq. (15-42) yields

$$\frac{Ke^{-at_i}}{(b-a)}[1 - Ae^{a\Delta t} - Be^{2a\Delta t}] - \frac{Ke^{-bt_i}}{(b-a)}[1 - Ae^{b\Delta t} - Be^{2b\Delta t}] = 0$$

$$(15\text{-}44)$$

Assuming that K and $(b-a)$ are nonzero, the only way Eq. (15-44) can be zero for all values of t_i is for each of the bracketed quantities to be zero. Hence, the following two relationships are obtained:

$$Ae^{a\Delta t} + Be^{2a\Delta t} = 1 \quad \text{and} \quad Ae^{b\Delta t} + Be^{2b\Delta t} = 1 \quad (15\text{-}45)$$

Solving for A and B gives

$$A = e^{-a\Delta t} + e^{-b\Delta t} \quad \text{and} \quad B = -e^{-(a+b)\Delta t} \quad (15\text{-}46)$$

Also, solving Eq. (15-46) for $e^{-a\Delta t}$ and $e^{-b\Delta t}$ in terms of A and B yields

$$e^{-a\Delta t} = \frac{A + \sqrt{A^2 + 4B}}{2} \quad \text{and} \quad e^{-b\Delta t} = \frac{A - \sqrt{A^2 + 4B}}{2}$$

$$(15\text{-}47)$$

From Eq. (15-46) it is seen that for a second-order difference equation to be an exact fit for Eq. (15-41), it is necessary that A be nonzero and B be less than zero. If a difference equation satisfies these restrictions A, B, and Δt can be used in Eq. (15-47) to determine a and b, thereby establishing the poles of $H(s)$.

Analysis of the type described above leads to several interesting and useful conclusions.

1. An mth order difference equation can be used as an exact fit for any function of time $h(t)$ having a Laplace transform $H(s)$ which possesses an mth order polynomial for its denominator.

2. Knowledge of the coefficients $A, B, C, \ldots, M$ of the difference equation in addition to Δt is sufficient information to determine the position of all poles of $H(s)$.

3. The number of restrictions on the coefficients $A, B, C, \ldots, M$ of the difference equation is equal to the order of the difference equation.

4. The restrictions on the coefficients $A, B, C, \ldots, M$ are the same for all functions of time having Laplace transforms with the same poles.

Proof of the first two conclusions can be obtained by assuming that $h(t)$ is represented by the summation of m exponential terms of the form

$$h(t) = \sum_{k=1}^{m} K_k e^{s_k t} \tag{15-48}$$

Writing this function at times $t, (t - \Delta t), (t - 2\Delta t), \ldots, (t - m\Delta t)$, substituting the results in Eq. (15-34) and regrouping terms gives

$$K_1 e^{-s_1 t}[1 - A e^{s_1 \Delta t} - B e^{2s_1 \Delta t} - \cdots - M e^{m s_1 \Delta t}]$$

$$-K_2 e^{-s_2 t}[1 - A e^{s_2 \Delta t} - B e^{2s_2 \Delta t} - \cdots - M e^{m s_2 \Delta t}]$$

$$\cdot \quad \cdot \quad \cdot \quad \cdot \quad \cdot \quad \cdot \quad \cdot \quad \cdot \quad \cdot \quad \cdot$$

$$-K_m e^{-s_m t}[1 - A e^{s_m \Delta t} - B e^{2s_m \Delta t} - \cdots - M e^{m s_m \Delta t}] = 0 \tag{15-49}$$

Since $K_1, K_2, \ldots, K_m$ are nonzero, the only way Eq. (15-49) can be zero for all time is for the quantities in the brackets to be zero. This yields a set of m simultaneous equations in m unknowns. Consequently, it is possible to solve for $A, B, C, \ldots, M$ in terms of $s_1, s_2, s_3, \ldots, s_m$ and Δt. The resulting relationships are given by

$$A = e^{-s_1 \Delta t} + e^{-s_2 \Delta t} + \cdots + e^{-s_m \Delta t}$$

$$-B = e^{-(s_1 + s_2)\Delta t} + e^{-(s_1 + s_3)\Delta t} + \cdots$$
(all combinations of s_i taken two at a time)

$$C = e^{-(s_1 + s_2 + s_3)\Delta t} + e^{-(s_1 + s_2 + s_4)\Delta t} + \cdots$$
(all combinations of s_i taken three at a time)

$$-D = e^{-(s_1 + s_2 + s_3 + s_4)\Delta t} + \cdots$$
(all combinations of s_i taken four at a time)

$$\cdot \quad \cdot \quad \cdot \quad \cdot \quad \cdot \quad \cdot \quad \cdot \quad \cdot \quad \cdot$$

$$M = e^{-(s_1 + s_2 + \cdots + s_m)\Delta t}$$
(the only combination taken m at a time) $\tag{15-50}$

Solution of this set of equations yields the poles of $H(s)$, given by the Laplace transformation of Eq. (15-48). However, the K_k coefficients of Eq. (15-48) do not influence the poles of $H(s)$, since they do not appear in Eq. (15-50).

Further consideration of Eq. (15-49) reveals that each bracketed quantity is of the same general form. For instance, if a new variable $x = e^{s_1 \Delta t}$ is substituted in the first bracketed quantity, it becomes

$$[1 - Ax - Bx^2 - \cdots - Mx^m] = 0 \qquad (15\text{-}51)$$

Similarly, letting $(x = e^{s_2 \Delta t})$ causes the second bracketed quantity to take the same form. Applying this substitution to each bracketed quantity in turn causes all the resulting polynomials to take the form of Eq. (15-51). Consequently, since each polynomial is of the same order and possesses the same coefficients, it is only necessary to factor one such expression to obtain the roots for all. Therefore, solving Eq. (15-51) for all m roots and denoting these roots by $x_1, x_2, \ldots, x_m$, one can solve for the desired parameters $s_1, s_2, \ldots, s_m$ by applying the relationship $(x_m = e^{s_m \Delta t})$ where Δt is presumed to be known.

When the substitution of variables is performed, the third and fourth conclusions listed above can be ignored. These restrictions are only a consequence of the derivation and do not rule out any realizable functions. For instance, even though A and B of Eq. (15-47) were restricted, an exact fit is obtained for Eq. (15-41) without placing restrictions on the poles $(s = -a)$ and $(s = -b)$ of Eq. (15-40). These poles can be located anywhere in the s-plane. Likewise, the restriction on A of Eq. (15-39) does not prevent the single real pole of Eq. (15-35) from falling anywhere on the real axis of the s-plane. By this line of reasoning, the m restrictions on the coefficients of an mth order difference equation do not restrict the m poles of $H(s)$ from any regions of the s-plane, nor do they prevent multiple-order poles. A brief summary including some general functions and a few of their special cases including the related restrictions on difference-equation coefficients is presented in Table 15-2. Additional cases are easily derived by the procedures outlined above.

A number of different functions of time can be fitted exactly by a difference equation of a given order. This should be clear from consideration of Table 15-2 and follows from the fact that a difference equation, like a differential equation, only contains information pertaining to the relationship between a function and its derivatives. Because it does not contain information pertaining to initial conditions, information must be added to completely identify a particular function of time. This can be accomplished by assuming that the zeros of $H^*(s)$ are represented by a polynomial $P(s)$ of the form

$$P(s) = K_n s^n + K_{(n-1)} s^{n-1} + \cdots + K_1 s + K_0$$

where $\qquad\qquad (n \leq m - 1) \qquad\qquad (15\text{-}52)$

To determine $K_n, K_{(n-1)}, \ldots, K_1$, and K_0, it is possible to use the specified data or function and successive application of the initial value

TABLE 15-2

Difference Equations and Laplace Transform Relationships

Order of difference equation	Restrictions on coefficients	Relationship of parameters	Form of $H(s)$
First order: $h_t - Ah_{(t-\Delta t)} = 0$	1. $A > 0$ (general case)	$e^{-a\Delta t} = A$	$\dfrac{K_0}{(s+a)}$
Second order: $h_t - Ah_{(t-\Delta t)} - Bh_{(t-2\Delta t)} = 0$	2. $A = 2\sqrt{-B}$, $A > 0$	$e^{-a\Delta t} = \dfrac{A}{2}$	$\dfrac{P(s)}{(s+a)^2}$
	3. $A^2 + 4B < 0$, $B < 0$	$e^{-2a\Delta t} = -B$, $\cos b\Delta t = A/2\sqrt{-B}$	$\dfrac{P(s)}{(s+a)^2 + b^2}$
	4. $A > 0$, $B > 0$ (general case)	$e^{-a\Delta t} = \dfrac{A + \sqrt{A^2 + 4B}}{2}$ $\quad e^{-b\Delta t} = \dfrac{A - \sqrt{A^2 + 4B}}{2}$	$\dfrac{P(s)}{(s+a)(s+b)}$
Third order: $h_t - Ah_{(t-\Delta t)} - Bh_{(t-2\Delta t)} - Ch_{(t-3\Delta t)} = 0$	5. $A = \sqrt{-3B}$, $A = 3\sqrt[3]{C}$, $A > 0$	$e^{-a\Delta t} = C$, $\cos b\Delta t = (A - C)/2$	$\dfrac{P(s)}{(s+a)^3}$
	6. $A = C - (B+1)/2$, $-2 \leqq (A - C) \leqq 2$, $C > 0$	$e^{-a\Delta t} = C$, $\cos b\Delta t = (A - C)/2$	$\dfrac{P(s)}{(s+a)(s^2 + b^2)}$
	7. $A > 0$, $B > 0$, $C > 0$ (general case)	$e^{-a\Delta t} = E + F + A/3$ $e^{-b\Delta t} = -\dfrac{(E+F)}{2} + \dfrac{(E-F)\sqrt{-3}}{2} + \dfrac{A}{3}$ $e^{-c\Delta t} = -\dfrac{(E+F)}{2} - \dfrac{(E-F)\sqrt{-3}}{2} + \dfrac{A}{3}$ where: $E = \sqrt[3]{-\dfrac{H}{2} + \sqrt{\dfrac{H^2}{4} + \dfrac{G^3}{27}}}$; $\quad G = -\dfrac{(A^2 + 3B)}{3}$ $F = \sqrt[3]{-\dfrac{H}{2} - \sqrt{\dfrac{H^2}{4} + \dfrac{G^3}{27}}}$; $\quad H = \dfrac{-(2A^3 + 9AB + 27C)}{27}$	$\dfrac{P(s)}{(s+a)(s+b)(s+c)}$

theorem and its derivatives. For instance, the initial value theorem is given by Eq. (15-11) and can be used to relate $sH^*(s)$ as s approaches infinity to the first sample of data $h(0)$. Hence, for a given order difference equation, it is possible to establish the highest order of s, n in the polynomial $P(s)$ and the coefficient K_n.

The remainder of $P(s)$ can be written in general terms, and the coefficients can be determined in two ways. One way is to transform $H^*(s)$ including its unknown coefficients to $h^*(t)$, after which the coefficients can be computed by various techniques from the specified data or function. An easier approach is based on applying the initial value theorem to derivatives of the data at $(t = 0)$. Analytically, the Laplace transform for the derivative of $h(t)$ is given by

$$H'(s) = sH(s) - \lim_{t \to 0} h(t) \tag{15-53}$$

where $H'(s)$ is the Laplace transform of $h'(t)$, the first derivative of $h(t)$. Applying the initial value theorem to the derivative function yields

$$\lim_{s \to \infty} sH'(s) = \lim_{t \to 0} h'(t) \tag{15-54}$$

Successive application of this approach using higher-order derivatives of $h(t)$ at $(t = 0)$ for the derivatives of $h^*(t)$ will yield the coefficients of $P(s)$ directly. The problem of finding derivatives of $h(t)$ at $(t = 0)$ can be solved in several ways. If $h(t)$ is given as a function, its derivatives can be evaluated directly; however, if it is given as a table of data, it is possible to use the difference equation established in Step 2 of the procedure, along with the first few samples of data, to construct artificial "data" back through negative time. This data centered at $(t = 0)$ can then be fit by a polynomial such that subsequent differentiation and evaluation will yield the necessary derivatives. However, determination of the zeros of $P(s)$ by use of the initial value theorem may suffer from the standpoint of accuracy if higher derivatives are based on approximations of tabulated data.

Once an mth order difference equation has been selected, its coefficients must be computed according to some criterion. Because a least-square criterion tends to minimize uncorrelated random noise in $h(t)$ while yielding the desired approximations, the following technique has been selected. The difference equation is first written as

$$h_{c(i)} = Ah_{p(i-1)} + Bh_{p(i-2)} + Ch_{p(i-3)} + \cdots + Mh_{p(i-m)} \tag{15-55}$$

where $h_{c(i)}$ is the computed value at time t_i based on the prescribed values h_p as obtained from $h(t)$ at times $(i-1)$, $(i-2)$, ..., $(i-m)$.

The error E_i between the prescribed and computed values of h_i at time t_i is given by $E_i = h_{p(i)} - h_{c(i)}$. Hence, for a least-square solution, the values of $A, B, C, \ldots, M$ are determined such that the sum of the squares of E_i will be a minimum. Therefore, substituting Eq. (15-55) into the error function, squaring both sides, and summing over all values of i from $(m + 1)$ to q yields

$$\sum_{m+1}^{q} E_i^2 = \sum_{m+1}^{q} [h_{p(i)} - Ah_{p(i-1)} - Bh_{p(i-2)} - Ch_{p(i-3)} - \cdots - Mh_{p(i-m)}]^2$$

$$(15\text{-}56)$$

where q is the number of samples. Note that E_i does not exist for $i = 1, 2, 3, \ldots, m$ since $h_{c(i)}$, as defined by Eq. (15-55), is also nonexistent for these values.

To obtain values for $A, B, C, \ldots, M$ such that Eq. (15-56) is a minimum, equate each of the partial derivatives with respect to $A, B, C, \ldots, M$ equal to zero. This yields a set of m linear simultaneous equations in terms of the m coefficients and the prescribed data of $h(t)$. These equations can be expressed in matrix form as follows, and can be solved directly for the desired coefficients:

$$\begin{bmatrix} \sum_{m+1}^{q} h_{p(i-1)}^2 & \sum_{m+1}^{q} h_{p(i-1)}h_{p(i-2)} \cdots & \sum_{m+1}^{q} h_{p(i-1)}h_{p(i-m)} \\ \sum_{m+1}^{q} h_{p(i-1)}h_{p(i-2)} & \sum_{m+1}^{q} h_{p(i-2)}^2 & \cdots \sum_{m+1}^{q} h_{p(i-2)}h_{p(i-m)} \\ \cdot & \cdot & \cdot \\ \cdot & \cdot & \cdot \\ \sum_{m+1}^{q} h_{p(i-1)}h_{p(i-m)} & \sum_{m+1}^{q} h_{p(i-2)}h_{p(i-m)} \cdots & \sum_{m+1}^{q} h_{p(i-m)}^2 \end{bmatrix} \begin{bmatrix} A \\ B \\ \cdot \\ \cdot \\ M \end{bmatrix} = \begin{bmatrix} \sum_{m+1}^{q} h_{p(i)}h_{p(i-1)} \\ \sum_{m+1}^{q} h_{p(i)}h_{p(i-2)} \\ \cdot \\ \cdot \\ \sum_{m+1}^{q} h_{p(i)}h_{p(i-m)} \end{bmatrix}$$

$$(15\text{-}57)$$

Choice of the time interval or sampling period must take into account the highest and lowest frequency variations in the data that are important. However, a minimum of $2m$ samples are required in writing m independent equations in terms of $A, B, C, \ldots, M$. The maximum number of samples is not limited, but if too many are used over a given time interval the value of the determinant of Eq. (15-57) approaches zero. Finally, if an $(m + 1)$st-order difference equation is used to approximate data which can be fit exactly by an mth-order difference equation, the determinant will identically equal zero.

As an example of the above procedure, consider the data provided in Table 15-3. A first-order approximation could be made to fit this data;

however, because the data exhibits higher-order variations, a second-order approximation will be used. Consequently, the following summations, necessary to solve Eq. (15-57), can be made from the data.

$$\sum_3^{16} h_p{}^2{}_{(i-1)} = 57.97353 \qquad \sum_3^{16} h_{p(i-1)}h_{p(i-2)} = 52.95918$$

$$\sum_3^{16} h_p{}^2{}_{(i-2)} = 63.10823$$

$$\sum_3^{16} h_{p(i)}h_{p(i-1)} = 42.84900 \qquad \sum_3^{16} h_{p(i)}h_{p(i-2)} = 29.26925$$

$$(15\text{-}58)$$

Substituting these summations into Eq. (15-57) and solving for A and B yields $A = 1.351452$ and $B = -0.670318$. Hence, the second-order difference equation that approximates the data can be written as

$$h_t - 1.351452h_{(t-\Delta t)} + 0.670318h_{(t-2\Delta t)} = 0 \qquad (15\text{-}59)$$

TABLE 15-3

Data for Example Problem

t	$h(t)$	t	$h(t)$	t	$h(t)$
0	2.28013	0.6	−1.45083	1.2	0.57689
0.1	4.43683	0.7	−1.62210	1.3	0.47376
0.2	4.46775	0.8	−1.21968	1.4	0.25356
0.3	3.06387	0.9	−0.56100	1.5	0.02511
0.4	1.14586	1.0	0.05940		
0.5	−0.50519	1.1	0.45633		

Inspection of Eq. (15-59) reveals that A and B satisfy both Forms 3 and 4 of Table 15-2. Using the "Relationship of Parameters" for Form 3 and $\Delta t = 0.1$ second leads to $a = 2.0000$ and $b = 6.0000$ radians/sec. The same results can be obtained directly by changing variables in Eq. (15-59) such that $(x^2 - 1.351452x + 0.670318 = 0)$. The roots of this function occur at $x = 0.6757 \pm j0.4623$ and can be expressed in exponential form as

$$x = e^{-0.20000 \pm j0.60000} \qquad (15\text{-}60)$$

Consequently, for $\Delta t = 0.1$ sec, $a = 2.0000$ and $b = 6.0000$ and $H^*(s)$ becomes

$$H^*(s) = \frac{P(s)}{(s + 2.0000)^2 + (6.0000)^2} \qquad (15\text{-}61)$$

Applying the initial-value theorem of Eq. (15-11) and using the initial value of data from Table 15-2 gives

$$\lim_{s \to \infty} \frac{sP(s)}{(s + 2.0000)^2 + (6.0000)^2} = \lim_{t \to 0} h(t) = 2.28013 \qquad (15\text{-}62)$$

It follows that $P(s) = K_1 s + K_0 = 2.28013s + K_0$, and this result can be substituted back in Eq. (15-61), after which K_0 can be determined by either of two methods. For instance, $H^*(s)$ can be inverse-transformed, in which case K_0 may be chosen to fit $h^*(t)$ to $h(t)$. The second approach will be demonstrated here and involves the use of Eq. (15-59) to extend the data back into negative time.

Time	$h^*(t)$	
$t_{-2} = -2\,\Delta t$	-7.47807	Computed "data" from Eq. (15-59)
$t_{-1} = -\Delta t$	-2.02194	
$t_0 = 0$	2.28013	
$t_1 = \Delta t$	4.43683	Prescribed data from Table 15-3
$t_2 = 2\,\Delta t$	4.46775	(15-63)

Fitting a third-order polynomial through these five points gives $c(t) = 0.52641 + 33.0274t - 0.930t^2 - 6.37t^3$, which has a derivative of 33.0274 at $(t = 0)$. Combining the above results to determine the derivative function $H^{*\prime}(s)$ in the form of Eq. (15-53) yields

$$H^{*\prime}(s) = \frac{s(2.28013s + K_0)}{(s + 2.0000)^2 + (6.0000)^2} - 2.28013 =$$

$$\frac{(K_0 - 9.12052)s - 91.2052}{(s + 2.0000)^2 + (6.0000)^2} \qquad (15\text{-}64)$$

Applying Eq. (15-54) to this result gives

$$\lim_{s \to \infty} sH^{*\prime}(s) = \lim_{s \to \infty} \frac{s[(K_0 - 9.12052)s - 91.2052]}{(s + 2.0000)^2 + (6.0000)^2} = 33.0274$$

or

$$K_0 = 42.1479 \qquad (15\text{-}65)$$

This completes the approximation, since it is possible from Eqs. (15-61) and (15-65) to write

$$H^*(s) = \frac{(2.28013s + 42.1479)}{(s + 2.0000)^2 + (6.0000)} \qquad (15\text{-}66)$$

The inverse transform of this function is given by

$$h^*(t) = 6.6667e^{-2.0000t} \sin(6.0000 + 19°59'59.5'') \qquad (15\text{-}67)$$

The tabulated data of Table 15-3 for this example was derived from $h(t) = (20/3)e^{-2t} \sin(6t + 20°)$.

Pole positions determined by this procedure are only "best" in the sense of least squares if the function to be approximated satisfies an mth order difference equation. Functions which do not satisfy such equations may have mean-square errors in the approximation which are larger than when the pole positions are determined by some other technique. Since the above example does not contain noise, a question remains concerning the ability of the procedure to filter noise from the data. In the case of first-order approximations, the least-square technique of Eq. (15-57) has been applied to a number of problems for which the rms-signal-to-rms-noise ratio had been determined in advance. The results of these computations are shown in Fig. 15-10.

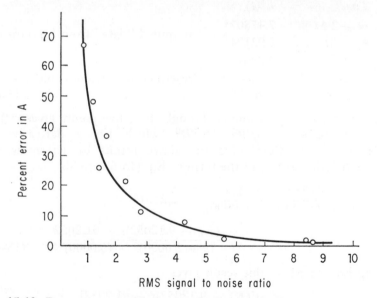

Fig. 15-10. Percent error in A of a first order difference equation as a function of the signal to noise ratio of the specified time response.

In conclusion, it is seen that this procedure tends to minimize the effect of uncorrelated random noise present in the specified data. However, computational difficulties increase significantly if least squares are used to determine both the coefficients and exponents of the exponential terms of $h^*(t)$, since nonlinear relationships exist between the parameters. Furthermore, the accuracy of the approximation can be progressively improved in most cases by increasing the order of the difference equation. Poles and zeros of $H^*(s)$ are not restricted from any region of the finite s-plane, and multiple-order poles and/or zeros are permitted. Finally, the procedure is best suited for fitting smooth functions of time and does not accurately approximate idealized discontinuous functions.

Fortunately these functions are not generally realizable in terms of practical elements except in the limit as the order of the approximation or the number of elements approaches infinity.

References

Although a number of time-domain approximation techniques have been developed, only a few texts offer detailed presentations on the subject. A notable example is J. E. Storer, *Passive Network Synthesis* (New York: McGraw-Hill Book Co., Inc., 1957), Chap. 31, which covers techniques closely related to the time-moment procedure of Sec. 15-1. Guillemin's text, *Synthesis of Passive Networks* (New York: John Wiley & Sons, Inc., 1957), Chap. 15, provides a detailed description of his impulse procedure plus techniques developed by his students. Guillemin's impulse procedure is also presented in J. G. Truxal, *Control System Synthesis* (New York: McGraw-Hill Book Co., Inc., 1955), Sec. 6.6. The remaining procedures of this chapter can be found only in the references provided in the footnotes. However, the following references outline other useful time-domain approximation procedures:

1. John D. Brule, "Improving the Approximation to a Prescribed Time Response," *IRE Trans. Circuit Theory*, vol. CT-6, no. 4, December 1959, pp. 355–361.
2. John D. Brule, "Comments on an Approximation Procedure," *IRE Trans. Circuit Theory*, vol. CT-8, no. 1, March 1961, pp. 81–82.
3. W. H. Kautz, "Transient Synthesis in the Time Domain," *IRE Trans. Circuit Theory*, vol. CT-1, no. 3, September 1954, pp. 29–39.
4. B. Liu, "A Time Domain Approximation Method and its Application to Lumped Delay Lines," *IRE Trans. Circuit Theory*, vol. CT-9, no. 3, September 1962, pp. 256–261.
5. M. Strieby, "A Fourier Method for Time Domain Synthesis," *Proceedings of the Symposium on Modern Network Synthesis*, Vol. V, Polytechnic Institute of Brooklyn (April 13–15, 1955), pp. 197–211. This book also contains other useful procedures including an interesting technique by A. Papoulis entitled "Network Response in Terms of Behavior at Imaginary Frequencies."
6. D. Teasdale, "Time Domain Approximation by Use of Padé Approximants," *IRE Convention Record*, Part 5, March 23–26, 1953, pp. 89–94.

Problems

15-1. Using the parabolas of Eq. (15-29), determine an approximation for the curve of Fig. 15-6 by the procedure of time moments (Sec. 15-1). Check the results by determining a rational fraction approximation and inverse transforming it to yield $h^*(t)$.

15-2. Using the procedure of time moments, approximate the function $h(t) = 1/(1 + t)$. Verify the results by determining the approximate function $h^*(t)$. Repeat the problem for $h(t) = (1 - t)e^{-t}$.

15-3. Apply Baker's procedure to the approximation of the desired straight-line response of Fig. 15-1. Reduce the error magnitude at all points between $t = 0$ and $t = 0.9$ to less than 20 percent.

15-4. Approximate the function $h(t) = \sin t/\pi t$ by Baker's procedure and reduce the error magnitude to less than 50 percent in the interval $0 \leq t \leq 6$. Is the resulting approximation realizable as a driving-point function?

15-5. Approximate the following functions by Guillemin's impulse procedure. (Convert the approximations to rational fraction form, then inverse-transform the results to check the accuracy.)

$$h(t) = \frac{2}{(2 + 2t + t^2)} \quad \text{and} \quad h(t) = \frac{1}{\sqrt{1 + t}}$$

15-6. The impulse response for a desired network is specified by the idealized functions, $h(t) = 1 - t$ for $0 \leq t \leq 1$ and $h(t) = 0$ for $1 \leq t < \infty$. Apply the least-square procedure of Sec. 15-4 to determine first- and second-order approximations that lead to realizable driving-point functions. Use a minimum of 10 sample points between $t = 0$ and $t = 1$.

15-7. Using the curve for $h(t)$ of Fig. 15-6, perform a third-order least-square approximation. The polynomial $p_1(t)$ of Eq. (15-29) can be used to establish derivatives of $h(t)$ at $t = 0$.

15-8. Perform a second-order least-square approximation of the idealized triangular pulse defined by $h(t) = t$ for $0 \leq t \leq 0.5$; $h(t) = 1 - t$ for $0.5 \leq t \leq 1$, and $h(t) = 0$ for $t > 1$. Also approximate this pulse using time moments, and finally, apply Guillemin's impulse method to obtain a third approximation. Discuss the results in each case concerning the amount of labor required and the accuracy of the approximation.

Index